Student Solutions Manual

Laurel Technical Services

COLLEGE ALGEBRA

SECOND EDITION

Robert Blitzer

Upper Saddle River, NJ 07458

Executive Editor: Sally Yagan
Supplement Editor: Joanne Wendelken
Special Projects Manager: Barbara A. Murray
Production Editor: James Buckley
Supplement Cover Manager: Paul Gourhan
Supplement Cover Designer: PM Workshop Inc.
Manufacturing Buyer: Lisa McDowell

Printed in the United States of America

10 9 8 7 6 5 4 3 2

ISBN 0-13-089410-9

Prentice-Hall International (UK) Limited, London
Prentice-Hall of Australia Pty. Limited, Sydney
Prentice-Hall Canada, Inc., Toronto
Prentice-Hall Hispanoamericana, S.A., Mexico
Prentice-Hall of India Private Limited, New Delhi
Pearson Education Asia Pte. Ltd., Singapore
Prentice-Hall of Japan, Inc., Tokyo
Editora Prentice-Hall do Brazil, Ltda., Rio de Janeiro

Table of Contents

Chapter P

Section P.1

Check Point Exercises

1. a. $\left|1-\sqrt{2}\right|$

Because $\sqrt{2} \approx 1.4$, the number inside the absolute value bars is negative. The absolute value of x when $x < 0$ is $-x$. Thus,

$\left|1-\sqrt{2}\right| = -\left(1-\sqrt{2}\right) = \sqrt{2}-1.$

b. $|\pi - 3|$

Because $\pi \approx 3.14$, the number inside the absolute value bars is positive. The absolute value of a positive number is the number itself. Thus,

$|\pi - 3| = \pi - 3.$

c. $\frac{|x|}{x}$ if $x > 0$

If $x > 0$, then $|x| = x$. Thus,

$\frac{|x|}{x} = \frac{x}{x} = 1.$

2. Because the distance between a and b is given by $|a-b|$, the distance between -4 and 5 is

$|-4-5| = |-9| = 9.$

3. Begin by substituting 100 for x. Because $x =$ 100, we will be finding the U.S. population 100 years after 1980, in the year 2080.

$2.35(100) + 179.5$
$= 235 + 179.5$
$= 414.5$

Thus, in 2080, the population of the United States will be 414.5 million.

4. Simplify: $7(4x - 3y) + 2(5x + y)$.
Use the distributive property to remove the parentheses. Then, multiply and group like terms. Finally combine like terms.

$7(4x - 3y) + 2(5x + y).$
$= 7 \cdot 4x - 7 \cdot 3y + 2 \cdot 5x + 2 \cdot y$
$= 28x - 21y + 10x + 2y$
$= (28x + 10x) + (2y - 21y)$
$= 38x - 19y$

Exercise Set P.1

For Exercises 1 and 3:

a. The natural numbers are used for counting, $\{1, 2, 3, 4, 5\ldots\}$.

b. The whole numbers add 0 to the set of natural numbers, $\{0, 1, 2, 3, 4, 5, \ldots\}$.

c. The integers add the negative of the natural numbers to the set of whole numbers,
$\{\ldots, -5, -4, -3, -2, -1, 0, 1, 2, 3, 4, 5, \ldots\}$.

d. The rational numbers can be expressed as an integer divided by a nonzero integer or a terminating or repeating decimal.

e. The irrational numbers cannot be expressed as a quotient of integers or a terminating or repeating decimal.

1. a. $\sqrt{100}$

b. $0, \sqrt{100}$

c. $-9, 0, \sqrt{100}$

d. $-9, \frac{-4}{5}, 0, 0.25, 9.2, \sqrt{100}$

e. $\sqrt{3}$

3. **a.** $\sqrt{64}$

b. $0, \sqrt{64}$

c. $-11, 0, \sqrt{64}$

d. $-11, \frac{-5}{6}, 0, 0.75, \sqrt{64}$

e. $\sqrt{5}, \pi$

5. 0

7. Answers may vary.

9. True; –13 is to the left of –2 on the number line.

11. True; 4 is to the right of –7 on the number line.

13. True; $-\pi = -\pi$

15. $|300| = 300$

17. $|12 - \pi| = 12 - \pi$

19. $|\sqrt{2} - 5| = 5 - \sqrt{2}$

21. $\frac{-3}{|-3|} = \frac{-3}{3} = -1$

23. $|17 - 2| = |15| = 15$

25. $|5 - (-2)| = |7| = 7$

27. $|-4 - (-19)| = |15| = 15$

29. $|-1.4 - (-3.6)| = |2.2| = 2.2$

31. $5x + 7 = 5\ (4) + 7 = 27$

33. $4(x+3) - 11 = 4[(-5)+3] - 11$
$= 4(-2) - 11 = -19$

35. $\frac{5}{9}(F - 32) = \frac{5}{9}(77 - 32)$
$= \frac{5}{9}(45)$
$= 25$

37. $\frac{5(x+2)}{2x - 14} = \frac{5(10+2)}{2(10) - 14}$
$= \frac{5(12)}{6}$
$= 5 \cdot 2$
$= 10$

39. $6 + (-4) = (-4) + 6$; commutative property of addition

41. $6 + (2 + 7) = (6 + 2) + 7$; associative property of addition

43. $(2 + 3) + (4 + 5) = (4 + 5) + (2 + 3)$; commutative property of addition

45. $-2 - (-8 + 6) = -16 + 12$; distributive property of multiplication over addition

47. $5(3x+4) - 4 = 5 \cdot 3x + 5 \cdot 4 - 4$
$= 15x + 20 - 4$
$= 15x + 16$

49. $5(3x - 2) + 12x = 5 \cdot 3x - 5 \cdot 2 + 12x$
$= 15x - 10 + 12x$
$= 27x - 10$

51. $7(3y - 5) + 2(4y + 3)$
$= 7 \cdot 3y - 7 \cdot 5 + 2 \cdot 4y + 2 \cdot 3$
$= 21y - 35 + 8y + 6$
$= 29y - 29$

53. $-(-14x) = 14x$

55. $-(2x - 3y - 6) = -2x + 3y + 6$

57. $\frac{1}{3}(3x) + [(4y) + (-4y)] = x + 0$
$= x$

59. Yes; The order in which you put on your shoes does not matter.

61. Answers may vary.

63. $962x + 18{,}667 = 962(7) + 18{,}667$
$= 6734 + 18{,}667$
$= 25{,}401$
$1990 + 7 = 1997$
In 1997, the average yearly earnings in the United States was \$25,401.

65. a. $0.6(220 - a) = 0.6(220) - 0.6(a)$
$= 132 - 0.6a$

b. Let $a = 20$
$0.6(220 - a) = 0.6(220 - 20)$
$= 0.6(200)$
$= 120$
$132 - 0.6a = 132 - 0.6(20)$
$= 132 - 12 = 120$

67.–71. Answers may vary.

73. a. False; For example, 1.7 is a rational number and it is not an integer.

b. False; All whole numbers, $\{0, 1, 2, 3, \ldots\}$, are also integers.

c. True; –7.5 is a rational number and it is not positive.

d. False; $-\pi$ is an irrational number that is also negative.

(c) is true.

75. $\sqrt{2} \approx 1.4$
$1.4 < 1.5$
$\sqrt{2} < 1.5$

77.
$-\frac{3.14}{2} = -1.57$
$-\frac{\pi}{2} \approx -1.571$
$-1.57 > -1.571$
$-\frac{3.14}{2} > -\frac{\pi}{2}$

Section P.2

Check Point Exercises

1. $(-4)^3 \cdot 2^2 = (-4)(-4)(-4) \cdot 2 \cdot 2$
$= -64 \cdot 4$
$= -256$

2. a. $2^{-3} = \frac{1}{2^3} = \frac{1}{2 \cdot 2 \cdot 2} = \frac{1}{8}$

b. $\frac{1}{6^{-2}} = \frac{1}{\frac{1}{6^2}} = 6^2 = 36$

3. a. $3^3 \cdot 3^2 = 3^{3+2} = 3^5 = 243$

b. $2^4 \cdot 2^{-7} = 2^{4+(-7)} = 2^{-3} = \frac{1}{2^3} = \frac{1}{8}$

c. $x^{-5} \cdot x^{11} = x^{-5+11} = x^6$

4. a. $(3^3)^2 = 3^{3 \cdot 2} = 3^6 = 729$

b. $(y^7)^4 = y^{7 \cdot 4} = y^{28}$

c. $(x^{-4})^2 = x^{-4 \cdot 2} = x^{-8} = \frac{1}{x^8}$

5. a. $\frac{3^6}{3^4} = 3^{6-4} = 3^2 = 9$

b. $\frac{x^5}{x^{12}} = x^{5-12} = x^{-7} = \frac{1}{x^7}$

c. $\frac{y^2}{y^{-7}} = y^{2-(-7)} = y^{2+7} = y^9$

6. $(-4x)^3 = (-4)^3 x^3 = -64x^3$

7. a. $\left(\frac{3}{4}\right)^3 = \frac{3^3}{4^3} = \frac{27}{64}$

b. $\left(-\frac{2}{y}\right)^5 = \frac{(-2)^5}{y^5} = \frac{-32}{y^5} = -\frac{32}{y^5}$

8. a. $(2x^3y^6)^4 = (2)^4(x^3)^4(y^6)^4$
$= (2)^4x^{3\cdot4}y^{6\cdot4}$
$= 16x^{12}y^{24}$

b. $(-6x^2y^5) = (-6)(3)x^2xy^5y3$
$= -18x^{2+1}y^{5+3}$
$= -18x^3y^8$

c. $\dfrac{100x^{12}y^2}{20x^{16}y^{-4}} = \left(\dfrac{100}{20}\right)\left(\dfrac{x^{12}}{x^{16}}\right)\left(\dfrac{y^2}{y^{-4}}\right)$
$= 5x^{12-16}y^{2-(-4)}$
$= 5x^{-4}y^6$
$= \dfrac{5y^6}{x^4}$

d. $\left(\dfrac{5x}{y^4}\right)^{-2} = \dfrac{5^{-2}x^{-2}}{(y^4)^{-2}}$
$= \dfrac{5^{-2}x^{-2}}{y^{-8}}$
$= \dfrac{y^8}{5^2x^2}$
$= \dfrac{y^8}{25x^2}$

9. a. Express 7.4×10^9 in decimal notation by moving the decimal point in 7.4 nine places to the right.
$7.4\times10^9 = 7,400,000,000$

b. Express 3.017×10^{-6} in decimal notation by moving the decimal point in 3.017 six places to the left.
$3.017\times10^{-6} = 0.000003017$

10. a. To express 7,410,000,000 in scientific notation, the decimal point needs to move nine places. The exponent on 10 is positive since 7,410,000,000 is greater than 10.
$7,410,000,000 = 7.41\times10^9$

b. To express 0.000000092 in scientific notation, the decimal points needs to move eight places. The exponent on 10 is negative since 0.000000092 is between 0 and 1.
$0.000000092 = 9.2\times10^{-8}$

11. The total distance covered by all runners is the number of people who run in the New York City Marathon, 2×10^4, multiplied by the distance of the Marathon, 26 miles.
$(2\times10^4)\times(26) = (2\times26)\times(10^4)$
$= 52\times10^4$
$= 5.2\times10^5$
Thus, the total distance covered by all runners is 5.2×10^5 miles.

Exercise Set P.2

1. $5^2\cdot2 = (5\cdot5)\cdot2 = 25\cdot2 = 50$

3. $(-2)^6 = (-2)(-2)(-2)(-2)(-2)(-2) = 64$

5. $-2^6 = -2\cdot2\cdot2\cdot2\cdot2\cdot2 = -64$

7. $(-3)^0 = 1$

9. $-3^0 = -1$

11. $4^{-3} = \dfrac{1}{4^3} = \dfrac{1}{4\cdot4\cdot4} = \dfrac{1}{64}$

13. $2^2\cdot2^3 = 2^{2+3} = 2^5 = 2\cdot2\cdot2\cdot2\cdot2 = 32$

15. $(2^2)^3 = 2^{2\cdot3} = 2^6 = 2\cdot2\cdot2\cdot2\cdot2\cdot2 = 64$

17. $\dfrac{2^8}{2^4} = 2^{8-4} = 2^4 = 2\cdot2\cdot2\cdot2 = 16$

19. $3^{-3}\cdot3 = 3^{-3+1} = 3^{-2} = \dfrac{1}{3^2} = \dfrac{1}{3\cdot3} = \dfrac{1}{9}$

21. $\dfrac{2^3}{2^7} = 2^{3-7} = 2^{-4} = \dfrac{1}{2^4} = \dfrac{1}{2\cdot2\cdot2\cdot2} = \dfrac{1}{16}$

23. $x^{-2}y = \dfrac{1}{x^2}\cdot y = \dfrac{y}{x^2}$

25. $x^0y^5 = 1\cdot y^5 = y^5$

27. $x^3 \cdot x^7 = x^{3+7} = x^{10}$

29. $x^{-5} \cdot x^{10} = x^{-5+10} = x^5$

31. $(x^3)^7 = x^{3\cdot 7} = x^{21}$

33. $(x^{-5})^3 = x^{-5\cdot 3} = x^{-15} = \frac{1}{x^{15}}$

35. $\frac{x^{14}}{x^7} = x^{14-7} = x^7$

37. $\frac{x^{14}}{x^{-7}} = x^{14-(-7)} = x^{14+7} = x^{21}$

39. $(8x^3)^2 = 8^2(x^3)^2 = 8^2x^{3\cdot 2} = 64x^6$

41. $\left(-\frac{4}{x}\right)^3 = \frac{(-4)^3}{x^3} = -\frac{64}{x^3}$

43. $(-3x^2y^5)^2 = (-3)^2(x^2)^2 \cdot (y^5)^2$
$= 9x^{2\cdot 2}y^{5\cdot 2}$
$= 9x^4y^{10}$

45. $(3x^4)(2x^7) = 3 \cdot 2x^4 \cdot x^7 = 6x^{4+7} = 6x^{11}$

47. $(-9x^3y)(-2x^6y^4) = (-9)(-2)x^3x^6yy^4$
$= 18x^{3+6}y^{1+4}$
$= 18x^9y^5$

49. $\frac{8x^{20}}{2x^4} = \left(\frac{8}{2}\right)\left(\frac{x^{20}}{x^4}\right) = 4x^{20-4} = 4x^{16}$

51. $\frac{25a^{13} \cdot b^4}{-5a^2 \cdot b^3} = \left(\frac{25}{-5}\right)\left(\frac{a^{13}}{a^2}\right)\left(\frac{b^4}{b^3}\right)$
$= -5a^{13-2}b^{4-3}$
$= -5a^{11}b$

53. $\frac{14b^7}{7b^{14}} = \left(\frac{14}{7}\right)\left(\frac{b^7}{b^{14}}\right) = 2 \cdot b^{7-14} = 2b^{-7} = \frac{2}{b^7}$

55. $(4x^3)^{-2} = (4^{-2})(x^3)^{-2}$
$= 4^{-2}x^{-6}$
$= \frac{1}{4^2x^6}$
$= \frac{1}{16x^6}$

57. $\frac{24x^3 \cdot y^5}{32x^7y^{-9}} = \frac{3}{4}x^{3-7}y^{5-(-9)}$
$= \frac{3}{4}x^{-4}y^{14}$
$= \frac{3y^{14}}{4x^4}$

59. $\left(\frac{5x^3}{y}\right)^{-2} = \frac{5^{-2}x^{3\cdot(-2)}}{y^{-2}}$
$= \frac{5^{-2} \cdot x^{-6}}{y^{-2}}$
$= \frac{y^2}{5^2 \cdot x^6}$
$= \frac{y^2}{25x^6}$

61. $4.7 \times 10^3 = 4700$

63. $4 \times 10^6 = 4{,}000{,}000$

65. $7.86 \times 10^{-4} = 0.000786$

67. $3.18 \times 10^{-6} = 0.00000318$

69. $3600 = 3.6 \times 10^3$

71. $220{,}000{,}000 = 2.2 \times 10^8$

73. $0.027 = 2.7 \times 10^{-2}$

75. $0.000763 = 7.63 \times 10^{-4}$

77. $(2\times10^3)(3\times10^2) = (2\times3)\times(10^3\times10^2)$
$= 6\times10^{3+2}$
$= 6\times10^5$
$= 600,000$

79. $(4.1\times10^2)(3\times10^{-4}) = (4.1\times3)\times(10^2\times10^{-4})$
$= 12.3\times10^{2+(-4)}$
$= 12.3\times10^{-2}$
$= 0.123$

81. $\dfrac{12\times10^6}{4\times10^2} = \left(\dfrac{12}{4}\right)\times\left(\dfrac{10^6}{10^2}\right)$
$= 3\times10^{6-2}$
$= 3\times10^4$
$= 30,000$

83. $\dfrac{6.3\times10^3}{3\times10^5} = \left(\dfrac{6.3}{3}\right)\times\left(\dfrac{10^3}{10^5}\right)$
$= 2.1\times10^{3-5} = 2.1\times10^{-2}$
$= 0.021$

85. 1,694,000 million $= (1.694\times10^6)(1\times10^6)$
$= 1.694\times10^{6+6}$
$= 1.694\times10^{12}$

87. 60 billion $= (6.0\times10)(1\times10^9) = 6.0\times10^{10}$

89. $(2.7\times10^8)(120) = (2.7\times10^8)(1.2\times10^2)$
$= (2.7\times1.2)\times(10^8\times10^2)$
$= 3.24\times10^{8+2}$
$= 3.24\times10^{10}$

91.–97. Answers may vary.

99. $1-(2^{-1}+2^{-2}) = 1-\left(\dfrac{1}{2}+\dfrac{1}{2^2}\right)$
$= 1-\left(\dfrac{1}{2}+\dfrac{1}{4}\right)$
$= 1-\left(\dfrac{3}{4}\right)$
$= \dfrac{1}{4}$

Section P.3

Check Point Exercises

1. a. Since $\sqrt{a^2} = |a|$,
$\sqrt{3^2} = 3$.

b. $\sqrt{5x}\cdot\sqrt{10x} = \sqrt{5x\cdot10x}$
$= \sqrt{50x^2}$
$= \sqrt{25x^2\cdot2}$
$= \sqrt{25x^2}\sqrt{2}$
$= \sqrt{25}\sqrt{x^2}\sqrt{2}$
$= 5|x|\sqrt{2}$

2. a. $\sqrt{\dfrac{25}{16}} = \dfrac{\sqrt{25}}{\sqrt{16}} = \dfrac{5}{4}$

b. $\dfrac{\sqrt{150x^3}}{\sqrt{2x}} = \sqrt{\dfrac{150x^3}{2x}} = \sqrt{75x^2}$
$= \sqrt{25x^2}\sqrt{3}$
$= \sqrt{25}\sqrt{x^2}\sqrt{3}$
$= 5|x|\sqrt{3}$

3. a. $8\sqrt{13}+9\sqrt{13} = (8+9)\sqrt{3}$
$= 17\sqrt{13}$

b. $\sqrt{17x}-20\sqrt{17x}$
$= 1\sqrt{17x}-20\sqrt{17x}$
$= (1-20)\sqrt{17x}$
$= -19\sqrt{17x}$

4. a. $5\sqrt{27}+\sqrt{12}$
$= 5\sqrt{9\cdot3}+\sqrt{4\cdot3}$
$= 5\cdot3\sqrt{3}+2\sqrt{3}$
$= 15\sqrt{3}+2\sqrt{3}$
$= (15+2)\sqrt{3}$
$= 17\sqrt{3}$

b. $6\sqrt{18x} - 4\sqrt{8x}$
$= 6\sqrt{9 \cdot 2x} - 4\sqrt{4 \cdot 2x}$
$= 6 \cdot 3\sqrt{2x} - 4 \cdot 2\sqrt{2x}$
$= 18\sqrt{2x} - 8\sqrt{2x}$
$= (18 - 8)\sqrt{2x}$
$= 10\sqrt{2x}$

5. a. If we multiply numerator and denominator by $\sqrt{3}$, the denominator becomes $\sqrt{3} \cdot \sqrt{3} = \sqrt{9} = 3$. Therefore, multiply by 1, choosing $\frac{\sqrt{3}}{\sqrt{3}}$ for 1.

$$\frac{5}{\sqrt{3}} = \frac{5}{\sqrt{3}} \cdot \frac{\sqrt{3}}{\sqrt{3}} = \frac{5\sqrt{3}}{\sqrt{9}} = \frac{5\sqrt{3}}{3}$$

b. The *smallest* number that will produce a perfect square in the denominator of $\frac{6}{\sqrt{12}}$ is $\sqrt{3}$ because $\sqrt{12} \cdot \sqrt{3} = \sqrt{36} = 6$. So multiply by 1, choosing $\frac{\sqrt{3}}{\sqrt{3}}$ for 1.

$$\frac{6}{\sqrt{12}} = \frac{6}{\sqrt{12}} \cdot \frac{\sqrt{3}}{\sqrt{3}} = \frac{6\sqrt{3}}{\sqrt{36}} = \frac{6\sqrt{3}}{6} = \sqrt{3}$$

6. The denominator will not contain a radical if multiplied by $4 - \sqrt{5}$. Therefore, multiply by 1, choosing $\frac{4-\sqrt{5}}{4-\sqrt{5}}$ for 1.

$$\frac{8}{4+\sqrt{5}} = \frac{8}{4+\sqrt{5}} \cdot \frac{4-\sqrt{5}}{4-\sqrt{5}}$$
$$= \frac{8(4-\sqrt{5})}{4^2 - (\sqrt{5})^2}$$
$$= \frac{8(4-\sqrt{5})}{16-5}$$
$$= \frac{8(4-\sqrt{5})}{11} \text{ or } \frac{32 - 8\sqrt{5}}{11}$$

7. a. $\sqrt[3]{40} = \sqrt[3]{8 \cdot 5} = \sqrt[3]{8} \cdot \sqrt[3]{5} = 2\sqrt[3]{5}$

b. $\sqrt[5]{8} \cdot \sqrt[5]{8} = \sqrt[5]{8 \cdot 8}$
$= \sqrt[5]{64}$
$= \sqrt[5]{32} \cdot \sqrt[5]{2}$
$= 2\sqrt[5]{2}$
5_2

c. $\sqrt[3]{\frac{125}{27}} = \frac{\sqrt[3]{125}}{\sqrt[3]{27}} = \frac{5}{3}$

8. $3\sqrt[3]{81} - 4\sqrt[3]{3}$
$= 3\sqrt[3]{27 \cdot 3} - 4\sqrt[3]{3}$
$= 3 \cdot 3\sqrt[3]{3} - 4\sqrt[3]{3}$
$= 9\sqrt[3]{3} - 4\sqrt[3]{3}$
$= (9 - 4)\sqrt[3]{3}$
$= 5\sqrt[3]{3}$

9. a. $81^{1/2} = \sqrt{81} = 9$

b. $27^{1/3} = \sqrt[3]{27} = 3$

c. $32^{-1/5} = \frac{1}{32^{1/5}} = \frac{1}{\sqrt[5]{32}} = \frac{1}{2}$

10. a. $4^{3/2} = (\sqrt{4})^3 = 2^3 = 8$

b. $32^{-2/5} = \frac{1}{32^{2/5}} = \frac{1}{(\sqrt[5]{32})^2} = \frac{1}{2^2} = \frac{1}{4}$

11. a. $\left(2x^{4/3}\right)\left(5x^{8/3}\right)$
$= 2 \cdot 5x^{4/3} - x^{8/3}$
$= 10x^{(4/3)+(8/3)}$
$= 10x^{12/3}$
$= 10x^4$

b. $\frac{20x^4}{5x^{3/2}} = \left(\frac{20}{5}\right)\left(\frac{x^4}{x^{3/2}}\right)$
$= 4x^{4-(3/2)}$
$= 4x^{(8/2)-(3/2)}$
$= 4x^{5/2}$

12. $\sqrt[6]{x^3} = x^{3/6} = x^{1/2} = \sqrt{x}$

Exercise Set P.3

1. $\sqrt{36} = \sqrt{6^2} = 6$

3. $\sqrt{-36}$ is not a real number.

5. $\sqrt{(-13)^2} = |-13| = 13$

7. $\sqrt{50} = \sqrt{25 \cdot 2} = \sqrt{25}\sqrt{2} = 5\sqrt{2}$

9. $$\begin{aligned}\sqrt{45x^2} &= \sqrt{9x^2 \cdot 5}\\ &= \sqrt{9x^2}\sqrt{5}\\ &= \sqrt{9}\sqrt{x^2}\sqrt{5}\\ &= 3|x|\sqrt{5}\end{aligned}$$

11. $$\begin{aligned}\sqrt{2x} \cdot \sqrt{6x} &= \sqrt{2x \cdot 6x}\\ &= \sqrt{12x^2}\\ &= \sqrt{4x^2 \cdot 3}\\ &= \sqrt{4x^2}\sqrt{3}\\ &= \sqrt{4}\sqrt{x^2}\sqrt{3}\\ &= 2|x|\sqrt{3}\end{aligned}$$

13. $\sqrt{x^3} = \sqrt{x^2 \cdot x} = |x|\sqrt{x}$

15. $$\begin{aligned}\sqrt{2x^2} \cdot \sqrt{6x} &= \sqrt{2x^2 \cdot 6x}\\ &= \sqrt{12x^3}\\ &= \sqrt{4x^2}\sqrt{x}\\ &= 2|x|\sqrt{3x}\end{aligned}$$

17. $\sqrt{\dfrac{1}{81}} = \dfrac{\sqrt{1}}{\sqrt{81}} = \dfrac{1}{9}$

19. $\sqrt{\dfrac{49}{16}} = \dfrac{\sqrt{49}}{\sqrt{16}} = \dfrac{7}{4}$

21. $\dfrac{\sqrt{48x^3}}{\sqrt{3x}} = \sqrt{\dfrac{48x^3}{3x}} = \sqrt{16x^2} = 4|x|$

23. $$\begin{aligned}\frac{\sqrt{150x^4}}{\sqrt{3x}} &= \sqrt{\frac{150x^4}{3x}}\\ &= \sqrt{50x^3}\\ &= \sqrt{25x^2}\sqrt{2x}\\ &= 5|x|\sqrt{2x}\end{aligned}$$

25. $7\sqrt{3} + 6\sqrt{3} = (7+6)\sqrt{3} = 13\sqrt{3}$

27. $6\sqrt{17x} - 8\sqrt{17x} = (6-8)\sqrt{17x} = -2\sqrt{17x}$

29. $$\begin{aligned}\sqrt{8} + 3\sqrt{2} &= \sqrt{4 \cdot 2} + 3\sqrt{2}\\ &= 2\sqrt{2} + 3\sqrt{2}\\ &= (2+3)\sqrt{2}\\ &= 5\sqrt{2}\end{aligned}$$

31. $$\begin{aligned}\sqrt{50x} - \sqrt{8x} &= \sqrt{25 \cdot 2x} - \sqrt{4 \cdot 2x}\\ &= 5\sqrt{2x} - 2\sqrt{2x}\\ &= (5-2)\sqrt{2x}\\ &= 3\sqrt{2x}\end{aligned}$$

33. $$\begin{aligned}3\sqrt{18} + 5\sqrt{50} &= 3\sqrt{9 \cdot 2} + 5\sqrt{25 \cdot 2}\\ &= 3 \cdot 3\sqrt{2} + 5 \cdot 5\sqrt{2}\\ &= 9\sqrt{2} + 25\sqrt{2}\\ &= (9+25)\sqrt{2}\\ &= 34\sqrt{2}\end{aligned}$$

35. $\dfrac{1}{\sqrt{7}} = \dfrac{1}{\sqrt{7}} \cdot \dfrac{\sqrt{7}}{\sqrt{7}} = \dfrac{\sqrt{7}}{7}$

37. $\dfrac{\sqrt{2}}{\sqrt{5}} = \dfrac{\sqrt{2}}{\sqrt{5}} \cdot \dfrac{\sqrt{5}}{\sqrt{5}} = \dfrac{\sqrt{10}}{5}$

39. $$\begin{aligned}\frac{13}{3+\sqrt{11}} &= \frac{13}{3+\sqrt{11}} \cdot \frac{3-\sqrt{11}}{3-\sqrt{11}}\\ &= \frac{13(3-\sqrt{11})}{3^2 - (\sqrt{11})^2}\\ &= \frac{13(3-\sqrt{11})}{9-11}\\ &= \frac{13(3-\sqrt{11})}{-2}\end{aligned}$$

41. $\frac{7}{\sqrt{5}-2}=\frac{7}{\sqrt{5}-2}\cdot\frac{\sqrt{5}+2}{\sqrt{5}+2}$
$=\frac{7(\sqrt{5}+2)}{(\sqrt{5})^2-2^2}$
$=\frac{7(\sqrt{5}+2)}{5-4}$
$=7(\sqrt{5}+2)$

43. $\frac{6}{\sqrt{5}+\sqrt{3}}=\frac{6}{\sqrt{5}+\sqrt{3}}\cdot\frac{\sqrt{5}-\sqrt{3}}{\sqrt{5}-\sqrt{3}}$
$=\frac{6(\sqrt{5}-\sqrt{3})}{(\sqrt{5})^2-(\sqrt{3})^2}$
$=\frac{6(\sqrt{5}-\sqrt{3})}{5-3}$
$=\frac{6(\sqrt{5}-\sqrt{3})}{2}$
$=3(\sqrt{5}-\sqrt{3})$

45. $\sqrt[3]{125}=\sqrt[3]{5^3}=5$

47. $\sqrt[3]{-8}=\sqrt[3]{(-2)^3}=-2$

49. $\sqrt[4]{-16}$ is not a real number.

51. $\sqrt[4]{(-3)^4}=|-3|=3$

53. $\sqrt[5]{(-3)^5}=-3$

55. $\sqrt[3]{32}=\sqrt[3]{8\cdot 4}=\sqrt[3]{8}\sqrt[3]{4}=2\cdot\sqrt[3]{4}$

57. $\sqrt[3]{x^4}=\sqrt[3]{x^3\cdot x}=x\cdot\sqrt[3]{x}$

59. $\sqrt[3]{9}\cdot\sqrt[3]{6}=\sqrt[3]{54}=\sqrt[3]{27\cdot 2}=\sqrt[3]{27}\sqrt[3]{2}=3\sqrt[3]{2}$

61. $\frac{\sqrt[5]{64x^6}}{\sqrt[5]{2x}}=\sqrt[5]{\frac{64x^6}{2x}}=\sqrt[5]{32x^5}=2x$

63. $36^{1/2}=\sqrt{36}=6$

65. $8^{1/3}=\sqrt[3]{8}=2$

67. $125^{2/3}=\left(\sqrt[3]{125}\right)^2=5^2=25$

69. $32^{-4/5}=\frac{1}{32^{4/5}}=\frac{1}{2^4}=\frac{1}{16}$

71. $\left(7x^{1/3}\right)\left(2x^{1/4}\right)=7\cdot 2x^{1/3}\cdot x^{1/4}$
$=14\cdot x^{1/3+1/4}$
$=14x^{7/12}$

73. $\frac{20x^{1/2}}{5x^{1/4}}=\left(\frac{20}{5}\right)\left(\frac{x^{1/2}}{x^{1/4}}\right)$
$=4\cdot x^{1/2-1/4}$
$=4x^{1/4}$

75. $\left(x^{2/3}\right)^3=x^{2/3\cdot 3}=x^2$

77. $(25x^4y^6)^{1/2}=25^{1/2}x^{4\cdot 1/2}y^{6\cdot 1/2}=5x^2|y|^3$

79. $\sqrt[4]{5^2}=5^{2/4}=5^{1/2}=\sqrt{5}$

81. $\sqrt[3]{x^6}=x^{6/3}=x^2$

83. $\sqrt[6]{x^4}=x^{4/6}=|x|^{2/3}$

85. $2\sqrt{5L}$ with $L=40$ gives
$2\sqrt{5\cdot 40}=2\sqrt{200}$
$=2\sqrt{100\cdot 2}$
$=2\cdot 10\sqrt{2}$
$=20\sqrt{2}$
The speed of the car prior to the accident was $20\sqrt{2}$ miles per hour.

87. $\frac{w}{h} = \frac{2}{\sqrt{5}-1}$
$= \frac{2}{\sqrt{5}-1} \cdot \frac{\sqrt{5}+1}{\sqrt{5}+1}$
$= \frac{2(\sqrt{5}+1)}{(\sqrt{5})^2 - 1^2}$
$= \frac{2(\sqrt{5}+1)}{5-1}$
$= \frac{2(\sqrt{5}+1)}{4}$
$= \frac{\sqrt{5}+1}{2}$
≈ 1.62

89. $\frac{7\sqrt{2 \cdot 2 \cdot 3}}{6} = \frac{7\sqrt{2^2 \cdot 3}}{6}$
$= \frac{7\sqrt{2^2}\sqrt{3}}{6}$
$= \frac{7 \cdot 2\sqrt{3}}{6}$
$= \frac{7}{3}\sqrt{3}$

91. $0.07d^{3/2} = 0.07 \cdot 9^{3/2}$
$= 0.07(\sqrt{9})^3$
$= 0.07 \cdot 3^3$
$= 0.07 \cdot 27$
$= 1.89$
The duration of a storm whose diameter is 9 miles is 1.89 hours.

93.–97. Answers may vary.

99. $60.19x^{0.025}$

x	$60.19x^{0.025}$	x	$60.19x^{0.025x}$
1	60.19	17	64.61
2	61.24	18	64.70
3	61.87	19	64.79
4	62.31	20	64.87
5	62.66	21	64.95
6	62.95	22	65.03
7	63.19	23	65.10
8	63.40	24	65.17
9	63.59	25	65.23
10	63.76	26	65.30
11	63.91	27	65.36
12	64.05	28	65.42
13	64.18	29	65.48
14	64.30	30	65.53
15	64.41	31	65.59
16	64.51		

At the beginning of 1990, the expected lifespan was 64.95 years. During 1990, the lifespan of African American men first exceeded 65 years. At the beginning of 1991, the expected lifespan was 65.03 years.

101. **a.** False; $(-8)^{1/3} = \sqrt[3]{-8} = -2$, which is a real number.

b. False; $\sqrt{x^2 + y^2} \neq \sqrt{(x+y)^2} = x + y$, if $x + y \geq 0$.

c. False; $\frac{1}{2} = 8^{-1/3} \neq -2$

d. True; $2^1 = 2^{1/2}2^{1/2} = 2$

(d) is true.

103. $\sqrt{\square \cdot x^{\square}} = 5 \cdot x^7$

$\left(\square \cdot x^{\square}\right)^{1/2} = 5 \cdot x^7$

Square both sides.

$\square \cdot x^{\square} = 25 \cdot x^{14}$

Let $\square = 25$ and $\square = 14$.

105. a. $3^{1/2} \square 3^{1/3}$

Square both sides. $3 \square 3^{2/3} = 9^{1/3}$

Raise to the third power on both sides.

$3^3 = 27 \boxed{>} \left(9^{1/3}\right)^3 = 9$

b. $\sqrt{7} + \sqrt{18} \square \sqrt{7+18}$

$\sqrt{7} + \sqrt{18} \square \sqrt{7+18} = \sqrt{25} = 5$

Square both sides.

$(\sqrt{7} + \sqrt{18})^2 = 7 + 2\sqrt{126} + 18$

$= 25 + 3\sqrt{14} \boxed{>} 25$

Section P.4

Check Point Exercises

1. a. $(-17x^3 + 4x^2 - 11x - 5) + (16x^3 - 3x^2 + 3x - 15)$

$= (-17x^3 + 16x^3) + (4x^2 - 3x^2) + (-11x + 3x) + (-5 - 15)$

$= -x^3 + x^2 - 8x - 20$

b. $(13x^3 - 9x^2 - 7x + 1) - (7x^3 + 2x^2 - 5x + 9)$

$= (13x^3 - 9x^2 - 7x + 1) + (7x^3 - 2x^2 + 5x - 9)$

$= (13x^3 + 7x^3) + (-9x^2 - 2x^2) + (-7x + 5x) + (1 - 9)$

$= 20x^3 - 11x^2 - 2x - 8$

2. $(5x - 2)(3x^2 - 5x + 4)$

$= 5x(3x^2 - 5x + 4) - 2(3x^2 - 5x + 4)$

$= 5x \cdot 3x^2 - 5x \cdot 5x + 5x \cdot 4 - 2 \cdot 3x^2 + 2 \cdot 5x - 2 \cdot 4$

$= 15x^3 - 25x^2 + 20x - 6x^2 + 10x - 8$

$= 15x^3 - 31x^2 + 30x - 8$

3. $(7x-5)(4x-3) = 7x \cdot 4x + 7x(-3) + (-5)4x + (-5)(-3)$
$= 28x^2 - 21x - 20x + 15$
$= 28x^2 - 41x + 15$

4. a. Use the special-product formula shown.
$(A+B)(A-B) = A^2 - B^2$
$(7x+8)(7x-8) = (7x)^2 - (8)^2$
$= 49x^2 - 64$

b. Use the special-product formula shown.
$(A+B)(A-B) = A^2 - B^2$
$(2y^3-5)(2y^3+5) = (2y^3+5)(2y^3-5) = (2y^3)^2 - (5)^2 = 4y^6 - 25$

5. a. Use the special-product formula shown.
$(A+B)^2 = A^2 + 2AB + B^2$
$(x+10)^2 = x^2 + 2 \cdot x \cdot 10 + 10^2$
$= x^2 + 20x + 100$

b. Use the special-product formula shown.
$(A+B)^2 = A^2 + 2AB + B^2$
$(5x+4)^2 = (5x)^2 + 2(5x)(4) + 4^2$
$= 25x^2 + 40x + 16$

6. a. Use the special-product formula shown.
$(A-B)^2 = A^2 - 2AB + B^2$
$(x-9)^2 = x^2 - 2 \cdot x \cdot 9 + 9^2$
$= x^2 - 18x + 81$

b. Use the special-product formula shown.
$(A-B)^2 = A^2 - 2AB + B^2$
$(7x-3)^2 = (7x)^2 - 2(7x)(3) + 3^2$
$= 49x^2 - 42x + 9$

7. $(x^3 - 4x^2y + 5xy^2 - y^3) - (x^3 - 6x^2y + y^3)$
$= (x^3 - 4x^2y + 5xy^2 - y^3) + (-x^3 + 6x^2y - y^3)$
$= (x^3 - x^3) + (-4x^2y + 6x^2y) + (5xy^2) + (-y^3 - y^3)$
$= 2x^2y + 5xy^2 - 2y^3$

8. a. $(7x-6y)(3x-y) = (7x)(3x)+(7x)(-y)+(-6y)(3x)+(-6y)(-y)$
$= 21x^2 - 7xy - 18xy + 6y^2$
$= 21x^2 - 25xy + 6y^2$

b. $(x^2+5y)^2 = (x^2)^2 + 2(x^2)(5y) + (5y)^2$
$= x^4 + 10x^2y + 25y^2$

Exercise Set P.4

1. Yes; $2x + 3x^2 - 5 = 3x^2 + 2x - 5$

3. No; The form of a polynomial involves addition and subtraction, not division.

5. $3x^2$ has degree 2
$-5x$ has degree 1
4 has degree 0
$3x^2 - 5x + 4$ has degree 2.

7. x^2 has degree 2
$-4x^3$ has degree 3
$9x$ has degree 1
$-12x^4$ has degree 4
63 has degree 0
$x^2 - 4x^3 + 9x - 12x^4 + 63$ has degree 4.

9. $(-6x^3 + 5x^2 - 8x + 9) + (17x^3 + 2x^2 - 4x - 13) = (-6x^3 + 17x^3) + (5x^2 + 2x^2) + (-8x - 4x) + (9 - 13)$
$= 11x^3 + 7x^2 - 12x - 4$
The degree is 3.

11. $(17x^3 - 5x^2 + 4x - 3) - (5x^3 - 9x^2 - 8x + 11) = (17x^3 - 5x^2 + 4x - 3) + (-5x^3 + 9x^2 + 8x - 11)$
$= (17x^3 - 5x^3) + (-5x^2 + 9x^2) + (4x + 8x) + (-3 - 11)$
$= 12x^3 + 4x^2 + 12x - 14$
The degree is 3.

13. $(5x^2 - 7x - 8) + (2x^2 - 3x + 7) - (x^2 - 4x - 3) = (5x^2 - 7x - 8) + (2x^2 - 3x + 7) + (-x^2 + 4x + 3)$
$= (5x^2 + 2x^2 - x^2) + (-7x - 3x + 4x) + (-8 + 7 + 3)$
$= 6x^2 - 6x + 2$
The degree is 2.

15. $(x+1)(x^2 - x + 1) = x(x^2) - x \cdot x + x \cdot 1 + 1(x^2) - 1 \cdot x + 1 \cdot 1$
$= x^3 - x^2 + x + x^2 - x + 1$
$= x^3 + 1$

17. $(2x-3)(x^2-3x+5) = (2x)(x^2)+(2x)(-3x)+(2x)(5)+(-3)(x^2)+(-3)(-3x)+(-3)(5)$
$= 2x^3-6x^2+10x-3x^2+9x-15$
$= 2x^3-9x^2+19x-15$

19. $(x+7)(x+3) = x^2+3x+7x+21 = x^2+10x+21$

21. $(x-5)(x+3) = x^2+3x-5x-15 = x^2-2x-15$

23. $(3x+5)(2x+1) = (3x)(2x)+3x(1)+5(2x)+5 = 6x^2+3x+10x+5 = 6x^2+13x+5$

25. $(2x-3)(5x+3) = (2x)(5x)+(2x)(3)+(-3)(5x)+(-3)(3)$
$= 10x^2+6x-15x-9$
$= 10x^2-9x-9$

27. $(5x^2-4)(3x^2-7) = (5x^2)(3x^2)+(5x^2)(-7)+(-4)(3x^2)+(-4)(-7)$
$= 15x^4-35x^2-12x^2+28$
$= 15x^4-47x^2+28$

29. $(x+3)(x-3) = x^2-3^2$
$= x^2-9$

31. $(3x+2)(3x-2) = (3x)^2-2^2$
$= 9x^2-4$

33. $(5-7x)(5+7x) = 5^2-(7x)^2$
$= 25-49x^2$

35. $(4x^2+5x)(4x^2-5x) = (4x^2)^2-(5x)^2$
$= 16x^4-25x^2$

37. $(x+2)^2 = x^2+2\cdot x\cdot 2+2^2 = x^2+4x+4$

39. $(2x+3)^2 = (2x)^2+2(2x)(3)+3^2$
$= 4x^2+12x+9$

41. $(x-3)^2 = x^2-2\cdot x\cdot 3+3^2 = x^2-6x+9$

43. $(4x^2-1)^2$
$= (4x^2)^2-2(4x^2)(1)+1^2$
$= 16x^4-8x^2+1$

45. $(7-2x)^2 = 7^2 - 2(7)(2x) + (2x)^2$
$= 49 - 28x + 4x^2$
$= 4x^2 - 28x + 49$

47. $(x+1)^3 = x^3 + 3\cdot x^2 \cdot 1 + 3x \cdot 1^2 + 1^3$
$= x^3 + 3x^2 + 3x + 1$

49. $(2x+3)^3$
$= (2x)^3 + 3\cdot(2x)^2 \cdot 3 + 3(2x)\cdot 3^2 + 3^3$
$= 8x^3 + 36x^2 + 54x + 27$

51. $(x-3)^3 = x^3 - 3\cdot x^3 \cdot 3 + 3\cdot x \cdot 3^2 - 3^3$
$= x^3 - 9x^2 + 27x - 27$

53. $(3x-4)^3 = (3x)^3 - 3(3x)^2 \cdot 4 + 3(3x)\cdot 4^2 - 4^3$
$= 27x^3 - 108x^2 + 144x - 64$

55. $(5x^2y - 3xy) + (2x^2y - xy) = (5x^2y + 2x^2y) + (-3xy - xy)$
$= (5+2)x^2y + (-3-1)xy$
$= 7x^2y - 4xy$ is of degree 3.

57. $(4x^2y + 8xy + 11) + (-2x^2y + 5xy + 2) = (4x^2y - 2x^2y) + (8xy + 5xy) + (11+2)$
$= (4-2)x^2y + (8+5)xy + 13$
$= 2x^2y + 13xy + 13$ is of degree 3.

59. $(x^3 + 7xy - 5y^2) - (6x^3 - xy + 4y^2) = (x^3 + 7xy - 5y^2)$
$= (x^3 - 6x^3) + (7xy + xy) + (-5y^2 - 4y^2)$
$= (1-6)x^3 + (7+1)xy + (-5-4)y^2$
$= -5x^3 + 8xy - 9y^2$ is of degree 3.

61. $(3x^4y^2 + 5x^3y - 3y) - (2x^4y^2 - 3x^3y - 4y + 6x) = (3x^4y^2 + 5x^3y - 3y) + (-2x^4y^2 + 3x^3y + 4y - 6x)$
$= (3x^4y^2 - 2x^4y^2) + (5x^3y + 3x^3y) + (-3y + 4y) - 6x$
$= (3-2)x^4y^2 + (5+3)x^3y + (-3+4)y - 6x$
$= x^4y^2 + 8x^3y + y - 6x$ is of degree 6.

63. $(x+5y)(7x+3y) = x(7x) + x(3y) + (5y)(7x) + (5y)(3y)$
$= 7x^2 + 3xy + 35xy + 15y^2$
$= 7x^2 + 38xy + 15y^2$

65. $(x-3y)(2x+7y) = x(2x) + x(7y) + (-3y)(2x) + (-3y)(7y)$
$= 2x^2 + 7xy - 6xy - 21y^2$
$= 2x^2 + xy - 21y^2$

67. $(3xy-1)(5xy+2) = (3xy)(5xy) + (3xy)(2) + (-1)(5xy) + (-1)(2)$
$= 15x^2y^2 + 6xy - 5xy - 2$
$= 15x^2y^2 + xy - 2$

69. $(7x+5y)^2 = (7x)^2 + 2(7x)(5y) + (5y)^2 = 49x^2 + 70xy + 25y^2$

71. $(x^2y^2-3)^2 = (x^2y^2)^2 - 2(x^2y^2)(3) + 3^2 = x^4y^4 - 6x^2y^2 + 9$

73. $(x-y)(x^2+xy+y^2) = x(x^2) + x(xy) + x(y^2) + (-y)(x^2) + (-y)(xy) + (-y)(y^2)$
$= x^3 + x^2y + xy^2 - x^2y - xy^2 - y^3$
$= x^3 - y^3$

75. $(3x+5y)(3x-5y) = (3x)^2 - (5y)^2 = 9x^2 - 25y^2$

77. $0.018x^2 - 0.757x + 9.047$ when $x = 40$ yields
$0.018(40)^2 - 0.757(40) + 9.047 = 28.8 - 30.28 + 9.047 = 7.567$
A person earning $40,000 feels underpaid $7567.

79. Let $A = 20$
$-0.02A^2 + 2A + 22$
$= -0.02(20)^2 + 2(20) + 22$
$= -8 + 40 + 22$
$= 54$
Let $A = 50$
$-0.02A^2 + 2A + 22$
$= -0.02(50)^2 + 2(50) + 22$
$= -50 + 100 + 22$
$= 72$
Let $A = 80$
$-0.02A^2 + 2A + 22$
$= -0.02(80)^2 + 2(80) + 22$
$= -128 + 160 + 22$
$= 54$
Performance increases as enthusiasm goes from 1 to 50, then performance decreases as enthusiasm goes from 50 to 100.

81. Number of people still ill t weeks after January 1 = (Number of people who catch cold t weeks after January 1) – (Number of people who recover t weeks after January 1)

$$= (5t - 3t^2 + t^3) - \left(t - t^2 + \frac{1}{3}t^3\right)$$
$$= (5t - 3t^2 + t^3) + \left(-t + t^2 - \frac{1}{3}t^3\right)$$
$$= (5t - t) + (-3t^2 + t^2) + \left(t^3 - \frac{1}{3}t^3\right)$$
$$= 4t - 2t^2 + \frac{2}{3}t^3$$

83. $(x+3)(x+9) - (x+1)(x+5)$

$$= (x^2 + 9x + 3x + 27) - (x^2 + 5x + x + 5)$$
$$= (x^2 + 12x + 27) - (x^2 + 6x + 5)$$
$$= (x^2 + 12x + 27) + (-x^2 - 6x - 6)$$
$$= (x^2 - x^2) + (12x - 6x) + (27 - 5)$$
$$= 6x + 22$$

85.–91. Answers may vary.

93.

x	$-3.08x^2 + 40.35x$ $+305.89$	# of aggravated assaults in US per 100,000	x	$-3.08x^2 + 40.35x$ $+305.89$	# of aggravated assaults in US per 100,000
0	305.89	306 in 1986	8	431.57	432 in 1994
1	343.16	343 in 1987	9	419.56	420 in 1995
2	374.27	374 in 1988	10	401.39	401 in 1996
3	399.22	399 in 1989	11	377.06	377 in 1997
4	418.01	418 in 1990	12	346.57	347 in 1998
5	430.64	431 in 1991	13	309.92	310 in 1999
6	437.11	437 in 1992	14	267.11	267 in 2000
7	437.42	437 in 1993			

The number of aggravated assaults in US per 100,000 was the greatest during 1992 and 1993.

95. $[(7x+5)+4y][(7x+5)-4y] = (7x+5)^2 - 4y^2$
$= (7x)^2 + 2(7x)(5) + 5^2 - 16y^2$
$= 49x^2 + 70x + 25 - 16y^2$

97. $(x+y)(x-y)(x^2+y^2) = (x^2-y^2)(x^2+y^2)$
$= (x^2)^2 - (y^2)^2$
$= x^4 - y^4$

Section P.5

Check Point Exercises

1. a. $10x^3 - 4x^2$
$= 2x^2(5x) - 2x^2(2)$
$= 2x^2(5x-2)$

b. $2x(x-7) + 3(x-7)$
$= (x-7)(2x+3)$

2. $x^3 + 5x^2 - 2x - 10$
$= (x^3 + 5x^2) - (2x + 10)$
$= x^2(x+5) - 2(x+5)$
$= (x+5)(x^2-2)$

3. a. Find two numbers whose product is 40 and whose sum is 13. The required integers are 8 and 5. Thus,
$x^2 + 13x + 40 = (x+5)(x+8)$ or $(x+8)(x+5)$

b. Find two numbers whose product is –14 and whose sum is –5. The required integers are –7 and 2. Thus,
$x^2 - 5x - 14 = (x-7)(x+2)$ or $(x+2)(x-7)$.

4. Find two First terms whose product is $6x^2$.
$6x^2 + 19x - 7 \stackrel{?}{=} (6x \quad\;)(x \quad\;)$
$6x^2 + 19x - 7 = (3x \quad\;)(2x \quad\;)$

Find two Last terms whose product is –7.
The possible factors are $1(-7)$ and $-1(7)$.

Try various combinations of these factors to find the factorization in which the sum of the Outside and Inside products is $19x$.

Possible Factors of $6x^2+19x-7$	Sum of Outside and Inside Products (Should Equal $19x$)
$(6x+1)(x-7)$	$-42x+x=-41x$
$(6x-7)(x+1)$	$6x-7x=-x$
$(6x-1)(x+7)$	$42x-x=41x$
$(6x+7)(x-1)$	$-6x+7x=x$
$(3x+1)(2x-7)$	$-21x+2x=-19x$
$(3x-7)(2x+1)$	$3x-14x=-11x$
$(3x-1)(2x+7)$	$21x-2x=19x$
$(3x+7)(2x-1)$	$-3x+14x=11x$

Thus, $6x^2+19x-7=(3x-1)(2x+7)$ or $(2x+7)(3x-1)$.

5. Express each term as the square of some monomial. Then use the formula for factoring A^2-B^2.

a. $x^2-81=x^2-9^2=(x+9)(x-9)$

b. $36x^2-25=(6x)^2-5^2=(6x+5)(6x-5)$

6. Express $81x^4-16$ as the difference of two squares and use the formula for factoring A^2-B^2.
$81x^4-16=(9x^2)^2-4^2=(9x^2+4)(9x^2-4)$

The factor $9x^2-4$ is the difference of two squares and can be factored. Express $9x^2-4$ as the difference of two squares and again use the formula for factoring A^2-B^2.
$(9x^2+4)(9x^2-4)=(9x^2+4)\left[(3x)^2-2^2\right]=(9x^2+4)(3x+2)(3x-2)$

Thus, factored completely,
$81x^4-16=(9x^2+4)(3x+2)(3x-2)$.

7. a. $x^2+14x+49=x^2+2\cdot x\cdot 7+7^2=(x+7)^2$

b. Since $16x^2=(4x)^2$ and $49=7^2$, check to see if the middle term can be expressed as twice the product of $4x$ and 7. Since $2\cdot 4x\cdot 7=56x$, $16x^2-56x+49$ is a perfect square trinomial. Thus,

$$\begin{aligned}16x^2-56x+49&=(4x)^2-2\cdot 4x\cdot 7+7^2\\&=(4x-7)^2\end{aligned}$$

8. a. $x^3+1=x^3+1^3$
$=(x+1)(x^2-x\cdot 1+1^2)$
$=(x+1)(x^2-x+1)$

b. $125x^3-8=(5x)^3-2^3$
$=(5x-2)\left[(5x)^2+(5x)(2)+2^2\right]$
$=(5x-2)(25x^2+10x+4]$

9. a. Factor out the greatest common factor.
$2x^3-24x^2+72x=2x(x^2-12x+36)$

Factor the perfect square trinomial.
$2x(x^2-12x+36)=2x(x-6)^2$
Thus, $2x^3-24x^2+72x=2x(x-6)^2$.

b. Group the terms with common factors and factor each group.
$x^3-4x^2-9x+36=(x^3-4x^2)-(9x-36)$
$=x^2(x-4)-9(x-4)$

Factor out the common binomial factor and factor completely by factoring x^2-9 as the difference of two squares.
$x^2(x-4)-9(x-4)=(x-4)(x^2-9)$
$=(x-4)(x+3)(x-3)$
Thus, $x^3-4x^2-9x+36=(x-4)(x+3)(x-3)$.

Exercise Set P.5

1. $18x+27=9\cdot 2x+9\cdot 3$
$=9(2x+3)$

3. $3x^2+6x=3x\cdot x+3x\cdot 2$
$=3x(x+2)$

5. $9x^4-18x^3+27x^2$
$=9x^2(x^2)+9x^2(-2x)+9x^2(3)$
$=9x^2(x^2-2x+3)$

7. $x(x+5)+3(x+5)=(x+5)(x+3)$

9. $x^2(x-3)+12(x-3)=(x-3)(x^2+12)$

11. $x^3-2x^2+5x-10=x^2(x-2)+5(x-2)$
$=(x^2+5)(x-2)$

13. $x^3 - x^2 + 2x - 2 = x^2(x-1) + 2(x-1)$
$= (x-1)(x^2+2)$

15. $3x^3 - 2x^2 - 6x + 4 = x^2(3x-2) - 2(3x-2)$
$= (3x-2)(x^2-2)$

17. $x^2 + 5x + 6 = (x+2)(x+3)$

19. $x^2 - 2x - 15 = (x-5)(x+3)$

21. $x^2 - 8x + 15 = (x-5)(x-3)$

23. $3x^2 - x - 2 = (3x+2)(x-1)$

25. $3x^2 - 25x - 28 = (3x-28)(x+1)$

27. $6x^2 - 11x + 4 = (2x-1)(3x-4)$

29. $4x^2 + 16x + 15 = (2x+3)(2x+5)$

31. $x^2 - 100 = x^2 - 10^2 = (x+10)(x-10)$

33. $36x^2 - 49 = (6x)^2 - 7^2 = (6x+7)(6x-7)$

35. $9x^2 - 25y^2 = (3x)^2 - (5y)^2$
$= (3x+5y)(3x-5y)$

37. $x^4 - 16 = (x^2)^2 - 4^2$
$= (x^2+4)(x^2-4)$
$= (x^2+4)(x+2)(x-2)$

39. $16x^4 - 81 = (4x^2)^2 - 9^2$
$= (4x^2+9)(4x^2-9)$
$= (4x^2+9)[(2x)^2 - 3^2]$
$= (4x^2+9)(2x+3)(2x-3)$

41. $x^2 + 2x + 1 = x^2 + 2 \cdot x \cdot 1 + 1^2 = (x+1)^2$

43. $x^2 - 14x + 49 = x^2 - 2 \cdot x \cdot 7 + 7^2$
$= (x-7)^2$

45. $4x^2 + 4x + 1 = (2x)^2 + 2 \cdot 2x \cdot 1 + 1^2$
$= (2x+1)^2$

47. $9x^2 - 6x + 1 = (3x)^2 - 2 \cdot 3x \cdot 1 + 1^2$
$= (3x-1)^2$

49. $x^3 + 27 = x^3 + 3^3$
$= (x+3)(x^2 - x \cdot 3 + 3^2)$
$= (x+3)(x^2 - 3x + 9)$

51. $x^3 - 64 = x^3 - 4^3$
$= (x-4)(x^2 + x \cdot 4 + 4^2)$
$= (x-4)(x^2 + 4x + 16)$

53. $8x^3 - 1 = (2x)^3 - 1^3$
$= (2x-1)[(2x)^2 + (2x)(1) + 1^2]$
$= (2x-1)(4x^2 + 2x + 1)$

55. $64x^3 + 27 = (4x)^3 + 3^3$
$= (4x+3)[(4x)^2 - (4x)(3) + 3^2]$
$= (4x+3)(16x^2 - 12x + 9)$

57. $3x^3 - 3x = 3x(x^2-1) = 3x(x+1)(x-1)$

59. $4x^2 - 4x - 24 = 4(x^2 - x - 6)$
$= 4(x+2)(x-3)$

61. $2x^4 - 162 = 2(x^4 - 81)$
$= 2[(x^2)^2 - 9^2]$
$= 2(x^2+9)(x^2-9)$
$= 2(x^2+9)(x^2-3^2)$
$= 2(x^2+9)(x+3)(x-3)$

63. $x^3 + 2x^2 - 9x - 18 = (x^3 + 2x^2) - (9x + 18)$
$= x^2(x+2) - 9(x+2)$
$= (x^2-9)(x+2)$
$= (x^2-3^2)(x+2)$
$= (x-3)(x+3)(x+2)$

65. $2x^2 - 2x - 112 = 2(x^2 - x - 56)$
$= 2(x-8)(x+7)$

67. $x^3 - 4x = x(x^2 - 4)$
$= x(x^2 - 2^2)$
$= x(x-2)(x+2)$

69. $x^2 + 64$ is prime.

71. $x^3 + 2x^2 - 4x - 8 = (x^3 + 2x^2) + (-4x - 8)$
$= x^2(x+2) - 4(x+2)$
$= (x^2 - 4)(x+2)$
$= (x^2 - 2^2)(x+2)$
$= (x-2)(x+2)(x+2)$
$= (x-2)(x+2)^2$

73. $y^5 - 81y = y(y^4 - 81)$
$= y[(y^2)^2 - 9^2]$
$= y(y^2+9)(y^2-9)$
$= y(y^2+9)(y^2-3^2)$
$= y(y^2+9)(y+3)(y-3)$

75. $20y^4 - 45y^2 = 5y^2(4y^2 - 9)$
$= 5y^2[(2y)^2 - 3^2]$
$= 5y^2(2y+3)(2y-3)$

77. $-16t^2 + 16t + 32 = -16(t^2 - t - 2)$
$= -16(t-2)(t+1)$

79. $(3x)(3x) - 2 \cdot 2 = (3x)^2 - 2^2$
$= (3x+2)(3x-2)$

81.–87. Answers may vary.

89. a. False; $x^3 + 1 = (x+1)(x^2 - x + 1)$

b. False; this is not a product.

c. False; $(x-4)^3 = x^3 - 12x^2 + 48x - 64$

d. True

(d) is true.

91. $-x^2 - 4x + 5 = -(x^2 + 4x - 5)$
$= -(x+5)(x-1)$

93. $x^4 - y^4 - 2x^3y + 2xy^3$
$= (x^4 - y^4 + (-2x^3y + 2xy^3)$
$= [(x^2)^2 - (y^2)^2] - 2xy(x^2 - y^2)$
$= (x^2 - y^2)(x^2 + y^2) - 2xy(x^2 - y^2)$
$= (x^2 - y^2)(x^2 + y^2 - 2xy)$
$= (x-y)(x+y)(x-y)^2$
$= (x-y)^3(x+y)$

95. For the polynomial $x^2 + 4x + b$ to be factorable, b needs to be any product of two integers whose sum is 4. So if $x^2 + 4x + b$ equals
$x(x + 4)$ then $b = 0$
$(x + 1)(x + 3)$ then $b = 3$
$(x+2)^2$ then $b = 4$
$(x - 1)(x + 5)$ then $b = -5$
$(x - 2)(x + 6)$ then $b = -12$
In fact, given any positive integer c and $c + 4$, we can set $b = -c \cdot (c+4)$. Then $x^2 + 4x + b$ is factorable.
So $b = 0, 3, 4, -c(c + 4)$, where $c > 0$ is an integer.

Section P.6

Check Point Exercises

1. a. The denominator would equal zero if $x = -5$, so -5 must be excluded from the domain.

b. $x^2 - 36 = (x+6)(x-6)$
The denominator would equal zero if $x = -6$ or $x = 6$, so -6 and 6 must both be excluded from the domain.

2. a. $\frac{x^3+3x^2}{x+3}=\frac{x^2(x+3)}{x+3}$ Because the denominator is $x+3$, $x \neq -3$

$=\frac{x^2(x+3)}{x+3}$

$=x^2,\ x\neq -3$

b. $\frac{x^2-1}{x^2+2x+1}=\frac{(x+1)(x-1)}{(x+1)(x+1)}$ Because the denominator is $(x+1)(x-1)$, $x\neq -1$ and $x\neq 1$.

$=\frac{(x+1)(x-1)}{(x+1)(x+1)}$

$=\frac{x-1}{x+1},\ x\neq -1 \text{ and } x\neq 1$

3. $\frac{x+3}{x^2-4}\cdot\frac{x^2-x-6}{x^2+6x+9}$

$=\frac{x+3}{(x+2)(x-2)}\cdot\frac{(x-3)(x+2)}{(x+3)(x+3)}$ Because the denominator has factors of $x+2$, $x-2$, and $x+3$, $x\neq -2$, $x\neq 2$, and $x\neq -3$.

$=\frac{x+3}{(x+2)(x-2)}\cdot\frac{(x-3)(x+2)}{(x+3)(x+3)}$

$=\frac{x-3}{(x-2)(x+3)},\ x\neq -2,\ x\neq 2,\ x\neq -3$

4. $\frac{x^2-2x+1}{x^3+x}\div\frac{x^2+x-2}{3x^2+3}$

$=\frac{x^2-2x+1}{x^3+x}\cdot\frac{3x^2+3}{x^2+x-2}$

$=\frac{(x-1)(x-1)}{x(x^2+1)}\cdot\frac{3(x^2+1)}{(x+2)(x-1)}$ For nonzero denominators, $x\neq 0$, $x\neq -2$, $x\neq 1$.

$=\frac{3(x-1)}{x(x+2)},\ x\neq 0,\ x\neq -2,\ x\neq 1$

5. $\frac{x}{x+1}-\frac{3x+2}{x+1}$

$=\frac{x-(3x+2)}{x+1}$

$=\frac{x-3x-2}{x+1}$

$=\frac{-2x-2}{x+1}$

$=\frac{-2(x+1)}{x+1}$ For a nonzero denominator, $x\neq -1$.

$=\frac{-2(x+1)}{x+1}$

$=-2,\ x\neq -1$

6. $\frac{3}{x+1}+\frac{5}{x-1}$

$=\frac{3x(x-1)+5(x+1)}{(x+1)(x-1)}$

$=\frac{3x-3+5x+5}{(x+1)(x-1)}$

$=\frac{8x+2}{(x+1)(x-1)}$

$=\frac{2(4x+1)}{(x+1)(x-1)}$ For a nonzero denominator, $x \neq -1$ and $x \neq 1$.

$=\frac{2(4x+1)}{(x+1)(x-1)}, x \neq -1, x \neq 1$

7. Factor each denominator completely.

$x^2-6x+9=(x-3)^2$

$x^2-9=(x+3)(x-3)$

List the factors of the first denominator.

$x-3, x-3$

Add any unlisted factors from the second denominator.

$x-3, x-3, x+3$

The least common denominator is the product of all factors in the final list.

$(x-3)(x-3)(x+3)$ or $(x-3)^2(x+3)$

is the least common denominator.

8. Find the least common denominator.

$x^2-10x+25=(x-5)^2$

$2x-10=2(x-5)$

The least common denominator is $2(x-5)(x-5)$.

Write all rational expressions in terms of the least common denominator.

$\frac{x}{x^2-10x+25}-\frac{x-4}{2x-10}$

$=\frac{x}{(x-5)(x-5)}-\frac{x-4}{2(x-5)}$

$=\frac{2x}{2(x-5)(x-5)}-\frac{(x-4)(x-5)}{2(x-5)(x-5)}$

Add numerators, putting this sum over the least common denominator.

$$=\frac{2x-(x-4)(x-5)}{2(x-5)(x-5)}$$

$$=\frac{2x-(x^2-5x-4x+20)}{2(x-5)(x-5)}$$

$$=\frac{2x-x^2+5x+4x-20}{2(x-5)(x-5)}$$

$$=\frac{2x-x^2+5x+4x-20}{2(x-5)(x-5)}$$

$$=\frac{-x^2+11x-20}{2(x-5)(x-5)}$$

$$=\frac{-x^2+11x-20}{2(x-5)^2},\ x\neq 5$$

9. $\frac{\frac{1}{x}-\frac{3}{2}}{\frac{1}{x}+\frac{3}{4}}=\frac{\frac{2}{2x}-\frac{3x}{2x}}{\frac{4}{4x}+\frac{3x}{4x}},\ x\neq 0$

$$=\frac{\frac{2-3x}{2x}}{\frac{4+3x}{4x}},\ x\neq\frac{-4}{3}$$

$$=\frac{2-3x}{2x}\div\frac{4+3x}{4x}$$

$$=\frac{2-3x}{2x}\cdot\frac{4x}{4+3x}$$

$$=\frac{2-3x}{4+3x}\cdot\frac{4}{2}$$

$$=\frac{2-3x}{4+3x}\cdot\frac{2}{1}$$

$$=\frac{2(2-3x)}{4+3x},\ x\neq 0 \text{ and } x\neq\frac{-4}{3}$$

Exercise Set P.6

1. $\frac{7}{x-3},\ x\neq 3$

3. $\frac{x+5}{x^2-25}=\frac{x+5}{(x+5)(x-5)},\ x\neq 5,-5$

5. $\frac{x-1}{x^2+11x+10}=\frac{x-1}{(x+1)(x+10)},\ x\neq -1,-10$

7. $\frac{3x-9}{x^2-6x+9}=\frac{3(x-3)}{(x-3)(x-3)}$

$$=\frac{3}{x-3},\ x\neq 3$$

9. $\frac{x^2-12x+36}{4x-24}=\frac{(x-6)(x-6)}{4(x-6)}=\frac{x-6}{4}$,

$x\neq 6$

11. $\frac{y^2+7y-18}{y^2-3y+2}=\frac{(y+9)(y-2)}{(y-2)(y-1)}=\frac{y+9}{y-1}$,

$y\neq 1, 2$

13. $\frac{x^2+12x+36}{x^2-36}=\frac{(x+6)^2}{(x+6)(x-6)}=\frac{x+6}{x-6}$,

$x\neq 6, -6$

15. $\frac{x-2}{3x+9}\cdot\frac{2x+6}{2x-4}=\frac{x-2}{3(x+3)}\cdot\frac{2(x+3)}{2(x-2)}$

$$=\frac{2}{6}=\frac{1}{3},\ x\neq 2,-3$$

17. $\frac{x^2-9}{x^2}\cdot\frac{x^2-3x}{x^2+x-12}$

$$=\frac{(x-3)(x+3)}{x^2}\cdot\frac{x(x-3)}{(x+4)(x-3)}$$

$$=\frac{(x-3)(x+3)}{x(x+4)},\ x\neq 0,-4,3$$

19. $\frac{x^2-5x+6}{x^2-2x-3}\cdot\frac{x^2-1}{x^2-4}$

$$=\frac{(x-3)(x-2)}{(x-3)(x+1)}\cdot\frac{(x+1)(x-1)}{(x-2)(x+2)}$$

$$=\frac{x-1}{x+2},\ x\neq -2,-1,2,3$$

21. $\frac{x^3-8}{x^2-4}\cdot\frac{x+2}{3x}=\frac{(x-2)(x^2+2x+4)}{(x-2)(x+2)}\cdot\frac{x+2}{3x}$

$$=\frac{x^2+2x+4}{3x},\ x\neq -2,0,2$$

23. $\frac{x+1}{3} \div \frac{3x+3}{7} = \frac{x+1}{3} \div \frac{3(x+1)}{7}$
$= \frac{x+1}{3} \cdot \frac{7}{3(x+1)}$
$= \frac{7}{9}, \ x \neq -1$

25. $\frac{x^2-4}{x} \div \frac{x+2}{x-2} = \frac{(x-2)(x+2)}{x} \div \frac{x+2}{x-2}$
$= \frac{(x-2)(x+2)}{x} \cdot \frac{x-2}{x+2}$
$= \frac{(x-2)^2}{x}, \ x \neq 0, -2, 2$

27. $\frac{4x^2+10}{x-3} \div \frac{6x^2+15}{x^2-9}$
$= \frac{2(2x^2+5)}{x-3} \div \frac{3(2x^2+5)}{(x-3)(x+3)}$
$= \frac{2(2x^2+5)}{x-3} \cdot \frac{(x-3)(x+3)}{3(2x^2+5)}$
$= \frac{2(x+3)}{3}, \ x \neq 3, -3$

29. $\frac{x^2-25}{2x-2} \div \frac{x^2+10x+25}{x^2+4x-5}$
$= \frac{(x-5)(x+5)}{2(x-1)} \div \frac{(x+5)^2}{(x+5)(x-1)}$
$= \frac{(x-5)(x+5)}{2(x-1)} \cdot \frac{(x+5)(x-1)}{(x+5)^2}$
$= \frac{x-5}{2}, \ x \neq 1, -5$

31. $\frac{4x+1}{6x+5} + \frac{8x+9}{6x+5} = \frac{4x+1+8x+9}{6x+5}$
$= \frac{12x+10}{6x+5}$
$= \frac{2(6x+5)}{6x+5} = 2, \ x \neq -\frac{5}{6}$

33. $\frac{x^2-2x}{x^2+3x} + \frac{x^2+x}{x^2+3x} = \frac{x^2-2x+x^2+x}{x^2+3x}$
$= \frac{2x^2-x}{x^2+3x}$
$= \frac{x(2x-1)}{x(x+3)}$
$= \frac{2x-1}{x+3}, \ x \neq 0, -3$

35. $\frac{4x-10}{x-2} - \frac{x-4}{x-2} = \frac{4x-10-(x-4)}{x-2}$
$= \frac{4x-10-x+4}{x-2}$
$= \frac{3x-6}{x-2}$
$= \frac{3(x-2)}{x-2}$
$= 3, \ x \neq 2$

37. $\frac{x^2+3x}{x^2+x-12} - \frac{x^2-12}{x^2+x-12}$
$= \frac{x^2+3x-(x^2-12)}{x^2+x-12}$
$= \frac{x^2+3x-x^2+12}{x^2+x-12}$
$= \frac{3x+12}{x^2+x-12}$
$= \frac{3(x+4)}{(x+4)(x-3)}$
$= \frac{3}{x-3}, \ x \neq 3, -4$

39. $\frac{3}{x+4} + \frac{6}{x+5} = \frac{3(x+5)+6(x+4)}{(x+4)(x+5)}$
$= \frac{3x+15+6x+24}{(x+4)(x+5)}$
$= \frac{9x+39}{(x+4)(x+5)}, \ x \neq -4, -5$

41. $\frac{3}{x+1} - \frac{3}{x} = \frac{3x-3(x+1)}{x(x+1)}$
$= \frac{3x-3x-3}{x(x+1)} = -\frac{3}{x(x+1)}, \ x \neq -1, 0$

43. $\frac{2x}{x+2}+\frac{x+2}{x-2}=\frac{2x(x-2)+(x+2)(x+2)}{(x+2)(x-2)}$

$=\frac{2x^2-4x+x^2+4x+4}{(x+2)(x-2)}$

$=\frac{3x^2+4}{(x+2)(x-2)}, x\neq -2, 2$

45. $\frac{x+5}{x-5}+\frac{x-5}{x+5}$

$=\frac{(x+5)(x+5)+(x-5)(x-5)}{(x-5)(x+5)}$

$=\frac{x^2+10x+25+x^2-10x+25}{(x-5)(x+5)}$

$=\frac{2x^2+50}{(x-5)(x+5)}, x\neq -5, 5$

47. $\frac{4}{x^2+6x+9}+\frac{4}{x+3}=\frac{4}{(x+3)^2}+\frac{4}{x+3}$

$=\frac{4+4(x+3)}{(x+3)^2}=\frac{4+4x+12}{(x+3)^2}=\frac{4x+16}{(x+3)^2},$

$x\neq -3$

49. $\frac{3x}{x^2+3x-10}-\frac{2x}{x^2+x-6}$

$=\frac{3x}{(x+5)(x-2)}-\frac{2x}{(x+3)(x-2)}$

$=\frac{3x(x+3)-2x(x+5)}{(x+5)(x-2)(x+3)}$

$=\frac{3x^2+9x-2x^2-10x}{(x+5)(x-2)(x+3)}$

$=\frac{x^2-x}{(x+5)(x-2)(x+3)}, x\neq -5, 2, -3$

51. $\frac{\frac{x}{3}-1}{x-3}=\frac{3\left[\frac{x}{3}-1\right]}{3[x-3]}=\frac{x-3}{3(x-3)}=\frac{1}{3}, \; x\neq 3$

53. $\frac{1+\frac{1}{x}}{3-\frac{1}{x}}=\frac{x\left[1+\frac{1}{x}\right]}{x\left[3-\frac{1}{x}\right]}=\frac{x+1}{3x-1}, \;\; x\neq 0, \; \frac{1}{3}$

55. $\frac{\frac{1}{x}+\frac{1}{y}}{x+y}=\frac{xy\left[\frac{1}{x}+\frac{1}{y}\right]}{xy[x+y]}=\frac{y+x}{xy(x+y)}=\frac{1}{xy},$

$x\neq 0, y\neq 0, x\neq -y$

57. $\frac{x-\frac{x}{x+3}}{x+2}=\frac{(x+3)\left[x-\frac{x}{x+3}\right]}{(x+3)(x+2)}=\frac{x(x+3)-x}{(x+3)(x+2)}$

$=\frac{x^2+3x-x}{(x+3)(x+2)}=\frac{x^2+2x}{(x+3)(x+2)}$

$=\frac{x(x+2)}{(x+3)(x+2)}=\frac{x}{x+3}, x\neq -2, -3$

59. $\frac{\frac{3}{x-2}-\frac{4}{x+2}}{\frac{7}{x^2-4}}=\frac{\frac{3}{x-2}-\frac{4}{x+2}}{\frac{7}{(x-2)(x+2)}}$

$=\frac{\left[\frac{3}{x-2}-\frac{4}{x+2}\right](x-2)(x+2)}{\left[\frac{7}{(x-2)(x+2)}\right](x-2)(x+2)}$

$=\frac{3(x+2)-4(x-2)}{7}$

$=\frac{3x+6-4x+8}{7}=\frac{-x+14}{7}$

$=-\frac{x-14}{7} \quad x\neq -2, 2$

61. Adjust the polynomial that describes the total yearly cost to millions of dollars by multiplying the polynomial by 1000: $540t^2+12,640t+107,100$.
The average cost per person (in dollars) is
$\frac{540t^2+12,640t+107,100}{-0.14t^2+0.51t+31.6}$

63. a. $\frac{130x}{100-x}$ is equal to

1. $\frac{130\cdot 40}{100-40}=\frac{130\cdot 40}{60}=86.67$,
when $x=40$
2. $\frac{130\cdot 80}{100-80}=\frac{130\cdot 80}{20}=520$,
when $x=80$
3. $\frac{130\cdot 90}{100-90}=\frac{130\cdot 90}{10}=1170$,
when $x=90$

It costs $86,670,000 to inoculate 40% of the population against this strain of flu, and $520,000,000 to inoculate 80% of the population, and $1,170,000,000 to inoculate 90% of the population.

b. For $x = 100$, the function is not defined.

c. As x approaches close to 100, the value of the function increases rapidly. So it costs an astronomical amount of money to inoculate almost all of the people, and it is impossible to inoculate 100% of the population.

65. $$\frac{2d}{\frac{d}{r_1}+\frac{d}{r_2}}=\frac{2d}{\frac{d}{r_1}+\frac{d}{r_2}}\cdot\frac{r_1r_2}{r_1r_2}$$
$$=\frac{2dr_1r_2}{dr_2+dr_1}$$
$$=\frac{d(2r_1r_2)}{d(r_2+r_1)}$$
$$=\frac{2r_1r_2}{r_1+r_2},$$

Let $r_1=30$ and $r_2=20$. The average speed is $\frac{2(30)(20)}{30+20}=\frac{1200}{50}=24$ miles per hour.

The reason that the average speed is not $\frac{30+20}{2}=25$ is that the average of speeds is defined by

$\frac{\text{total distance travelled}}{\text{total time}}$, not by

$\frac{\text{sum of every speed}}{\text{number of the speeds being added}}$.

67.–77. Answers may vary.

79.

t	$f(t)$	Amount paid per recipient of Medicaid in \$	t	$f(t)$	Amount paid per recipient of Medicaid in \$
8	1105.87	1105 in 1988	15	412.84	412.84 in 1995
9	968.29	968.29 in 1989	16	364.54	364.54 in 1996
10	837.74	837.74 in 1990	17	323.94	323.94 in 1997
11	721.97	721.97 in 1991	18	289.60	289.60 in 1998
12	623.00	623.00 in 1992	19	260.36	260.36 in 1999
13	539.89	539.89 in 1993	20	235.29	235.29 in 2000
14	470.60	470.60 in 1994			

where $f(t)=\dfrac{413.48t^2+185.72t+24{,}031.95}{0.004t^4+0.02t^3+0.01t^2-0.24t+21.66}$

In 1990, the amount paid per recipient fell below \$900.

81. $$\frac{3x}{x-5}+\frac{\square}{5-x}=\frac{7x+1}{x-5}$$
$$\frac{3x}{x-5}+\frac{\square}{-1(x-5)}=\frac{7x+1}{x-5}$$
$$\frac{3x-\square}{x-5}=\frac{7x+1}{x-5}$$
$$3x-\square=7x+1$$
$$\square=-4x-1$$

83. It cubes x, $x\neq 0$.

Section P.7

Check Point Exercises

1. a. $(5-2i)+(3+3i)$
$=5-2i+3+3i$
$=(5+3)+(-2+3)i$
$=8+i$

b. $(2+6i)-(12-4i)$
$=2+6i-12+4i$
$=(2-12)+(6+4)i$
$=-10+10i$

2. a. $7i(2-9i) = 7i(2) - 7i(9i)$
$= 14i - 63i^2$
$= 14i - 63(-1)$
$= 63 + 14i$

b. $(5+4i)(6-7i) = 30 - 35i + 24i - 28i^2$
$= 30 - 35i + 24i - 28(-1)$
$= 30 + 28 - 35i + 24i$
$= 58 - 11i$

c. $\frac{-14+\sqrt{-12}}{2} = \frac{-14+i\sqrt{12}}{2}$
$= \frac{-14+2i\sqrt{3}}{2}$
$= \frac{-14}{2} + \frac{2i\sqrt{3}}{2}$
$= -7 + i\sqrt{3}$

3. The complex conjugate of the denominator, $4-2i$, is $4+2i$, so multiply the numerator and denominator by $4+2i$.

$$\frac{5+4i}{4-2i} = \frac{(5+4i)}{(4-2i)} \cdot \frac{(4+2i)}{(4+2i)}$$
$$= \frac{20+10i+16i+8i^2}{4^2+2^2}$$
$$= \frac{20+26i+8(-1)}{20}$$
$$= \frac{12+26i}{20}$$
$$= \frac{12}{20} + \frac{26}{20}i$$
$$= \frac{3}{5} + \frac{13}{10}i$$

4. a. $\sqrt{-27} + \sqrt{-48} = i\sqrt{27} + i\sqrt{48}$
$= i\sqrt{9 \cdot 3} + i\sqrt{16 \cdot 3}$
$= 3i\sqrt{3} + 4i\sqrt{3}$
$= 7i\sqrt{3}$

b. $(-2+\sqrt{-3})^2 = (-2+i\sqrt{3})^2$
$= (-2)^2 + 2(-2)(i\sqrt{3}) + (i\sqrt{3})^2$
$= 4 - 4i\sqrt{3} + 3i^2$
$= 4 - 4i\sqrt{3} + 3(-1)$
$= 1 - 4i\sqrt{3}$

Exercise Set P.7

1. $(7 + 2i) + (1 - 4i) = 7 + 2i + 1 - 4i$
$= 7 + 1 + 2i - 4i$
$= 8 - 2i$

3. $(3 + 2i) - (5 - 7i) = 3 - 5 + 2i + 7i$
$= 3 + 2i - 5 + 7i$
$= -2 + 9i$

5. $6 - (-5 + 4i) - (-13 - 11i)$
$= 6 + 5 - 4i + 13 + 11i$
$= 24 + 7i$

7. $8i - (14 - 9i) = 8i - 14 + 9i$
$= -14 + 8i + 9i$
$= -14+17i$

9. $-3i(7i - 5) = -21i^2 + 15i$
$= -21(-1) + 15i$
$= 21 + 15i$

11. $(-5 + 4i)(3 + 7i) = -15 - 35i + 12i + 28i^2$
$= -15 - 35i + 12i + 28(-1)$
$= -43 - 23i$

13. $(7 - 5i)(-2 - 3i) = -14 - 21i + 10i + 15i^2$
$= -14 - 15 - 11i$
$= -29 - 11i$

15. $(3 + 5i)(3 - 5i) = 9 - 25i^2 = 9 + 25 = 34$

17. $(-5 + 3i)(-5 - 3i) = 25 - 9i^2 = 25 + 9 = 34$

19. $(2 + 3i)^2 = 4 + 12i + 9i^2$
$= 4 + 12i - 9$
$= -5 + 12i$

21. $\frac{2}{3-i} = \frac{2}{3-i} \cdot \frac{3+i}{3+i}$
$= \frac{2(3+i)}{9+1}$
$= \frac{2(3+i)}{10}$
$= \frac{3+i}{5}$
$= \frac{3}{5} + \frac{1}{5}i$

23. $\frac{2i}{1+i} = \frac{2i}{1+i} \cdot \frac{1-i}{1-i} = \frac{2i-2i^2}{1+1} = \frac{2+2i}{2} = 1+i$

25. $\frac{8i}{4-3i} = \frac{8i}{4-3i} \cdot \frac{4+3i}{4+3i}$
$= \frac{32i+24i^2}{16+9}$
$= \frac{-24+32i}{25}$
$= -\frac{24}{25} + \frac{32}{25}i$

27. $\frac{2+3i}{2+i} = \frac{2+3i}{2+i} \cdot \frac{2-i}{2-i}$
$= \frac{4+4i-3i^2}{4+1}$
$= \frac{7+4i}{5}$
$= \frac{7}{5} + \frac{4}{5}i$

29. $\sqrt{-64} - \sqrt{-25} = i\sqrt{64} - i\sqrt{25}$
$= 8i - 5i = 3i$

31. $5\sqrt{-16} + 3\sqrt{-81} = 5(4i) + 3(9i)$
$= 20i + 27i = 47i$

33. $\left(-2+\sqrt{-4}\right)^2 = (-2+2i)^2$
$= 4 - 8i + 4i^2$
$= 4 - 8i - 4$
$= -8i$

35. $\left(-3-\sqrt{-7}\right)^2 = \left(-3-i\sqrt{7}\right)^2$
$= 9 + 6i\sqrt{7} + i^2(7)$
$= 9 - 7 + 6i\sqrt{7}$
$= 2 + 6i\sqrt{7}$

37. $\frac{-8+\sqrt{-32}}{24} = \frac{-8+i\sqrt{32}}{24}$
$= \frac{-8+i\sqrt{16\cdot 2}}{24}$
$= \frac{-8+4i\sqrt{2}}{24}$
$= -\frac{1}{3} + \frac{\sqrt{2}}{6}i$

39. $\frac{-6-\sqrt{-12}}{48} = \frac{-6-i\sqrt{12}}{48}$
$= \frac{-6-i\sqrt{4\cdot 3}}{48}$
$= \frac{-6-2i\sqrt{3}}{48}$
$= -\frac{1}{8} - \frac{\sqrt{3}}{24}i$

41. $\sqrt{-8}\left(\sqrt{-3}-\sqrt{5}\right) = i\sqrt{8}(i\sqrt{3}-\sqrt{5})$
$= 2i\sqrt{2}\left(i\sqrt{3}-\sqrt{5}\right)$
$= -2\sqrt{6} - 2i\sqrt{10}$

43. $\left(3\sqrt{-5}\right)\left(-4\sqrt{-12}\right) = \left(3i\sqrt{5}\right)\left(-8i\sqrt{3}\right)$
$= -24i^2\sqrt{15}$
$= 24\sqrt{15}$

45.–51. Answers may vary.

53. a. False; all irrational numbers are complex numbers.

b. False; $(3 + 7i)(3 - 7i) = 9 + 49 = 58$ is a real number.

c. False; $\frac{7+3i}{5+3i} = \frac{7+3i}{5+3i} \cdot \frac{5-3i}{5-3i}$

$= \frac{44-6i}{34} = \frac{22}{17} - \frac{3}{17}i$

d. True; $(x+yi)(x-yi) = x^2 - (yi)^2 = x^2 + y^2$

(d) is true.

55.
$$\begin{aligned}\frac{4}{(2+i)(3-i)} &= \frac{4}{6+i-i^2}\\ &= \frac{4}{6+i+1}\\ &= \frac{4}{7+i}\\ &= \frac{4}{7+i} \cdot \frac{7-i}{7-i}\\ &= \frac{4(7-i)}{49+1}\\ &= \frac{28-4i}{50}\\ &= \frac{28}{50} - \frac{4}{50}i\\ &= \frac{14}{25} - \frac{2}{25}i\end{aligned}$$

57. $x^2 - 2x + 2$ for $x = 1 + i$
$$\begin{aligned}x^2 - 2x + 2 &= (1+i)^2 - 2(1+i) + 2\\ &= 1 + 2i - 1 - 2 - 2i + 2\\ &= 0\end{aligned}$$

Section P.8

Check Point Exercises

1.

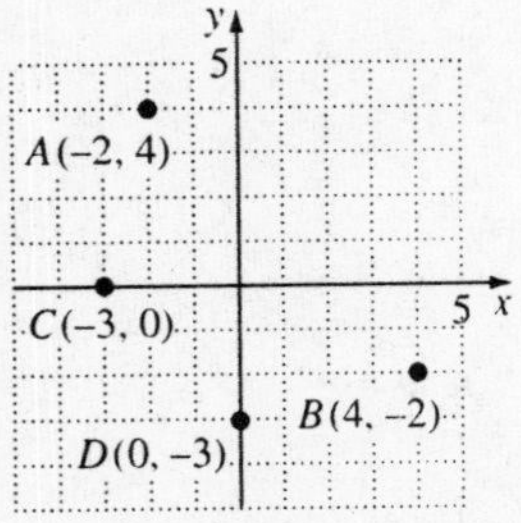

y
5
A(−2, 4)
C(−3, 0)
5 x
B(4, −2)
D(0, −3)

2.

x	$y = 2x - 4$	Ordered Pair (x, y)
-1	$y = 2(-1) - 4 = -2 - 4 = -6$	$(-1, -6)$
0	$y = 2(0) - 4 = 0 - 4 = -4$	$(0, -4)$
1	$y = 2(1) - 4 = 2 - 4 = -2$	$(1, -2)$
2	$y = 2(2) - 4 = 4 - 4 = 0$	$(2, 0)$
3	$y = 2(3) - 4 = 6 - 4 = 2$	$(3, 2)$

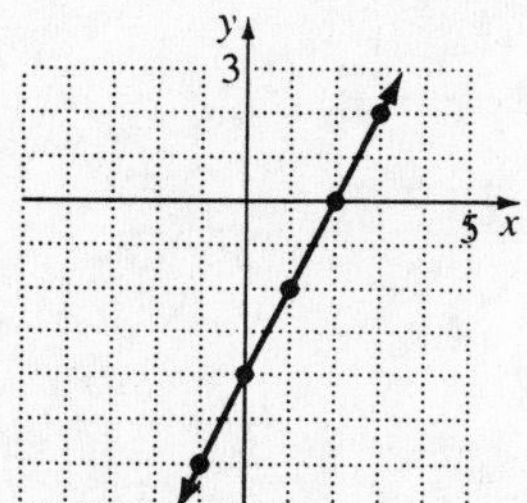

3. The minimum x-value is -100 and the maximum x-value is 100. The distance between consecutive tick marks is 50. The minimum y-value is -100 and the maximum y-value is 100. The distance between consecutive tick marks is 10.

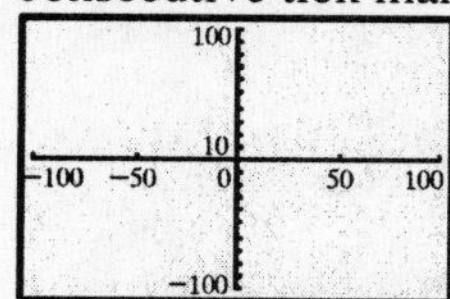

4. Letting $(x_1, y_1) = (2, -2)$ and $(x_2, y_2) =$ $(5, 2)$, we obtain

$$\begin{aligned} d &= \sqrt{(x_2 - x_1)^2 + (y_2 - y_1)^2} \\ &= \sqrt{(5-2)^2 + (2-(-2))^2} \\ &= \sqrt{(5-2)^2 + (2+2)^2} \\ &= \sqrt{3^2 + 4^2} \\ &= \sqrt{9+16} \\ &= \sqrt{25} \\ &= 5 \end{aligned}$$

The distance between the given points is 5 units.

5. To find the coordinates of the midpoint, we average the coordinates of the endpoints.

$$\text{Midpoint} = \left(\frac{1+7}{2}, \frac{2+(-3)}{2}\right)$$
$$= \left(\frac{8}{2}, \frac{-1}{2}\right)$$
$$= \left(4, -\frac{1}{2}\right)$$

6. Minimum sales correspond to the lowest point on the graph. The coordinates of this point are approximately (1991, 800). This means that in 1991 ticket sales reached a minimum. The sales for that year were about $800 million.

Exercise Set P.8

1.

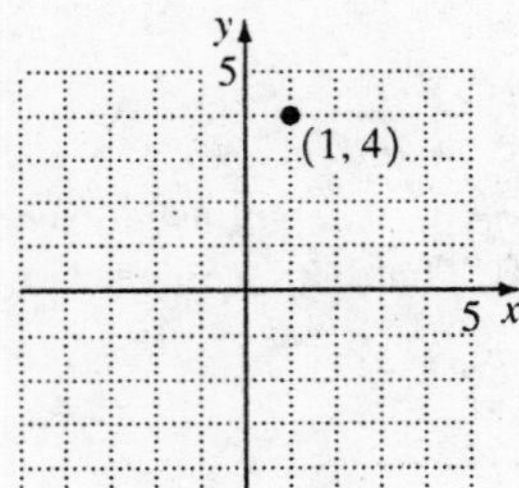

3.

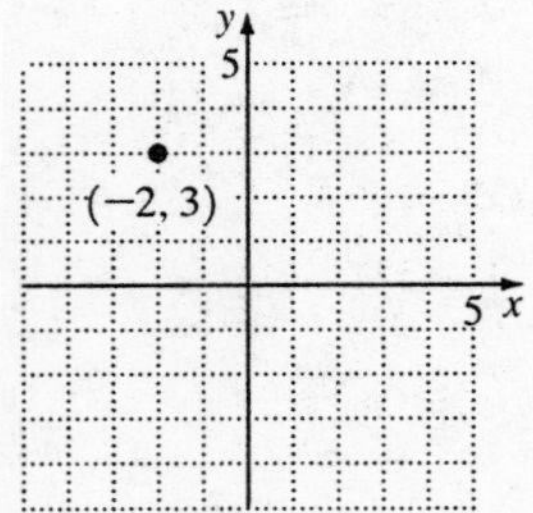

5.

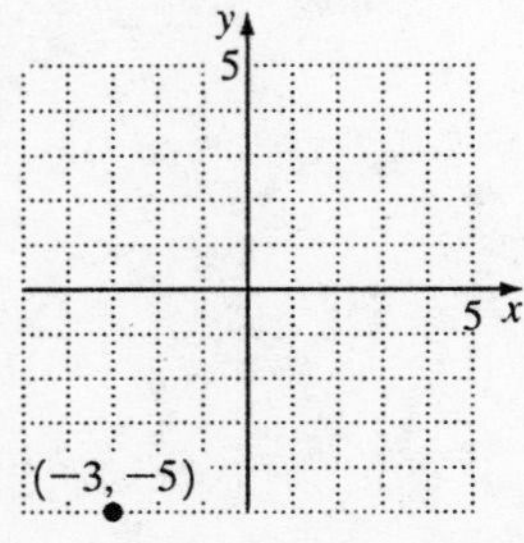

7.

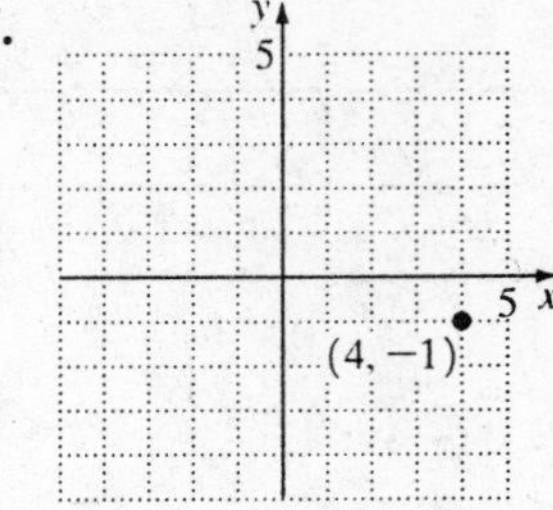

9.

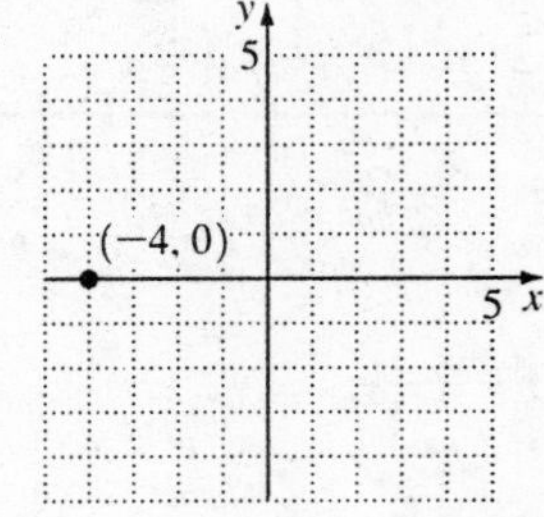

11.

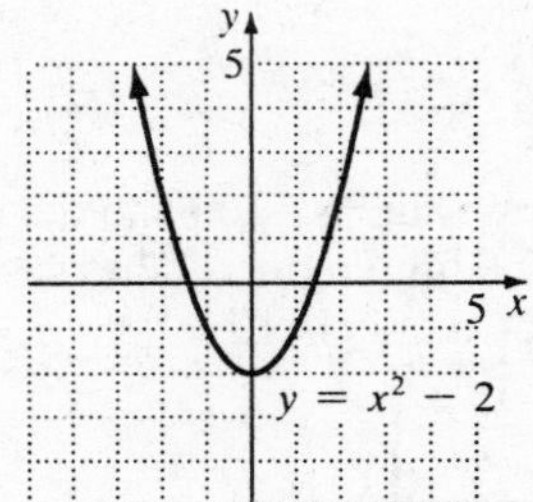

$x = -3,\ y = 7$
$x = -2,\ y = 2$
$x = -1,\ y = -1$
$x = 0,\ y = -2$
$x = 1,\ y = -1$
$x = 2,\ y = 2$
$x = 3,\ y = 7$

13.

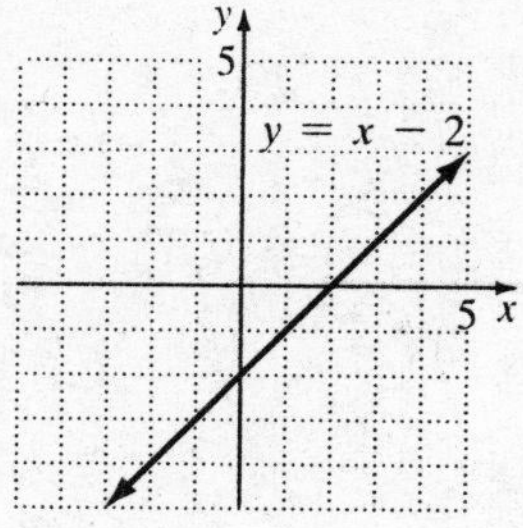

$x = -3,\ y = -5$
$x = -2,\ y = -4$
$x = -1,\ y = -3$
$x = 0,\ y = -2$
$x = 1,\ y = -1$
$x = 2,\ y = 0$
$x = 3,\ y = 1$

15.

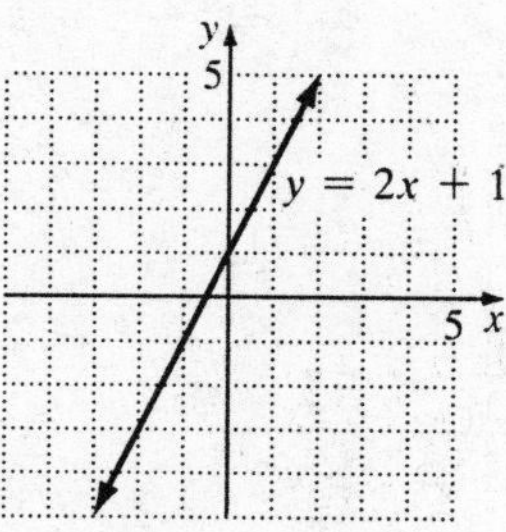

$x = -3,\ y = -5$
$x = -2,\ y = -3$
$x = -1,\ y = -1$
$x = 0,\ y = 1$
$x = 1,\ y = 3$
$x = 2,\ y = 5$
$x = 3,\ y = 7$

17.

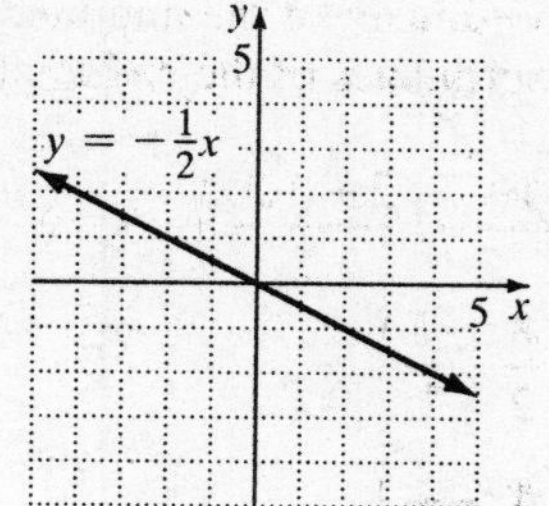

$x = -3,\ y = \frac{3}{2}$
$x = -2,\ y = 1$
$x = -1,\ y = \frac{1}{2}$
$x = 0,\ y = 0$
$x = 1,\ y = -\frac{1}{2}$
$x = 2,\ y = -1$
$x = 3,\ y = -\frac{3}{2}$

19.

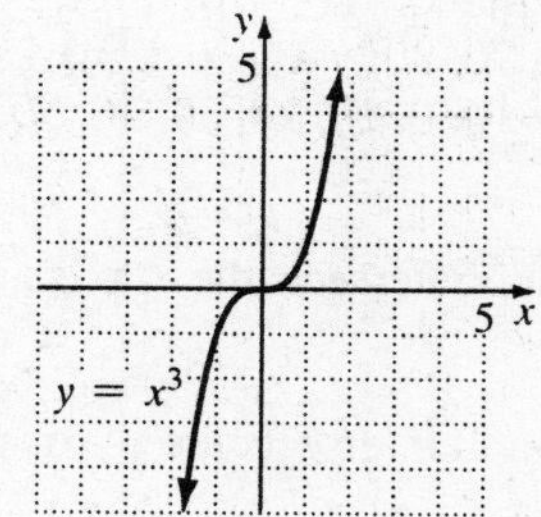

$x = -3,\ y = -27$
$x = -2,\ y = -8$
$x = -1,\ y = -1$
$x = 0,\ y = 0$
$x = 1,\ y = 1$
$x = 2,\ y = 8$
$x = 3,\ y = 27$

21.

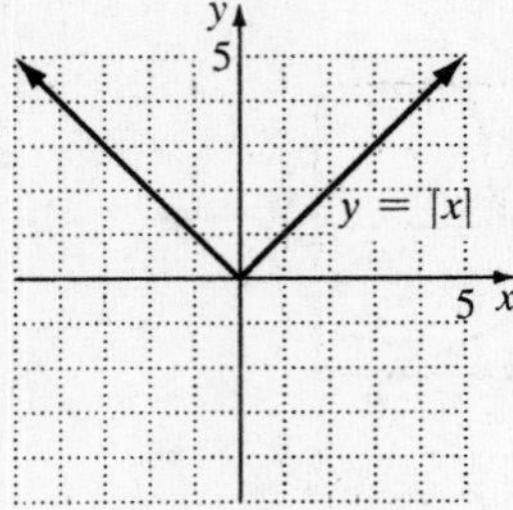

$x = -3,\ y = 3$
$x = -2,\ y = 2$
$x = -1,\ y = 1$
$x = 0,\ y = 0$
$x = 1,\ y = 1$
$x = 2,\ y = 2$
$x = 3,\ y = 3$

23. (c); x-axis tick marks –5, –4, –3, –2, –1, 0, 1, 2, 3, 4, 5; y-axis tick marks are the same.

25. (b); x-axis tick marks –20, –10, 0, 10, 20, 30, 40, 50, 60, 70, 80; y-axis tick marks –30, –20, –10, 0, 10, 20, 30, 40, 50, 60, 70

27. a. 2; The graph intersects the x-axis at (2, 0).

b. –4; The graph intersects the y-axis at (0,–4).

29. a. 1, –2; The graph intersects the x-axis at (1, 0) and (–2, 0).

b. 2; The graph intersects the y-axis at (0, 2).

31. a. –1; The graph intersects the x-axis at (–1, 0).

b. None; The graph does not intersect the y-axis.

33. a.

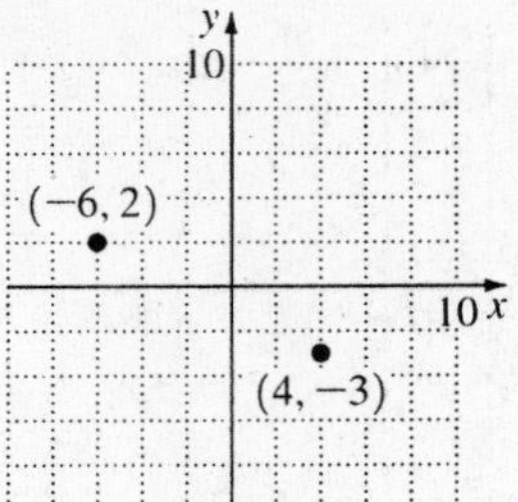

b. $\sqrt{[4-(-6)]^2+[-3-2]^2} = \sqrt{100+25}$
$= \sqrt{125}$
$= 5\sqrt{5}$

c. $\left(\frac{4-6}{2}, \frac{-3+2}{2}\right) = \left(\frac{-2}{2}, \frac{-1}{2}\right)$
$= \left(-1, -\frac{1}{2}\right)$

35. a.

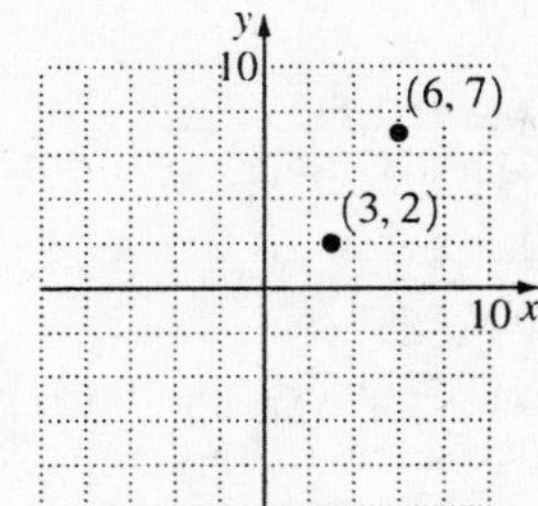

b. $\sqrt{(3-6)^2+(2-7)^2} = \sqrt{9+25} = \sqrt{34}$

c. $\left(\frac{3+6}{2}, \frac{2+7}{2}\right) = \left(\frac{9}{2}, \frac{9}{2}\right)$

37. a.

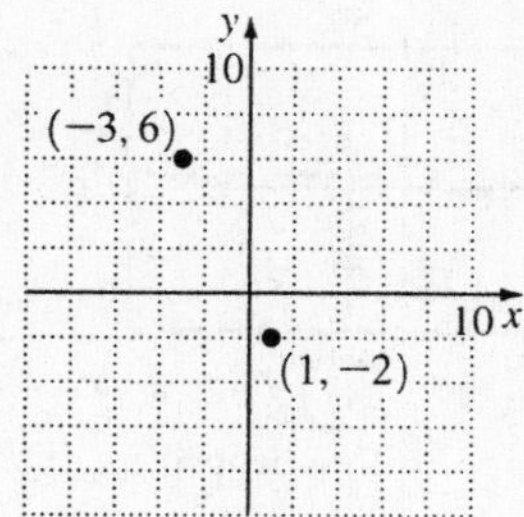

b. $\sqrt{[1-(-3)]^2+(-2-6)^2} = \sqrt{16+64}$
$= \sqrt{80}$
$= 4\sqrt{5}$

c. $\left(\frac{1-3}{2}, \frac{-2+6}{2}\right) = (-1,\ 2)$

39. The point on the graph is about (1970, 5). The unemployment rate in 1970 was about 5%.

41. The maximum point is about (1982, 9.7). Therefore the maximum rate of 9.7% was in 1982.

43. (1970, 61)
In 1970, the population of US for people under 16 was about 61 million.

45. (1990, 60)
In 1990, the population of US for people under 16 was about 60 million.

47. a. The maximum height of the graph, i.e., from where the ball was dropped, is (0, 1250). Therefore, the height of the building is 1250 ft.

b. The point on the graph which represents when the ball hit the ground is (8.8, 0). Therefore, the ball hit the ground after 8.8 seconds.

49.–53. Answers may vary.

55. Exercise 11

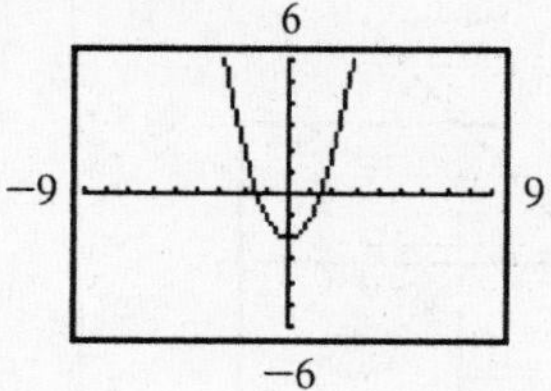

Exercise 13

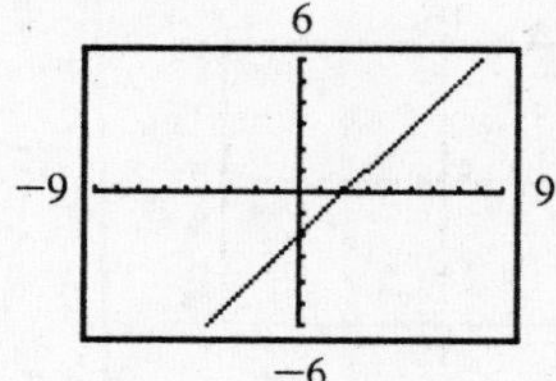

Exercise 15

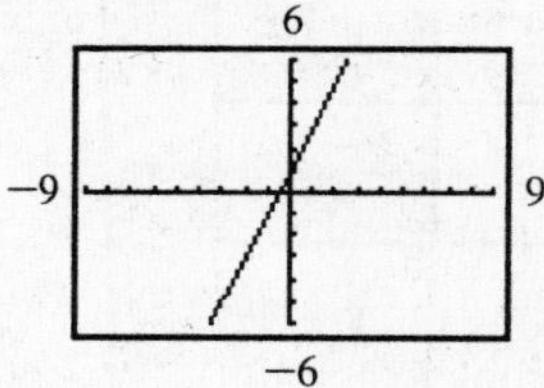

Exercise 17

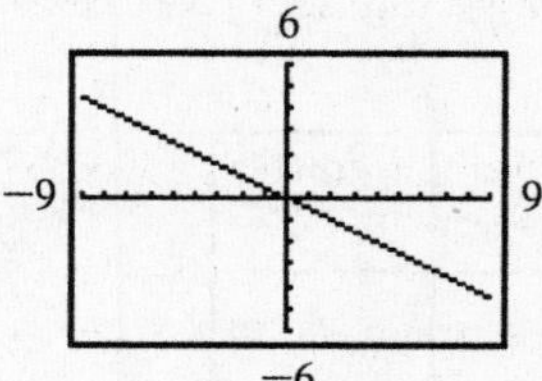

Exercise 19

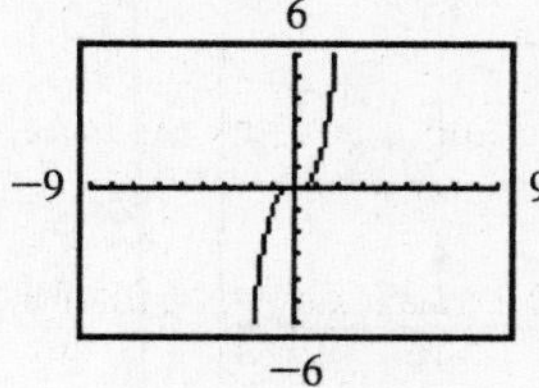

57. $y = x^2 + 10$

a.

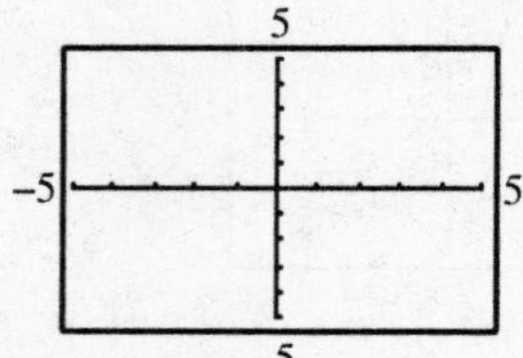

b.

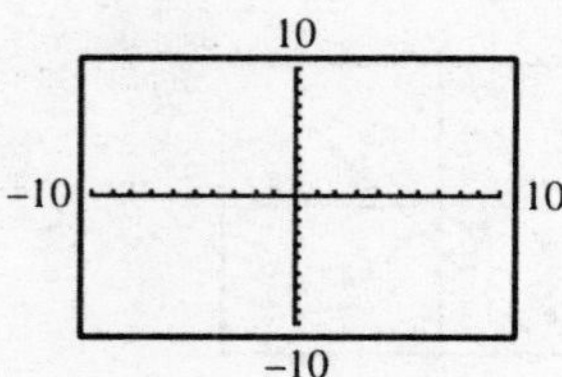

c.

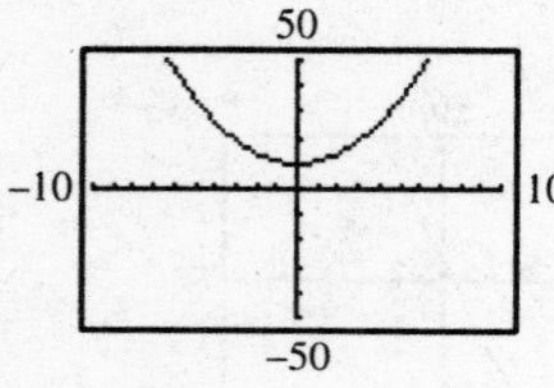

(c) gives a complete graph.

59. $y = \sqrt{x + 18}$

a.

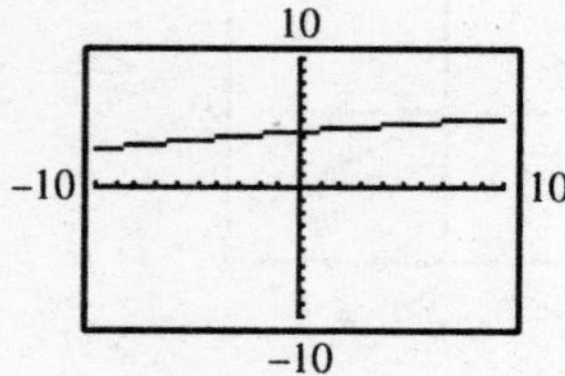

b.

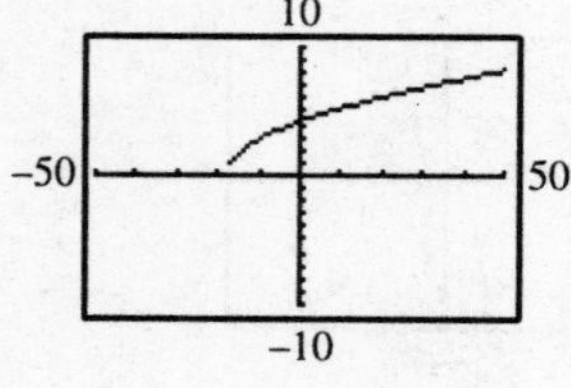

c.

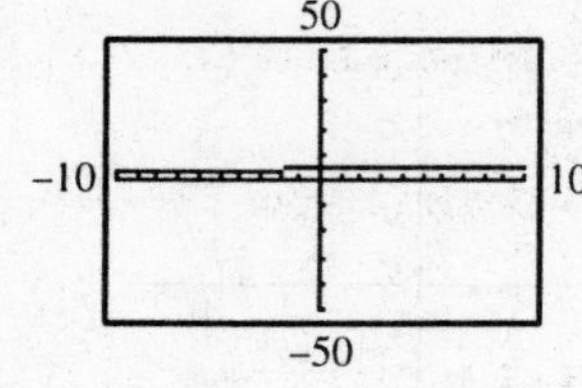

(b) gives a complete graph.

61. **a.** False; (x, y) can be in quadrant III.

b. False; when $x = 2$ and $y = 5$,
$3y - 2x = 3(5) - 2(2) = 11$.

c. False; if a point is on the x-axis, $y = 0$.

d. True; all of the above are false.

(d) is true.

63. a. d_1 = distance from (x, y) to $\left(\frac{x_1+x_2}{2}, \frac{y_1+y_2}{2}\right)$

d_2 = distance from $\left(\frac{x_1+x_2}{2}, \frac{y_1+y_2}{2}\right)$ to $(x_2 y_2)$

$$d_1 = \sqrt{\left(x_1 - \frac{x_1+x_2}{2}\right)^2 + \left(y_1 - \frac{y_1+y_2}{2}\right)^2}$$

$$d_1 = \sqrt{\left(\frac{2x_1 - x_1 - x_2}{2}\right)^2 + \left(\frac{2y_1 - y_1 - y_2}{2}\right)^2}$$

$$d_1 = \sqrt{\left(\frac{x_1 - x_2}{2}\right)^2 + \left(\frac{y_1 - y_2}{2}\right)^2}$$

$$d_1 = \sqrt{\frac{x_1^2 - 2x_1x_2 + x_2^2}{4} + \frac{y_1^2 - 2y_1y_2 + y_2^2}{4}}$$

$$d_1 = \frac{1}{2}\sqrt{x_1^2 - 2x_1x_2 + x_2^2 + y_1^2 - 2y_1y_2 + y_2^2}$$

$$d_2 = \sqrt{\left(x_2 - \frac{x_1+x_2}{2}\right)^2 + \left(y_2 - \frac{y_1+y_2}{2}\right)^2}$$

$$d_2 = \sqrt{\left(\frac{2x_2 - x_1 - x_2}{2}\right)^2 + \left(\frac{2y_2 - y_1 - y_2}{2}\right)^2}$$

$$d_2 = \sqrt{\left(\frac{x_2 - x_1}{2}\right)^2 + \left(\frac{y_2 - y_1}{2}\right)^2}$$

$$d_2 = \sqrt{\frac{x_2^2 - 2x_1x_2 + x_1^2}{4} + \frac{y_2^2 - 2y_1y_2 + y_1^2}{4}}$$

$$d_2 = \frac{1}{2}\sqrt{x_1^2 - 2x_1x_2 + x_2^2 + y_1^2 - 2y_1y_2 + y_2^2}$$

$$d_1 = d_2$$

b. $d_1 + d_2 = \sqrt{x_1^2 - 2x_1x_2 + x_2^2 + y_1^2 - 2y_1y_2 + y_2^2}$

distance from $(x_1 y_1)$ to (x_2, y_2)

$$d_3 = \sqrt{(x_1 - x_2)^2 + (y_1 - y_2)^2}$$

$$d_3 = \sqrt{x_1^2 - 2x_1x_2 + x_2^2 + y_1^2 - 2y_1y_2 + y_2^2}$$

$$d_1 + d_2 = d_3$$

Review Exercises

1. a. $\sqrt{81}$

b. $0, \sqrt{81}$

c. $-17, 0, \sqrt{81}$

d. $-17, -\frac{9}{13}, 0, 0.75, \sqrt{81}$

e. $\sqrt{2}, \pi$

2. $|-103| = 103$

3. $|\sqrt{2}-1| = \sqrt{2}-1$

4. $|3-\sqrt{17}| = \sqrt{17}-3$ since $\sqrt{17}$ is greater than 3.

5. $|4-(-17)| = |4+17| = |21| = 21$

6. $\frac{5}{9}(F-32) = \frac{5}{9}(68-32) = \frac{5}{9}(36) = 20$

7. $\frac{8(x+5)}{3x+8} = \frac{8(2+5)}{3\cdot 2+8} = \frac{8\cdot 7}{6+8} = \frac{56}{14} = 4$

8. $3 + 17 = 17 + 3$;
commutative property of addition.

9. $(6\cdot 3)\cdot 9 = 6\cdot(3\cdot 9)$;
associative property of multiplication.

10. $\sqrt{3}(\sqrt{5}+\sqrt{3}) = \sqrt{15}+3$;
distributive property of multiplication over addition.

11. $(6\cdot 9)\cdot 2 = 2\cdot(6\cdot 9)$;
commutative property of multiplication.

12. $\sqrt{3}(\sqrt{5}+\sqrt{3}) = (\sqrt{5}+\sqrt{3})\sqrt{3}$;
commutative property of multiplication.

13. $(3\cdot 7)+(4\cdot 7) = (4\cdot 7)+(3\cdot 7)$;
commutative property of addition.

14. $3(7x - 5y) - 2(4y - x + 1)$
$= 21x - 15y - 8y + 2x - 2$
$= (21x + 2x) + (-15y - 8y) - 2$
$= 23x - 23y - 2$

15. $\frac{1}{5}(5x)+[(3y)+(-3y)]-(-x) = x + x = 2x$

16. $(-3)^3(-2)^2 = (-27)\cdot(4) = -108$

17. $2^{-4}+4^{-1} = \frac{1}{2^4}+\frac{1}{4}$
$= \frac{1}{16}+\frac{1}{4}$
$= \frac{1}{16}+\frac{4}{16}$
$= \frac{5}{16}$

18. $5^{-3}\cdot 5 = 5^{-3}5^1 = 5^{-3+1} = 5^{-2} = \frac{1}{5^2} = \frac{1}{25}$

19. $\frac{3^3}{3^6} = 3^{3-6} = 3^{-3} = \frac{1}{3^3} = \frac{1}{27}$

20. $(-2x^4y^3)^3 = (-2)^3(x^4)^3(y^3)^3$
$= (-2)^3x^{4\cdot 3}y^{3\cdot 3}$
$= -8x^{12}y^9$

21. $(-5x^3y^2)(-2x^{-11}y^{-2})$
$= (-5)(-2)x^3x^{-11}y^2y^{-2}$
$= 10\cdot x^{3-11}y^{2-2}$
$= 10x^{-8}y^0$
$= \frac{10}{x^8}$

22. $(2x^3)^{-4} = (2)^{-4}(x^3)^{-4}$
$= 2^{-4}x^{-12}$
$= \frac{1}{2^4x^{12}}$
$= \frac{1}{16x^{12}}$

23. $\frac{7x^5y^6}{28x^{15}y^{-2}} = \left(\frac{7}{28}\right)(x^{5-15})(y^{6-(-2)})$
$= \frac{1}{4}x^{-10}y^8$
$= \frac{y^8}{4x^{10}}$

24. $3.74 \times 10^4 = 37,400$

25. $7.45 \times 10^{-5} = 0.0000745$

26. $3,590,000 = 3.59 \times 10^6$

27. $0.00725 = 7.25 \times 10^{-3}$

28. $(3 \times 10^3)(1.3 \times 10^2) = (3 \times 1.3) \times (10^3 \times 10^2)$
$= 3.9 \times 10^5$

29. $\frac{6.9 \times 10^3}{3 \times 10^5} = \left(\frac{6.9}{3}\right) \times 10^{3-5}$
$= 2.3 \times 10^{-2}$

30. $\frac{10^9}{10^6} = 10^{9-6} = 10^3$
It would take 10^3 or 1000 years to accumulate $1 billion.

31. $(2.7 \times 10^8) \times (150)$
$= (2.7 \times 10^8) \times (1.5 \times 10^2)$
$= (2.7 \times 1.5) \times (10^8 \times 10^2)$
$= 4.05 \times 10^{10}$
The total annual spending on movies is $\$4.05 \times 10^{10}$.

32. $\sqrt{300} = \sqrt{100 \cdot 3} = \sqrt{100} \cdot \sqrt{3} = 10\sqrt{3}$

33. $\sqrt{12x^2} = \sqrt{4x^2 \cdot 3} = \sqrt{4x^2} \cdot \sqrt{3} = 2|x|\sqrt{3}$

34. $\sqrt{10x} \cdot \sqrt{2x} = \sqrt{20x^2}$
$= \sqrt{4x^2 \cdot 5}$
$= \sqrt{4x^2} \cdot \sqrt{5}$
$= 2|x|\sqrt{5}$

35. $\sqrt{r^3} = \sqrt{r^2 \cdot r} = |r|\sqrt{r}$

36. $\sqrt{\frac{121}{4}} = \frac{\sqrt{121}}{\sqrt{4}} = \frac{11}{2}$

37. $\frac{\sqrt{96x^3}}{\sqrt{2x}} = \sqrt{\frac{96x^3}{2x}}$
$= \sqrt{48x^2}$
$= \sqrt{16x^2 \cdot 3}$
$= \sqrt{16x^2} \cdot \sqrt{3}$
$= 4|x|\sqrt{3}$

38. $7\sqrt{5} + 13\sqrt{5} = (7+13)\sqrt{5} = 20\sqrt{5}$

39. $2\sqrt{50} + 3\sqrt{8} = 2\sqrt{25 \cdot 2} + 3\sqrt{4 \cdot 2}$
$= 2 \cdot 5\sqrt{2} + 3 \cdot 2\sqrt{2}$
$= 10\sqrt{2} + 6\sqrt{2}$
$= 16\sqrt{2}$

40. $4\sqrt{72} - 2\sqrt{48} = 4\sqrt{36 \cdot 2} - 2\sqrt{16 \cdot 3}$
$= 4 \cdot 6\sqrt{2} - 2 \cdot 4\sqrt{3}$
$= 24\sqrt{2} - 8\sqrt{3}$

41. $\frac{30}{\sqrt{5}} = \frac{30}{\sqrt{5}} \cdot \frac{\sqrt{5}}{\sqrt{5}} = \frac{30\sqrt{5}}{5} = 6\sqrt{5}$

42. $\frac{\sqrt{2}}{\sqrt{3}} = \frac{\sqrt{2}}{\sqrt{3}} \cdot \frac{\sqrt{3}}{\sqrt{3}} = \frac{\sqrt{6}}{3}$

43. $\frac{5}{6+\sqrt{3}} = \frac{5}{6+\sqrt{3}} \cdot \frac{6-\sqrt{3}}{6-\sqrt{3}}$
$= \frac{5(6-\sqrt{3})}{36-3}$
$= \frac{5(6-\sqrt{3})}{33}$

44. $\frac{14}{\sqrt{7}-\sqrt{5}} = \frac{14}{\sqrt{7}-\sqrt{5}} \cdot \frac{\sqrt{7}+\sqrt{5}}{\sqrt{7}+\sqrt{5}}$
$= \frac{14(\sqrt{7}+\sqrt{5})}{7-5}$
$= \frac{14(\sqrt{7}+\sqrt{5})}{2}$
$= 7(\sqrt{7}+\sqrt{5})$

45. $\sqrt[3]{125} = 5$

46. $\sqrt[5]{-32} = -2$

47. $\sqrt[4]{-125}$ is not a real number.

48. $\sqrt[4]{(-5)^4} = \sqrt[4]{625} = \sqrt[4]{5^4} = 5$

49. $\sqrt[3]{81} = \sqrt[3]{27 \cdot 3} = \sqrt[3]{27} \cdot \sqrt[3]{3} = 3\sqrt[3]{3}$

50. $\sqrt[3]{y^5} = \sqrt[3]{y^3 y^2} = y\sqrt[3]{y^2}$

51. $\sqrt[4]{8} \cdot \sqrt[4]{10} = \sqrt[4]{80} = \sqrt[4]{16 \cdot 5} = \sqrt[4]{16} \cdot \sqrt[4]{5} = 2\sqrt[4]{5}$

52. $4\sqrt[3]{16} + 5\sqrt[3]{2} = 4\sqrt[3]{8 \cdot 2} + 5\sqrt[3]{2}$
$= 4 \cdot 2\sqrt[3]{2} + 5\sqrt[3]{2}$
$= 8\sqrt[3]{2} + 5\sqrt[3]{2}$
$= 13\sqrt[3]{2}$

53. $\frac{\sqrt[4]{32x^5}}{\sqrt[4]{16x}} = \sqrt[4]{\frac{32x^5}{16x}} = \sqrt[4]{2x^4} = |x|\sqrt[4]{2}$

54. $16^{1/2} = \sqrt{16} = 4$

55. $25^{-1/2} = \frac{1}{25^{1/2}} = \frac{1}{\sqrt{25}} = \frac{1}{5}$

56. $125^{1/3} = \sqrt[3]{125} = 5$

57. $27^{-1/3} = \frac{1}{27^{1/3}} = \frac{1}{\sqrt[3]{27}} = \frac{1}{3}$

58. $64^{2/3} = (\sqrt[3]{64})^2 = 4^2 = 16$

59. $27^{-4/3} = \frac{1}{27^{4/3}} = \frac{1}{(\sqrt[3]{27})^4} = \frac{1}{3^4} = \frac{1}{81}$

60. $(5x^{2/3})(4x^{1/4}) = 5 \cdot 4x^{2/3+1/4} = 20x^{11/12}$

61. $\frac{15x^{3/4}}{5x^{1/2}} = \left(\frac{15}{5}\right)x^{3/4-1/2} = 3x^{1/4}$

62. $(125 \cdot x^6)^{2/3} = (\sqrt[3]{125x^6})^2$
$= (5x^2)^2$
$= 25x^4$

63. $\sqrt[6]{y^3} = (y^3)^{1/6} = y^{3 \cdot 1/6} = y^{1/2}$

64. $(-6x^3+7x^2-9x+3)+(14x^3+3x^2-11x-7)=(-6x^3+14x^3)+(7x^2+3x^2)+(-9x-11x)+(3-7)$
$=8x^3+10x^2-20x-4$
The degree is 3.

65. $(13x^4-8x^3+2x^2)-(5x^4-3x^3+2x^2-6)=(13x^4-8x^3+2x^2)+(-5x^4+3x^3-2x^2+6)$
$=(13x^4-5x^4)+(-8x^3+3x^3)+(2x^2-2x^2)+6$
$=8x^4-5x^3+6$
The degree is 4.

66. $(3x-2)(4x^2+3x-5)=(3x)(4x^2)+(3x)(3x)+(3x)(-5)+(-2)(4x^2)+(-2)(3x)+(-2)(-5)$
$=12x^3+9x^2-15x-8x^2-6x+10$
$=12x^3+x^2-21x+10$

67. $(3x-5)(2x+1)=(3x)(2x)+(3x)(1)+(-5)(2x)+(-5)(1)$
$=6x^2+3x-10x-5$
$=6x^2-7x-5$

68. $(4x+5)(4x-5)=(4x^2)-5^2=16x^2-25$

69. $(2x+5)^2=(2x)^2+2(2x)\cdot 5+5^2=4x^2+20x+25$

70. $(3x-4)^2=(3x)^2-2(3x)\cdot 4+(-4)^2=9x^2-24x+16$

71. $(2x+1)^3=(2x)^3+3(2x)^2(1)+3(2x)(1)^2+1^3=8x^3+12x^2+6x+1$

72. $(5x-2)^3=(5x)^3-3(5x)^2(2)+3(5x)(2)^2-2^3=125x^3-150x^2+60x-8$

73. $(7x^2-8xy+y^2)+(-8x^2-9xy-4y^2)=(7x^2-8x^2)+(-8xy-9xy)+(y^2-4y^2)$
$=-x^2-17xy-3y^2$
The degree is 2.

74. $(13x^3y^2-5x^2y-9x^2)-(-11x^3y^2-6x^2y+3x^2-4)$
$=(13x^3y^2-5x^2y-9x^2)+(11x^3y^2+6x^2y-3x^2+4)$
$=(13x^3y^2+11x^3y^2)+(-5x^2y+6x^2y)+(-9x^2-3x^2)+4$
$=24x^3y^2+x^2y-12x^2+4$
The degree is 5.

75. $(x+7y)(3x-5y)=x(3x)+(x)(-5y)+(7y)(3x)+(7y)(-5y)$
$=3x^2-5xy+21xy-35y^2$
$=3x^2+16xy-35y^2$

76. $(3x-5y)^2=(3x)^2-2(3x)(5y)+(-5y)^2$
$=9x^2-30xy+25y^2$

77. $(3x^2+2y)^2 = (3x^2)^2 + 2(3x^2)(2y) + (2y)^2$
$= 9x^4 + 12x^2y + 4y^2$

78. $(7x+4y)(7x-4y) = (7x)^2 - (4y)^2$
$= 49x^2 - 16y^2$

79. $(a-b)(a^2+ab+b^2)$
$= a(a^2) + a(ab) + a(b^2) + (-b)(a^2)$
$+(-b)(ab) + (-b)(b^2)$
$= a^3 + a^2b + ab^2 - a^2b - ab^2 - b^3$
$= a^3 - b^3$

80. $15x^3 + 3x^2 = 3x^2 \cdot 5x + 3x^2 \cdot 1$
$= 3x^2(5x+1)$

81. $x^2 - 11x + 28 = (x-4)(x-7)$

82. $15x^2 - x - 2 = (3x+1)(5x-2)$

83. $64 - x^2 = 8^2 - x^2 = (8-x)(8+x)$

84. $x^2 + 16$ is prime.

85. $3x^4 - 9x^3 - 30x^2 = 3x^2(x^2 - 3x - 10)$
$= 3x^2(x-5)(x+2)$

86. $20x^7 - 36x^3 = 4x^3(5x^4 - 9)$

87. $x^3 - 3x^2 - 9x + 27 = x^2(x-3) - 9(x-3)$
$= (x^2-9)(x-3)$
$= (x+3)(x-3)(x-3)$
$= (x+3)(x-3)^2$

88. $16x^2 - 40x + 25 = (4x-5)(4x-5)$
$= (4x-5)^2$

89. $x^4 - 16 = (x^2)^2 - 4^2$
$= (x^2+4)(x^2-4)$
$= (x^2+4)(x+2)(x-2)$

90. $y^3 - 8 = y^3 - 2^3 = (y-2)(y^2+2y+4)$

91. $x^3 + 64 = x^3 + 4^3 = (x+4)(x^2-4x+16)$

92. $3x^4 - 12x^2 = 3x^2(x^2-4)$
$= 3x^2(x-2)(x+2)$

93. $27x^3 - 125 = (3x)^3 - 5^3$
$= (3x-5)[(3x)^2 + (3x)(5) + 5^2]$
$= (3x-5)(9x^2+15x+25)$

94. $x^5 - x = x(x^4-1)$
$= x(x^2-1)(x^2+1)$
$= x(x-1)(x+1)(x^2+1)$

95. $x^3 + 5x^2 - 2x - 10 = x^2(x+5) - 2(x+5)$
$= (x^2-2)(x+5)$

96. $\dfrac{x^3+2x^2}{x+2} = \dfrac{x^2(x+2)}{x+2} = x^2, x \neq -2$

97. $\dfrac{x^2+3x-18}{x^2-36} = \dfrac{(x+6)(x-3)}{(x+6)(x-6)} = \dfrac{x-3}{x-6},$
$x \neq -6, 6$

98. $\dfrac{x^2+2x}{x^2+4x+4} = \dfrac{x(x+2)}{(x+2)^2} = \dfrac{x}{x+2},$
$x \neq -2$

99. $\dfrac{x^2+6x+9}{x^2-4} \cdot \dfrac{x+3}{x-2} = \dfrac{(x+3)^2}{(x-2)(x+2)} \cdot \dfrac{x+3}{x-2}$
$= \dfrac{(x+3)^3}{(x-2)^2(x+2)},$
$x \neq 2, -2$

100. $\frac{6x+2}{x^2-1} \div \frac{3x^2+x}{x-1}$
$= \frac{2(3x+1)}{(x-1)(x+1)} \div \frac{x(3x+1)}{x-1}$
$= \frac{2(3x+1)}{(x-1)(x+1)} \cdot \frac{x-1}{x(3x+1)}$
$= \frac{2}{x(x+1)},$
$x \neq 0,\ 1,\ -1,\ -\frac{1}{3}$

101. $\frac{x^2-5x-24}{x^2-x-12} \div \frac{x^2-10x+16}{x^2+x-6}$
$= \frac{(x-8)(x+3)}{(x-4)(x+3)} \div \frac{(x-2)(x-8)}{(x+3)(x-2)}$
$= \frac{x-8}{x-4} \cdot \frac{x+3}{x-8}$
$= \frac{x+3}{x-4},$
$x \neq -3, 4, 2, 8$

102. $\frac{2x-7}{x^2-9} - \frac{x-10}{x^2-9} = \frac{2x-7-(x-10)}{x^2-9}$
$= \frac{x+3}{(x+3)(x-3)}$
$= \frac{1}{x-3},$
$x \neq 3, -3$

103. $\frac{3x}{x+2} + \frac{x}{x-2} = \frac{3x}{x+2} \cdot \frac{x-2}{x-2} + \frac{x}{x-2} \cdot \frac{x+2}{x+2}$
$= \frac{3x^2-6x+x^2+2x}{(x+2)(x-2)}$
$= \frac{4x^2-4x}{(x+2)(x-2)}$
$= \frac{4x(x-1)}{(x+2)(x-2)},$
$x \neq 2, -2$

104. $\frac{x}{x^2-9} + \frac{x}{x^2-5x+6}$
$= \frac{x}{(x-3)(x+3)} + \frac{x}{(x-2)(x-3)}$
$= \frac{x}{(x-3)(x+3)} \cdot \frac{x-2}{x-2}$
$+ \frac{x}{(x-2)(x-3)} \cdot \frac{x+3}{x+3}$
$= \frac{x(x-2)+x(x+3)}{(x-3)(x+3)(x-2)}$
$= \frac{2x^2+x}{(x-3)(x+3)(x-2)}$
$= \frac{x(2x+1)}{(x-3)(x+3)(x-2)}$
$x \neq 3, -3, 2$

105. $\frac{4x-1}{2x^2+5x-3} - \frac{x+3}{6x^2+x-2}$
$= \frac{4x-1}{(2x-1)(x+3)} - \frac{x+3}{(2x-1)(3x+2)}$
$= \frac{4x-1}{(2x-1)(x+3)} \cdot \frac{3x+2}{3x+2}$
$- \frac{x+3}{(2x-1)(3x+2)} \cdot \frac{x+3}{x+3}$
$= \frac{12x^2+8x-3x-2-x^2-6x-9}{(2x-1)(x+3)(3x+2)}$
$= \frac{11x^2-x-11}{(2x-1)(x+3)(3x+2)},$
$x \neq \frac{1}{2},\ -3,\ -\frac{2}{3}$

106. $\frac{\frac{1}{x}-\frac{1}{2}}{\frac{1}{3}-\frac{x}{6}} = \frac{\frac{1}{x}-\frac{1}{2}}{\frac{1}{3}-\frac{x}{6}} \cdot \frac{6x}{6x}$
$= \frac{6-3x}{2x-x^2}$
$= \frac{-3(x-2)}{-x(x-2)}$
$= \frac{3}{x},$
$x \neq 0, 2$

107. $\dfrac{3+\frac{12}{x}}{1-\frac{16}{x^2}} = \dfrac{3+\frac{12}{x}}{1-\frac{16}{x^2}} \cdot \dfrac{x^2}{x^2}$
$= \dfrac{3x^2+12x}{x^2-16}$
$= \dfrac{3x(x+4)}{(x+4)(x-4)}$
$= \dfrac{3x}{x-4},$
$x \neq 0, 4, -4$

108. $\dfrac{3-\frac{1}{x+3}}{3+\frac{1}{x+3}} = \dfrac{3-\frac{1}{x+3}}{3+\frac{1}{x+3}} \cdot \dfrac{x+3}{x+3}$
$= \dfrac{3(x+3)-1}{3(x+3)+1}$
$= \dfrac{3x+9-1}{3x+9+1}$
$= \dfrac{3x+8}{3x+10},$
$x \neq -3, -\dfrac{10}{3}$

109. $(8-3i)-(17-7i) = 8-3i-17+7i$
$= -9+4i$

110. $4i(3i-2) = (4i)(3i)+(4i)(-2)$
$= 12i^2 - 8i$
$= -12 - 8i$

111. $(7-5i)(2+3i)$
$= 7\cdot 2 + 7(3i) + (-5i)(2) + (-5i)(3i)$
$= 14 + 21i - 10i + 15$
$= 29 + 11i$

112. $(3-4i)^2 = 3^2 + 2\cdot 3(-4i) + (-4i)^2$
$= 9 - 24i - 16$
$= -7 - 24i$

113. $(7+8i)(7-8i) = 7^2 + 8^2 = 49 + 64 = 113$

114. $\dfrac{6}{5+i} = \dfrac{6}{5+i}\cdot\dfrac{5-i}{5-i}$
$= \dfrac{6(5-i)}{25+1}$
$= \dfrac{6(5-i)}{26}$
$= \dfrac{3(5-i)}{13} = \dfrac{15}{13} - \dfrac{3}{13}i$

115. $\dfrac{3+4i}{4-2i} = \dfrac{3+4i}{4-2i}\cdot\dfrac{4+2i}{4+2i}$
$= \dfrac{12+6i+16i+8i^2}{4^2+2^2}$
$= \dfrac{12+22i-8}{16+4}$
$= \dfrac{4+22i}{20}$
$= \dfrac{1}{5} + \dfrac{11}{10}i$

116. $\sqrt{-32} - \sqrt{-18} = i\sqrt{32} - i\sqrt{18}$
$= i\sqrt{16\cdot 2} - i\sqrt{9\cdot 2}$
$= 4i\sqrt{2} - 3i\sqrt{2}$
$= (4i - 3i)\sqrt{2}$
$= i\sqrt{2}$

117. $(-2+\sqrt{-100})^2 = (-2 + i\sqrt{100})^2$
$= (-2+10i)^2$
$= 4 - 40i + (10i)^2$
$= 4 - 40i - 100$
$= -96 - 40i$

118. $\dfrac{4+\sqrt{-8}}{2} = \dfrac{4+i\sqrt{8}}{2} = \dfrac{4+2i\sqrt{2}}{2} = 2 + i\sqrt{2}$

119. $y = 2x - 2$

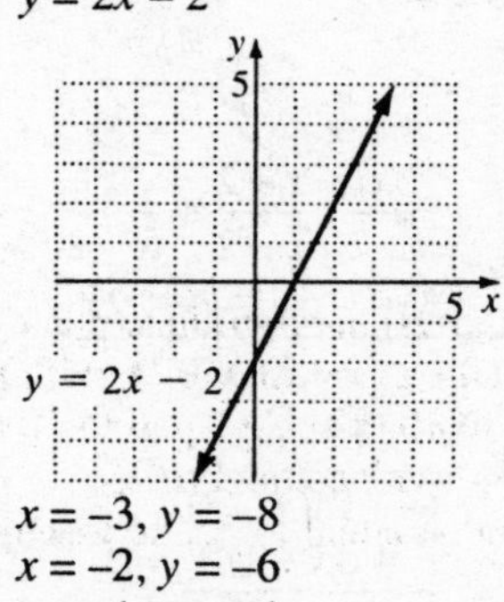

$x = -3, y = -8$
$x = -2, y = -6$
$x = -1, y = -4$
$x = 0, y = -2$
$x = 1, y = 0$
$x = 2, y = 2$
$x = 3, y = 4$

120. $y = x^2 - 3$

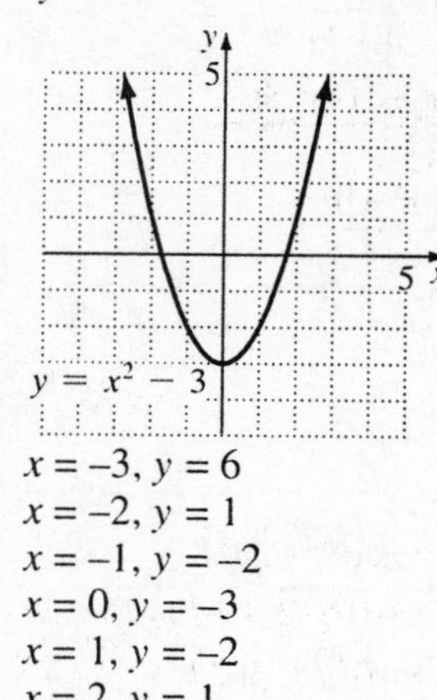

$x = -3, y = 6$
$x = -2, y = 1$
$x = -1, y = -2$
$x = 0, y = -3$
$x = 1, y = -2$
$x = 2, y = 1$
$x = 3, y = 6$

121. $y = x$

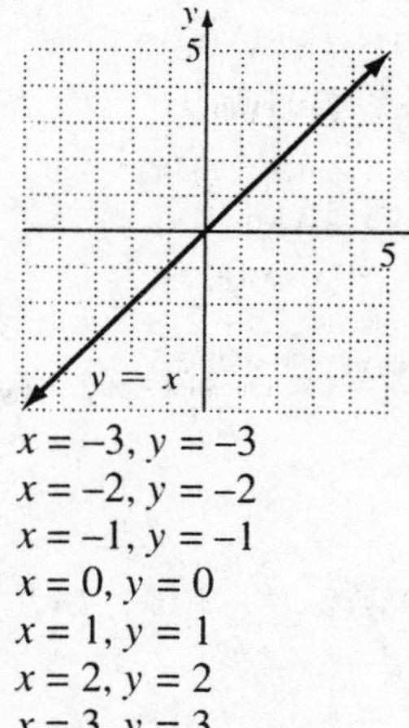

$x = -3, y = -3$
$x = -2, y = -2$
$x = -1, y = -1$
$x = 0, y = 0$
$x = 1, y = 1$
$x = 2, y = 2$
$x = 3, y = 3$

122. A portion of Cartesian coordinate plane with minimum x-value equal to –20, maximum x-value equal to 40, x-scale equal to 10 and with minimum y-value equal to –5, maximum y-value equal to 5, and y-scale equal to 1.

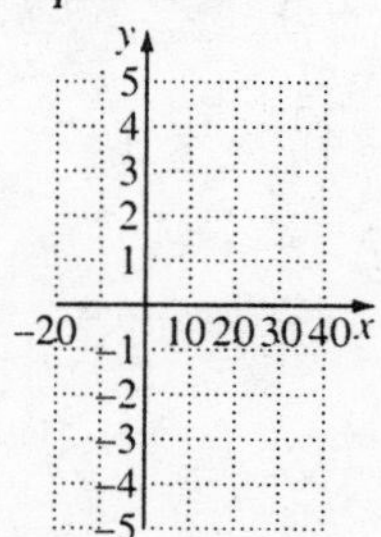

123. x-intercept: –2; The graph intersects the x-axis at (–2, 0).
y-intercept: 2; The graph intersects the y-axis at (0, 2).

124. x-intercepts: 2, –2; The graph intersects the x-axis at (–2, 0) and (2, 0).
y-intercept: –4; The graph intercepts the y-axis at (0, –4).

125. x-intercept: 5; The graph intersects the x-axis at (5, 0).
y-intercept: None; The graph does not intersect the y-axis.

126. a.

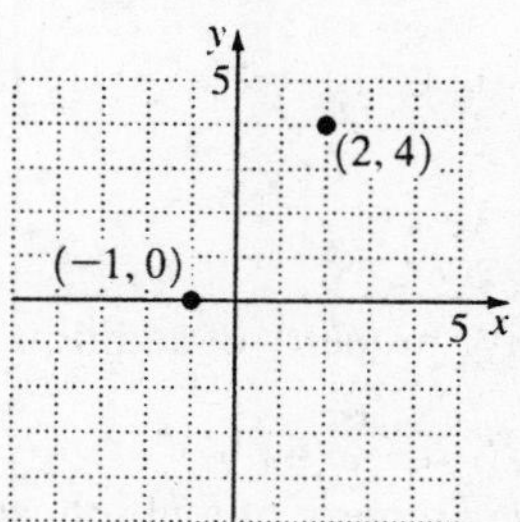

b. $$\sqrt{[2-(-1)]^2 + (4-0)^2} = \sqrt{3^2 + 4^2} = \sqrt{9+16} = \sqrt{25} = 5$$

c. $$\left(\frac{-1+2}{2}, \frac{0+4}{2}\right) = \left(\frac{1}{2}, 2\right)$$

127. a.

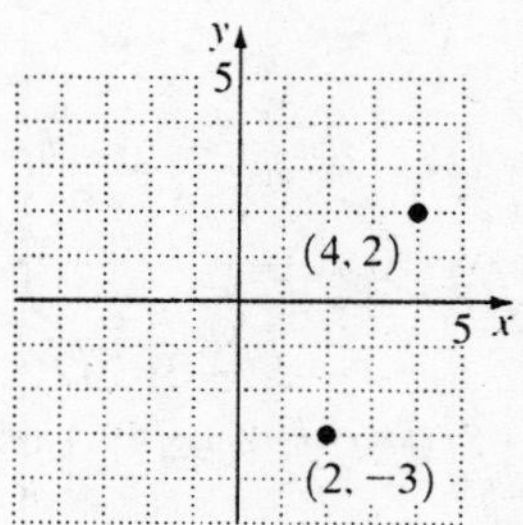

b. $$\sqrt{(4-2)^2 + [2-(-3)^2} = \sqrt{4+25} = \sqrt{29}$$

c. $$\left(\frac{2+4}{2}, \frac{-3+2}{2}\right) = \left(3, -\frac{1}{2}\right)$$

128. a. 1991 because the maximum point is at (1991, 100). The number of applicants for 1991 is 100,000.

b. (1990, 30). The number of medical school applicants in 1990 is about 30,000.

c. The coordinates of A are approximately (1998, 70). In 1998 there were about 70,000 law school applicants.

Chapter P Test

1. $-7, -\frac{4}{5}, 0, 0.25, \sqrt{4}, \frac{22}{7}$ are rational numbers.

2. 3(2 + 5) = 3(5 + 2);
commutative property of addition

3. $6(7+4) = 6\cdot 7 + 6\cdot 4$
distributive property of multiplication over addition

4. $0.00076 = 7.6\times 10^{-4}$

5. $9(10x - 2y) - 5(x - 4y + 3)$
$= 90x - 18y - 5x + 20y - 15$
$= 85x + 2y - 15$

6. $\frac{30x^3y^4}{6x^9y^{-4}} = 5x^{3-9}y^{4-(-4)} = 5x^{-6}y^8 = \frac{5y^8}{x^6}$

7. $\sqrt{6r}\sqrt{3r} = \sqrt{18r^2} = \sqrt{9r^2\cdot 2} = 3|r|\sqrt{2}$

8. $4\sqrt{50} - 3\sqrt{18} = 4\sqrt{25\cdot 2} - 3\sqrt{9\cdot 2}$
$= 4\cdot 5\sqrt{2} - 3\cdot 3\sqrt{2}$
$= 20\sqrt{2} - 9\sqrt{2}$
$= 11\sqrt{2}$

9. $\frac{3}{5+\sqrt{2}} = \frac{3}{5+\sqrt{2}}\cdot\frac{5-\sqrt{2}}{5-\sqrt{2}}$
$= \frac{3(5-\sqrt{2})}{25-2}$
$= \frac{3(5-\sqrt{2})}{23}$

10. $\sqrt[3]{16x^4} = \sqrt[3]{8x^3\cdot 2x}$
$= \sqrt[3]{8x^3}\cdot\sqrt[3]{2x}$
$= 2x\sqrt[3]{2x}$

11. $\frac{x^2+2x-3}{x^2-3x+2} = \frac{(x+3)(x-1)}{(x-2)(x-1)} = \frac{x+3}{x-2}$,
$x \neq 2, 1$

12. $27^{-5/3} = \frac{1}{27^{5/3}} = \frac{1}{\left(\sqrt[3]{27}\right)^5} = \frac{1}{3^5} = \frac{1}{243}$

13. $(2x-5)(x^2-4x+3)$
$= 2x^3 - 8x^2 + 6x - 5x^2 + 20x - 15$
$= 2x^3 - 13x^2 + 26x - 15$

14. $(5x+3y)^2 = (5x)^2 + 2(5x)(3y) + (3y)^2$
$= 25x^2 + 30xy + 9y^2$

15. $x^2 - 9x + 18 = (x-3)(x-6)$

16. $x^3 + 2x^2 + 3x + 6 = x^2(x+2) + 3(x+2)$
$= (x^2+3)(x+2)$

17. $25x^2 - 9 = (5x)^2 - 3^2 = (5x-3)(5x+3)$

18. $36x^2 - 84x + 49 = (6x)^2 - 2(6x)\cdot 7 + 7^2$
$= (6x-7)^2$

19. $y^3 - 125 = y^3 - 5^3 = (y-5)(y^2+5y+25)$

20. $\frac{2x+8}{x-3} \div \frac{x^2+5x+4}{x^2-9}$
$= \frac{2(x+4)}{x-3} \div \frac{(x+1)(x+4)}{(x-3)(x+3)}$
$= \frac{2(x+4)}{x-3}\cdot\frac{(x-3)(x+3)}{(x+1)(x+4)}$
$= \frac{2(x+3)}{x+1}$,
$x \neq 3, -1, -4, -3$

21. $\frac{x}{x+3}+\frac{5}{x-3}$
$=\frac{x}{x+3}\cdot\frac{x-3}{x-3}+\frac{5}{x-3}\cdot\frac{x+3}{x+3}$
$=\frac{x(x-3)+5(x+3)}{(x+3)(x-3)}$
$=\frac{x^2-3x+5x+15}{(x+3)(x-3)}$
$=\frac{x^2+2x+15}{(x+3)(x-3)},\ x\neq 3,\ -3$

22. $\frac{2x+3}{x^2-7x+12}-\frac{2}{x-3}$
$=\frac{2x+3}{(x-3)(x-4)}-\frac{2}{x-3}$
$=\frac{2x+3}{(x-3)(x-4)}-\frac{2}{x-3}\cdot\frac{x-4}{x-4}$
$=\frac{2x+3-2(x-4)}{(x-3)(x-4)}$
$=\frac{2x+3-2(x-4)}{(x-3)(x-4)}$
$=\frac{2x+3-2x+8}{(x-3)(x-4)}$
$=\frac{11}{(x-3)(x-4)},$
$x\neq 3,\ 4$

23. $\frac{\frac{1}{x}-\frac{1}{3}}{\frac{1}{x}}=\frac{\frac{1}{x}-\frac{1}{3}}{\frac{1}{x}}\cdot\frac{3x}{3x}=\frac{3-x}{3},$
$x\neq 0$

24. $(6-7i)(2+5i)=12+30i-14i-35i^2$
$=12+16i+35$
$=47+16i$

25. $\frac{5}{2-i}=\frac{5}{2-i}\cdot\frac{2+i}{2+i}$
$=\frac{5(2+i)}{4+i}$
$=\frac{5(2+i)}{5}$
$=2+i$

26. $2\sqrt{-49}+3\sqrt{-64}=2(7i)+3(8i)$
$=14i+24i$
$=38i$

27.

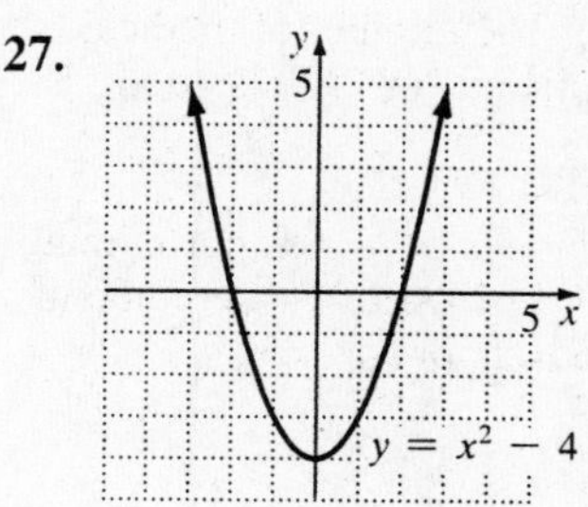

$x=-3,\ y=5$
$x=-2,\ y=0$
$x=-1,\ y=-3$
$x=0,\ y=4$
$x=1,\ y=-3$
$x=2,\ y=0$
$x=3,\ y=5$

28. (2, 9) and (6, 3)
$\sqrt{(6-2)^2+(3-9)^2}=\sqrt{16+36}$
$=\sqrt{52}$
$=\sqrt{4\cdot 13}$
$=2\sqrt{13}$

Chapter 1

Section 1.1

Check Point Exercises

1.
$$\begin{aligned} 5x-8&=72\\ 5x-8+8&=72+8\\ 5x&=80\\ \frac{5x}{5}&=\frac{80}{5}\\ x&=16 \end{aligned}$$

Check:
$$\begin{aligned} 5x-8&=72\\ 5(16)-8&\stackrel{?}{=}72\\ 80-8&\stackrel{?}{=}72\\ 72&=72 \end{aligned}$$
The solution set is $\{16\}$.

2.
$$\begin{aligned} 4(2x+1)-29&=3(2x-5)\\ 8x+4-29&=6x-15\\ 8x-25&=6x-15\\ 8x-25-6x&=6x-15-6x\\ 2x-25&=-15\\ 2x-25+25&=-15+25\\ 2x&=10\\ \frac{2x}{2}&=\frac{10}{2}\\ x&=5 \end{aligned}$$

Check:
$$\begin{aligned} 4(2x+1)-29&\stackrel{?}{=}3(2x-5)\\ 4[2(5)+1]-29&\stackrel{?}{=}3[2(5)-5]\\ 4(10+1)-29&\stackrel{?}{=}3(10-5)\\ 4(11)-29&\stackrel{?}{=}3(5)\\ 44-29&\stackrel{?}{=}15\\ 15&\stackrel{?}{=}15 \end{aligned}$$
The solution set is $\{5\}$.

3.
$$\begin{aligned} \frac{x}{4}&=\frac{2x}{3}+\frac{5}{6}\\ 12\cdot\frac{x}{4}&=12\left(\frac{2x}{3}+\frac{5}{6}\right)\\ 12\cdot\frac{x}{4}&=12\cdot\frac{2x}{3}+12\cdot\frac{5}{6}\\ 3x&=8x+10\\ 3x-8x&=8x+10-8x\\ -5x&=10\\ \frac{-5x}{-5}&=\frac{10}{-5}\\ x&=-2 \end{aligned}$$

Check:
$$\begin{aligned} \frac{x}{4}&=\frac{2x}{3}+\frac{5}{6}\\ \frac{-2}{4}&\stackrel{?}{=}\frac{2(-2)}{3}+\frac{5}{6}\\ \frac{-1}{2}&\stackrel{?}{=}\frac{-4}{3}+\frac{5}{6}\\ \frac{-1}{2}&=\frac{-1}{2} \end{aligned}$$
The solution set is $\{-2\}$.

4.
$$\begin{aligned} \frac{5}{2x}&=\frac{17}{18}-\frac{1}{3x},\ x\neq 0\\ 18x\cdot\frac{5}{2x}&=18x\left(\frac{17}{18}-\frac{1}{3x}\right)\\ 18\cdot\frac{5}{2x}&=18x\cdot\frac{17}{18}-18x\cdot\frac{1}{3x}\\ 45&=17x-6\\ 45+6&=17x-6+6\\ 51&=17x\\ \frac{51}{17}&=\frac{17x}{17}\\ 3&=x \end{aligned}$$
The solution set is $\{3\}$.

5.
$$\frac{x}{x-2}=\frac{2}{x-2}-\frac{2}{3}, x\neq 2$$
$$3(x-2)\cdot\frac{x}{x-2}=3(x-2)\left[\frac{2}{x-2}-\frac{2}{3}\right]$$
$$3(x-2)\cdot\frac{x}{x-2}=(3x-2)\cdot\frac{2}{x-2}-3(x-2)\cdot\frac{2}{3}$$
$$3x=6-(x-2)\cdot 2$$
$$3x=6-2(x-2)$$
$$3x=6-2x+4$$
$$3x=10-2x$$
$$3x+2x=10-2x+2x$$
$$5x=10$$
$$\frac{5x}{5}=\frac{10}{5}$$
$$x=2$$
The solution set is the empty set, $\varnothing$.

6. $2(x+1)=2x+2$
$2x+2=2x+2$
The given equation is an identity.

Exercise Set 1.1

1. $5x-8=72$
$5x=80$
$x=16$
The solution set is $\{16\}$.

Check:
$5x-8=72$
$5(16)-8\overset{?}{=}72$
$80-8\overset{?}{=}72$
$72=72$

3. $11x-(6x-5)=40$
$11x-6x+5=40$
$5x+5=40$
$5x=35$
$x=7$
The solution set is $\{7\}$.

Check:
$11x-(6x-5)=40$
$11(7)-[6(7)-5]\overset{?}{=}40$
$77-(42-5)\overset{?}{=}40$
$77-37\overset{?}{=}40$
$40=40$

5. $2x-7=6+x$
$x-7=6$
$x=13$
The solution set is $\{13\}$.

Check:
$2x-7=6+x$
$2(13)-7\overset{?}{=}6+13$
$26-7\overset{?}{=}19$
$19=19$

7. $7x+4=x+16$
$6x+4=16$
$6x=12$
$x=2$
The solution set is $\{2\}$.

Check:
$7x+4=x+16$
$7(2)+4\overset{?}{=}2+16$
$14+4=18$
$18=18$

9. $3(x-2)+7=2(x+5)$
$3x-6+7=2x+10$
$3x+1=2x+10$
$x+1=10$
$x=9$
The solution set is $\{9\}$.

Check:
$3(x-2)+7=2(x+5)$
$3(9-2)+7\overset{?}{=}2(9+5)$
$3(7)+7\overset{?}{=}2(14)$
$21+7=28$
$28=28$

11. $3(x-4)-4(x-3)=x+3-(x-2)$
$3x-12-4x+12=x+3-x+2$
$-x=5$
$x=-5$
The solution set is $\{-5\}$.

Check:
$3(x-4)-4(x-3)=x+3-(x-2)$
$3(-5-4)-4(-5-3)\overset{?}{=}-5+3-(5-2)$
$3(-9)-4(-8)\overset{?}{=}-2-(-7)$
$-27+32=-2+7$
$5=5$

13. $16 = 3(x-1)-(x-7)$
$16 = 3x-3-x+7$
$16 = 2x+4$
$12 = 2x$
$6 = x$
$x = 6$
The solution set is $\{6\}$.

Check:
$16 = 3(x-1)-(x-7)$
$16 \stackrel{?}{=} 3(6-1)-(6-7)$
$16 \stackrel{?}{=} 3(5)-(-1)$
$16 = 15+1$
$16 = 16$

15. $25-[2+5y-3(y+2)] = -3(2y-5)-[5(y-1)-3y+3]$
$25-[2+5y-3y-6] = -6y+15-[5y-5-3y+3]$
$25-[2y-4] = -6y+15-[2y-2]$
$25-2y+4 = -6y+15-2y+2$
$-2y+29 = -8y+17$
$6y = -12$
$y = -2$
The solution set is $\{-2\}$.

Check:
$25-[2+5y-3(y+2)] = -3(2y-5)-[5(y-1)-3y+3]$
$25-[2+5(-2)-3(-2+2)] \stackrel{?}{=} -3[2(-2)-5]-[5(-2-1)-3(-2)+3]$
$25-[2-10-3(0)] \stackrel{?}{=} -3(-4-5)-[5(-3)+6+3]$
$25+8 \stackrel{?}{=} 27-(-6)$
$33 = 33$

17. $\frac{x}{3} = \frac{x}{2}-2$
$6\left[\frac{x}{3} = \frac{x}{2}-2\right]$
$2x = 3x-12$
$12 = 3x-2x$
$x = 12$
The solution set is $\{12\}$.

19. $20-\frac{x}{3}=\frac{x}{2}$

$6\left[20-\frac{x}{3}=\frac{x}{2}\right]$

$120-2x=3x$

$120=3x+2x$

$120=5x$

$x=\frac{120}{5}$

$x=24$

The solution set is $\{24\}$.

21. $\frac{3x}{5}=\frac{2x}{3}+1$

$15\left[\frac{3x}{5}=\frac{2x}{3}+1\right]$

$9x=10x+15$

$9x-10x=15$

$-x=15$

$x=-15$

The solution set is $\{-15\}$.

23. $\frac{3x}{5}-x=\frac{x}{10}-\frac{5}{2}$

$10\left[\frac{3x}{5}-x=\frac{x}{10}-\frac{5}{2}\right]$

$6x-10x=x-25$

$-4x-x=-25$

$-5x=-25$

$x=5$

The solution set is $\{5\}$.

25. $\frac{x+3}{6}=\frac{3}{8}+\frac{x-5}{4}$

$24\left[\frac{x+3}{6}=\frac{3}{8}+\frac{x-5}{4}\right]$

$4x+12=9+6x-30$

$4x-6x=-21-12$

$-2x=-33$

$x=\frac{33}{2}$

The solution set is $\left\{\frac{33}{2}\right\}$.

27. $\frac{x}{4}=2+\frac{x-3}{3}$

$12\left[\frac{x}{4}=2+\frac{x-3}{3}\right]$

$3x=24+4x-12$

$3x-4x=12$

$-x=12$

$x=-12$

The solution set is $\{-12\}$.

29. $\frac{x+1}{3}=5-\frac{x+2}{7}$

$21\left[\frac{x+1}{3}=5-\frac{x+2}{7}\right]$

$7x+7=105-3x-6$

$7x+3x=99-7$

$10x=92$

$x=\frac{92}{10}$

$x=\frac{46}{5}$

The solution set is $\left\{\frac{46}{5}\right\}$.

31. a. $\frac{4}{x}=\frac{5}{2x}+3 \ (x\neq 0)$

b. $\frac{4}{x}=\frac{5}{2x}+3$

$8=5+6x$

$3=6x$

$\frac{1}{2}=x$

The solution set is $\left\{\frac{1}{2}\right\}$.

33. a. $\frac{2}{x}+3=\frac{5}{2x}+\frac{13}{4} \ (x\neq 0)$

b. $\frac{2}{x}+3=\frac{5}{2x}+\frac{13}{4}$

$8+12x=10+13x$

$-x=2$

$x=-2$

The solution set is $\{-2\}$.

35. a. $\frac{2}{3x}+\frac{1}{4}=\frac{11}{6x}-\frac{1}{3}$ $(x \neq 0)$

b. $\frac{2}{3x}+\frac{1}{4}=\frac{11}{6x}-\frac{1}{3}$
$$8+3x=22-4x$$
$$7x=14$$
$$x=2$$
The solution set is $\{2\}$.

37. a. $\frac{x-2}{2x}+1=\frac{x+1}{x}$ $(x \neq 0)$

b. $\frac{x-2}{2x}+1=\frac{x+1}{x}$
$$x-2+2x=2x+2$$
$$x-2=2$$
$$x=4$$
The solution set is $\{4\}$.

39. a. $\frac{1}{x-1}+5=\frac{11}{x-1}$ $(x \neq 1)$

b. $\frac{1}{x-1}+5=\frac{11}{x-1}$
$$1+5(x-1)=11$$
$$1+5x-5=11$$
$$5x-4=11$$
$$5x=15$$
$$x=3$$
The solution set is $\{3\}$.

41. a. $\frac{8x}{x+1}=4-\frac{8}{x+1}$ $(x \neq -1)$

b. $\frac{8x}{x+1}=4-\frac{8}{x+1}$
$$8x=4(x+1)-8$$
$$8x=4x+4-8$$
$$4x=-4$$
$$x=-1 \Rightarrow \text{ no solution}$$
The solution set is the empty set, $\varnothing$.

43. a. $\frac{3}{2x-2}+\frac{1}{2}=\frac{2}{x-1}$ $(x \neq 1)$

b. $\frac{3}{2x-2}+\frac{1}{2}=\frac{2}{x-1}$
$$\frac{3}{2(x-1)}+\frac{1}{2}=\frac{2}{x-1}$$
$$3+1(x-1)=4$$
$$3+x-1=4$$
$$x=2$$
The solution set is $\{2\}$.

45. a. $\frac{3}{x+2}+\frac{2}{x-2}=\frac{8}{(x+2)(x-2)}$

b. $\frac{3}{x+2}+\frac{2}{x-2}=\frac{8}{(x+2)(x-2)}$
$(x \neq 2,\ x \neq -2)$
$$3(x-2)+2(x+2)=8$$
$$3x-6+2x+4=8$$
$$5x=10$$
$$x=2 \Rightarrow \text{ no solution}$$
The solution set is the empty set, $\varnothing$.

47. a. $\frac{2}{x+1}-\frac{1}{x-1}=\frac{2x}{x^2-1}$ $(x \neq 1,\ x \neq -1)$

b. $\frac{2}{x+1}-\frac{1}{x-1}=\frac{2x}{x^2-1}$
$$\frac{2}{x+1}-\frac{1}{x-1}=\frac{2x}{(x+1)(x-1)}$$
$$2(x-1)-1(x+1)=2x$$
$$2x-2-x-1=2x$$
$$-x=3$$
$$x=-3$$
The solution set is $\{-3\}$.

49. a. $\frac{1}{x-4}-\frac{5}{x+2}=\frac{6}{x^2-2x-8}$

b. $\frac{1}{x-4}-\frac{5}{x+2}=\frac{6}{x^2-2x-8}$
$$\frac{1}{x-4}-\frac{5}{x+2}=\frac{6}{(x-4)(x+2)}$$
$(x \neq 4,\ x \neq -2)$
$$1(x+2)-5(x-4)=6$$
$$x+2-5x+20=6$$
$$-4x=-16$$
$$x=4 \Rightarrow \text{ no solution}$$
The solution set is the empty set, $\varnothing$.

51. $4(x-7) = 4x-28$
$4x-28 = 4x-28$
The given equation is an identity.

53. $2x+3 = 2x-3$
$3 = -3$
The given equation is an inconsistent equation.

55. $4x+5x = 8x$
$9x = 8x$
$x = 0$
The given equation is a conditional equation.

57. $\frac{2x}{x-3} = \frac{6}{x-3}+4$
$2x = 6+4(x-3)$
$2x = 6+4x-12$
$-2x = -6$
$x = 3 \Rightarrow$ no solution
The given equation is an inconsistent equation.

59. $\frac{x+5}{2}-4 = \frac{2x-1}{3}$
$3(x+5)-24 = 2(2x-1)$
$3x+15-24 = 4x-2$
$-x = 7$
$x = -7$
The solution set is $\{-7\}$.

61. $\frac{2}{x-2} = 3+\frac{x}{x-2}$
$2 = 3(x-2)+x$
$2 = 3x-6+x$
$-4x = -8$
$x = 2 \Rightarrow$ no solution
The solution set is the empty set, $\varnothing$.

63. $8x-(3x+2)+10 = 3x$
$8x-3x-2+10 = 3x$
$2x = -8$
$x = -4$
The solution set is $\{-4\}$.

65. $\frac{2}{x}+\frac{1}{2} = \frac{3}{4}$
$8+2x = 3x$
$-x = -8$
$x = 8$
The solution set is $\{8\}$.

67. $\frac{4}{x-2}+\frac{3}{x+5} = \frac{7}{(x+5)(x-2)}$
$4(x+5)+3(x-2) = 7$
$4x+20+3x-6 = 7$
$7x = -7$
$x = -1$
The solution set is $\{-1\}$.

69. a. Let $d = 500{,}000$.
$d = 5000c - 525{,}000$
$500{,}000 = 5000c - 525{,}000$
$1{,}025{,}000 = 5000c$
$205 = c$
In 1990, the average cholesterol level was 205 milligrams per deciliter.

b. Let $c = 180$.
$d = 5000c - 525{,}000$
$d = 5000(180) - 525{,}000$
$d = 375{,}000$
$500{,}000 - 375{,}000 = 125{,}000$
125,000 lives could be saved.

71. $p = 15+\frac{15d}{33}$
$201 = 15+\frac{15d}{33}$
$186 = \frac{15d}{33}$
$15d = 6138$
$d = 409\frac{1}{5}$ feet

Ferreras descended to $409\frac{1}{5}$ feet.

73.–83. Answers may vary.

85. Graph $y_1 = 9x + 3 - 3x$
$y_2 = 2(3x + 1)$

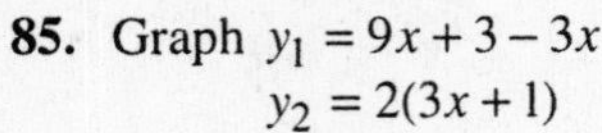

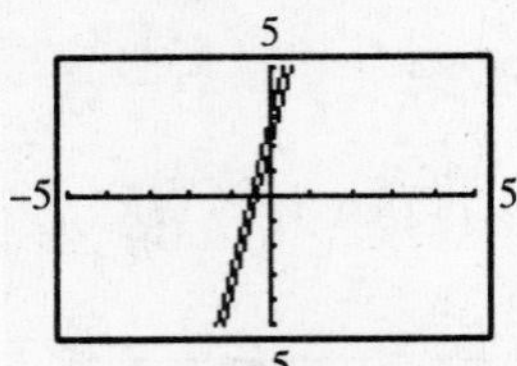

The given equation is an inconsistent equation.

87. Graph $y_1 = \frac{2x-1}{3} - \frac{x-5}{6}$
$y_2 = \frac{x-3}{4}$

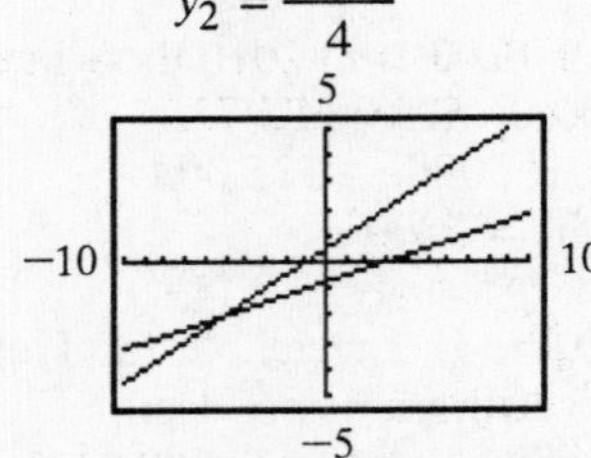

The given equation is a conditional equation.
The solution set is $\{-5\}$.

89. $ax + b = c$
$ax = c - b$
$x = \frac{c-b}{a}$

91. Answers may vary.

93. $\frac{4x-b}{x-5} = 3$
$4x - b = 3(x - 5)$
The solution set will be $\varnothing$ if x = 5.
$4(5) - b = 3(5 - 5)$
$20 - b = 0$
$20 = b$
$b = 20$

Section 1.2

Check Point Exercises

1. $D = 0.2F - 1$
$19 = 0.2F - 1$
$19 + 1 = 0.2F - 1 + 1$
$20 = 0.2F$
$\frac{20}{0.2} = \frac{0.2F}{0.2}$
$100 = F$
The daily fat intake for women in America is 100 grams.

2. Let x = the number (in millions) of copies of the Bee Gees album sold. Let $x + 5$ = the number (in millions) of copies the Morissette album sold.
Then $x + x + 5 = 27$
$2x + 5 = 27$
$2x + 5 - 5 = 27 - 5$
$2x = 22$
$\frac{2x}{2} = \frac{22}{2}$
$x = 11$
There were 11 million copies of the Bee Gees album sold, and 11 + 5 = 16 million copies of the Morisette album sold.

3. Let x = the number of hours of use.
Then $440 + 1.75x = 540.$
$440 + 1.75x - 440 = 540 - 440$
$1.75x = 100$
$\frac{1.75x}{1.75} = \frac{100}{1.75}$
$x \approx 57$
You are allowed 57 hours of use.

4. Let x = the amount invested at 9%.
Let $25,000 - x =$ the amount invested at 12%.
Then $0.09x + 0.12(25,000 - x) = 2550.$
$0.09x + 3000 - 0.12x = 2550$
$-0.03x + 3000 - 3000 = 2550 - 3000$
$-0.03x = -450$
$\frac{-0.03x}{-0.03} = \frac{-450}{-0.03}$
$x = 15,000$
\$15,000 should be invested at 9% and \$10,000 at 12%.

5. Let x = the width of the swimming pool.
Let $3x$ = the length of the swimming pool.
Then $2 \cdot 3x + 2 \cdot x = 320$

$$6x + 2x = 320$$
$$8x = 320$$
$$\frac{8x}{8} = \frac{320}{8}$$
$$x = 4$$
$$3x = 120$$

The length of the pool is 120 feet; its width is 40 feet.

6.
$$y = mx + b$$
$$y - b = mx + b - b$$
$$y - b = mx$$
$$\frac{y-b}{x} = \frac{mx}{x}$$
$$\frac{y-b}{x} = m$$
$$m = \frac{y-b}{x}$$

Exercise Set 1.2

1. $x + 9$

3. $20 - x$

5. $8 - 5x$

7. $15 \div x$

9. $2x + 20$

11. $7x - 30$

13. $4(x + 12)$

15. $x + 40 = 450$
$$x = 410$$
The solution set is $\{410\}$.

17. $5x - 7 = 123$
$$5x = 130$$
$$x = 26$$
The solution set is $\{26\}$.

19. $9x = 3x + 30$
$$6x = 30$$
$$x = 5$$
The solution set is $\{5\}$.

21.
$$R = 143 - 0.65A$$
$$117 = 143 - 0.65A$$
$$-0.65A = -26$$
$$A = 40$$
She is 40 years old. Find 117 on the vertical axis and follow it over to the Female graph.

23.
$$y = 2.5x + 198.73$$
$$273.73 = 2.5x + 198.73$$
$$75 = 2.5x$$
$$x = 30$$
30 years after 1980 or in 2010 the winning predicted speed will be 273.73.

25.
$$f = 0.432h - 10.44$$
$$16 = 0.432h - 10.44$$
$$26.44 = 0.432h$$
$$h \approx 61.2 \text{ inches}$$
Yes, the skeleton could be the missing woman's since the height (about 61.2 inches) is greater than 5 feet.

27. Let x = Sosa homeruns
$x + 4$ = McGwire homeruns
$$x + x + 4 = 136$$
$$2x + 4 = 136$$
$$2x = 132$$
$$x = 66$$
Sosa hit 66 homeruns.
McGwire hit 70 homeruns.

29. Let x = losing score
$x + 1$ = winning score
$$x + x + 1 = 39$$
$$2x + 1 = 39$$
$$2x = 38$$
$$x = 19$$
The losing score was 19.
The winning score was 20.

31. Let x = Sweden
$2x + 14$ = United States
$$x + 2x + 14 = 54.5$$
$$3x + 14 = 54.5$$
$$3x = 40.5$$
$$x = 13.5$$
Sweden = 13.5%
United States = 41%

33. Let x = number of miles
$$200 + 0.15x = 320$$
$$0.15x = 120$$
$$x = 800$$
You can travel 800 miles.

35. Let x = number of months
$$7 + 1.5x = 16$$
$$1.5x = 9$$
$$x = 6$$
After 6 months, a baby girl weighs 16 pounds.

37. Let x = the weight of unpeeled bananas.
$\frac{7}{8}x$ = weight of peeled bananas
$$x = \frac{7}{8}x + \frac{7}{8}$$
$$\frac{1}{8}x = \frac{7}{8}$$
$$x = 7$$
The banana with peel weighs 7 ounces.

39. a. with book: $21 + 0.5x$
without book: $1.25x$

b. $21 + 0.5x = 1.25x$
$$21 = 0.75x$$
$$x = 28$$
If the bus is used 28 times, the costs are the same.

41. Let x = amount at 9%
$25000 - x$ = amount at 12%
$$0.09x + 0.12(25000 - x) = 2250$$
$$0.09x + 3000 - 0.12x = 2250$$
$$-0.03x = -750$$
$$x = 25{,}000$$
\$25,000 at 9%
\$0 at 12%

43. Let x = width
$2x + 6$ = length
$$2x + 2(2x + 6) = 228$$
$$2x + 4x + 12 = 228$$
$$6x + 12 = 228$$
$$6x = 216$$
$$x = 36$$
$$2(36) + 6 = 78$$
The dimensions are 78 feet by 36 feet.

45. Let x = height
$3x$ = length
$$4(3x) + 3x = 60$$
$$12x + 3x = 60$$
$$15x = 60$$
$$x = 4$$
$$3(4) = 12$$
The length is 12 feet, the height is 4 feet.

47. Let x = number of hours
$35x$ = labor cost
$$35x + 63 = 448$$
$$35x = 385$$
$$x = 11$$
It took 11 hours.

49. Let x = original price
$$x - .35x = 81.90$$
$$.65x = 81.90$$
$$x = 126$$
Before the reduction, it cost \$126.

51. Let x = original price
$$x + .065x = 788.10$$
$$1.065x = 788.10$$
$$x = 740$$
Before taxes, the price was \$740.

53. Let x = dealer's cost
$$x + 0.25x = 584$$
$$1.25x = 584$$
$$x = 467.20$$
The dealer's cost is \$467.20.

55. Let x = inches over 5 feet
$$100 + 5x = 135$$
$$5x = 35$$
$$x = 7$$
A height of 5 feet 7 inches corresponds to 135 pounds.

57. $A = lw$

$w = \frac{A}{l}$;

area of rectangle

59. $A = \frac{1}{2}bh$

$2A = bh$

$b = \frac{2A}{h}$;

area of triangle

61. $I = Prt$

$P = \frac{I}{rt}$;

interest

63. $E = mc^2$

$m = \frac{E}{c^2}$;

energy

65. $T = D + pm$

$T - D = pm$

$p = \frac{(T - D)}{m}$

67. $A = \frac{1}{2}h(a + b)$

$2A = h(a + b)$

$\frac{2A}{h} = a + b$

$\frac{2A}{h} - b = a$;

area of trapezoid

69. $S = P + Prt$

$S - P = Prt$

$\frac{S - P}{Pt} = r$;

interest

71. $B = \frac{F}{S - V}$

$B(S - V) = F$

$S - V = \frac{F}{B}$

$S = \frac{F}{B} + V$

73.–75. Answers may vary.

77. a. $y = 3.82 + 0.3x$

b.

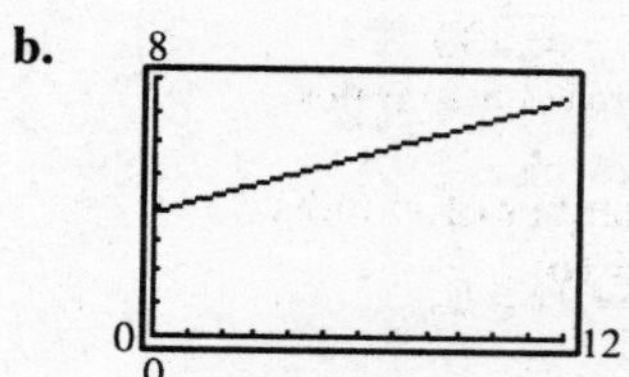

c. The trace feature shows x to be about 8 when $y = 6.22$. $1980 + 8 = 1988$

d. $6.22 = 3.82 + 0.3x$

$2.4 = 0.3x$

$x = 8$

$1980 + 8 = 1988$

79. Let x = student population of one school

$1000 - x$ = student population of the other school

$0.1x + 0.9(1000 - x) = .42(1000)$

$0.1x + 900 - 0.9x = 420$

$-0.8x + 900 = 420$

$-0.8x = -480$

$x = 600$

The school with 10% African Americans has 600 students. The other has 400 students.

81. Let x = woman's age

$3x$ = Coburn's age

$3x + 20 = 2(x + 20)$

$3x + 20 = 2x + 40$

$x + 20 = 40$

$x = 20$

Coburn is 60 years old the woman is 20 years old.

83. Let x = mother's amount
$2x$ = boy's amount
$\frac{x}{2}$ = girl's amount

$$x + 2x + \frac{x}{2} = 14,000$$
$$\frac{7}{2}x = 14,000$$
$$x = \$4,000$$

The mother got \$4000, the boy got \$8000, and the girl got \$2000.

Section 1.3

Check Point Exercises

1. a.
$$3x^2 - 9x = 0$$
$$3x(x-3) = 0$$
$$3x = 0 \text{ or } x - 3 = 0$$
$$x = 0 \qquad x = 3$$
The solution set is $\{0, 3\}$.

b.
$$2x^2 + x = 1$$
$$2x^2 + x - 1 = 0$$
$$(2x-1)(x+1) = 0$$
$$2x - 1 = 0 \text{ or } x + 1 = 0$$
$$2x = 1 \qquad x = -1$$
$$x = \frac{1}{2}$$
The solution set is $\left\{-1, \frac{1}{2}\right\}$.

2. a.
$$3x^2 = 21$$
$$\frac{3x^2}{3} = \frac{21}{3}$$
$$x^2 = 7$$
$$x = \pm\sqrt{7}$$
The solution set is $\{-\sqrt{7}, \sqrt{7}\}$.

b.
$$(x+5)^2 = 11$$
$$x + 5 = \pm\sqrt{11}$$
$$x = -5 \pm \sqrt{11}$$
The solution set is
$\{-5+\sqrt{11}, -5-\sqrt{11}\}$.

3. Add $\left(\frac{14}{2}\right)^2 = 49$.
$$x^2 - 14x + 7^2 = x^2 - 14x + 49 = (x-7)^2$$

4.
$$x^2 - 2x - 2 = 0$$
$$x^2 - 2x - 2 + 2 = 0 + 2$$
$$x^2 - 2x = 2$$
$$x^2 - 2x + 1 = 2 + 1$$
$$(x-1)^2 = 3$$
$$x - 1 = \pm\sqrt{3}$$
$$x = 1 \pm \sqrt{3}$$

The solution set is $\{1+\sqrt{3}, 1-\sqrt{3}\}$.

5. $2x^2 + 2x - 1 = 0$
$a = 2,\ b = 2,\ c = -1$
$$x = \frac{-b \pm \sqrt{b^2 - 4ac}}{2a}$$
$$= \frac{-2 \pm \sqrt{2^2 - 4(2)(-1)}}{2(2)}$$
$$= \frac{-2 \pm \sqrt{4+8}}{4}$$
$$= \frac{-2 \pm \sqrt{12}}{4}$$
$$= \frac{-2 \pm 2\sqrt{3}}{4}$$
$$= \frac{2(-1 \pm \sqrt{3})}{4}$$
$$= \frac{-1 \pm \sqrt{3}}{2}$$

The solution set is $\left\{\frac{-1+\sqrt{3}}{2}, \frac{-1-\sqrt{3}}{2}\right\}$.

6. $x^2 - 2x + 2 = 0$

$a = 1,\ b = -2,\ c = 2$

$$x = \frac{-b \pm \sqrt{b^2 - 4ac}}{2a}$$
$$= \frac{-(-2) \pm \sqrt{(-2)^2 - 4(1)(2)}}{2(1)}$$
$$= \frac{2 + \sqrt{-4}}{2}$$
$$= \frac{2 + 2i}{2}$$
$$= \frac{2(1+i)}{2}$$
$$= 1 + i$$

The solution set is $\{1+i,\ 1-i\}$.

7. $3x^2 - 2x + 5 = 0$

$a = 3,\ b = -2,\ c = 5$

$b^2 - 4ac = (-2)^2 - 4 \cdot 3 \cdot 5 = 4 - 60 = -56$

The discriminant is –56. The equation has two complex imaginary solutions.

8. $P = -10x^2 + 475x + 3500$

$7250 = -10x^2 + 475x + 3500$

$= 10x^2 + 475x - 3750 = 0$

$a = -10,\ b = 475,\ c = -3750$

$$x = \frac{-b \pm \sqrt{b^2 - 4ac}}{2a}$$
$$= \frac{-475 \pm \sqrt{(475)^2 - 4(-10)(-3750)}}{2(-10)}$$
$$= \frac{-475 \pm \sqrt{75,625}}{-20}$$

$x = \dfrac{-475 + \sqrt{75,625}}{-20}$ or $x = \dfrac{-475 - \sqrt{75,625}}{-20}$

$= 10$ $\qquad = 37.5$

It will take 10 years.

9. $w^2 + 9^2 = 15^2$

$w^2 + 81 = 225$

$w^2 = 144$

$w = \pm\sqrt{144}$

$w = \pm 12$

The width of the television is 12 inches.

Exercise Set 1.3

1. $x^2 - 3x - 10 = 0$

$(x+2)(x-5) = 0$

$x + 2 = 0$ or $x - 5 = 0$

$x = -2$ or $x = 5$

The solution set is $\{-2, 5\}$.

3. $x^2 = 8x - 15$

$x^2 - 8x + 15 = 0$

$(x-3)(x-5) = 0$

$x - 3 = 0$ or $x - 5 = 0$

$x = 3$ or $x = 5$

The solution set is $\{3, 5\}$.

5. $6x^2 + 11x - 10 = 0$

$(2x+5)(3x-2) = 0$

$2x + 5 = 0$ or $3x - 2 = 0$

$2x = -5$ $\qquad 3x = 2$

$x = -\frac{5}{2}$ or $x = \frac{2}{3}$

The solution set is $\left\{-\frac{5}{2}, \frac{2}{3}\right\}$.

7. $3x^2 - 2x = 8$

$3x^2 - 2x - 8 = 0$

$(3x+4)(x-2) = 0$

$3x + 4 = 0$ or $x - 2 = 0$

$3x = -4$

$x = -\frac{4}{3}$ or $x = 2$

The solution set is $\left\{-\frac{4}{3}, 2\right\}$.

9. $3x^2 + 12x = 0$

$3x(x+4) = 0$

$3x = 0$ or $x + 4 = 0$

$x = 0$ or $x = -4$

The solution set is $\{-4, 0\}$.

11. $2x(x-3)=5x^2-7x$

$2x^2-6x-5x^2+7x=0$

$-3x^2+x=0$

$x(-3x+1)=0$

$x=0$ or $-3x+1=0$

$-3x=-1$

$x=\frac{1}{3}$

The solution set is $\left\{0, \frac{1}{3}\right\}$.

13. $7-7x=(3x+2)(x-1)$

$7-7x=3x^2-x-2$

$7-7x-3x^2+x+2=0$

$-3x^2-6x+9=0$

$-3(x+3)(x-1)=0$

$x+3=0$ or $x-1=0$

$x=-3$ or $x=1$

The solution set is $\{-3, 1\}$.

15. $3x^2=27$

$x^2=9$

$x=\pm\sqrt{9}=\pm 3$

The solution set is $\{-3, 3\}$.

17. $5x^2+1=51$

$5x^2=50$

$x^2=10$

$x=\pm\sqrt{10}$

The solution set is $\left\{-\sqrt{10}, \sqrt{10}\right\}$.

19. $(x+2)^2=25$

$x+2=\pm\sqrt{25}=\pm 5$

$x=-2\pm 5$

The solution set is $\{-7, 3\}$.

21. $(3x+2)^2=9$

$3x+2=\pm\sqrt{9}=\pm 3$

$3x+2=-3$ or $3x+2=3$

$3x=-5$ $\quad 3x=1$

$x=-\frac{5}{3}$ or $x=\frac{1}{3}$

The solution set is $\left\{-\frac{5}{3}, \frac{1}{3}\right\}$.

23. $(5x-1)^2=7$

$5x-1=\pm\sqrt{7}$

$5x=1\pm\sqrt{7}$

$x=\frac{1\pm\sqrt{7}}{5}$

The solution set is $\left\{\frac{1-\sqrt{7}}{5}, \frac{1+\sqrt{7}}{5}\right\}$.

25. $(3x-4)^2=8$

$3x-4=\pm\sqrt{8}=\pm 2\sqrt{2}$

$3x=4\pm 2\sqrt{2}$

$x=\frac{4\pm 2\sqrt{2}}{3}$

The solution set is $\left\{\frac{4-2\sqrt{2}}{3}, \frac{4+2\sqrt{2}}{3}\right\}$.

27. x^2+12x

$\left(\frac{12}{2}\right)^2=6^2=36$

$x^2+12x+36=(x+6)^2$

29. x^2-10x

$\left(\frac{10}{2}\right)^2=5^2=25$

$x^2-10x+25=(x-5)^2$

31. x^2+3x

$\left(\frac{3}{2}\right)^2=\frac{9}{4}$

$x^2+3x+\frac{9}{4}=\left(x+\frac{3}{2}\right)^2$

33. x^2-7x

$\left(\frac{7}{2}\right)^2=\frac{49}{4}$

$x^2-7x+\frac{49}{4}=\left(x-\frac{7}{2}\right)^2$

35. $x^2 - \frac{2}{3}x$

$$\left(\frac{\frac{2}{3}}{2}\right)^2 = \left(\frac{1}{3}\right)^2 = \frac{1}{9}$$

$$x^2 - \frac{2}{3}x + \frac{1}{9} = \left(x - \frac{1}{3}\right)^2$$

37. $x^2 - \frac{1}{3}x$

$$\left(\frac{\frac{1}{3}}{2}\right)^2 = \left(\frac{1}{6}\right)^2 = \frac{1}{36}$$

$$x^2 - \frac{1}{3}x + \frac{1}{36} = \left(x - \frac{1}{6}\right)^2$$

39.
$$x^2 + 6x = 7$$
$$x^2 + 6x + 9 = 7 + 9$$
$$(x+3)^2 = 16$$
$$x + 3 = \pm 4$$
$$x = -3 \pm 4$$
The solution set is $\{-7, 1\}$.

41.
$$x^2 - 2x = 2$$
$$x^2 - 2x + 1 = 2 + 1$$
$$(x-1)^2 = 3$$
$$x - 1 = \pm\sqrt{3}$$
$$x = 1 \pm \sqrt{3}$$
The solution set is $\left\{1+\sqrt{3},\ 1-\sqrt{3}\right\}$.

43. $x^2 - 6x - 11 = 0$
$$x^2 - 6x = 11$$
$$x^2 - 6x + 9 = 11 + 9$$
$$(x-3)^2 = 20$$
$$x - 3 = \pm\sqrt{20}$$
$$x = 3 \pm 2\sqrt{5}$$
The solution set is $\left\{3+2\sqrt{5},\ 3-2\sqrt{5}\right\}$.

45. $x^2 + 4x + 1 = 0$
$$x^2 + 4x = -1$$
$$x^2 + 4x + 4 = -1 + 4$$
$$(x+2)^2 = 3$$
$$x + 2 = \pm\sqrt{3}$$
$$x = -2 \pm \sqrt{3}$$
The solution set is $\left\{-2+\sqrt{3},\ -2-\sqrt{3}\right\}$.

47. $x^2 + 3x - 1 = 0$
$$x^2 + 3x = 1$$
$$x^2 + 3x + \frac{9}{4} = 1 + \frac{9}{4}$$
$$\left(x + \frac{3}{2}\right)^2 = \frac{13}{4}$$
$$x + \frac{3}{2} = \pm\frac{\sqrt{13}}{2}$$
$$x = \frac{-3 \pm \sqrt{13}}{2}$$
The solution set is $\left\{\frac{-3+\sqrt{13}}{2},\ \frac{-3-\sqrt{13}}{2}\right\}$.

49. $2x^2 - 7x + 3 = 0$
$$x^2 - \frac{7}{2}x + \frac{3}{2} = 0$$
$$x^2 - \frac{7}{2}x = \frac{-3}{2}$$
$$x^2 - \frac{7}{2}x + \frac{49}{16} = -\frac{3}{2} + \frac{49}{16}$$
$$\left(x - \frac{7}{4}\right)^2 = \frac{25}{16}$$
$$x - \frac{7}{4} = \pm\frac{5}{4}$$
$$x = \frac{7}{4} \pm \frac{5}{4}$$
The solution set is $\left\{\frac{1}{2},\ 3\right\}$.

51. $4x^2 - 4x - 1 = 0$

$$4x^2 - 4x - 1 = 0$$
$$x^2 - x - \frac{1}{4} = 0$$
$$x^2 - x = \frac{1}{4}$$
$$x^2 - x + \frac{1}{4} = \frac{1}{4} + \frac{1}{4}$$
$$\left(x - \frac{1}{2}\right)^2 = \frac{2}{4}$$
$$x - \frac{1}{2} = \frac{\pm\sqrt{2}}{2}$$
$$x = \frac{1 \pm \sqrt{2}}{2}$$

The solution set is $\left\{\frac{1+\sqrt{2}}{2}, \frac{1-\sqrt{2}}{2}\right\}$.

53. $3x^2 - 2x - 2 = 0$

$$x^2 - \frac{2}{3}x - \frac{2}{3} = 0$$
$$x^2 - \frac{2}{3}x = \frac{2}{3}$$
$$x^2 - \frac{2}{3}x + \frac{1}{9} = \frac{2}{3} + \frac{1}{9}$$
$$\left(x - \frac{1}{3}\right)^2 = \frac{7}{9}$$
$$x - \frac{1}{3} = \frac{\pm\sqrt{7}}{3}$$
$$x = \frac{1 \pm \sqrt{7}}{3}$$

The solution set is $\left\{\frac{1+\sqrt{7}}{3}, \frac{1-\sqrt{7}}{3}\right\}$.

55. $x^2 + 8x + 15 = 0$

$$x = \frac{-8 \pm \sqrt{8^2 - 4(1)(15)}}{2(1)}$$
$$x = \frac{-8 \pm \sqrt{64 - 60}}{2}$$
$$x = \frac{-8 \pm \sqrt{4}}{2}$$
$$x = \frac{-8 \pm 2}{2}$$

The solution set is $\{-5, -3\}$.

57. $x^2 + 5x + 3 = 0$

$$x = \frac{-5 \pm \sqrt{5^2 - 4(1)(3)}}{2(1)}$$
$$x = \frac{-5 \pm \sqrt{25 - 12}}{2}$$
$$x = \frac{-5 \pm \sqrt{13}}{2}$$

The solution set is $\left\{\frac{-5+\sqrt{13}}{2}, \frac{-5-\sqrt{13}}{2}\right\}$.

59. $3x^2 - 3x - 4 = 0$

$$x = \frac{3 \pm \sqrt{(-3)^2 - 4(3)(-4)}}{2(3)}$$
$$x = \frac{3 \pm \sqrt{9 + 48}}{6}$$
$$x = \frac{3 \pm \sqrt{57}}{6}$$

The solution set is $\left\{\frac{3+\sqrt{57}}{6}, \frac{3-\sqrt{57}}{6}\right\}$

61. $4x^2 = 2x + 7$

$4x^2 - 2x - 7 = 0$

$x = \frac{2 \pm \sqrt{(-2)^2 - 4(4)(-7)}}{2(4)}$

$x = \frac{2 \pm \sqrt{4 + 112}}{8}$

$x = \frac{2 \pm \sqrt{116}}{8}$

$x = \frac{2 \pm 2\sqrt{29}}{8}$

$x = \frac{1 \pm \sqrt{29}}{4}$

The solution set is $\left\{\frac{1+\sqrt{29}}{4}, \frac{1-\sqrt{29}}{4}\right\}$.

63. $x^2 - 6x + 10 = 0$

$x = \frac{6 \pm \sqrt{(-6)^2 - 4(1)(10)}}{2(1)}$

$x = \frac{6 \pm \sqrt{36 - 40}}{2}$

$x = \frac{6 \pm \sqrt{-4}}{2}$

$x = \frac{6 \pm 2i}{2}$

$x = 3 \pm i$

The solution set is $\{3+i, 3-i\}$.

65. $x^2 - 4x - 5 = 0$

$(-4)^2 - 4(1)(-5)$

$= 16 + 20$

$= 36$; 2 unequal real solutions

67. $2x^2 - 11x + 3 = 0$

$(-11)^2 - 4(2)(3)$

$= 121 - 24$

$= 97$; 2 unequal real solutions

69. $x^2 - 2x + 1 = 0$

$(-2)^2 - 4(1)(1)$

$= 4 - 4$

$= 0$; 1 real solution

71. $x^2 - 3x - 7 = 0$

$(-3)^2 - 4(1)(-7)$

$= 9 + 28$

$= 37$; 2 unequal real solutions

73. $2x^2 - x = 1$

$2x^2 - x - 1 = 0$

$(2x+1)(x-1) = 0$

$2x + 1 = 0$ or $x - 1 = 0$

$2x = -1$

$x = -\frac{1}{2}$ or $x = 1$

The solution set is $\left\{-\frac{1}{2}, 1\right\}$.

75. $5x^2 + 2 = 11x$

$5x^2 - 11x + 2 = 0$

$(5x-1)(x-2) = 0$

$5x - 1 = 0$ or $x - 2 = 0$

$5x = 1$

$x = \frac{1}{5}$ or $x = 2$

The solution set is $\left\{\frac{1}{5}, 2\right\}$.

77. $3x^2 = 60$

$x^2 = 20$

$x = \pm\sqrt{20}$

$x = \pm 2\sqrt{5}$

The solution set is $\left\{-2\sqrt{5}, 2\sqrt{5}\right\}$.

79. $x^2 - 2x = 1$

$x^2 - 2x + 1 = 1 + 1$

$(x-1)^2 = 2$

$x - 1 = \pm\sqrt{2}$

$x = 1 \pm \sqrt{2}$

The solution set is $\left\{1+\sqrt{2}, 1-\sqrt{2}\right\}$.

81. $(2x+3)(x+4)=1$

$2x^2+8x+3x+12=1$

$2x^2+11x+11=0$

$x=\frac{-11\pm\sqrt{11^2-4(2)(11)}}{2(2)}$

$x=\frac{-11\pm\sqrt{121-88}}{4}$

$x=\frac{-11\pm\sqrt{33}}{4}$

The solution set is

$\left\{\frac{-11+\sqrt{33}}{4}, \frac{-11-\sqrt{33}}{4}\right\}$.

83. $(3x-4)^2=16$

$3x-4=\pm\sqrt{16}$

$3x-4=\pm4$

$3x=4\pm4$

$3x=8$ or $3x=0$

$x=\frac{8}{3}$ or $x=0$

The solution set is $\left\{0, \frac{8}{3}\right\}$.

85. $3x^2-12x+12=0$

$x^2-4x+4=0$

$(x-2)(x-2)=0$

$x-2=0$

$x=2$

The solution set is $\{2\}$.

87. $4x^2-16=0$

$4x^2=16$

$x^2=4$

$x=\pm2$

The solution set is $\{-2, 2\}$.

89. $x^2-6x+13=0$

$x^2-6x=-13$

$x^2-6x+9=-13+9$

$(x-3)^2=-4$

$x-3=\pm2i$

$x=3\pm2i$

The solution set is $\{3+2i, 3-2i\}$.

91. $x^2=4x-7$

$x^2-4x=-7$

$x^2-4x+4=-7+4$

$(x-2)^2=-3$

$x-2=\pm i\sqrt{3}$

$x=2\pm i\sqrt{3}$

The solution set is $\{2+i\sqrt{3}, 2-i\sqrt{3}\}$.

93. $2x^2-7x=0$

$x(2x-7)=0$

$x=0$ or $2x-7=0$

$2x=7$

$x=0$ or $x=\frac{7}{2}$

The solution set is $\left\{0, \frac{7}{2}\right\}$.

95.
$$45 = 0.0075x^2 - 0.2676x + 14.8$$
$$0 = 0.0075x^2 - 0.2676x - 30.2$$
$$x = \frac{0.2676 \pm \sqrt{(-0.2676)^2 - 4(0.0075)(-30.2)}}{2(0.0075)}$$
$$x = \frac{0.2676 \pm \sqrt{0.07160976 + 0.906}}{0.015}$$
$$x = \frac{0.2676 \pm \sqrt{0.97760976}}{0.015}$$
$$x = \frac{0.2676 \pm 0.9887415031}{0.015}$$
$$x \approx \frac{1.2563}{0.015} \text{ or } x \approx \frac{-0.7211}{0.015}$$
$$\Rightarrow x \approx 83.76 \text{ or } -48.1$$
$$\Rightarrow 1940 + 84 = 2024$$

Fuel efficiency reached 45 miles per gallon in 2024.

97.
$$4.1 = 0.4x^2 + 0.5$$
$$3.6 = 0.4x^2$$
$$x^2 = 9$$
$$x = \pm 3$$

1996 + 3 = 1999

In 1999 4.1 million Americans use modems. The formula gives a number that is slightly larger than the actual number of users. The formula describes the number of users very well.

99.
$$690,515 = 29,035t^2 + 429,200$$
$$29,035t^2 = 261,315$$
$$t^2 = 9$$
$$t = \pm 3$$

1983 + 3 = 1986

It occurred in 1986.

101.
$$740 = 2x^2 + 22x + 320$$
$$0 = 2x^2 + 22x - 420$$
$$0 = x^2 + 11x - 210$$
$$x = \frac{-11 \pm \sqrt{11^2 - 4(1)(-210)}}{2(1)}$$
$$x = \frac{-11 \pm \sqrt{121 + 840}}{2}$$
$$x = \frac{-11 \pm \sqrt{961}}{2}$$
$$x = \frac{-11 \pm 31}{2}$$
$$x = \frac{-42}{2},\ \frac{20}{2}$$
$$x = -21,\ 10$$

1980 + 10 = 1990; actual number: 739,980; The formula describes very well.

103.
$$330 = -1.65x^2 + 51.8x + 111.44$$
$$0 = -1.65x^2 + 51.8x - 218.56$$
$$x = \frac{-51.8 \pm \sqrt{51.8^2 - 4(-1.65)(-218.56)}}{2(-1.65)}$$
$$x = \frac{-51.8 \pm \sqrt{2683.24 - 1442.496}}{-3.3}$$
$$x = \frac{-51.8 \pm \sqrt{1240.744}}{-3.3}$$
$$x \approx \frac{-51.8 \pm 35.22}{-3.3}$$
$$x \approx \frac{-16.58}{-3.3},\ \frac{-87.024}{-3.3}$$
$$x \approx 5.024,\ 26.37$$

$1990 + 5.024 \approx 1995$; actual number: 340,000; The formula is fairly close.

105.
$$90^2 + 90^2 = x^2$$
$$8100 + 8100 = x^2$$
$$16200 = x^2$$
$$x \approx \pm 127.28$$

The distance is 127.28 feet.

107. $15^2 + 8^2 = x^2$

$225 + 64 = x^2$

$289 = x^2$

$x = \pm 17$

$17 \times 2 = 34$

The total length is 34 feet.

109. Let x = width

$x + 5$ = length

$x(x+5) = 300$

$x^2 + 5x = 300$

$x^2 + 5x - 300 = 0$

$(x+20)(x-15) = 0$

$x + 20 = 0 \quad x - 15 = 0$

$x = -20 \quad x = 15$

The width is 15 feet, the length is 20 feet.

111. $x(x)(2) = 200$

$2x^2 = 200$

$x^2 = 100$

$x = \pm 10$

The length and width are 10 inches.

113.–119. Answers may vary.

121. Exercises 55 and 57

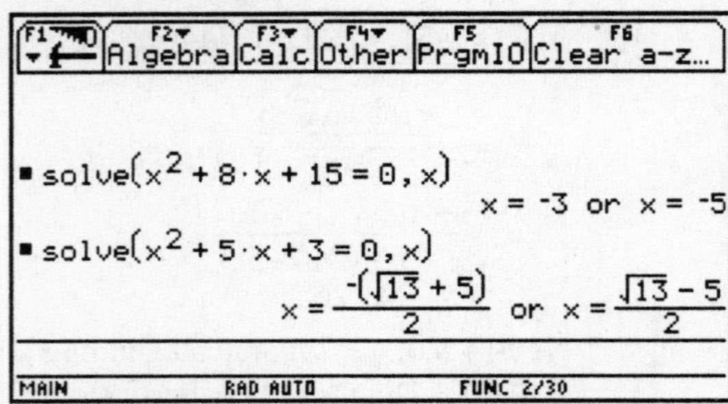

Exercises 59 and 61

F1 F2 Algebra F3 Calc F4 Other F5 PrgmIO F6 Clear a-z...

■ solve(3·x^2 − 3·x − 4 = 0, x)

$x = \frac{\sqrt{57} + 3}{6}$ or $x = \frac{-(\sqrt{57} - 3)}{6}$

■ solve(4·x^2 = 2·x + 7, x)

$x = \frac{\sqrt{29} + 1}{4}$ or $x = \frac{-(\sqrt{29} - 1)}{4}$

MAIN RAD AUTO FUNC 2/30

Exercise 63

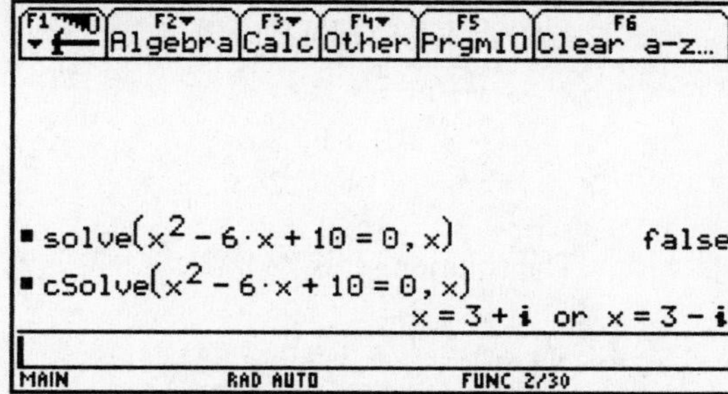

123. **a.** False;

$(2x-3)^2 = 25$

$2x - 3 = \pm 5$

b. False;

Consider $x^2 = 0$, then $x = 0$ is the only distinct solution.

c. True

d. False;

$ax^2 + c = 0$

$$x = \frac{0 \pm \sqrt{0-4ac}}{2a} = \frac{2i\sqrt{ac}}{2a} = \frac{i\sqrt{ac}}{a}$$

(c) is true.

125.

$$(x+3)(x-5) = 0$$
$$x^2 - 5x + 3x - 15 = 0$$
$$x^2 - 2x - 15 = 0$$

127. $19 = -2x^2 + 36x$

$-2x^2 + 36x - 19 = 0$

$36^2 - 4(-2)(-19)$

$1296 - 152$

1144; it is possible, the applicant should be hired.

Section 1.4

Check Point Exercises

1. $4x^4 = 12x^2$

$4x^4 - 12x^2 = 0$

$4x^2(x^2 - 3) = 0$

$4x^2 = 0$ or $x^2 - 3 = 0$

$x^2 = 0$ $\quad x^2 = 3$

$x = \pm\sqrt{0}$ $\quad x = \pm\sqrt{3}$

$x = 0$ $\quad x = \pm\sqrt{3}$

The solution set is $\left\{-\sqrt{3},\ 0,\ \sqrt{3}\right\}$.

2. $2x^3 + 3x^2 = 8x + 12$

$x^2(2x + 3) - 4(2x + 3) = 10$

$(2x + 3)(x^2 - 4) = 0$

$2x + 3 = 0$ or $x^2 - 4 = 0$

$2x = -3$ $\quad x^2 = 4$

$x = -\dfrac{3}{2}$ $\quad x = \pm 2$

The solution set is $\left\{-2,\ -\dfrac{3}{2},\ 2\right\}$.

3. $\sqrt{6x + 7} - x = 2$

$\sqrt{6x + 7} = x + 2$

$6x + 7 = (x + 2)^2$

$6x + 7 = x^2 + 4x + 4$

$0 = x^2 - 2x - 3$

$0 = (x - 3)(x + 1)$

$x - 3 = 0$ or $x + 1 = 0$

$x = 3$ $\quad x = -1$

Check 3:

$\sqrt{6(3) + 7} - 3 \stackrel{?}{=} 2$

$\sqrt{18 + 7} - 3 \stackrel{?}{=} 2$

$\sqrt{25} - 3 \stackrel{?}{=} 2$

$5 - 3 \stackrel{?}{=} 2$

$2 = 2$

Check 1:

$\sqrt{6(-1) + 7} - (-1) \stackrel{?}{=} 2$

$\sqrt{-6 + 7} + 1 \stackrel{?}{=} 2$

$\sqrt{1} + 1 \stackrel{?}{=} 2$

$1 + 1 \stackrel{?}{=} 2$

$2 = 2$

The solution set is $\{-1,\ 3\}$.

4. $\sqrt{x + 5} - \sqrt{x - 3} = 2$

$\sqrt{x + 5} = \sqrt{x - 3} + 2$

$x + 5 = \left(\sqrt{x - 3} + 2\right)^2$

$x + 5 = x - 3 + 4\sqrt{x - 3} + 4$

$x + 5 = x + 1 + 4\sqrt{x - 3}$

$4 = 4\sqrt{x - 3}$

$1 = \sqrt{x - 3}$

$1 = x - 3$

$4 = x$

$x - 3 = 0$ or $x + 1 = 0$

$x = 3$ $\quad x = -1$

Check:

$\sqrt{4 + 5} - \sqrt{4 - 3} \stackrel{?}{=} 2$

$\sqrt{9} - \sqrt{1} \stackrel{?}{=} 2$

$3 - 1 \stackrel{?}{=} 2$

$2 = 2$

The solution set is $\{4\}$.

5. $5x^{3/2} - 25 = 0$

$5x^{3/2} = 25$

$x^{3/2} = 5$

$x = 5^{2/3}$

Check:

$5\left(5^{2/3}\right)^{3/2} - 25 \stackrel{?}{=} 0$

$5(5) - 25 \stackrel{?}{=} 0$

$0 = 0$

The solution set is $\left\{5^{2/3}\right\}$.

6. $x^4 - 5x^2 + 6 = 0$

$\left(x^2\right)^2 - 5x^2 + 6 = 0$

Let $t = x^2$.

$t^2 - 5t + 6 = 0$

$(t-3)(t-2) = 0$

$t - 3 = 0$ or $t - 2 = 0$

$t = 3$ or $t = 2$

$x^2 = 3$ or $x^2 = 2$

$x = \pm\sqrt{3}$ or $x = \pm\sqrt{2}$

The solution set is $\left\{-\sqrt{3},\ \sqrt{3},\ -\sqrt{2},\ \sqrt{2}\right\}$.

7. $3x^{2/3} - 11x^{1/3} - 4 = 0$

Let $t = x^{1/3}$.

$3t^2 - 11t - 4 = 0$

$(3t+1)(t-4) = 0$

$3t + 1 = 0$ or $t - 4 = 0$

$3t = -1$

$t = -\frac{1}{3}$ $\quad$ $t = 4$

$x^{1/3} = -\frac{1}{3}$ $\quad$ $x^{1/3} = 4$

$x = \left(-\frac{1}{3}\right)^3$ $\quad$ $x = 4^3$

$x = -\frac{1}{27}$ $\quad$ $x = 64$

The solution set is $\left\{-\frac{1}{27},\ 64\right\}$.

8. $|2x - 1| = 5$

$2x - 1 = 5$ or $2x - 1 = -5$

$2x = 6$ $\quad$ $2x = -4$

$x = 3$ $\quad$ $x = -2$

The solution set is $\{-2, 3\}$.

Exercise Set 1.4

1. $3x^4 - 48x^2 = 0$

$3x^2(x^2 - 16) = 0$

$3x^2(x+4)(x-4) = 0$

$3x^2 = 0$ $\quad$ $x + 4 = 0$ $\quad$ $x - 4 = 0$

$x^2 = 0$ $\quad$ $x = -4$ $\quad$ $x = 4$

$x = 0$

The solution set is $\{0, -4, 4\}$.

3. $2x^4 = 16x$

$2x^4 - 16x = 0$

$2x\left(x^3 - 8\right) = 0$

$2x = 0$ $\quad$ $x^3 - 8 = 0$

$x^3 = 8$

$x = 0$ $\quad$ $x = 2$

The solution set is $\{0, 2\}$.

5. $3x^3 + 2x^2 = 12x + 8$

$3x^3 + 2x^2 - 12x - 8 = 0$

$x^2(3x+2) - 4(3x+2) = 0$

$(3x+2)(x^2 - 4) = 0$

$3x + 2 = 0$ $\quad$ $x^2 - 4 = 0$

$3x = -2$ $\quad$ $x^2 = 4$

$x = -\frac{2}{3}$ $\quad$ $x = \pm 2$

The solution set is $\left\{-\frac{2}{3},\ 2,\ -2\right\}$.

7. $2x - 3 = 8x^3 - 12x^2$

$8x^3 - 12x^2 - 2x + 3 = 0$

$4x^2(2x-3) - (2x-3) = 0$

$(2x-3)(4x^2 - 1) = 0$

$2x - 3 = 0$ $\quad$ $4x^2 - 1 = 0$

$2x = 3$ $\quad$ $4x^2 = 1$

$x^2 = \frac{1}{4}$

$x = \frac{3}{2}$ $\quad$ $x = \pm\frac{1}{2}$

The solution set is $\left\{\frac{3}{2},\ \frac{1}{2},\ -\frac{1}{2}\right\}$.

9.
$$4y^3 - 2 = y - 8y^2$$
$$4y^3 + 8y^2 - y - 2 = 0$$
$$4y^2(y+2) - (y+2) = 0$$
$$(y+2)(4y^2 - 1) = 0$$
$$y+2=0 \quad 4y^2 - 1 = 0$$
$$4y^2 = 1$$
$$y^2 = \frac{1}{4}$$
$$y = -2 \quad y = \pm\frac{1}{2}$$
The solution set is $\left\{-2, \frac{1}{2}, -\frac{1}{2}\right\}$.

11.
$$\sqrt{3x+18} = x$$
$$3x+18 = x^2$$
$$x^2 - 3x - 18 = 0$$
$$(x+3)(x-6) = 0$$
$$x+3=0 \quad x-6=0$$
$$x=-3 \quad x=6$$
$$\sqrt{3(-3)+18} = -3 \quad \sqrt{3(6)+18} = 6$$
$$\sqrt{-9+18} = -3 \quad \sqrt{18+18} = 6$$
$$\sqrt{9} = -3 \text{ False} \quad \sqrt{36} = 6$$
The solution set is $\{6\}$.

13.
$$\sqrt{x+3} = x-3$$
$$x+3 = x^2 - 6x + 9$$
$$x^2 - 7x + 6 = 0$$
$$(x-1)(x-6) = 0$$
$$x-1=0 \quad x-6=0$$
$$x=1 \quad x=6$$
$$\sqrt{1+3} = 1-3 \quad \sqrt{6+3} = 6-3$$
$$\sqrt{4} = -2 \text{ False} \quad \sqrt{9} = 3$$
The solution set is $\{6\}$.

15.
$$\sqrt{2x+13} = x+7$$
$$2x+13 = (x+7)^2$$
$$2x+13 = x^2 + 14x + 49$$
$$x^2 + 12x + 36 = 0$$
$$(x+6)^2 = 0$$
$$x+6 = 0$$
$$x = -6$$
$$\sqrt{2(-6)+13} = -6+7$$
$$\sqrt{-12+13} = 1$$
$$\sqrt{1} = 1$$
The solution set is $\{-6\}$.

17.
$$x - \sqrt{2x+5} = 5$$
$$x - 5 = \sqrt{2x+5}$$
$$(x-5)^2 = 2x+5$$
$$x^2 - 10x + 25 = 2x + 5$$
$$x^2 - 12x + 20 = 0$$
$$(x-2)(x-10) = 0$$
$$x-2=0 \quad x-10=0$$
$$x=2 \quad x=10$$
$$2 - \sqrt{2(2)+5} = 5 \quad 10 - \sqrt{2(10)+5} = 5$$
$$2 - \sqrt{9} = 5 \quad 10 - \sqrt{25} = 5$$
$$2 - 3 = 5 \text{ False} \quad 10 - 5 = 5$$
The solution set is $\{10\}$.

19.
$$\sqrt{3x} + 10 = x + 4$$
$$\sqrt{3x} = x - 6$$
$$3x = (x-6)^2$$
$$3x = x^2 - 12x + 36$$
$$x^2 - 15x + 36 = 0$$
$$(x-12)(x-3) = 0$$
$$x - 12 = 0 \quad x - 3 = 0$$
$$x = 12 \quad x = 3$$
$$\sqrt{3(12)} + 10 = 12 + 4 \quad \sqrt{3(3)} + 10 = 3 + 4$$
$$\sqrt{36} + 10 = 16 \quad \sqrt{9} + 10 = 7$$
$$6 + 10 = 16 \quad 3 + 10 = 7 \text{ False}$$
The solution set is $\{12\}$.

21. $\sqrt{x+8}-\sqrt{x-4}=2$

$\sqrt{x+8}=\sqrt{x-4}+2$

$x+8=(\sqrt{x-4}+2)^2$

$x+8=x-4+4\sqrt{x-4}+4$

$x+8=x+4\sqrt{x-4}$

$8=4\sqrt{x-4}$

$2=\sqrt{x-4}$

$4=x-4$

$x=8$

$\sqrt{8+8}-\sqrt{8-4}=2$

$\sqrt{16}-\sqrt{4}=2$

$4-2=2$

The solution set is $\{8\}$.

23. $\sqrt{x-5}-\sqrt{x-8}=3$

$\sqrt{x-5}=\sqrt{x-8}+3$

$x-5=(\sqrt{x-8}+3)^2$

$x-5=x-8+6\sqrt{x-8}+9$

$x-5=x+1+6\sqrt{x-8}$

$-6=6\sqrt{x-8}$

$-1=\sqrt{x-8}$

$1=x-8$

$x=9$

$\sqrt{9-5}-\sqrt{9-8}=3$

$\sqrt{4}-\sqrt{1}=3$

$2-1=3$ False

The solution set is the empty set, $\varnothing$.

25. $\sqrt{2x+3}+\sqrt{x-2}=2$

$\sqrt{2x+3}=2-\sqrt{x-2}$

$2x+3=(2-\sqrt{x-2})^2$

$2x+3=4-4\sqrt{x-2}+x-2$

$x+1=-4\sqrt{x-2}$

$(x+1)^2=16(x-2)$

$x^2+2x+1=16x-32$

$x^2-14x+33=0$

$(x-11)(x-3)=0$

$x-11=0 \quad x-3=0$

$x=11 \qquad x=3$

$\sqrt{2(11)+3}+\sqrt{11-2}=2$

$\sqrt{22+3}+\sqrt{9}=2$

$5+3=2$ False

$\sqrt{2(3)+3}+\sqrt{3-2}=2$

$\sqrt{6+3}+\sqrt{1}=2$

$3+1=2$ False

The solution set is the empty set, $\varnothing$.

27. $\sqrt{3\sqrt{x+1}}=\sqrt{3x-5}$

$3\sqrt{x+1}=3x-5$

$9(x+1)=9x^2-30x+25$

$9x^2-39x+16=0$

$x=\dfrac{39\pm\sqrt{945}}{18}=\dfrac{13\pm\sqrt{105}}{6}$

Check proposed solutions.

The solution set is $\left\{\dfrac{13+\sqrt{105}}{6}\right\}$.

29. $x^{3/2}=8$

$(x^{3/2})^{2/3}=8^{2/3}$

$x=\sqrt[3]{8}^2$

$x=2^2$

$x=4$

$4^{3/2}=8$

$\sqrt{4}^3=8$

$2^3=8$

The solution set is $\{4\}$.

31. $(x-4)^{3/2}=27$

$((x-4)^{3/2})^{2/3}=27^{2/3}$

$x-4=\sqrt[3]{27}^2$

$x-4=3^2$

$x-4=9$

$x=13$

$(13-4)^{3/2}=27$

$9^{3/2}=27$

$\sqrt{9}^3=27$

$3^3=27$

The solution set is $\{13\}$.

33. $6x^{5/2}-12=0$

$6x^{5/2}=12$

$x^{5/2}=2$

$(x^{5/2})^{2/5}=2^{2/5}$

$x=\sqrt[5]{2^2}$

$x=\sqrt[5]{4}$

$6(\sqrt[5]{4})^{5/2}-12=0$

$6(4^{1/5})^{5/2}-12=0$

$6(4^{1/2})-12=0$

$6(2)-12=0$

The solution set is $\left\{\sqrt[5]{4}\right\}$.

35. $(x^2-x-4)^{3/4}-2=6$

$(x^2-x-4)^{3/4}=8$

$((x^2-x-4)^{3/4})^{4/3}=8^{4/3}$

$x^2-x-4=\sqrt[3]{8}^4$

$x^2-x-4=2^4$

$x^2-x-4=16$

$x^2-x-20=0$

$(x-5)(x+4)=0$

$x-5=0 \quad x+4=0$

$x=5 \quad x=-4$

$(5^2-5-4)^{3/4}-2=6$

$(25-9)^{3/4}-2=6$

$16^{3/4}-2=6$

$\sqrt[4]{16}^3-2=6$

$2^3-2=6$

$8-2=6$

$((-4)^2-(-4)-4)^{3/4}-2=6$

$(16+4-4)^{3/4}-2=6$

$16^{3/4}-2=6$

$\sqrt[4]{16}^3-2=6$

$2^3-2=6$

$8-2=6$

The solution set is {5, –4}.

37. $x^4-5x^2+4=0$ let $t=x^2$

$t^2-5t+4=0$

$(t-1)(t-4)=0$

$t-1=0 \quad t-4=0$

$t=1 \quad t=4$

$x^2=1 \quad x^2=4$

$x=\pm 1 \quad x=\pm 2$

The solution set is {1, –1, 2, –2}

39. $9x^4=25x^2-16$

$9x^4-25x^2+16=0$ let $t=x^2$

$9t^2-25t+16=0$

$(9t-16)(t-1)=0$

$9t-16=0$

$9t=16$

$t=\frac{16}{9} \quad t-1=0$

$t=1$

$x^2=\frac{16}{9} \quad x^2=1$

$x=\pm 1$

$x=\pm\frac{4}{3}$

The solution set is $\left\{1,-1,\frac{4}{3},-\frac{4}{3}\right\}$.

41. $x^6+8x^3+15=0$ let $t=x^3$

$t^2+8t+15=0$

$(t+5)(t+3)=0$

$t+5=0 \quad t+3=0$

$t=-5 \quad t=-3$

$x^3=-5 \quad x^3=-3$

$x=-\sqrt[3]{5} \quad x=-\sqrt[3]{3}$

The solution set is $\left\{-\sqrt[3]{5},-\sqrt[3]{5}\right\}$.

43. $5x^6 + x^3 = 18$ let $t = x^3$

$5t^2 + t - 18 = 0$

$(5t - 9)(t + 2) = 0$

$5t - 9 = 0$

$5t = 9$

$t = \frac{9}{5}$ $\quad t + 2 = 0$

$t = -2$

$x^3 = \frac{9}{5}$ $\quad x^3 = -2$

$x = -\sqrt[3]{2}$

$x = \sqrt[3]{\frac{9}{5}}$

The solution set is $\left\{\sqrt[3]{\frac{9}{5}}, -\sqrt[3]{2}\right\}$.

45. $x^{2/3} - x^{1/3} - 6 = 0$ let $t = x^{1/3}$

$t^2 - t - 6 = 0$

$(t - 3)(t + 2) = 0$

$t - 3 = 0 \quad t + 2 = 0$

$t = 3 \quad t = -2$

$x^{1/3} = 3 \quad x^{1/3} = -2$

$x = 3^3 \quad x = (-2)^3$

$x = 27 \quad x = -8$

The solution set is {27, –83}.

47. $x^{3/2} - 2x^{3/4} + 1 = 0$ let $t = x^{3/4}$

$t^2 - 2t + 1 = 0$

$(t - 1)(t - 1) = 0$

$t - 1 = 0$

$t = 1$

$x^{3/4} = 1$

$x = 1^{4/3}$

$x = 1$

The solution set is {1}.

49. $2x - 3x^{1/2} + 1 = 0$ let $t = x^{1/2}$

$2t^2 - 3t + 1 = 0$

$(2t - 1)(t - 1) = 0$

$2t - 1 = 0 \quad t - 1 = 0$

$2t = 1$

$t = \frac{1}{2} \quad t = 1$

$x^{1/2} = \frac{1}{2} \quad x^{1/2} = 1$

$x = \left(\frac{1}{2}\right)^2 \quad x = 1^2$

$x = \frac{1}{4} \quad x = 1$

The solution set is $\left\{\frac{1}{4}, 1\right\}$.

51. $(x - 5)^2 - 4(x - 5) - 21 = 0$ let $t = x - 5$

$t^2 - 4t - 21 = 0$

$(t + 3)(t - 7) = 0$

$t + 3 = 0 \quad t - 7 = 0$

$t = -3 \quad t = 7$

$x - 5 = -3 \quad x - 5 = 7$

$x = 2 \quad x = 12$

The solution set is {2, 12}.

53. $\left(x^2 - x\right)^2 - 14\left(x^2 - x\right) + 24 = 0$

Let $t = x^2 - x$.

$t^2 - 14t + 24 = 0$

$(t - 2)(t - 12) = 0$

$t = 2$ or $t = 12$

$x^2 - x = 2$ or $x^2 - x = 12$

$x^2 - x - 2 = 0 \quad x^2 - x - 12 = 0$

$(x - 2)(x + 1) = 0 \quad (x - 4)(x + 3) = 0$

The solution set is {–3, –1, 2, 4}.

55. $\left(y-\frac{8}{y}\right)^2+5\left(y-\frac{8}{y}\right)-14=0$

Let $t=y-\frac{8}{y}$.

$t^2+5t-14=0$
$(t+7)(t-2)=0$
$t=-7$ or $t=2$

$y-\frac{8}{y}=-7$ or $y-\frac{8}{y}=2$

$y^2+7y-8=0$ $\quad y^2-2y-8=0$

$(y+8)(y-1)=0$ $\quad (y-4)(y+2)=0$

The solution set is $\{-8, -2, 1, 4\}$.

57. $|x|=8$
$x=8, x=-8$
The solution set is $\{8, -8\}$.

59. $|x-2|=7$
$x-2=7$ $\quad x-2=-7$
$x=9$ $\quad x=-5$
The solution set is $\{9, -5\}$.

61. $|2x-1|=5$
$2x-1=5$ $\quad 2x-1=-5$
$2x=6$ $\quad 2x=-4$
$x=3$ $\quad x=-2$
The solution set is $\{3, -2\}$.

63. $x+2\sqrt{x}-3=0$ let $t=\sqrt{x}$
$t^2+2t-3=0$
$(t-1)(t+3)=0$
$t-1=0$ $\quad t+3=0$
$t=1$ $\quad t=-3$
$\sqrt{x}=1$ $\quad \sqrt{x}=-3$
$x=1$ $\quad x=9$
The solution set is $\{1\}$.

65. $(x+4)^{3/2}=8$
$x+4=8^{2/3}$
$x+4=\sqrt[3]{8}^2$
$x+4=2^2$
$x+4=4$
$x=0$
The solution set is $\{0\}$.

67. $\sqrt{4x+15}-2x=0$
$\sqrt{4x+15}=2x$
$4x+15=4x^2$
$4x^2-4x-15=0$
$(2x-5)(2x+3)=0$
$2x-5=0$ $\quad 2x+3=0$
$2x=5$ $\quad 2x=-3$
$x=\frac{5}{2}$ $\quad x=\frac{-3}{2}$
The solution set is $\left\{\frac{5}{2}\right\}$.

69. $|x^2+2x-36|=12$
$x^2+2x-36=12$ $\quad x^2+2x-36=-12$
$x^2+2x-48=0$ $\quad x^2+2x-24=0$
$(x-6)(x+8)=0$ $\quad (x+6)(x-4)=0$
$x-6=0$ $\quad x+8=0$ $\quad x+6=0$ $\quad x-4=0$
$x=6$ $\quad x=-8$ $\quad x=-6$ $\quad x=4$
The solution set is $\{6, -8, -6, 4\}$.

71. $x^3-2x^2=x-2$
$x^3-2x^2-x+2=0$
$x^2(x-2)-(x-2)=0$
$(x-2)(x^2-1)=0$
$x-2=0$ $\quad x^2-1=0$
$x=2$ $\quad x^2=1$
$x=\pm1$
The solution set is $\{1, -1, 2\}$

73. $N=5000\sqrt{100-x}$
$40000=5000\sqrt{100-x}$
$8=\sqrt{100-x}$
$64=100-x$
$x=36$
They will survive to 36 years old.

75. $N = 1220\sqrt[3]{x+42} + 4900$

$9780 = 1220\sqrt[3]{x+42} + 4900$

$4880 = 1220\sqrt[3]{x+42}$

$4 = \sqrt[3]{x+42}$

$64 = x + 42$

$x = 22$

$1930 + 22 = 1952$

9780 aides were assigned in 1952.

77. $T = \dfrac{T_0}{\sqrt{1-\dfrac{v^2}{c^2}}}$

$$4 = \frac{2}{\sqrt{1-\dfrac{v^2}{c^2}}}$$

$$\sqrt{1-\frac{v^2}{c^2}} = \frac{2}{4}$$

$$\sqrt{1-\frac{v^2}{(186,000)^2}} = \frac{1}{2}$$

$$1-\frac{v^2}{(186,000)^2} = \frac{1}{4}$$

$$-\frac{v^2}{(186,000)^2} = -\frac{3}{4}$$

$$v^2 = \frac{3}{4}(186,000)^2$$

$$v \approx 161,081$$

The ship is traveling about 161,081 miles/second.

79. a. $p = 30 - \sqrt{0.01(0)+1}$

$p = 29$

There will be no demand for CD sets at a price of $29.

b. $27.76 = 30 - \sqrt{0.01x+1}$

$\left(\sqrt{0.01x+1}\right)^2 = (2.24)^2$

$0.01x + 1 = 5.0176$

$x = 401.76 \approx 402$

402 CD sets will sell weekly.

81. a.

$$\sqrt{6^2+x^2}+\sqrt{3^2+(12-x)^2}=15$$
$$\sqrt{36+x^2}=15-\sqrt{9+144-24x+x^2}$$
$$36+x^2=225-30\sqrt{153-24x+x^2}+x^2-24x+153$$
$$30\sqrt{x^2-24x+153}=-24x+342$$
$$5\sqrt{x^2-24x+153}=-4x+157$$
$$25(x^2-24x+153)=16x^2-456x+3249$$
$$25x^2-600x+3825=16x^2-456x+3249$$
$$9x^2-144x+576=0$$
$$x^2-16x+64=0$$
$$(x-8)(x-8)=0$$
$$x=8$$

b. You may either position the roads $1\frac{5}{7}$ miles from A and $10\frac{2}{7}$ miles from B *or* directly below B..

83.–89. Answers may vary.

91. $-x^4+4x^3-4x^2=0$

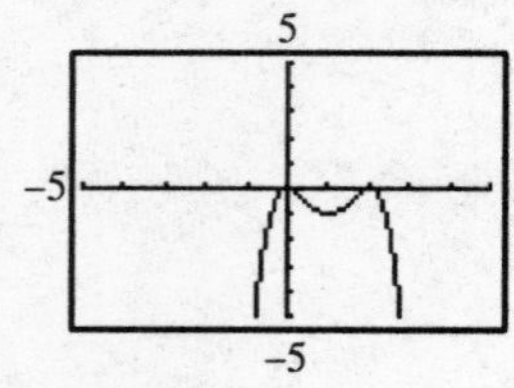

$x=0, 2$

$$-(0)^4+4(0)^3-4(0)=0$$
$$0+0-0=0$$
$$-2^4+4(2)^3-4(2)^2=0$$
$$-16+4(8)-4(4)=0$$
$$-16+32-16=0$$

The solution set is $\{0, 2\}$.

93. $\sqrt{2x+13}-x-5=0$

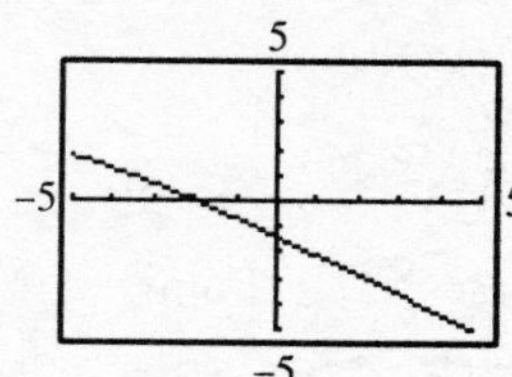

$$x=-2$$
$$\sqrt{2(-2)+13}-(-2)-5=0$$
$$\sqrt{-4+13}+2-5=0$$
$$\sqrt{9}-3=0$$
$$3-3=0$$

The solution set is $\{-2\}$.

95.

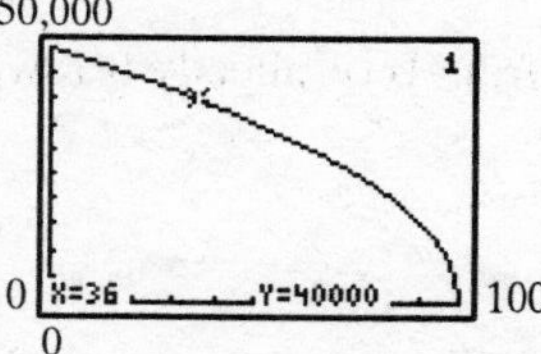

Tracing along the curve shows the point (36, 40,000) on the graph.

97. **a.** False;

$$\left(\sqrt{y+4}+\sqrt{y-1}\right)^2 \neq y+4+y-1$$

b. False; if $t=(x^2-2x)^3$, the original equation can be written as $t^3-5t+6=0$, not a quadratic form.

c. False; the other value may be a solution.

d. True

(d) is true

99. $5-\frac{2}{x}=\sqrt{5-\frac{2}{x}}$

$$5-\frac{2}{x}=0 \quad \text{or} \quad 5-\frac{2}{x}=1$$
$$5=\frac{2}{x} \qquad -\frac{2}{x}=-4$$
$$5x=2 \qquad -4x=-2$$
$$x=\frac{2}{5} \qquad x=\frac{1}{2}$$

The solution set is $\left\{\frac{2}{5},\frac{15}{2}\right\}$.

101. $x^{5/6} + x^{2/3} - 2x^{1/2} = 0$
$x^{1/2}(x^{2/6} + x^{1/6} - 2) = 0$ let $t = x^{1/6}$
$x^{1/2}(t^2 + t - 2) = 0$
$x^{1/2} = 0 \quad t^2 + t - 2 = 0$
$(t-1)(t+2) = 0$
$t - 1 = 0 \quad t + 2 = 0$
$t = 1 \quad t = -2$
$x^{1/6} = 1 \quad x^{1/6} = -2$
$x = 1^6 \quad x = (-2)^6$
$x = 0 \quad x = 1 \quad x = 64$
The solution set is {0, 1, 64}.

Section 1.5

Check Point Exercises

1. a. 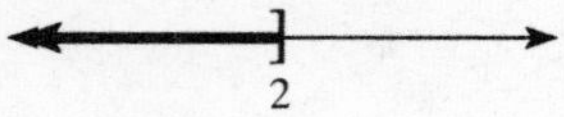 (number line: shaded to the left, closed at 2)

b. 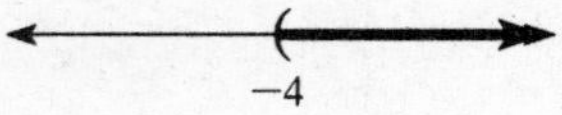 (number line: shaded to the right, open at −4)

c.  (number line: closed at 2, open at 6)

2. a. $[-2, 5) = \{x|-2 \le x < 5\}$
(number line: closed at −2, open at 5)

b. $[1, 3.5] = \{x|1 \le x \le 3.5\}$
(number line: closed at 1, closed at 3.5)

c. $[-\infty, -1) = \{x|x < -1\}$
(number line: shaded to the left, open at −1)

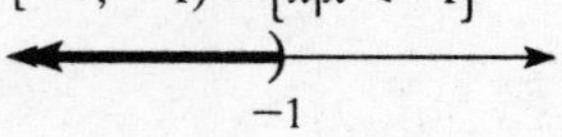

3. $2 - 3x \le 5$
$-3x \le 3$
$x \ge -1$
The solution set is $\{x|x \ge -1\}$ or $[-1, \infty)$.
(number line: closed at −1, shaded to the right)

4. $6 - 3x \le 5x - 2$
$8 - 3x \le 5x$
$8 \le 8x$
$1 \le x$
$x \ge 1$
The solution set is $\{x|x \ge 1\}$ or $[1, \infty)$.
(number line: closed at 1, shaded to the right)

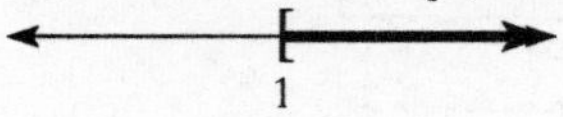

5. $1 \le 2x + 3 < 11$
$-2 \le 2x < 8$
$-1 \le x < 4$
The solution set is $\{x|-1 \le x < 4\}$ or $[-1, 4)$.
(number line: closed at −1, open at 4)

6. $|x - 2| < 5$
$-5 < x - 2 < 5$
$-3 < x < 7$
The solution set is $\{x|-3 < x < 7\}$ or $(-3, 7)$.
(number line: open at −3, open at 7)

7. $|2x - 5| \ge 3$
$2x - 5 \le -3$ or $2x - 5 \ge 3$
$2x \le 2$ or $2x \ge 8$
$x \le 1$ or $x \ge 4$
The solution set is $\{x|x \le 1 \text{ or } x \ge 4\}$, that is, all x in $(-\infty, 1]$ or $[4, \infty)$.
(number line: shaded left of 1 closed, shaded right of 4 closed)

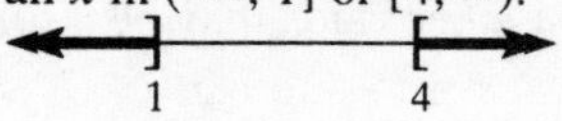

8. Let x = the number of miles driven in a week.
$260 < 80 + 0.25x$
$180 < 0.25x$
$720 < x$
Driving more than 720 miles in a week makes Basic the better deal.

Exercise Set 1.5

1. 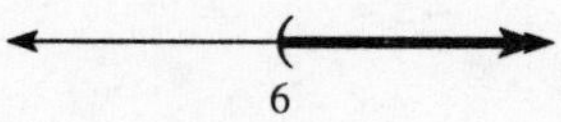 (number line: open at 6, shaded to the right)

3. 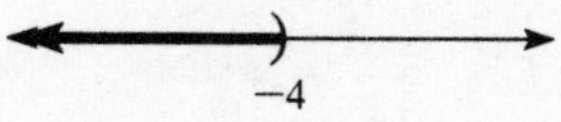 (number line: shaded to the left, open at −4)

5.
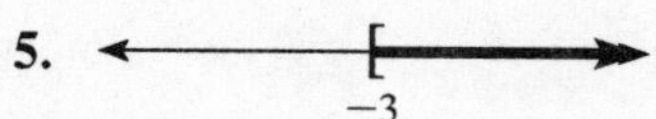

7. 4

9. 2 5

11. −1 4

13. $1 < x \le 6$

1 6

15. $-5 \le x < 2$

−5 2

17. $-3 \le x \le 1$

−3 1

19. $x > 2$

2

21. $x \ge -3$

−3

23. $x < 3$

3

25. $x < 5.5$

5.5

27. $5x + 11 < 26$
$5x < 15$
$x < 3$
The solution set is $\{x | x < 3\}$, or $(-\infty, 3)$.

3

29. $3x - 7 \ge 13$
$3x \ge 20$
$x \ge \frac{20}{3}$

The solution set is $\left\{x \middle| x > \frac{20}{3}\right\}$, or $\left[\frac{20}{3}, \infty\right)$.

$\frac{20}{3}$

31. $-9x \ge 36$
$x \le -4$
The solution set is $\{x | x \le -4\}$, or $(-\infty, -4]$.

−4

33. $8x - 11 \le 3x - 13$
$8x - 3x \le -13 + 11$
$5x \le -2$
$x \le -\frac{2}{5}$

The solution set is $\left\{x \middle| x \le -\frac{2}{5}\right\}$, or $\left(-\infty, -\frac{2}{5}\right]$.

$-\frac{2}{5}$

35. $4(x + 1) + 2 \ge 3x + 6$
$4x + 4 + 2 \ge 3x + 6$
$4x + 6 \ge 3x + 6$
$4x - 3x \ge 6 - 6$
$x \ge 0$
The solution set is $\{x | x > 0\}$, or $[0, \infty)$.

0

37. $2x - 11 < -3(x + 2)$
$2x - 11 < -3x - 6$
$5x < 5$
$x < 1$
The solution set is $\{x | x < 1\}$, or $(-\infty, 1)$.

1

39. $1-(x+3)\ge 4-2x$
$1-x-3\ge 4-2x$
$-x-2\ge 4-2x$
$x\ge 6$
The solution set is $\{x|\,x\ge 6\}$, or $[6,\infty)$.

41. $\frac{x}{4}-\frac{3}{5}\le\frac{x}{2}+1$
$-\frac{8}{5}\le\frac{x}{4}$
$x\ge-\frac{32}{5}$
The solution set is $\left\{x\middle|\,x\ge-\frac{32}{5}\right\}$, or $\left[-\frac{32}{5},\infty\right)$.

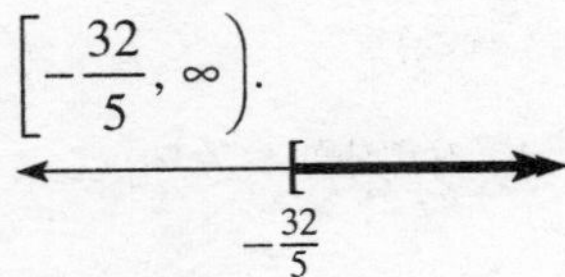

43. $1-\frac{x}{2}>4$
$-\frac{x}{2}>3$
$x<-6$
The solution set is $\{x|\,x,-6\}$, or $(-\infty,-6)$.

45. $\frac{x-4}{6}\ge\frac{x-2}{9}+\frac{5}{18}$
$3(x-4)\ge 2(x-2)+5$
$3x-12\ge 2x-4+5$
$x\ge 13$
The solution set is $\{x|\,x\ge 13\}$, or $(13,\infty)$.

47. $4(3x-2)-3x<3(1+3x)-7$
$12x-8-3x<3+9x-7$
$9x-8<-4+9x$
$-8<-4$
True for all x
The solution set is $\{x|\,x \text{ is any real number}\}$, or $(-\infty,\infty)$.

49. $6<x+3<8$
$6-3<x+3-3<8-3$
$3<x<5$
The solution set is $\{x|\,3<x<5\}$, or $(3, 5)$.

51. $-3\le x-2<1$
$-1\le x<3$
The solution set is $\{x|-1\le x<3\}$, or $[-1, 3)$.

53. $-11<2x-1\le-5$
$-10<2x\le-4$
$-5<x\le-2$
The solution set is $\{x|-5<x\le-2\}$, or $(-5,-2]$.

55. $-3\le\frac{2}{3}x-5<-1$
$2\le\frac{2}{3}x<4$
$3\le x<6$
The solution set is $\{x|\,3\le x<6\}$, or $[3, 6)$.

57. $|x|<3$
$-3<x<3$
The solution set is $\{x|-3<x<3\}$, or $(-3, 3)$.

59. $|x-1| \le 2$
$-2 \le x-1 \le 2$
$-1 \le x \le 3$
The solution set is $\{x|-1 \le x \le 3\}$, or $[-1, 3]$.

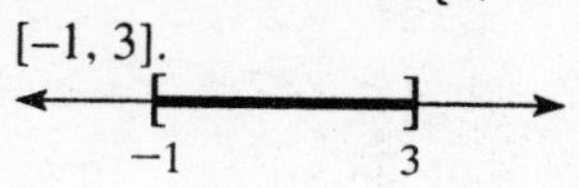

61. $|2x-6| < 8$
$-8 < 2x-6 < 8$
$-2 < 2x < 14$
$-1 < x < 7$
The solution set is $\{x|-1 < x < 7\}$, or $(-1, 7)$.

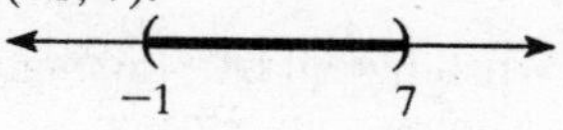

63. $|2(x-1)+4| \le 8$
$-8 \le 2(x-1)+4 \le 8$
$-8 \le 2x-2+4 \le 8$
$-8 \le 2x+2 \le 8$
$-10 \le 2x \le 6$
$-5 \le x \le 3$
The solution set is $\{x|-5 \le x \le 3\}$, or $[-5, 3]$.

65. $\left|\frac{2y+6}{3}\right| < 2$
$-2 < \frac{2y+6}{3} < 2$
$-6 < 2y+6 < 6$
$-12 < 2y < 0$
$-6 < y < 0$
The solution set is $\{x|-6 < y < 0\}$, or $(-6, 0)$.

67. $|x| > 3$
$x > 3$ or $x < -3$
The solution set is $\{x|x > 3 \text{ or } x < -3\}$, that is, $(-\infty, -3)$ or $(3, \infty)$.

69. $|x-1| \ge 2$
$x-1 \ge 2$ or $x-1 \le -2$
$x \ge 3$ $\quad$ $x \le -1$
The solution set is $\{x|x \le -1 \text{ or } x \ge 3\}$, that is, $(-\infty, -1]$ or $[3, \infty)$.

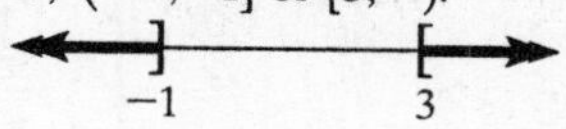

71. $|3x-8| > 7$
$3x-8 > 7$ or $3x-8 < -7$
$3x > 15$ $\quad$ $3x < 1$
$x > 5$ $\quad$ $x < \frac{1}{3}$
The solution set is $\left\{x \middle| x < \frac{1}{3} \text{ or } x > 5\right\}$, that is, $\left(-\infty, \frac{1}{3}\right)$ or $(5, \infty)$.

73. $\left|\frac{2x+2}{4}\right| \ge 2$
$\frac{2x+2}{4} \ge 2$ or $\frac{2x+2}{4} \le -2$
$2x+2 \ge 8$ $\quad$ $2x+2 \le -8$
$2x \ge 6$ $\quad$ $2x \le -10$
$x \ge 3$ $\quad$ $x \le -5$
The solution set is $\{x|x \le -5 \text{ or } x \ge 3\}$, that is, $(-\infty, -5]$ or $[3, \infty)$.

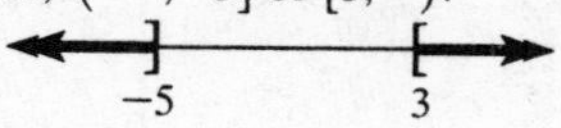

75. $\left|3-\frac{2}{3}x\right| > 5$
$3-\frac{2}{3}x > 5$ or $3-\frac{2}{3}x < -5$
$-\frac{2}{3}x > 2$ $\quad$ $-\frac{2}{3}x < -8$
$x < -3$ $\quad$ $x > 12$
The solution set is $\{x|x < -3 \text{ or } x > 12\}$, that is, $(-\infty, -3)$ or $(12, \infty)$.

77. $3|x-1|+2 \ge 8$
$3|x-1| \ge 6$
$|x-1| \ge 2$
$x-1 \ge 2$ or $x-1 \le -2$
$x \ge 3$ $\quad x \le -1$
The solution set is $\{x | x \le 1 \text{ or } x \ge 3\}$, that is, $(-\infty, -1]$ or $[3, \infty)$.

79. $3 < |2x-1|$
$2x-1 > 3$ or $2x-1 < -3$
$2x > 4$ $\quad 2x < -2$
$x > 2$ $\quad x < -1$
The solution set is $\{x | x < -1 \text{ or } x > 2\}$, that is, $(-\infty, -1)$ or $(2, \infty)$.

81. $12 < \left|-2x+\frac{6}{7}\right|+\frac{3}{7}$
$\frac{81}{7} < \left|-2x+\frac{6}{7}\right|$
$-2x+\frac{6}{7} > \frac{81}{7}$ or $-2x+\frac{6}{7} < -\frac{81}{7}$
$-2x > \frac{75}{7}$ $\quad -2x < -\frac{87}{7}$
$x < -\frac{75}{14}$ $\quad x > \frac{87}{14}$
The solution set is $\left\{x \middle| x < -\frac{75}{14} \text{ or } x > \frac{87}{14}\right\}$, that is, $\left(-\infty, -\frac{75}{14}\right)$ or $\left(\frac{87}{14}, \infty\right)$.

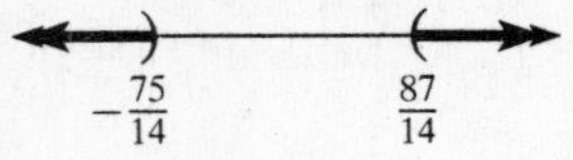

83. $4+\left|3-\frac{x}{3}\right| \ge 9$
$\left|3-\frac{x}{3}\right| \ge 5$
$3-\frac{x}{3} \ge 5$ or $3-\frac{x}{3} \le -5$
$-\frac{x}{3} \ge 2$ $\quad -\frac{x}{3} \le -8$
$x \le -6$ $\quad x \ge 24$
The solution set is $\{x | x \le -6 \text{ or } x \ge 24\}$, that is, $(-\infty, -6]$ or $[24, \infty)$.

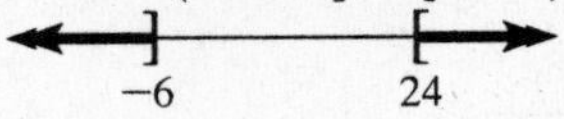

85. Raleigh, NC, Seattle, San Francisco, Austin, TX

87. San Diego

89. Austin, TX, Washington, DC, Lexington-Fayette, KY, Minneapolis, Boston, Arlington, TX

91. $11 \le 3x-4 \le 56$
$15 \le 3x \le 60$
$5 \le x \le 20$
This inequality includes 5.0 million, 17.5 million, and 17.6 million. The disorders are severe cognitive impairment, substance abuse disorders, and depressive: manic, major depression.

93. $y = 30x + 113$
$623 < 30x + 113$
$510 < 30x$
$17 < x$
$x > 17$
$1996 + 17 = 2013$
Liposuctions exceed 623 thousand in 2013.

95. $C = 18x + 250$
$322 < 18x + 250 < 412$
$72 < 18x < 162$
$4 < x < 9$
$2000 + 4 = 2004$; $2000 + 9 = 2009$
Cost ranges from 322 to 412 billion dollars between 2004 and 2009.

97. Let x = number of checks
$8 + 0.05x > 2 + 0.08x$
$6 > 0.03x$
$200 > x$
The number of checks that should be written is 199 checks or fewer.

99. a. $\dfrac{86+88+x}{3} \ge 90$
$\dfrac{174+x}{3} \ge 90$
$174 + x \ge 270$
$x \ge 96$
You must get at least a 96.

b. $\dfrac{86+88+x}{3} < 80$
$\dfrac{174+x}{3} < 80$
$174 + x < 240$
$x < 66$
This will happen if you get a grade less than 66.

101. Cost = 65,000 + 20x
Revenue = 85x
$85x - (65{,}000 + 20x) > 0$
$65x > 65{,}000$
$x > 1000$
The company should manufacture and sell 1001 or more pairs of shoes.

103.–111. Answers may vary.

113.

10
−10 10
−10

$x < -3$

115.

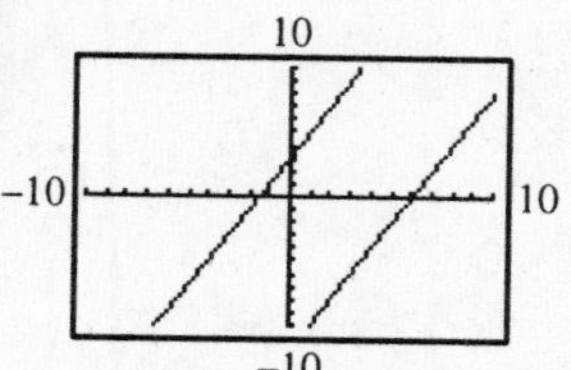

The graph of the left side of the inequality is always greater than the right side, therefore all real numbers are part of the solution.
$2x + 3 > 3(2x - 4) - 4x$
$2x + 3 > 6x - 12 - 4x$
$2x + 3 > 2x - 12$
$0 > -15$
You get a true statement with no variable.

117. a. False; $|2x - 3| > -7$ is true for any x because the absolute value is 0 or positive.

b. False; $2x > 6$, $x > 3$
3.1 is a real number that satisfies the inequality.

c. True; $|x - 4| > 0$ is not satisfied only when $x = 4$. Since 4 is rational, all irrational numbers satisfy the inequality.

d. False

(c) is true.

119. (−10, −8)

Section 1.6

Check Point Exercises

1. $x^2 + 2x - 3 < 0$

Solve $x^2 + 2x - 3 = 0$.

$(x-1)(x+3) = 0$

$x - 1 = 0$ or $x + 3 = 0$

$x = 1$ or $x = -3$

The boundary points are 1 and –3.
The test intervals are
$(-\infty, -3)$, $(-3, 1)$, and $(1, \infty)$.

Test –5: $(-5)^2 + 2(-5) - 3 < 0$

$25 - 10 - 3 < 0$

$12 < 0$ False

Test 0: $0^2 + 2(0) - 3 < 0$

$-3 = 0$ True

Test 2: $2^2 + 2(2) - 3 < 0$

$4 + 4 - 3 < 0$

$5 < 0$ False

The solution set is (–3, 1).

–3 1

2. $x^2 - x \ge 20$

$x^2 - x - 20 \ge 0$

Solve $x^2 - x - 20 = 0$.

$(x-5)(x+4) = 0$

$x - 5 = 0$ or $x + 4 = 0$

$x = 5$ or $4 = -4$

The boundary points are –4 and 5.
The test intervals are
$(-\infty, -4]$, $[-4, 5]$, and $[5, \infty)$.

Test –5: $(-5)^2 - (5) \ge 20$

$25 + 5 \ge 20$

$30 \ge 20$ True

Test 0: $0^2 - 0 \ge 20$

$0 \ge 20$ False

Test 6: $6^2 - 6 \ge 20$

$36 - 6 \ge 20$

$30 \ge 20$ True

The solution set is $(-\infty, -4]$ or $[5, \infty)$.

–4 5

3. $\dfrac{x-5}{x+2} > 0$

$x - 5 = 0$ $x + 2 = 0$

$x = 5$ $x = -2$

The boundary points are –2 and 5.
The test intervals are
$(-\infty, -2)$, $(-2, 5)$, and $(5, \infty)$.

Test –3: $\dfrac{-3-5}{-3+2} > 0$

$\dfrac{-8}{-1} > 0$ True

Test 0: $\dfrac{0-5}{0+2} > 0$

$\dfrac{-5}{2} > 0$ False

Test 6: $\dfrac{6-5}{6+2} > 0$

$\dfrac{1}{8} > 0$ True

The solution set is $(-\infty, -2)$ or $(5, \infty)$.

–2 5

4. $\frac{2x}{x+1} \le 1$

$\frac{2x}{x+1} - 1 \le 0$

$\frac{2x - x - 1}{x+1} \le 0$

$\frac{x-1}{x+1} \le 0$

$x - 1 = 0 \quad x + 1 = 0$

$x = 1 \qquad x = -1$

The boundary points are –1 and 1.
The test intervals are
$(-\infty, -1)$, $(-1, 1]$, and $[1, \infty)$.

Test –2: $\frac{2(2)}{-2+1} \le 1$

$\frac{-4}{-1} \le 1$

$4 \le 1$ False

Test 0: $\frac{2(0)}{0+1} \le 1$

$0 \le 1$ True

Test 2: $\frac{2(2)}{2+1} \le 1$

$\frac{4}{3} \le 1$ False

The solution set is $(-1, 1]$.

–1 1

5. $-16t^2 + 80t > 64$

$-16t^2 + 80t - 64 > 0$

$t^2 - 5t + 4 < 0$

Solve $t^2 - 5t + 4 = 0$

$(t-4)(t-1) = 0$

$t - 4 = 0$ or $t - 1 = 0$

$t = 4$ or $t = 1$

The boundary points are 1 and 4.
Note that the object is at ground level when $s = 0$.

$0 = 16t^2 + 80t$

$0 = -16t(t-5)$

$t = 0$ or $t = 5$

The test intervals are (0, 1), (1, 4), and (4, 5).

Test $\frac{1}{2}$: $-16\left(\frac{1}{2}\right)^2 + 80\left(\frac{1}{2}\right) > 64$

$-4 + 40 > 64$

$36 > 64$ False

Test 2: $-16(2)^2 + 80(2) > 64$

$-64 + 160 > 64$

$96 > 64$ True

Test $\frac{9}{2}$: $-16\left(\frac{9}{2}\right)^2 + 80\left(\frac{9}{2}\right) > 64$

$-324 + 360 > 64$

$36 > 64$ False

The object will be more than 64 feet above the ground between 1 and 4 seconds, excluding $t = 1$ and $t = 4$.

Exercise Set 1.6

1. $(x-4)(x+2) > 0$
$x = 4$ or $x = -2$

T	F	T

–2 4

Test –3: $(-3-4)(-3+2) > 0$

$7 > 0$ True

Test 0: $(0-4)(0+2) > 0$

$-8 > 0$ False

Test 5: $(5-4)(5+2) > 0$

$7 > 0$ True

$(-\infty, -2)$ or $(4, \infty)$

–2 4

3. $(x-7)(x+3) \le 0$
$x = 7$ or $x = -3$

F	T	F

–3 7

Test –4: $(-4-7)(-4+3) \le 0$

$11 \le 0$ False

Test 0: $(0-7)(0+3) \le 0$

$-21 \le 0$ True

Test 8: $(8-7)(8+3) \le 0$

$11 \le 0$ False

The solution set is $[-3, 7]$.

–3 7

5. $x^2 - 5x + 4 > 0$

$(x-4)(x-1) > 0$

$x = 4$ or $x = 1$

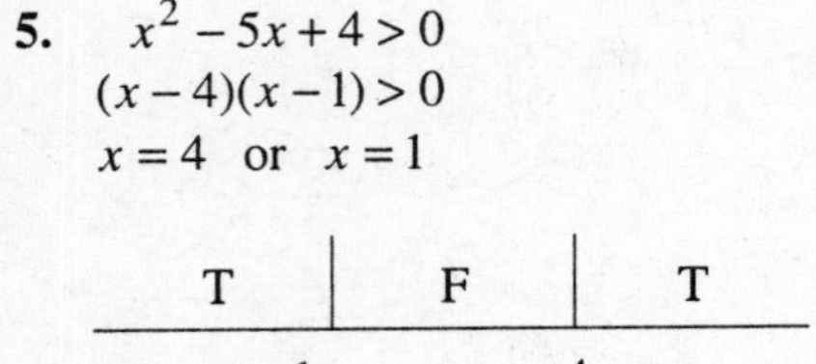

Test 0: $0^2 - 5(0) + 4 > 0$

$4 > 0$ True

Test 2: $2^2 - 5(2) + 4 > 0$

$-2 > 0$ False

Test 5: $5^2 - 5(5) + 4 > 0$

$4 > 0$ True

The solution set is $(-\infty,\ 1)$ or $(4,\ \infty)$.

1 4

7. $x^2 + 5x + 4 > 0$

$(x+1)(x+4) > 0$

$x = -1$ or $x = -4$

T | F | T

−4 −1

Test −5: $(-5)^2 + 5(-5) + 4 > 0$

$4 > 0$ True

Test −3: $(-3)^2 + 5(-3) + 4 > 0$

$-2 > 0$ False

Test 0: $0^2 + 5(0) + 4 > 0$

$4 > 0$ True

The solution set is $(-\infty,\ -4)$ or $(-1,\ \infty)$.

−4 1

9. $x^2 - 6x + 9 < 0$

$(x-3)(x-3) < 0$

$x = 0$

F | F

3

Test 0: $0^2 - 6(0) + 9 < 0$

$9 < 0$ False

Test 4: $4^2 - 6(4) + 9 < 0$

$1 < 0$ False

The solution set is the empty set, $\varnothing$.

11. $x^2 - 6x + 8 \le 0$

$(x-4)(x-2) \le 0$

$x = 4$ or $x = 2$

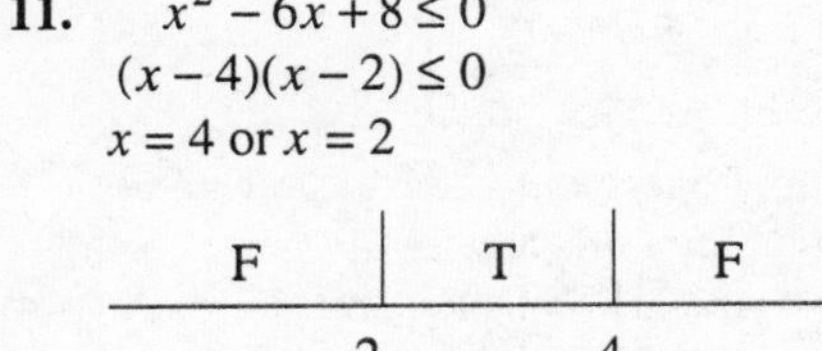

Test 0: $0^2 - 6(0) + 8 \le 0$

$8 \le 0$ False

Test 3: $3^2 - 6(3) + 8 \le 0$

$-1 \le 0$ True

Test 5: $5^2 - 6(5) + 8 \le 0$

$3 \le 0$ False

The solution set is $[2,\ 4]$.

2 4

13. $3x^2 + 10x - 8 \le 0$

$(3x-2)(x+4) \le 0$

$x = \frac{2}{3}$ or $x = -4$

F | T | F

-4 $\frac{2}{3}$

Test −5: $3(-5)^2 + 10(-5) - 8 \le 0$

$17 \le 0$ False

Test 0: $3(0)^2 + 10(0) - 8 \le 0$

$8 \le 0$ True

Test 1: $3(1)^2 + 10(1) - 8 \le 0$

$5 \le 0$ False

The solution set is $\left[-4,\ \frac{2}{3}\right]$.

-4 $\frac{2}{3}$

15.

$$2x^2 + x < 15$$
$$2x^2 + x - 15 < 0$$
$$(2x - 5)(x + 3) < 0$$
$$2x - 5 = 0 \quad \text{or} \quad x + 3 = 0$$
$$2x = 5$$
$$x = \frac{5}{2} \quad \text{or} \quad x = -3$$

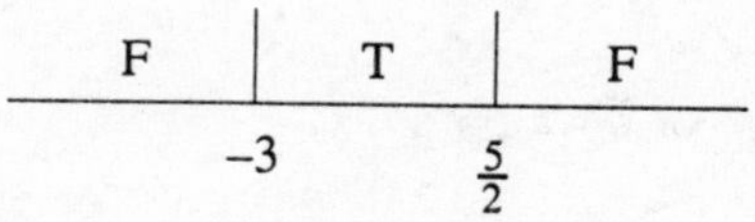

F | T | F on the number line, with boundary points -3 and $\frac{5}{2}$.

Test –4: $2(-4)^2 + (-4) < 15$
$28 < 15$ False

Test 0: $2(0)^2 + 0 < 15$
$0 < 15$ True

Test 3: $2(3)^2 + 3 < 15$
$21 < 15$ False

The solution set is $\left(-3, \frac{5}{2}\right)$.

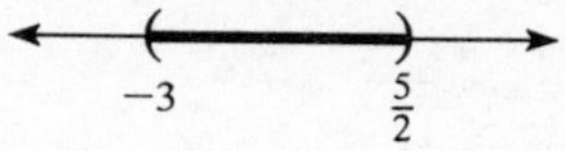

Number line: open interval from -3 to $\frac{5}{2}$.

17.

$$4x^2 + 7x < -3$$
$$4x^2 + 7x + 3 < 0$$
$$(4x + 3)(x + 1) < 0$$
$$4x + 3 = 0 \quad \text{or} \quad x + 1 = 0$$
$$4x \text{ - } 3 = 0$$
$$x = -\frac{3}{4} \quad \text{or} \quad x = -1$$

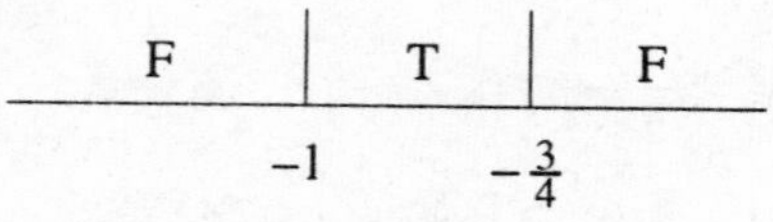

F | T | F on the number line, with boundary points -1 and $-\frac{3}{4}$.

Test –2: $4(-2)^2 + 7(-2) < -3$
$2 < -3$ False

Test $-\frac{7}{8}$: $4\left(-\frac{7}{8}\right)^2 + 7\left(-\frac{7}{8}\right) < -3$
$\frac{49}{16} - \frac{49}{8} < -3$
$-\frac{49}{16} < -3$ True

Test 0: $4(0)^2 + 7(0) < -3$
$0 < -3$ False

The solution set is $\left(-1, -\frac{3}{4}\right)$.

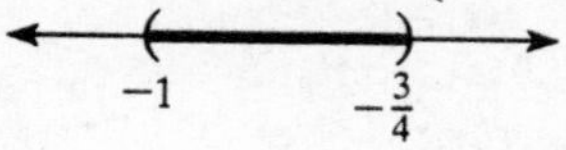

Number line: open interval from -1 to $-\frac{3}{4}$.

19.

$$5x \le 2 - 3x^2$$
$$3x^2 + 5x - 2 \le 0$$
$$(3x - 1)(x + 2) \le 0$$
$$3x - 1 = 0 \text{ or } x + 2 = 0$$
$$3x = 1$$
$$3x - 1 = 0 \quad \text{or} \quad x + 2 = 0$$
$$3x = 1$$
$$x = \frac{1}{3} \quad \text{or} \quad x = -2$$

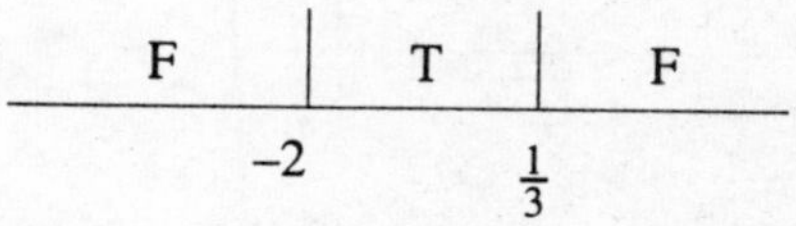

F | T | F on the number line, with boundary points -2 and $\frac{1}{3}$.

Test –3: $5(-3) \le 2 - 3(-3)^2$
$-15 \le -25$ False

Test 0: $5(0) \le 2 - 3(0)^2$
$0 \le 2$ True

Test 1: $5(1) \le 2 - 3(1)^2$
$5 \le -1$ False

Ths solution set is $\left[-2, \frac{1}{3}\right]$.

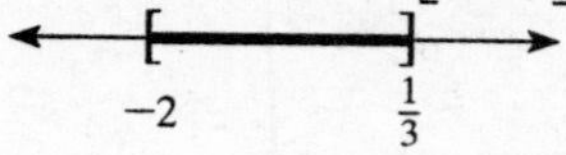

Number line: closed interval from -2 to $\frac{1}{3}$.

21. $x^2 - 4x \geq 0$

$x(x-4) \geq 0$

$x = 0$ or $x - 4 = 0$

$x = 4$

T | F | T

0 4

Test −1: $(-1)^2 - 4(-1) \geq 0$

$5 \geq 0$ True

Test 1: $(1)^2 - 4(1) \geq 0$

$-3 \geq 0$ False

$0 \leq 2$ True

Test 5: $5^2 - 4(5) \geq 0$

$5 \geq 0$ True

The solution set is $(-\infty, \ 0]$ or $[4, \ \infty)$.

0 4

23. $2x^2 + 3x > 0$

$x(2x+3) > 0$

$x = 0$ or $x = -\frac{3}{2}$

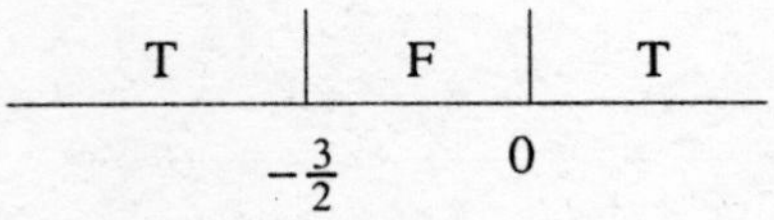

T | F | T

$-\frac{3}{2}$ 0

Test −2: $2(-2)^2 + 3(-2) > 0$

$2 > 0$ True

Test −1: $2(-1)^2 + 3(-1) > 0$

$-1 > 0$ False

Test 1: $2(1)^2 + 3(1) > 0$

$5 > 0$ True

The solution set is $\left(-\infty, \ -\frac{3}{2}\right)$ or $(0, \ \infty)$.

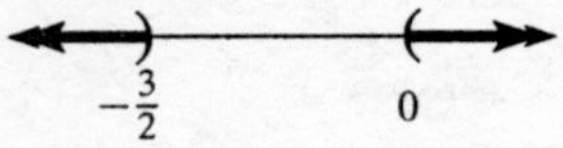

$-\frac{3}{2}$ 0

25. $-x^2 + x \geq 0$

$x^2 - x \leq 0$

$x(x-1) \leq 0$

$x = 0$ or $x = 1$

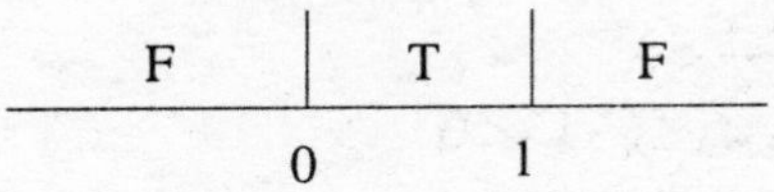

F | T | F

0 1

Test −1: $-(-1)^2 + (-1) \geq 0$

$-2 \geq 0$ False

Test $\frac{1}{2}$: $-\left(\frac{1}{2}\right)^2 + \left(\frac{1}{2}\right) \geq 0$

$\frac{1}{4} \geq 0$ True

Test 2: $-(2)^2 + 2 \geq 0$

$-2 \geq 0$ False

The solution set is $[0, \ 1]$.

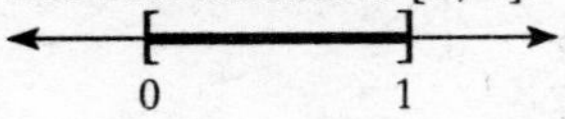

0 1

27. $\frac{x-4}{x+3} > 0$

$x - 4 = 0 \quad x + 3 = 0$

$x = 4 \qquad x = -3$

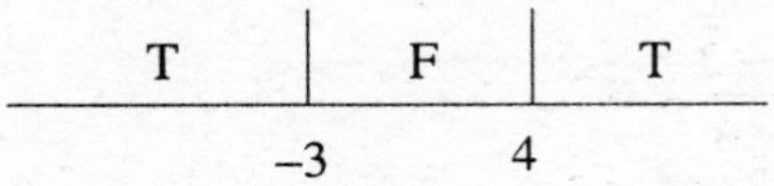

T | F | T

−3 4

Test −4: $\frac{-4-4}{-4+3} > 0$

$\frac{-8}{-1} > 0$

$8 > 0$ True

Test 0: $\frac{0-4}{0+3} > 0$

$-\frac{4}{3} > 0$ False

Test 5: $\frac{5-4}{5+3} > 0$

$\frac{1}{8} > 0$ True

The solution set is $(-\infty, \ -3)$ or $(4, \ \infty)$.

−3 4

29. $\frac{x+3}{x+4} < 0$

$x = -3$ or $x = -4$

F	T	F
	-4	-3

Test -5: $\frac{-5+3}{-5+4} < 0$

$2 < 0$ False

Test $-\frac{7}{2}$: $\frac{-\frac{7}{2}+3}{-\frac{7}{2}+4} < 0$

$-1 < 0$ True

Test 0: $\frac{0+3}{0+4} < 0$

$\frac{3}{4} < 0$ False

The solution set is $(-4, -3)$.

31. $\frac{-x+2}{x-4} \geq 0$

$x = 2$ or $x = 4$

F	T	F
	2	4

Test 0: $\frac{0+2}{0-4} \geq 0$

$-\frac{1}{2} \geq 0$ False

Test 3: $\frac{-3+2}{3-4} \geq 0$

$1 \geq 0$ True

Test 5: $\frac{-5+2}{5-4} \geq 0$

$-3 \geq 0$ False

The solution set is $[2, 4)$.

33. $\frac{4-2x}{3x+4} \leq 0$

$x = 2$ or $x = -\frac{4}{3}$

T	F	T
	$-\frac{4}{3}$	2

Test -2: $\frac{4-2(-2)}{3(-2)+4} \leq 0$

$-4 \leq 0$ True

Test 0: $\frac{4-2(0)}{3(0)+4} \leq 0$

$1 \leq 0$ False

Test 3: $\frac{4-2(3)}{3(3)+4} \leq 0$

$\frac{-2}{13} \leq 0$ True

The solution set is $\left(-\infty, \frac{-4}{3}\right)$ or $[2, \infty)$.

35. $\frac{x}{x-3} > 0$

$x = 0$ or $x = 3$

T	F	T
	0	3

Test -1: $\frac{-1}{-1-3} > 0$

$\frac{1}{4} > 0$ True

Test 2: $\frac{2}{2-3} > 0$

$-2 > 0$ False

Test 4: $\frac{4}{4-3} > 0$

$4 > 0$ True

The solution set is $(-\infty, 0)$ or $(3, \infty)$.

37.
$$\frac{x+1}{x+3} < 0$$
$$\frac{x+1}{x+3} - 2 < 0$$
$$\frac{x+1-2(x+3)}{x+3} < 0$$
$$\frac{x+1-2x-6}{x+3} < 0$$
$$\frac{-x-5}{x+3} < 0$$
$x =$ or $x = -3$

T	F	T
	−5	−3

Test −6: $\frac{-6+1}{-6+3} < 2$

$\frac{5}{3} < 2$ True

Test −4: $\frac{-4+1}{-4+3} < 2$

$3 < 2$ False

Test 0: $\frac{0+1}{0+3} < 2$

$\frac{1}{3} < 2$ True

The solution set is $(-\infty, -5)$ or $(-3, \infty)$.

−5 −3

39.
$$\frac{x+4}{2x-1} \le 3$$
$$\frac{x+4}{2x-1} - 3 \le 0$$
$$\frac{x+4-3(2x-1)}{2x-1} \le 0$$
$$\frac{x+4-6x+3}{2x-1} \le 0$$
$$\frac{-5x+7}{2x-1} \le 0$$
$x = \frac{7}{5}$ or $x = \frac{1}{2}$

T	F	T
	$\frac{1}{2}$	$\frac{7}{5}$

Test 0: $\frac{0+4}{2(0)-1} \le 3$

$-4 \le 3$ True

Test 1: $\frac{1+4}{2(1)-1} \le 3$

$5 \le 3$ False

Test 2: $\frac{2+4}{2(2)-1} \le 3$

$2 \le 3$ True

The solution set is $\left(-\infty, \frac{1}{2}\right)$ or $\left[\frac{7}{5}, \infty\right)$.

$\frac{1}{2}$ $\frac{7}{5}$

41. $\frac{x-2}{x+2} \le 2$

$\frac{x-2}{x+2} - 2 \le 0$

$\frac{x-2-2(x+2)}{x+2} \le 0$

$\frac{x-2-2x-4}{x+2} \le 0$

$\frac{-x-6}{x+2} \le 0$

$x = -6$ or $x = -2$

T	F	T
	-6	-2

Test −7: $\frac{-7-2}{-7+2} \le 2$

$\frac{9}{5} \le 2$ True

Test −3: $\frac{-3-2}{-3+2} \le 2$

$5 \le 2$ False

Test 0: $\frac{0-2}{0+2} \le 2$

$-1 \le 2$ True

The solution set is $(-\infty, -6]$ or $(-2, \infty)$.

43. $S = -16t^2 + v_0 t + s_0$

$96 < -16t^2 + 80t + 0$

$0 < -16t^2 + 80t - 96$

$0 < -16(t^2 - 5t + 6)$

$0 < -16(t-3)(t-2)$

F	T	F
	2	3

$2 < t < 3$

The projectile's height will exceed 96 feet between 2 and 3 seconds exclusive.

45. $S = -16t^2 + v_0 t + s_0$

$96 < -16t^2 + 64t + 80$

$0 < -16t^2 + 64t - 16$

$0 < -16(t^2 - 4t + 1)$

$t = \frac{4 \pm \sqrt{(-4)^2 - 4(1)(1)}}{2}$

$t = \frac{4 \pm 2\sqrt{3}}{2}$

$t = 2 \pm \sqrt{3}$

F	T	F
	$2-\sqrt{3}$	$2+\sqrt{3}$

$2 + \sqrt{3} - (2 - \sqrt{3}) = 2\sqrt{3} \approx 3.46$

The ball is higher than 96 feet for about 3.46 seconds.

47. $H = \frac{15}{8}x^2 - 30x + 200$

a. $H = \frac{15}{8}(0)^2 - 30(0) + 200$

$H = 200$ beats per minute

b. $110 < \frac{15}{8}x^2 - 30x + 200$

$880 < 15x^2 - 240x + 1600$

$0 < x^2 - 16x + 48$

$0 < (x-12)(x-4)$

$x = 12$ or $x = 4$

T	F	T
	4	12

Test 0:

$110 < \frac{15}{8}(0)^2 - 30(0) + 200$

$110 < 200$ True

Test 8: $110 < \frac{15}{8}(8)^2 - 30(8) + 200$

$110 < 80$ False

Test 16: $110 < \frac{15}{8}(16)^2 - 30(16) + 200$

$110 < 200$ True

Heart rate exceeds 110 beats per minute up to 4 minutes after work-out.

49. $y = -0.22x^2 + 4.32x + 26$

$41.3 > -0.22x^2 + 4.32x + 26$

$0 > -0.22x^2 + 4.32x - 15.3$

$0 > -22x^2 + 432x - 1530$

$0 < 11x^2 - 216x + 765$

$x = \frac{216 \pm \sqrt{(-216)^2 - 4(11)(765)}}{2(11)}$

$x = \frac{216 \pm \sqrt{46656 - 33660}}{22}$

$x = \frac{216 \pm \sqrt{12996}}{22}$

$x = \frac{216 \pm 114}{22}$

$x = 15,\ 4\frac{7}{11}$

T	F	T
	$4\frac{7}{11}$	15

Test 0: $41.3 > -0.22(0)^2 + 4.32(0) + 26$

$41.3 > 26$ True

Test 5: $41.3 > -0.22(5)^2 + 4.32(5) + 26$

$41.3 > 42.1$ False

Test 16: $41.3 > -0.22(16)^2 + 4.32(16) + 26$

$41.3 > 38.8$ True

1986 + 15 = 2001

After 2001 the number of visitors will be less than 41.3 million.

51. $C = \frac{4p}{100 - p}$
$6 > \frac{4p}{100 - p}$
$600 - 6p > 4p$
$600 > 10p$
$60 > p$
Less than 60% can be removed.

53. Answers may vary.

55. Graph $y_1 = x^2 + 3x - 10$ in a standard viewing window. The graph is above the x-axis, or zero, for $x < -5$ and $x > 2$.

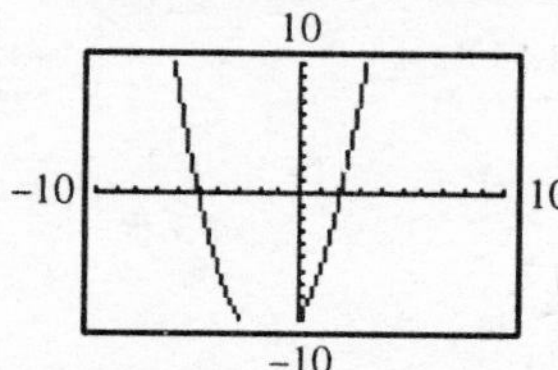

The solution set is $(-\infty, -5]$ or $(2, \infty)$.

57. Graph $y_1 = \frac{x - 4}{x - 1}$ in a standard viewing window. The graph is below the x-axis for $1 < x \le 4$.

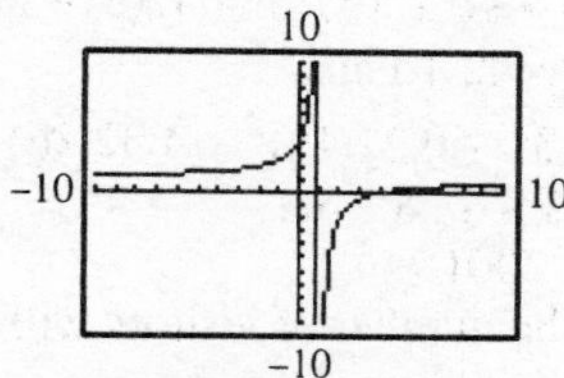

The solution set is $\{1, 4\}$.

59. Graph $y_1 = \frac{1}{x + 1}$ and $y_2 = \frac{2}{x + 4}$ in a standard viewing window. y_1 is below y_2 for $-4 < x < -1$.

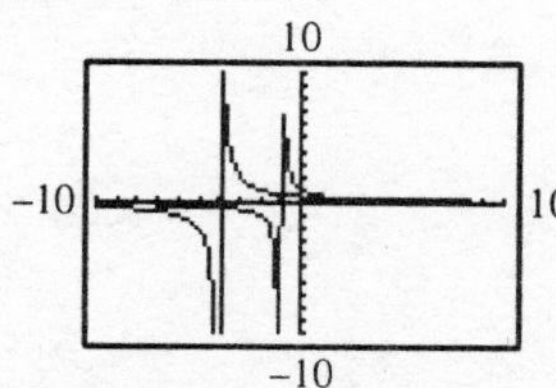

The solution set is $(-4, -1]$ or $(2, \infty)$.

61. $N = 14W^3 - 17W^2 - 6W + 34$
We want $46 < 14W^3 - 17W^2 - 6W + 34$.
Graph $y_1 = 14x^3 - 17x^2 - 6x + 34$ and $y_2 = 46$ for $1.5 \le x \le 3.5$. The graph of y_1 is above y_2 for approximately $x > 1.74$.

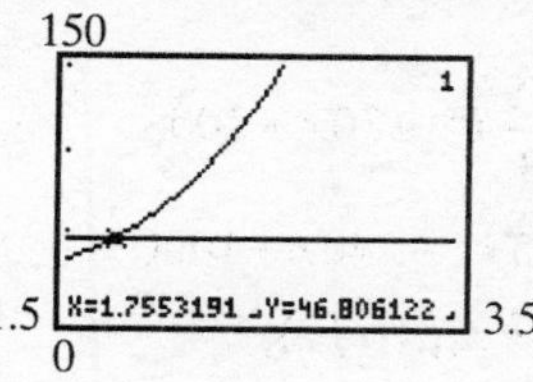

$(1.7, 3.5]$.
The abdominal width is from 1.7 mm to 3.5 mm.

63. Answers may vary.

65. Because any non-zero number squared is positive, the solution is all real numbers except 2.

67. Because any number squared is positive, the solution is the empty set, $\varnothing$.

69. **a.** The solution set is all real numbers.

b. The solution set is the empty set, $\varnothing$.

c. $4x^2 - 8x + 7 > 0$
$x = \frac{8 \pm \sqrt{(-8)^2 - 4(4)(7)}}{2(4)}$
$x = \frac{8 \pm \sqrt{64 - 112}}{8}$
$x = \frac{8 \pm \sqrt{-48}}{8} \Rightarrow$ imaginary
no critical values
Test 0: $4(0)^2 - 8(0) + 7 > 0$
$7 > 0$ True
The inequality is true for all numbers.

Chapter 1 Review Exercises

1. $2x - 5 = 7$
$2x = 12$
$x = 6$
$2(6) - 5 = 7$
$12 - 5 = 7$
The solution set is $\{6\}$.

2. $5x + 20 = 3x$
$2x = -20$
$x = -10$
$5(-10) + 20 = 3(-10)$
$-50 + 20 = -30$
The solution set is $\{-10\}$.

3. $7(x - 4) = x + 2$
$7x - 28 = x + 2$
$6x = 30$
$x = 5$
$7(5 - 4) = 5 + 2$
$7(1) = 7$
The solution set is $\{5\}$.

4. $1 - 2(6 - x) = 3x + 2$
$1 - 12 + 2x = 3x + 2$
$-11 - x = 2$
$-x = 13$
$x = -13$
$1 - 2[6 - (-13)] = 3(-13) + 2$
$1 - 2(19) = -39 + 2$
$1 - 38 = -37$
The solution set is $\{-13\}$.

5. $2(x-4) + 3(x+5) = 2x - 2$
$2x - 8 + 3x + 15 = 2x - 2$
$5x + 7 = 2x - 2$
$3x = -9$
$x = -3$
$2(-3 - 4) + 3(-3 + 5) = 2(-3) - 2$
$2(-7) + 3(2) = -6 - 2$
$-14 + 6 = -8$
The solution set is $\{-3\}$.

6. $2x - 4(5x + 1) = 3x + 17$
$2x - 20x - 4 = 3x + 17$
$-18x - 4 = 3x + 17$
$-21x = 21$
$x = -1$
$2(-1) - 4(5(-1) + 1) = 3(-1) + 17$
$-2 - 4(-4) = -3 + 17$
$-2 + 16 = 14$
The solution set is $\{-1\}$.

7. $\frac{2x}{3} = \frac{x}{6} + 1$
$2(2x) = x + 6$
$4x = x + 6$
$3x = 6$
$x = 2$
$\frac{2(2)}{3} = \frac{2}{6} + 1$
$\frac{4}{3} = \frac{1}{3} + \frac{3}{3}$
$\frac{4}{3} = \frac{4}{3}$
The solution set is $\{2\}$.

8. $\frac{x}{2} - \frac{1}{10} = \frac{x}{5} + \frac{1}{2}$
$5x - 1 = 2x + 5$
$3x = 6$
$x = 2$
$\frac{2}{2} - \frac{1}{10} = \frac{2}{5} + \frac{1}{2}$
$1 - \frac{1}{10} = \frac{4}{10} + \frac{5}{10}$
$\frac{9}{10} = \frac{9}{10}$
The solution set is $\{2\}$.

9. $\frac{2x}{3}=6-\frac{x}{4}$
$4(2x)=12(6)-3x$
$8x=72-3x$
$11x=72$
$x=\frac{72}{11}$
$\frac{2\left(\frac{72}{11}\right)}{3}=6-\frac{\frac{72}{11}}{4}$
$\frac{\frac{144}{11}}{3}=6-\frac{72}{11}\cdot\frac{1}{4}$
$\frac{144}{11}\cdot\frac{1}{3}=6-\frac{18}{11}$
$\frac{48}{11}=\frac{66}{11}-\frac{18}{11}$
$\frac{48}{11}=\frac{48}{11}$
The solution set is $\left\{\frac{72}{11}\right\}$.

10. $\frac{x}{4}=2+\frac{x-3}{3}$
$3x=12(2)+4(x-3)$
$3x=24+4x-12$
$-x=12$
$x=-12$
$\frac{-12}{4}=2+\frac{-12-3}{3}$
$-3=2+\frac{-15}{3}$
$-3=2-5$
The solution set is $\{-12\}$.

11. $\frac{3x+1}{3}-\frac{13}{2}=\frac{1-x}{4}$
$4(3x+1)-6(13)=3(1-x)$
$12x+4-78=3-3x$
$12x-74=3-3x$
$15x=77$
$x=\frac{77}{15}$
$\frac{3\left(\frac{77}{15}\right)+1}{3}-\frac{13}{2}=\frac{1-\frac{77}{15}}{4}$
$\frac{\frac{77}{5}+1}{3}-\frac{13}{2}=\frac{\frac{-62}{15}}{4}$
$\frac{82}{5}\cdot\frac{1}{3}-\frac{13}{2}=\frac{-62}{15}\cdot\frac{1}{4}$
$\frac{82}{15}-\frac{13}{2}=\frac{-31}{30}$
$\frac{164}{30}-\frac{195}{30}=\frac{-31}{30}$
The solution set is $\left\{\frac{77}{15}\right\}$.

12. **a.** $x\neq 0$

b. $\frac{9}{4}-\frac{1}{2x}=\frac{4}{x}$
$9x-2=16$
$9x=18$
$x=2$
The solution set is $\{2\}$.

13. **a.** $x\neq 5$

b.
$\frac{7}{x-5}+2=\frac{x+2}{x-5}$
$7+2(x-5)=x+2$
$7+2x-10=x+2$
$2x-3=x+2$
$x=5$
The solution set is the empty set, $\varnothing$.

14. **a.** $x \neq 1, x \neq -1$

b.
$$\frac{1}{x-1}-\frac{1}{x+1}=\frac{2}{x^2-1}$$
$$\frac{1}{x-1}-\frac{1}{x+1}=\frac{2}{(x+1)(x-1)}$$
$$x+1-(x-1)=2$$
$$x+1-x+1=2$$
$$2=2$$
The solution set is all real numbers except 1 and –1.

15. **a.** $x \neq -2, x \neq 4$

b.
$$\frac{4}{x+2}+\frac{2}{x-4}=\frac{30}{(x+2)(x-4)}$$
$$4(x-4)+2(x+2)=30$$
$$4x-16+2x+4=30$$
$$6x-12=30$$
$$6x=42$$
$$x=7$$
The solution set is {7}.

16. $\frac{1}{x+5}=0$
$1=0$
The given equation is an inconsistent equation.

17. $7x + 13 = 4x - 10 + 3x + 23$
$7x + 13 = 7x + 13$
$13 = 13$
The given equation is an identity.

18. $7x + 13 = 3x - 10 + 2x + 23$
$7x + 13 = 5x + 13$
$2x = 0$
$x = 0$
The given equation is a conditional equation.

19. $4080 = 420x + 720$
$3360 = 420x$
$x = 8$
$1989 + 8 = 1997$
Losses amounted to $4080 million in 1997.

20. $47{,}587 = 1321.7(x - 1980) + 21{,}153$
$26{,}434 = 1321.7(x - 1980)$
$20 = x - 1980$
$x = 2000$
The median income was $47,587 in 2000.

21. Let x = number of times bus is used
$1.50x$ = fare without coupon book
$25+.0.25x$ = fare with coupon book
$1.50x = 25 + 0.25x$
$1.25x = 25$
$x = 20$
The bus must be used 20 times.

22. Let x = number of unhealthy days per year in New York
$5x + 29$ = number of unhealthy days per year in Los Angeles.
$x+5x+29=185$
$6x+29=185$
$6x=156$
$x=26$
$5x = 29 = 159$
There are 26 unhealthy days per year in New York and 159 in Los Angeles.

23. Let x = amount at 8%
$10{,}000 - x$ = amount at 12%
$0.08x + 0.12(10{,}000 - x) = 950$
$0.08x + 1200 - 0.12x = 950$
$-0.04x = -250$
$x = \$6250$
Invest $6250 at 8%, $3750 at 12%.

24. Let x = width of field
$2x + 14$ = length of field
$2x + 2(2x + 14) = 346$
$2x + 4x + 28 = 346$
$6x = 318$
$x = 53$
$2(53) + 14 = 120$
The width is 53 meters, the length is 120 meters.

25. Let x = amount sold
$300 + 0.05x = 800$
$0.05x = 500$
$x = 10{,}000$
$10,000 in sales must be sold.

26. Let x = price before reduction
$$x - 0.45x = 247.50$$
$$0.55x = 247.50$$
$$x = 450$$
The price before reduction was $450.

27. Let x = number of concerts over 50
$$2627 = 2987 - 8x$$
$$8x = 360$$
$$x = 45$$
$$50 + 45 = 95$$
95 concerts should be given.

28. $V = \frac{1}{3}Bh$
$$3V = Bh$$
$$h = \frac{3V}{B}$$

29. $F = f(1 - M)$
$$F = f - fM$$
$$F - f = -fM$$
$$M = \frac{F - f}{-f}$$
$$M = \frac{f - F}{f}$$

30. $2x^2 + 15x = 8$
$$2x^2 + 15x - 8 = 0$$
$$(2x - 1)(x + 8) = 0$$
$$2x - 1 = 0 \quad x + 8 = 0$$
$$x = \frac{1}{2} \text{ or } x = -8$$
The solution set is $\left\{\frac{1}{2}, -8\right\}$.

31. $5x^2 + 20x = 0$
$$5x(x + 4) = 0$$
$$5x = 0 \quad x + 4 = 0$$
$$x = 0 \text{ or } x = -4$$
The solution set is $\{0, -4\}$.

32. $2x^2 - 3 = 125$
$$2x^2 = 128$$
$$x^2 = 64$$
$$x = \pm 8$$
The solution set is $\{8, -8\}$.

33. $(3x - 4)^2 = 18$
$$3x - 4 = \pm\sqrt{18}$$
$$3x = 4 \pm 3\sqrt{2}$$
$$x = \frac{4 \pm 3\sqrt{2}}{3}$$
The solution set is $\left\{\frac{4 + 3\sqrt{2}}{3}, \frac{4 - 3\sqrt{2}}{3}\right\}$.

34. $x^2 + 20x$
$$\left(\frac{20}{2}\right)^2 = 10^2 = 100$$
$$x^2 + 20x + 100 = (x + 10)^2$$

35. $x^2 - 3x$
$$\left(\frac{3}{2}\right)^2 = \frac{9}{4}$$
$$x^2 - 3x + \frac{9}{4} = \left(x - \frac{3}{2}\right)^2$$

36. $x^2 - 12x = -27$
$$x^2 - 12x + 36 = -27 + 36$$
$$(x - 6)^2 = 9$$
$$x - 6 = \pm 3$$
$$x = 6 \pm 3$$
$$x = 9, 3$$
The solution set is $\{9, 3\}$.

37. $3x^2 - 12x + 11 = 0$

$$x^2 - 4x = -\frac{11}{3}$$
$$x^2 - 4x + 4 = -\frac{11}{3} + 4$$
$$(x-2)^2 = \frac{1}{3}$$
$$x - 2 = \pm\sqrt{\frac{1}{3}}$$
$$x = 2 \pm \frac{\sqrt{3}}{3}$$

The solution set is $\left\{2 + \frac{\sqrt{3}}{3}, 2 - \frac{\sqrt{3}}{3}\right\}$.

38. $x^2 = 2x + 4$

$$x^2 - 2x - 4 = 0$$
$$x = \frac{2 \pm \sqrt{(-2)^2 - 4(1)(-4)}}{2(1)}$$
$$x = \frac{2 \pm \sqrt{4 + 16}}{2}$$
$$x = \frac{2 \pm \sqrt{20}}{2}$$
$$x = \frac{2 \pm 2\sqrt{5}}{2}$$
$$x = 1 \pm \sqrt{5}$$

The solution set is $\{1 + \sqrt{5}, 1 - \sqrt{5}\}$.

39. $x^2 - 2x + 19 = 0$

$$x = \frac{2 \pm \sqrt{(-2)^2 - 4(1)(19)}}{2(1)}$$
$$x = \frac{2 \pm \sqrt{4 - 76}}{2}$$
$$x = \frac{2 \pm \sqrt{-72}}{2}$$
$$x = \frac{2 \pm 6i\sqrt{2}}{2}$$
$$x = 1 \pm 3i\sqrt{2}$$

The solution set is $\{1 + 3i\sqrt{2}, 1 - 3i\sqrt{2}\}$.

40. $2x^2 = 3 - 4x$

$$2x^2 + 4x - 3 = 0$$
$$x = \frac{-4 \pm \sqrt{4^2 - 4(2)(-3)}}{2(2)}$$
$$x = \frac{-4 \pm \sqrt{16 + 24}}{4}$$
$$x = \frac{-4 \pm \sqrt{40}}{4}$$
$$x = \frac{-4 \pm 2\sqrt{10}}{4}$$
$$x = \frac{-2 \pm \sqrt{10}}{2}$$

The solution set is $\left\{\frac{-2 + \sqrt{10}}{2}, \frac{-2 - \sqrt{10}}{2}\right\}$.

41. $x^2 - 4x + 13 = 0$

$(-4)^2 - 4(1)(13)$
$= 16 - 52$
$= -36$; 2 complex imaginary solutions

42. $9x^2 = 2 - 3x$

$9x^2 + 3x - 2 = 0$
$3^2 - 4(9)(-2)$
$= 9 + 72$
$= 81$; 2 unequal real solutions

43. $2x^2 - 11x + 5 = 0$

$(2x - 1)(x - 5) = 0$
$2x - 1 = 0 \quad x - 5 = 0$
$x = \frac{1}{2}$ or $x = 5$

The solution set is $\left\{5, \frac{1}{2}\right\}$.

44. $(3x+5)(x-3)=5$

$3x^2+5x-9x-15=5$

$3x^2-4x-20=0$

$x=\dfrac{4\pm\sqrt{(-4)^2-4(3)(-20)}}{2(3)}$

$x=\dfrac{4\pm\sqrt{16+240}}{6}$

$x=\dfrac{4\pm\sqrt{256}}{6}$

$x=\dfrac{4\pm 16}{6}$

$x=\dfrac{20}{6},\ \dfrac{-12}{6}$

$x=\dfrac{10}{3},\ -2$

The solution set is $\left\{-2, \dfrac{10}{3}\right\}$.

45. $3x^2-7x+1=0$

$x=\dfrac{7\pm\sqrt{(-7)^2-4(3)(1)}}{2(3)}$

$x=\dfrac{7\pm\sqrt{49-12}}{6}$

$x=\dfrac{7\pm\sqrt{37}}{6}$

The solution set is $\left\{\dfrac{7+\sqrt{37}}{6}, \dfrac{7-\sqrt{37}}{6}\right\}$.

46. $x^2-9=0$

$x^2=9$

$x=\pm 3$

The solution set is $\{-3, 3\}$.

47. $(x-3)^2-25=0$

$(x-3)^2=25$

$x-3=\pm 5$

$x=3\pm 5$

$x=8,\ -2$

The solution set is $\{8, -2\}$.

48. $3x^2-x+2=0$

$x=\dfrac{1\pm\sqrt{(-1)^2-4(3)(2)}}{2(3)}$

$x=\dfrac{1\pm\sqrt{1-24}}{6}$

$x=\dfrac{1\pm\sqrt{-23}}{6}$

$x=\dfrac{1\pm i\sqrt{23}}{6}$

The solution set is $\left\{\dfrac{1+i\sqrt{23}}{6}, \dfrac{1-i\sqrt{23}}{6}\right\}$.

49. $W=3t^2$

$1200=3t^2$

$400=t^2$

$t=\pm 20$

Discard negative time; it will weigh 1200 grams in 20 weeks.

50. $N=0.337x^2-2.265x+3.962$

$10.9=0.337x^2-2.265x+3.962$

$0=0.337x^2-2.265x-6.938$

$x=\dfrac{2.265\pm\sqrt{(-2.265)^2-4(0.337)(-6.938)}}{2(0.337)}$

$x=\dfrac{2.265\pm\sqrt{5.130225+9.352424}}{0.674}$

$x=\dfrac{2.265\pm\sqrt{14.482649}}{0.674}$

$x\approx\dfrac{2.265\pm 3.8056}{0.674}$

$\approx\dfrac{6.0706}{0.674},\ \dfrac{-1.5406}{0.674}$

Discard negative value;

$x\approx 9$

10.9 million Amercians owned mountain bikes in 1989.

51. Let x = height
$x(15+x)=324$
$15x+x^2=324$
$x^2+15x-324=0$
$(x+27)(x-12)=0$
$x=-27$ or $x=12$
$12+15=27$
Disregard a negative length. The dimensions are 12 ft by 27 ft.

52. Let x = height of building
$2x$ = shadow height
$x^2+(2x)^2=300^2$
$x^2+4x^2=90{,}000$
$5x^2=90{,}000$
$x^2=18{,}000$
$x\approx\pm134.164$
Discard negative height.
The building is approximately 134.16 meters high.

53. $2x^4=50x^2$
$2x^4-50x^2=0$
$2x^2\left(x^2-25\right)=0$
$x=0$
$x=\pm5$
The solution set is $\{-5, 0, 5\}$.

54. $2x^3-x^2-18x+9=0$
$x^2(2x-1)-9(2x-1)=0$
$\left(x^2-9\right)(2x-1)=0$
$x=\pm3,\ x=\frac{1}{2}$
The solution set is $\left\{-3, \frac{1}{2}, 3\right\}$.

55. $\sqrt{2x-3}+x=3$
$\sqrt{2x-3}=3-x$
$2x-3=9-6x+x^2$
$x^2-8x+12=0$
$x^2-8x=-12$
$x^2-8x+16=-12+16$
$(x-4)^2=4$
$x-4=\pm2$
$x=4+2$
$x=6, 2$
The solution set is $\{2\}$.

56. $\sqrt{x-4}+\sqrt{x+1}=5$
$\sqrt{x-4}=5-\sqrt{x+1}$
$x-4=25-10\sqrt{x+1}+(x+1)$
$x-4=26+x-10\sqrt{x+1}$
$-30=-10\sqrt{x+1}$
$3=\sqrt{x+1}$
$9=x+1$
$x=8$
The solution set is $\{8\}$.

57. $3x^{3/4}-24=0$
$3x^{3/4}=24$
$x^{3/4}=8$
$x=8^{4/3}$
$x=16$
The solution set is $\{16\}$.

58. $(x-7)^{3/2}=125$
$x-7=125^{2/3}$
$x-7=\sqrt[3]{125}^2$
$x-7=5^2$
$x-7=25$
$x=32$
The solution set is $\{32\}$.

59. $x^4 - 5x^2 + 4 = 0$
Let $t = x^2$
$t^2 - 5t + 4 = 0$
$(t-4)(t-1) = 0$
$t = 4$ or $t = 1$
$x^2 = 4$ $x^2 = 1$
$x = \pm 2$ $x = \pm 1$
The solution set is $\{-2, -1, 1, 2\}$.

60. $x^{1/2} + 3x^{1/4} - 10 = 0$
Let $t = x^{1/4}$
$t^2 + 3t - 10 = 0$
$(t+5)(t-2) = 0$
$t = -5$ or $t = 2$
$x^{1/4} = -5$ or $x^{1/4} = 2$
$x = 625$ $x = 16$
The solution set is $\{16\}$.

61. $|2x+1| = 7$
$2x + 1 = 7$ or $2x + 1 = -7$
$2x = 6$ $2x = -8$
$x = 3$ or $x = -4$
The solution set is $\{-4, 3\}$.

62. $2|x-3| - 7 = 10$
$2|x-3| = 17$
$|x-3| = \frac{17}{2}$
$x - 3 = \frac{17}{2}$ or $x - 3 = -\frac{17}{2}$
$x = \frac{23}{2}$ or $x = -\frac{11}{2}$
The solution set is $\left\{-\frac{11}{2}, \frac{23}{2}\right\}$.

63. $3x^{4/3} - 5x^{2/3} + 2 = 0$
Let $t = x^{2/3}$.
$3t^2 - 5t + 2 = 0$
$(3t-2)(t-1) = 0$
$t = \frac{2}{3}$ or $t = 1$
$x^{2/3} = \frac{2}{3}$ $x^{2/3} = 1$
$x = \pm\left(\frac{2}{3}\right)^{3/2}$ $x = \pm 1^{3/2}$
$x = \pm\frac{2\sqrt{6}}{9}$ $x = \pm 1$
The solution set is $\left\{-1, -\frac{2\sqrt{6}}{9}, \frac{2\sqrt{6}}{9}, 1\right\}$.

64. $2\sqrt{x-1} = x$
$4(x-1) = x^2$
$4x - 4 = x^2$
$x^2 - 4x + 4 = 0$
$(x-2)^2 = 0$
$x = 2$
The solution set is $\{2\}$.

65. $|2x-5| - 3 = 0$
$|2x-5| = 3$
$2x - 5 = 3$ or $2x - 5 = -3$
$2x = 8$ $2x = 2$
$x = 4$ $x = 1$
The solution set is $\{4, 1\}$.

66. $x^3 + 2x^2 - 9x - 18 = 0$
$x^2(x+2) - 9(x+2) = 0$
$(x^2 - 9)(x+2) = 0$
$x + 2 = 0$ or $x^2 - 9 = 0$
$x = -2$ $x = -3, 3$
The solution set is $\{-3, -2, 3\}$.

67. $D = \sqrt{2H}$
$50 = \sqrt{2H}$
$2500 = 2H$
$H = 1250$
The mountain is 1250 feet high.

68. 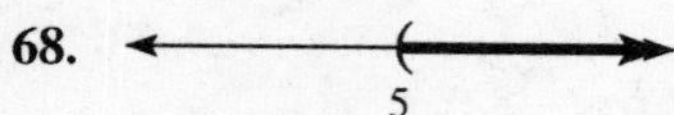

69. 1

70. −3 0

71. $-2 < x \le 3$

−2 3

72. $-1.5 \le x \le 2$

−1.5 2

73. $x > -1$

−1

74. $-6x + 3 \le 15$
$-6x \le 12$
$x \ge 2$

2

The solution set is $[-2, \infty)$.

75. $6x - 9 \ge -4x - 3$
$10x \ge 6$
$x \ge \frac{3}{5}$

$\frac{3}{5}$

The solution set is $\left[\frac{3}{5}, \infty\right)$.

76. $\frac{x}{3} - \frac{3}{4} - 1 > \frac{x}{2}$
$12\left(\frac{x}{3} - \frac{3}{4} - 1\right) > 12\left(\frac{x}{2}\right)$
$4x - 9 - 12 > 6x$
$-21 > 2x$
$-\frac{21}{2} > x$

$-\frac{21}{2}$

The solution set is $\left(-\infty, -\frac{21}{2}\right)$.

77. $6x + 5 > -2(x - 3) - 25$
$6x + 5 > -2x + 6 - 25$
$8x + 5 > -19$
$8x > -24$
$x > -3$

−3

The solution set is $(-3, \infty)$.

78. $3(2x - 1) - 2(x - 4) \ge 7 + 2(3 + 4x)$
$6x - 3 - 2x + 8 \ge 7 + 6 + 8x$
$4x + 5 \ge 8x + 13$
$-4x \ge 8$
$x \le -2$

−2

The solution set is $[-\infty, -2)$.

79. $7 < 2x + 3 \le 9$
$4 < 2x \le 6$
$2 < x \le 3$
(2, 3]

2 5

The solution set is $[2, 3)$.

80. $|2x + 3| \le 15$
$-15 \le 2x + 3 \le 15$
$-18 \le 2x \le 12$
$-9 \le x \le 6$

−9 6

The solution set is $[-9, 6]$.

81. $\left|\frac{2x+6}{3}\right|>2$

$\frac{2x+6}{3}>2 \quad \frac{2x+6}{3}<-2$

$2x+6>6 \quad 2x+6<-6$

$2x>0 \quad 2x<-12$

$x>0 \quad x<-6$

−6 0

The solution set is $(-\infty,-6)$ or $(0,\infty)$.

82. $|2x+5|-7\ge -6$

$|2x+5|\ge 1$

$2x+5\ge 1$ or $2x+5\le -1$

$2x\ge -4 \quad 2x\le -6$

$x\ge -2$ or $x\le -3$

−3 −2

The solution set is $(-\infty,-3]$ or $[-2,\infty)$.

83. $437\le 4x-7\le 1229$

$444\le 4x\le 1236$

$111\le x\le 309$

Canada, Former Soviet Union

84. $|x-320|>80$

$x-320>80$ or $x-320<-80$

$x>400$ or $x<240$

Australia, Canada, United States

85. $|h-6.5|\le 1$

$-1\le h-6.5\le 1$

$5.5\le h\le 7.5$

Most people sleep between 5.5 and 7.5 hours.

86. $15\le \frac{5}{9}(F-32)\le 35$

$27\le F-32\le 63$

$59\le F\le 95$

The range is between 59° and 95°, inclusively.

87. Option 1: $11+0.06x$

Option 2: $4+0.20x$

$11+0.06x<4+0.20x$

$-0.14x<-7$

$x>50$

More than 50 checks should be written.

88. Let x = number of years since 1984.

turntables: $1{,}644-82x$

CD players: $284+496x$

$284+496x>1644-82x$

$578x>1360$

$x>2.3529$

$1984+2.35=1986.35$

The first year was 1986.

89. $2x^2+7x\le 4$

$2x^2+7x-4\le 0$

$(2x-1)(x+4)\le 0$

$x=-4$ or $x=\frac{1}{2}$

F	T	F

−4 $\frac{1}{2}$

Test −5: $2(-5)^2+7(-5)\le 4$

$50-35\le 4$

$15\le 4$ False

Test 0: $2(0)^2+7(0)\le 4$

$0\le 4$ True

Test 1: $2(1)^2+7(1)\le 4$

$2+7\le 4$

$9\le 4$ False

The solution set is $\left[-4,\frac{1}{2}\right]$.

−4 $\frac{1}{2}$

90. $2x^2 > 6x - 3$

$2x^2 - 6x + 3 > 0$

$x = \dfrac{6 \pm \sqrt{(-6)^2 - 4(2)(3)}}{2(2)}$

$x = \dfrac{6 \pm 2\sqrt{3}}{4}$

$x = \dfrac{3 \pm \sqrt{3}}{2}$

T | F | T

$\frac{3-\sqrt{3}}{2}$ $\quad$ $\frac{3+\sqrt{3}}{2}$

Test 0: $2(0)^2 > 6(0) - 4$
$0 > -3$ True

Test 1: $2(1)^2 > 6(1) - 3$
$2 > 3$ True

Test 3: $2(3)^2 > 6(3) - 3$
$18 > 15$ True

The solution set is $\left(-\infty, \dfrac{3-\sqrt{3}}{2}\right)$ or $\left(\dfrac{3+\sqrt{3}}{2}, \infty\right)$.

$\frac{3-\sqrt{3}}{2}$ $\quad$ $\frac{3+\sqrt{3}}{2}$

91. $\dfrac{x-6}{x+2} > 0$

$x - 6 = 0$ or $x + 2 = 0$

$x = 6$ or $x = -2$

T | F | T

-2 $\quad$ 6

Test –3: $\dfrac{-3-6}{-3+2} > 0$
$9 > 0$ True

Test 0: $\dfrac{0-6}{0+2} > 0$
$-3 > 0$ False

Test 7: $\dfrac{7-6}{7+2} > 0$
$\dfrac{1}{9} > 0$ True

The solution set is $(-\infty, -2)$ or $(6, \infty)$.

-2 $\quad$ 6

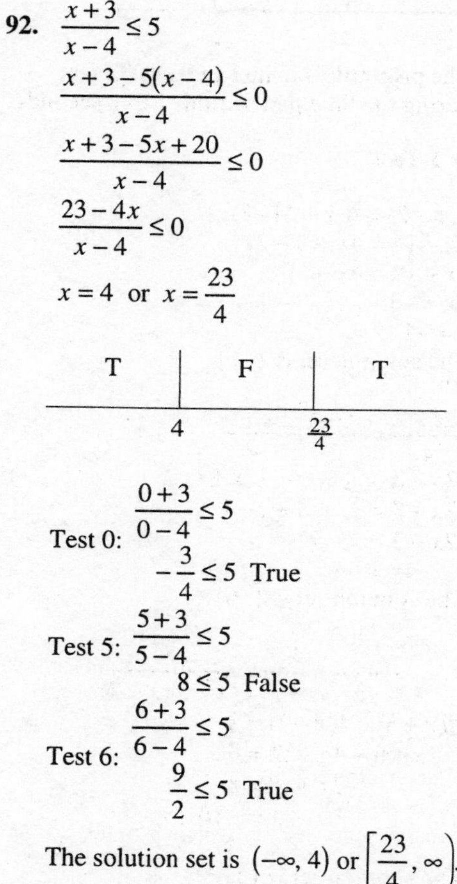

92. $\dfrac{x+3}{x-4} \le 5$

$\dfrac{x+3-5(x-4)}{x-4} \le 0$

$\dfrac{x+3-5x+20}{x-4} \le 0$

$\dfrac{23-4x}{x-4} \le 0$

$x = 4$ or $x = \dfrac{23}{4}$

T | F | T

4 $\quad$ $\frac{23}{4}$

Test 0: $\dfrac{0+3}{0-4} \le 5$
$-\dfrac{3}{4} \le 5$ True

Test 5: $\dfrac{5+3}{5-4} \le 5$
$8 \le 5$ False

Test 6: $\dfrac{6+3}{6-4} \le 5$
$\dfrac{9}{2} \le 5$ True

The solution set is $(-\infty, 4)$ or $\left[\dfrac{23}{4}, \infty\right)$.

4 $\quad$ $\frac{23}{4}$

93. $s = -16t^2 + v_0 t + s_0$
$32 < -16t^2 + 48t + 0$
$0 < -16t^2 + 48t - 32$
$0 < -16(t^2 - 3t + 2)$
$0 < -16(t-2)(t-1)$

F	T	F
	1	2

The projectile's height exceeds 32 feet during the time period from 1 to 2 seconds.

Chapter 1 Test

1. $7(x-2) = 4(x+1) - 21$
$7x - 14 = 4x + 4 - 21$
$7x - 14 = 4x - 17$
$3x = -3$
$x = -1$
The solution set is $\{-1\}$.

2. $\frac{2x-3}{4} = \frac{x-4}{2} - \frac{x+1}{4}$
$2x - 3 = 2(x-4) - (x+1)$
$2x - 3 = 2x - 8 - x - 1$
$2x - 3 = x - 9$
$x = -6$
The solution set is $\{-6\}$.

3. $\frac{2}{x-3} - \frac{4}{x+3} = \frac{8}{(x-3)(x+3)}$
$2(x+3) - 4(x-3) = 8$
$2x + 6 - 4x + 12 = 8$
$-2x + 18 = 8$
$-2x = -10$
$x = 5$
The solution set is $\{5\}$.

4. $2x^2 - 3x - 2 = 0$
$(2x+1)(x-2) = 0$
$2x + 1 = 0$ or $x - 2 = 0$
$x = -\frac{1}{2}$ or $x = 2$

The solution set is $\left\{-\frac{1}{2}, 2\right\}$.

5. $(3x-1)^2 = 75$
$3x - 1 = \pm\sqrt{75}$
$3x = 1 \pm 5\sqrt{3}$
$x = \frac{1 \pm 5\sqrt{3}}{3}$
The solution set is $\left\{\frac{1-5\sqrt{3}}{3}, \frac{1+5\sqrt{3}}{3}\right\}$.

6. $x(x-2) = 4$
$x^2 - 2x - 4 = 0$
$x = \frac{2 \pm \sqrt{(-2)^2 - 4(1)(-4)}}{2}$
$x = \frac{2 \pm 2\sqrt{5}}{2}$
$x = 1 \pm \sqrt{5}$
The solution set is $\{1-\sqrt{5}, 1+\sqrt{5}\}$.

7. $4x^2 = 8x - 5$
$4x^2 - 8x + 5 = 0$
$x = \frac{8 \pm \sqrt{(-8)^2 - 4(4)(5)}}{2(4)}$
$x = \frac{8 \pm \sqrt{-16}}{8}$
$x = \frac{8 \pm 4i}{8}$
$x = \frac{2 \pm i}{2}$
The solution set is $\left\{\frac{2-i}{2}, \frac{2+i}{2}\right\}$.

8. $x^3 - 4x^2 - x + 4 = 0$
$x^2(x-4) - 1(x-4) = 0$
$(x^2 - 1)(x-4) = 0$
$(x-1)(x+1)(x-4) = 0$
$x = 1$ or $x = -1$ or $x = 4$
The solution set is $\{-1, 1, 4\}$.

9. $\sqrt{x-3}+5=x$

$\sqrt{x-3}=x-5$

$x-3=x^2-10x+25$

$x^2-11x+28=0$

$x=\dfrac{11\pm\sqrt{11^2-4(1)(28)}}{2(1)}$

$x=\dfrac{11\pm\sqrt{121-112}}{2}$

$x=\dfrac{11\pm\sqrt{9}}{2}$

$x=\dfrac{11\pm 3}{2}$

$x=7$ or $x=4$

The solution set is {7}.

10. $\sqrt{x+4}+\sqrt{x-1}=5$

$\sqrt{x+4}=5-\sqrt{x-1}$

$x+4=25-10\sqrt{x-1}+(x-1)$

$x+4=25-10\sqrt{x-1}+x-1$

$-20=-10\sqrt{x-1}$

$2=\sqrt{x-1}$

$4=x-1$

$x=5$

The solution set is {5}.

11. $5x^{3/2}-10=0$

$5x^{3/2}=10$

$x^{3/2}=2$

$x=2^{2/3}$

$x=\sqrt[3]{4}$

The solution set is $\left\{\sqrt[3]{4}\right\}$.

12. $x^{2/3}-9x^{1/3}+8=0$ let $t=x^{1/3}$

$t^2-9t+8=0$

$(t-1)(t-8)=0$

$t=1 \quad t=8$

$x^{1/3}=1 \quad x^{1/3}=8$

$x=1 \quad x=512$

The solution set is {1, 512}.

13. $\left|\dfrac{2}{3}x-6\right|=2$

$\dfrac{2}{3}x-6=2 \quad \dfrac{2}{3}x-6=-2$

$\dfrac{2}{3}x=8 \quad \dfrac{2}{3}x=4$

$x=12 \quad x=6$

The solution set is {6, 12}.

14. $3(x+4)\ge 5x-12$

$3x+12\ge 5x-12$

$-2x\ge -24$

$x\le 12$

The solution set is $(-\infty, 12]$.

12

15. $\dfrac{x}{6}+\dfrac{1}{8}\le\dfrac{x}{2}-\dfrac{3}{4}$

$4x+3\le 12x-18$

$-8x\le -21$

$x\ge\dfrac{21}{8}$

The solution set is $\left[\dfrac{21}{8},\infty\right)$.

$\frac{21}{8}$

16. $-3\le\dfrac{2x+5}{3}<6$

$-9\le 2x+5<18$

$-14\le 2x<13$

$-7\le x<\dfrac{13}{2}$

The solution set is $\left[-7,\dfrac{13}{2}\right)$.

$-7 \quad \frac{13}{2}$

17. $|3x+2|\ge 3$

$3x+2\ge 3$ or $3x+2\le -3$

$3x\ge 1$ $\quad$ $3x\le -5$

$x\ge \frac{1}{3}$ $\quad$ $x\le -\frac{5}{3}$

The solution set is $\left(-\infty, -\frac{5}{3}\right]$ or $\left[\frac{1}{3}, \infty\right)$.

$-\frac{5}{3}$ $\quad$ $\frac{1}{3}$

18. $x^2 < x+12$

$x^2 - x - 12 < 0$

$(x-4)(x+3) < 0$

$x = 4$ or $x = -3$

F	T	F

-3 $\quad$ 4

Test -4: $(-4)^2 < -4+12$

$16 < 8$ False

Test 0: $0^2 < 0+12$

$0 < 12$ True

Test 5: $5^2 < 5+12$

$25 < 17$ False

The solution set is $(-3, 4)$.

-3 $\quad$ 4

19. $\frac{2x+1}{x-3} > 3$

$\frac{2x+1-3(x-3)}{x-3} > 0$

$\frac{2x+1-3x+9}{x-3} > 0$

$\frac{10-x}{x-3} > 0$

$x = 3$ or $x = 10$

F	T	F

3 $\quad$ 10

Test 0: $\frac{2(0)+1}{0-3} > 3$

$-\frac{1}{3} > 3$ False

Test 4: $\frac{2(4)+1}{4-3} > 3$

$9 > 3$ True

Test 11: $\frac{2(11)+1}{11-3} \ge 3$

$\frac{23}{8} > 3$ False

The solution set is [3, 10).

3 $\quad$ 10

20. a. $B = \frac{2}{5}w + \frac{1}{125}n$

$125B = 125\left(\frac{2}{5}w + \frac{1}{125}n\right)$

$125B = 50w + n$

$125B - 50w = n$

$n = 125B - 50w$

b. $n = 125(512) - 50(800)$

$n = 24{,}000$

An employee must work 24,000 years!

21. let x = years after 1980

$2795 + 89x$ = Arizona population

$3071 + 43x$ = South Carolina population

$2795 + 89x = 3071 + 43x$

$46x = 276$

$x = 6$

$1980 + 6 = 1986$

The populations were the same in 1986.

22. $4080 = 420x + 720$

$3360 = 420x$

$x = 8$

$1989 + 8 = 1997$

Losses amounted to $4080 million in 1997.

23. Let x = original salary

$1.09x = 45{,}780$

$x = 42{,}000$

The therapist's salary was $42,000.

24. let x = amount at 9%
$6000 - x$ = amount at 6%
$$0.09(x) + 0.06(6000 - x) = 480$$
$$0.09x + 360 - 0.06x = 480$$
$$0.03x = 120$$
$$x = 4000$$
$4000 was invested at 9%; $2000 at 6%.

25. $24^2 + x^2 = 26^2$
$$576 + x^2 = 676$$
$$x^2 = 100$$
$$x = \pm 10$$
The wire should be attached 10 feet up the pole.

26. $\frac{76 + 80 + 72 + x}{4} \geq 80$
$$76 + 80 + 72 + x \geq 320$$
$$228 + x \geq 320$$
$$x \geq 92$$
The student must earn at least a 92.

27. Option 1: $20
Option 2: $5 + 0.15x$
$$5 + 0.15x < 20$$
$$0.15x < 15$$
$$x < 100$$
Less than 100 hours make the second option a better deal.

Chapter 2

Section 2.1

Check Point Exercises

1. a. $m = \frac{-2-4}{-4-(-3)} = \frac{-6}{-1} = 6$

   b. $m = \frac{5-(-2)}{-1-4} = \frac{7}{-5} = -\frac{7}{5}$

2. $$\begin{aligned} y - y_1 &= m(x - x_1) \\ y-(-5) &= 6(x-2) \\ y+5 &= 6x-12 \\ y &= 6x-17 \end{aligned}$$

3. $m = \frac{-6-(-1)}{-1-(-2)} = \frac{-5}{1} = -5$,
   so the slope is –5. Using the point (–2, –1), we get the point slope equation:
   $$\begin{aligned} y - y_1 &= m(x - x_1) \\ y-(-1) &= -5[x-(-2)] \\ y+1 &= -5(x+2). \text{ Solve the equation for } y\text{:} \\ y+1 &= -5x-10 \\ y &= -5x-11. \end{aligned}$$

4. The slope m is $\frac{3}{5}$ and the y-intercept is 1, so one point on the line is (1, 0). We can find a second point on the line by using the slope $m = \frac{3}{5} = \frac{\text{Rise}}{\text{Run}}$: starting at the point (0, 1), move 3 units up and 5 units to the right, to obtain the point (5, 4).

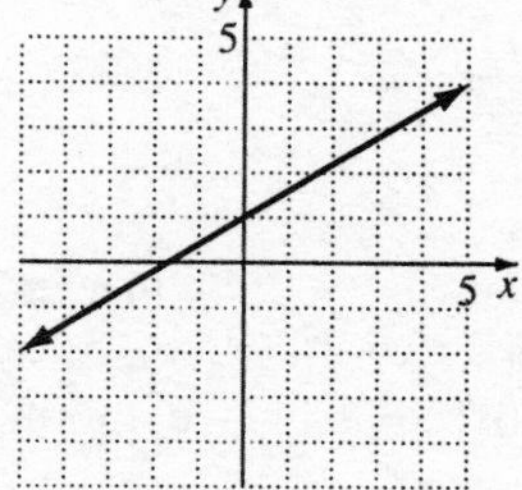

5. All points on the graph of $x = -1$ have a value of x that is always –1. For example, we could plot the points (–1, –2) and (–1, 3) and connect them.

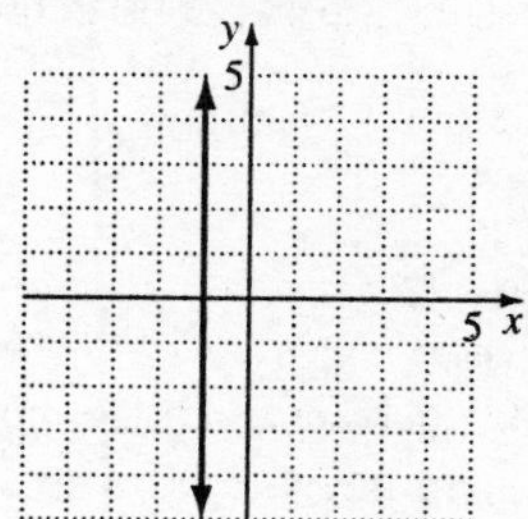

6. $$\begin{aligned} 3x+6y-12 &= 0 \\ 6y &= -3x+12 \\ y &= \frac{-3}{6}x + \frac{12}{6} \\ y &= -\frac{1}{2}x+2 \end{aligned}$$

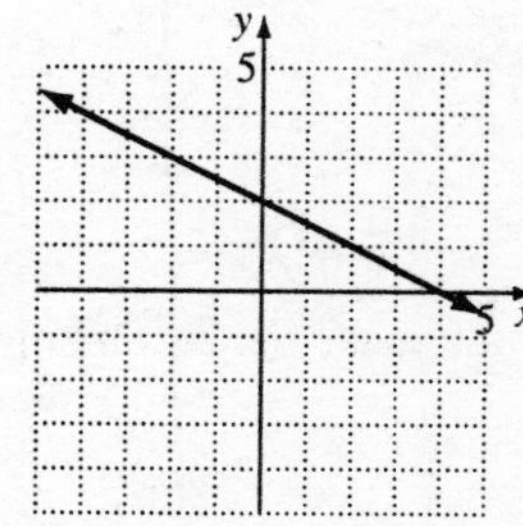

The slope is $-\frac{1}{2}$ and the y-intercept is 2.

7. Using the points (10, 203.3) and (20, 226.5), we obtain a slope of

$$m = \frac{\text{change in } y}{\text{change in } x} = \frac{226.5 - 203.3}{20 - 10} = \frac{23.2}{10} = 2.32.$$

Using the point (10, 203.3), the point slope equation of the line is given by:

$$y - y_1 = m(x - x_1)$$
$$y - 203.3 = 2.32(x - 10)$$
$$y - 203.3 = 2.32x - 23.2$$
$$y = 2.32x + 180.1.$$

The linear equation that models U.S. population, y, in millions, x years after 1960 is $y = 2.32x + 180.1$. To estimate the U.S. population in 2020, note that 2020 is $x = 60$ years after 1960, so substitute 60 for x and compute y. $y = 2.32(60) + 180.1 = 319.3$

Our equation predicts that the U.S. population in the year 2020 will be 319.3 million.

Exercise Set 2.1

1. $m = \frac{10 - 7}{8 - 4} = \frac{3}{4}$; rises

3. $m = \frac{2 - 1}{2 - (-2)} = \frac{1}{4}$; rises

5. $m = \frac{2 - (-2)}{3 - 4} = \frac{0}{-1} = 0$; horizontal

7. $m = \frac{-1 - 4}{-1 - (-2)} = \frac{-5}{1} = -5$; falls

9. $m = \frac{-2 - 3}{5 - 5} = \frac{-5}{0}$ undefined; vertical

11. $m = 2,\ x_1 = 3,\ y_1 = 5;$

point-slope form: $y - 5 = 2(x - 3)$;

slope-intercept form: $y - 5 = 2x - 6$

$$y = 2x - 1$$

13. $m = 6,\ x_1 = -2,\ y_1 = 5;$

point-slope form: $y - 5 = 6(x + 2)$;

slope-intercept form: $y - 5 = 6x + 12$

$$y = 6x + 17$$

15. $m = -3,\ x_1 = -2,\ y_1 = -3;$

point-slope form: $y + 3 = -3(x + 2)$;

slope-intercept form: $y + 3 = -3x - 6$

$$y = -3x - 9$$

17. $m = -4,\ x_1 = -4,\ y_1 = 0;$

point-slope form: $y - 0 = -4(x + 4)$;

slope-intercept form: $y = -4(x + 4)$

$$y = -4x - 16$$

19. $m = -1,\ x_1 = \frac{-1}{2},\ y_1 = -2;$

point-slope form: $y + 2 = -1\left(x + \frac{1}{2}\right)$;

slope-intercept form: $y + 2 = -x - \frac{1}{2}$

$$y = -x - \frac{5}{2}$$

21. $m = \frac{1}{2},\ x_1 = 0,\ y_1 = 0;$

point-slope form: $y - 0 = \frac{1}{2}(x - 0)$;

slope-intercept form: $y = \frac{1}{2}x$

23. $m = -\frac{2}{3},\ x_1 = 6,\ y_1 = -2;$

point-slope form: $y + 2 = -\frac{2}{3}(x - 6)$;

slope-intercept form: $y + 2 = -\frac{2}{3}x + 4$

$$y = -\frac{2}{3}x + 2$$

25. $m = \frac{10 - 2}{5 - 1} = \frac{8}{4} = 2$;

point-slope form: $y - 2 = 2(x - 1)$ using $(x_1, y_1) = (1, 2)$, or $y - 10 = 2(x - 5)$ using $(x_1, y_1) = (5, 10)$; slope-intercept form:

$$y - 2 = 2x - 2 \text{ or}$$
$$y - 10 = 2x - 10,$$
$$y = 2x$$

27. $m = \dfrac{3-0}{0-(-3)} = \dfrac{3}{3} = 1;$
point-slope form: $y - 0 = 1(x + 3)$ using $(x_1, y_1) = (-3, 0)$, or $y - 3 = 1(x - 0)$ using $(x_1, y_1) = (0, 3)$; slope-intercept form:
$y = x + 3$

29. $m = \dfrac{4-(-1)}{2-(-3)} = \dfrac{5}{5} = 1;$
point-slope form: $y + 1 = 1(x + 3)$ using $(x_1, y_1) = (-3, -1)$, or $y - 4 = 1(x - 2)$ using $(x_1, y_1) = (2, 4)$; slope-intercept form:
$y + 1 = x + 3$ or
$y - 4 = x - 2$
$y = x + 2$

31. $m = \dfrac{6-(-2)}{3-(-3)} = \dfrac{8}{6} = \dfrac{4}{3};$
point-slope form: $y + 2 = \dfrac{4}{3}(x + 3)$ using $(x_1, y_1) = (-3, -2)$, or $y - 6 = \dfrac{4}{3}(x - 3)$ using $(x_1, y_1) = (3, 6)$; slope-intercept form:
$y + 2 = \dfrac{4}{3x} + 4$ or
$y - 6 = \dfrac{4}{3}x - 4,$
$y = \dfrac{4}{3}x + 2$

33. $m = \dfrac{-1-(-1)}{4-(-3)} = \dfrac{0}{7} = 0;$
point-slope form: $y + 1 = 0(x + 3)$ using $(x_1, y_1) = (-3, -1)$, or $y + 1 = 0(x - 4)$ using $(x_1, y_1) = (4, -1)$; slope-intercept form:
$y + 1 = 0,$ so
$y = -1$

35. $m = \dfrac{0-4}{-2-2} = \dfrac{-4}{-4} = 1;$
point-slope form: $y - 4 = 1(x - 2)$ using $(x_1, y_1) = (2, 4)$, or $y - 0 = 1(x + 2)$ using $(x_1, y_1) = (-2, 0)$; slope-intercept form:
$y - 9 = x - 2,$ or
$y = x + 2$

37. $m = \dfrac{4-0}{0-\left(-\frac{1}{2}\right)} = \dfrac{4}{\frac{1}{2}} = 8;$
point-slope form: $y - 4 = 8(x - 0)$ using $(x_1, y_1) = (0, 4)$, or $y - 0 = 8\left(x + \frac{1}{2}\right)$ using $(x_1, y_1) = \left(-\frac{1}{2}, 0\right)$; or $y - 0 = 8\left(x + \frac{1}{2}\right)$
slope-intercept form: $y - 4 = 8x$ or
$y = 8x + 4$

39. $m = 2; b = 1$

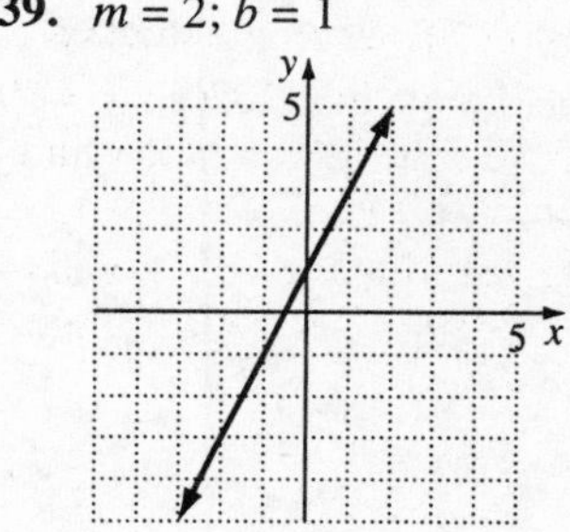

41. $m = -2; b = 1$

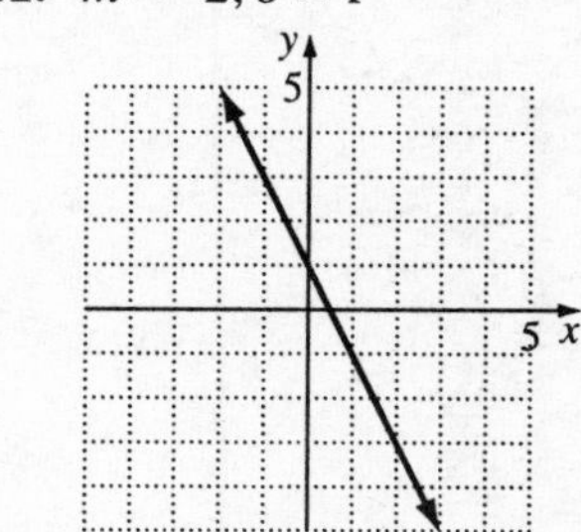

43. $m = \dfrac{3}{4};\ b = -2$

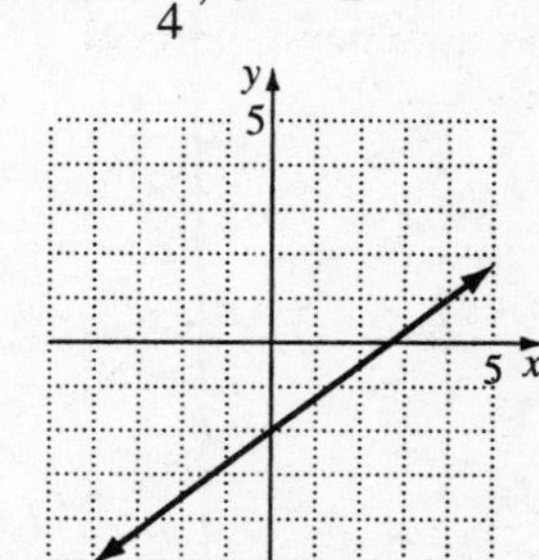

45. $m = -\frac{3}{5};\ b = 7$

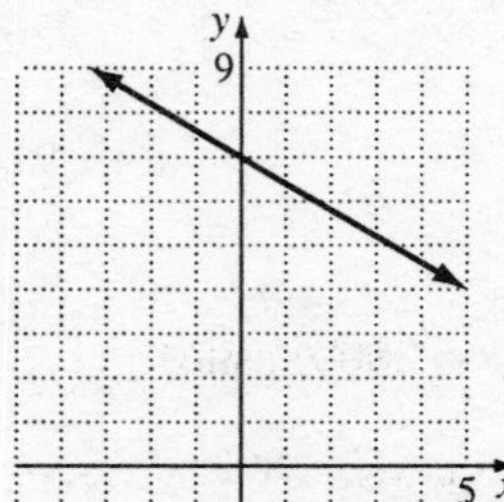

47.

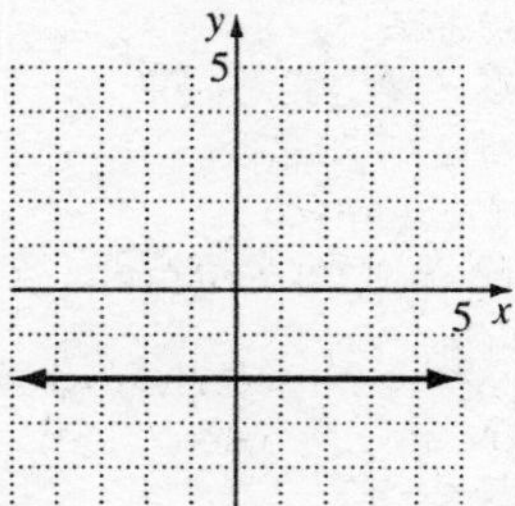

49.

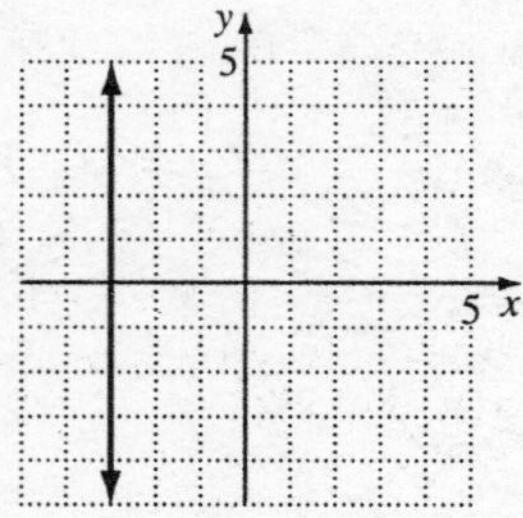

51.

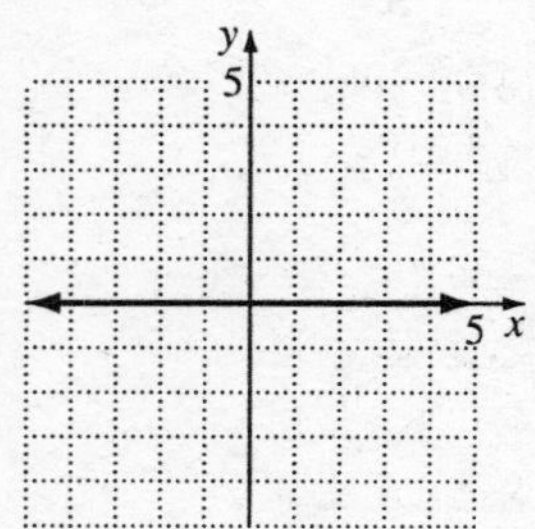

53. a.
$$\begin{aligned} 3x + y - 5 &= 0 \\ y - 5 &= -3x \\ y &= -3x + 5 \end{aligned}$$

b. $m = -3;\ b = 5$

c.

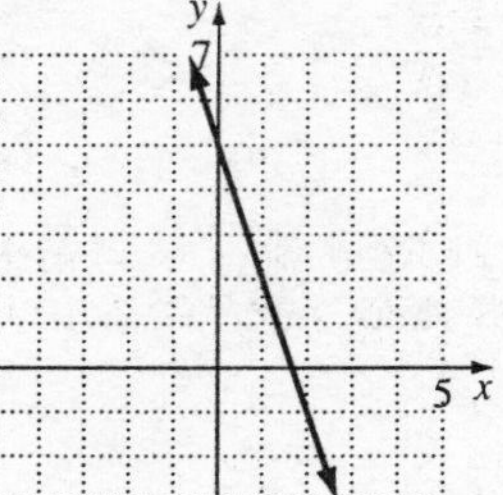

55. a.
$$\begin{aligned} 2x + 3y - 18 &= 0 \\ 2x - 18 &= -3y \\ -3y &= 2x - 18 \\ y &= \frac{2}{-3}x - \frac{18}{-3} \\ y &= -\frac{2}{3}x + 6 \end{aligned}$$

b. $m = -\frac{2}{3};\ b = 6$

c.

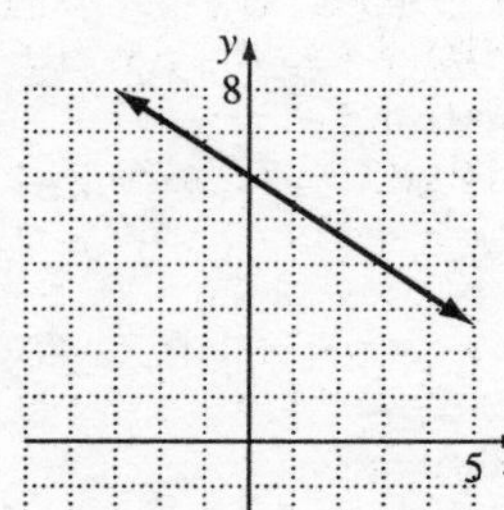

57. a.
$$\begin{aligned} 8x - 4y - 12 &= 0 \\ 8x - 12 &= 4y \\ 4y &= 8x - 12 \\ y &= \frac{8}{4}x - \frac{12}{4} \\ y &= 2x - 3 \end{aligned}$$

b. $m = 2;\ b = -3$

c.

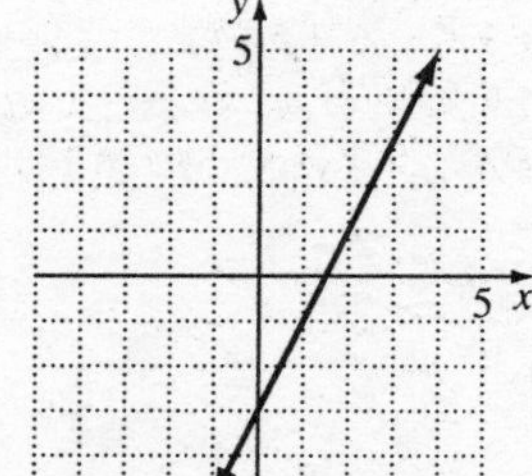

59. a. $3x - 9 = 0$
$3x = 9$
$x = 3$

b. m is undefined since the line is vertical; no y-intercept since all x values are 3.

c.

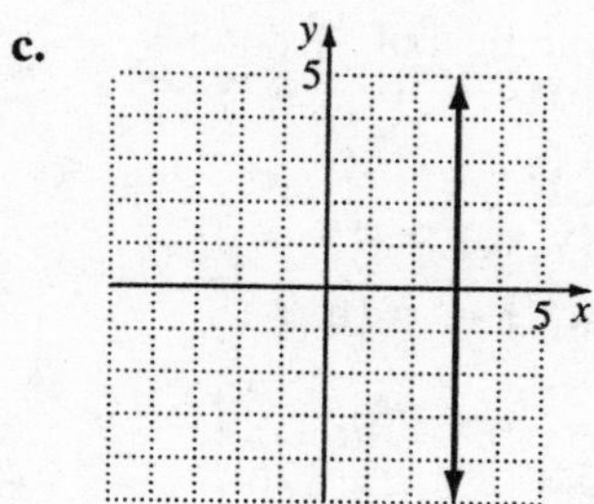

61. Answers may vary. The equation $y = 80$ is a reasonable approximation to model the data, since the data are almost constant.

63. In 2030, it will be $x = 70$ years after 1960, and $y = 2.35(70) + 179.5 = 344$ million U.S. people are predicted.
In 2040, it will be $x = 80$ years after 1960, and $y = 2.35(80) + 179.5 = 367.5$ million U.S. people are predicted.
In 2050, it will be $x = 90$ years after 1960, and $y = 2.35(90) + 179.5 = 391$ million U.S. people are predicted.
The equation models the projections well, but is slightly lower than the projections.

65. $m = \dfrac{5493.7 - 4459.2}{7 - 3} = \dfrac{1034.5}{4} = 258.625;$
point-slope form:
$y - 4459.2 = 258.625(x - 3)$ using $(x_1, y_1) = (3, 4459.2)$; slope-intercept form:
$y - 4459.2 = 258.625x - 775.875$
$y = 258.625x + 3683.325;$
2020 is 30 years after 1990, so
$y = 258.625(30) + 3683.325 = 11442.075;$
Consumers in the US are expected to spend about $11,442.075 billion in the year 2020.

67. $m = \dfrac{55 - 19}{2000 - 20{,}000}$
$= \dfrac{36}{-18{,}000}$
$= -\dfrac{1}{500}$
$= -0.002;$
$y - 55 = -0.002(x - 2000)$ using $(x_1, y_1) = (2000, 55)$;
slope-intercept equation:
$y - 55 = 0.002x + 4$
$y = -0.002x + 59$
When $y = 50$: $50 = -0.002x + 59$
$-9 = -0.002x$
$x = 4500$
4500 shirts can be sold for $50 each.

69. It appears that the regression line passes through the points (2, 9.5) and (12, 3).
$m = \dfrac{3 - 9.5}{12 - 2} = \dfrac{-6.5}{10} = -0.65;$
point-slope form: $y - 3 = -0.65(x - 12)$ using $(x_1, y_1) = (12, 3)$;
slope-intercept form: $y - 3 = -0.65x + 7.8$
$y = -0.65x + 10.8$
When $x = 7$; $y = -0.65(7) + 10.8 = 6.25$;
A person with 7 years education is predicted to have a score of about 6.25.

71.–77. Answers may vary.

79. Two points are (0, 6) and (10, –24).
$m = \dfrac{-24 - 6}{10 - 0} = \dfrac{-30}{10} = -3.$
Check: $y = mx + b$: $y = -3x + 6$.

10
–10 10
–10

81. Two points are (0, –2) and (10, 5.5).

$$m = \frac{5.5-(-2)}{10-0} = \frac{7.5}{10} = 0.75 \text{ or } \frac{3}{4}.$$

Check: $y = mx + b$: $y = \frac{3}{4}x - 2$.

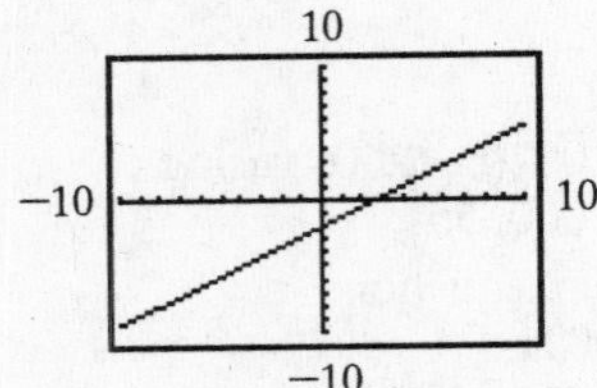

83. a. False; if $m = 0$, the graph does not rise.

b. False; the product of their slopes is –16.

c. True; the point (6, 0) satisfies the equation. Write the equation in slope-intercept form,

$y = -\frac{5}{6} + 5$, so the slope $m = -\frac{5}{6}$.

d. False; the graph of $y = 7$ is a horizontal line through (0, 7).

(c) is true

85. a. m_1, m_3, m_2, m_4

b. b_2, b_1, b_4, b_3

Section 2.2

Check Point Exercises

1. Since the line is to pass through the point (2, 5), in the point-slope formula we have $x_1 = -2$ and $y_1 = 5$. Also since the line is to be parallel to the line $y = 3x + 1$, the two lines must have the same slope $m = 3$.
point-slope form: $y - 5 = 3(x + 2)$
slope-intercept form:
$y - 5 = 3x + 6,\ y = 3x + 11$

2. $x + 3y - 12 = 0$

$$3y = -x + 12$$
$$y = -\frac{1}{3}x + 4$$

The given line has slope $m = \frac{-1}{3}$, so any line perpendicular to it has a slope that is the negative reciprocal of $\frac{-1}{3}$, or 3.

3. $h = 0,\ k = 0,\ r = 4;$

$$(x-0)^2 + (y-0)^2 = 4^2$$
$$x^2 + y^2 = 16$$

4. $h = 5,\ k = -6,\ r = 10;$

$$(x-5)^2 + [y-(-6)]^2 = 10^2$$
$$(x-5)^2 + (y+6)^2 = 100$$

5. $(x+3)^2 + (y-1)^2 = 4$

$[x-(-3)]^2 + (y-1)^2 = 2^2$

So in the standard form of the circle's equation $(x-h)^2 + (y-k)^2 = r^2$, we have $h = -3,\ k = 1,\ r = 2$.
center: $(h, k) = (-3, 1)$
radius: $r = 2$

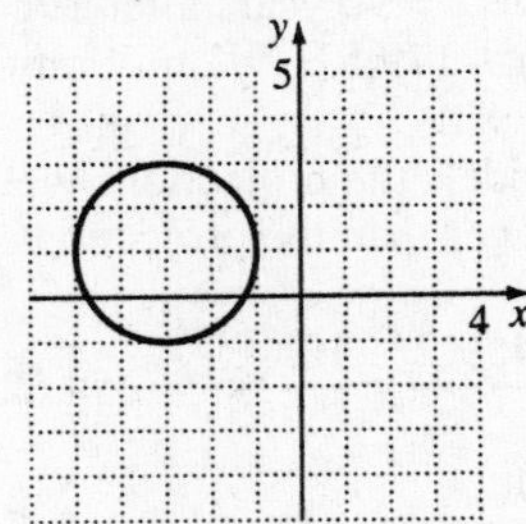

6.
$$x^2 + y^2 + 4x - 4y - 1 = 0$$
$$\left(x^2 + 4x \quad\right) + \left(y^2 - 4y \quad\right) = 0$$
$$\left(x^2 + 4x + 4\right) + \left(y^2 + 4y + 4\right) = 1 + 4 + 4$$
$$(x+2)^2 + (y-2)^2 = 9$$
$$[x-(-x)]^2 + (y-2)^2 = 3^2$$
So in the standard form of the circle's equation $(x-h)^2 + (y-k)^2 = r^2$, we have $h = -2$, $k = 2$, $r = 3$.

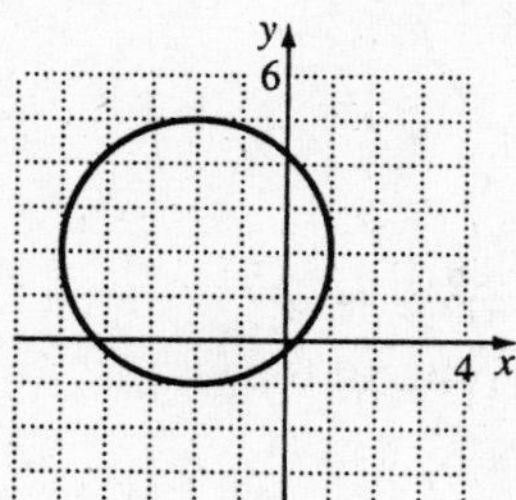

Exercise Set 2.2

1. a. 5

b. $-\frac{1}{5}$

3. a. –7

b. $\frac{1}{7}$

5. a. $\frac{1}{2}$

b. –2

7. a. $-\frac{2}{5}$

b. $\frac{5}{2}$

9. a. –4

b. $\frac{1}{4}$

11. a. $-\frac{1}{2}$

b. 2

13. a. $\frac{2}{3}$

b. $-\frac{3}{2}$

15. a. undefined

b. 0

17. L has slope 2 because it is parellel to $y = 2x$, and passes through (4, 2).
point-slope form: $y - 2 = 2(x - 4)$
slope-intercept form: $y - 2 = 2x - 8$
$$y = 2x - 6$$

19. L has slope $-\frac{1}{2}$ because it is perpendicular to $y = 2x$, and passes through (2, 4).
point-slope form: $y - 4 = -\frac{1}{2}(x - 2)$
slope-intercept form: $y - 4 = -\frac{1}{2}x + 1$
$$y = -\frac{1}{2}x + 5$$

21. $m = -4$ since the line is parallel to $y = -4x + 3$; $x_1 = -8$, $y_1 = -10$;
point-slope form: $y + 10 = -4(x + 8)$
slope-intercept form: $y + 10 = -4x - 32$
$$y = -4x - 42$$

23. $m = -5$ since the line is perpendicular to $y = \frac{1}{5}x + 6$; $x_1 = 2$, $y_1 = -3$;
point-slope form: $y + 3 = -5(x - 2)$
slope-intercept form: $y + 3 = -5x + 10$
$$y = -5x + 7$$

25. $2x - 3y - 7 = 0$
$$-3y = -2x + 7$$
$$y = \frac{2}{3}x - \frac{7}{3}$$
The slope of the given line is $\frac{2}{3}$, so $m = \frac{2}{3}$ since the lines are parallel.
point-slope form: $y - 2 = \frac{2}{3}(x + 2)$
slope-intercept form: $y = \frac{2}{3}x + \frac{10}{3}$

27. $x - 2y - 3 = 0$
$$-2y = -x + 3$$
$$y = \frac{1}{2}x - \frac{3}{2}$$
The slope of the given line is $\frac{1}{2}$, so $m = -2$ since the lines are perpendicular.
point-slope form: $y + 7 = -2(x - 4)$
slope-intercept form: $y + 7 = -2x + 8$
$$y = -2x + 1$$

29. $(x - 0)^2 + (y - 0)^2 = 7^2$
$$x^2 + y^2 = 49$$

31. $(x - 3)^2 + (y - 2)^2 = 5^2$
$$(x - 3)^2 + (y - 2)^2 = 25$$

33. $[x - (-1)]^2 + (y - 4)^2 = 2^2$
$$(x + 1)^2 + (y - 4)^2 = 4$$

35. $[x - (-3)]^2 + [y - (-1)]^2 = \left(\sqrt{3}\right)^2$
$$(x + 3)^2 + (y + 1)^2 = 3$$

37. $[x - (-4)]^2 + (y - 0)^2 = 10^2$
$$(x + 4)^2 + (y - 0)^2 = 100$$

39. $x^2 + y^2 = 16$
$(x - 0)^2 + (y - 0)^2 = y^2$
$h = 0,\ k = 0,\ r = 4;$
center = (0, 0)
radius = 4

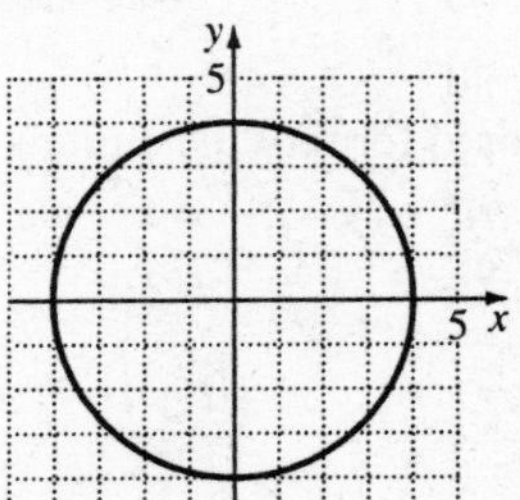

41. $(x - 3)^2 + (y - 1)^2 = 36$
$(x - 3)^2 + (y - 1)^2 = 6^2$
$h = 3,\ k = 1,\ r = 6;$
center = (3, 1)
radius = 6

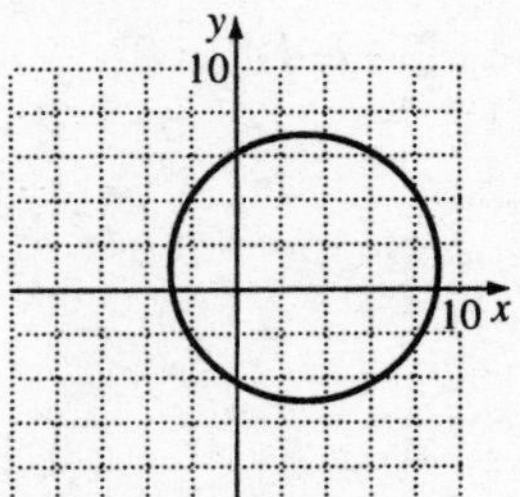

43. $(x + 3)^2 + (y - 2)^2 = 4$
$[x - (-3)]^2 + (y - 2)^2 = 2^2$
$h = -3,\ k = 2,\ r = 2$
center = (–3, 2)
radius = 2

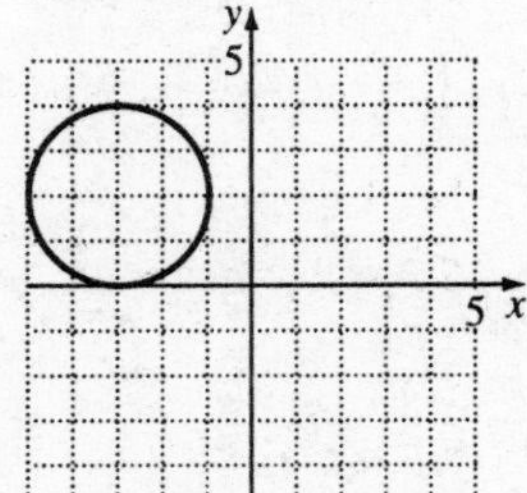

45.

$$(x+2)^2+(y+2)^2=4$$
$$[x-(-2)]^2+[y-(-2)]^2=2^2$$
$$h=-2,\ k=-2,\ r=2$$

center = (–2, –2)
radius = 2

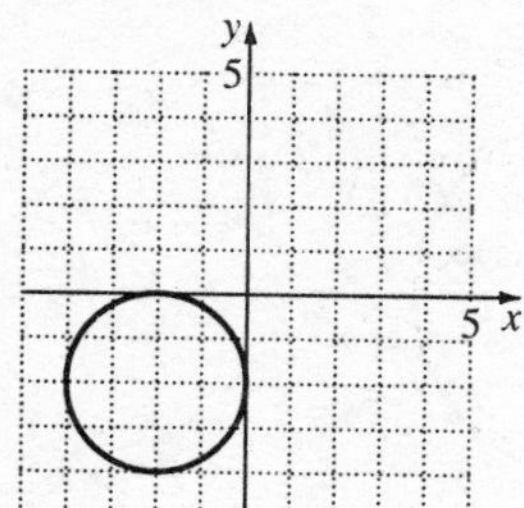

47.

$$x^2+y^2+6x+2y+6=0$$
$$\left(x^2+6x\right)+\left(y^2+2y\right)=-6$$
$$\left(x^2+6x+9\right)+\left(y^2+2y+1\right)=9+1-6$$
$$(x+3)^2+(y+1)^2=4$$
$$[x-(-3)]^2+[9-(-1)]^2=2^2$$

center = (–3, –1)
radius = 2

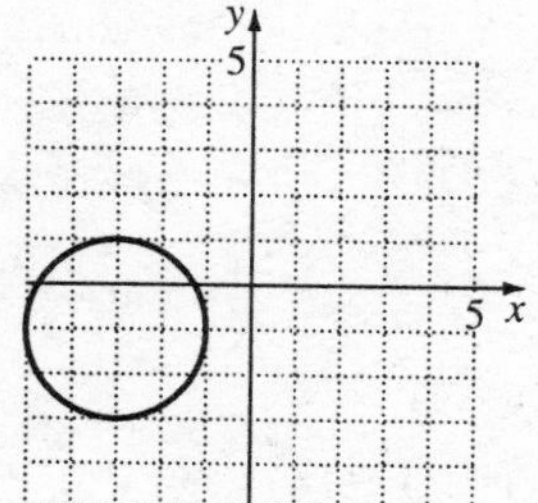

49.

$$x^2+y^2-10x-6y-30=0$$
$$\left(x^2-10x\right)+\left(y^2-6y\right)=30$$
$$\left(x^2-10x+25\right)+\left(y^2-6y+9\right)=25+9+30$$
$$(x-5)^2+(y-3)^2=64$$
$$(x-5)^2+(y-3)^2=8^2$$

center = (5, 3)
radius = 8

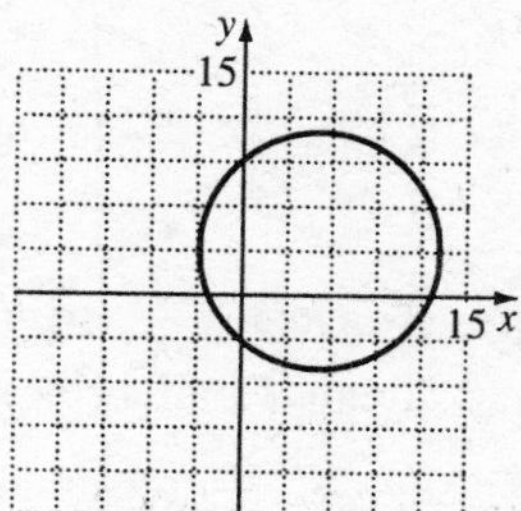

51.

$$x^2+y^2+8x-2y-8=0$$
$$\left(x^2+8x\right)+\left(y^2-2y\right)=8$$
$$\left(x^2+8x+16\right)+\left(y^2-2y+1\right)=16+1+8$$
$$(x+4)^2+(y-1)^2=25$$
$$[x-(-4)]^2+(y-1)^2=5^2$$

center = (–4, 1)
radius = 5

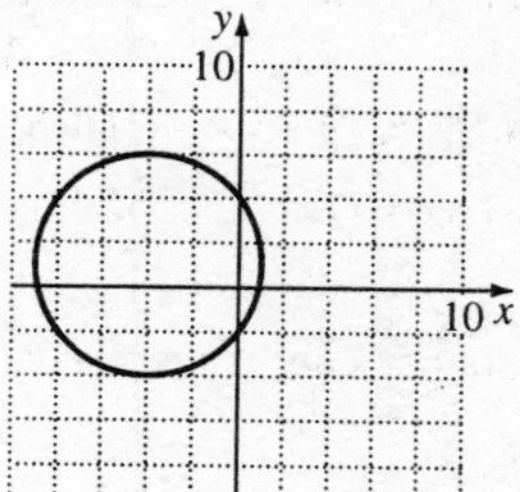

53.

$$x^2-2x+y^2-15=0$$
$$\left(x^2-2x\right)+y^2=15$$
$$\left(x^2-2x+1\right)+(y-0)^2=1+0+15$$
$$(x-1)^2+(y-0)^2=16$$
$$(x-1)^2+(y-0)^2=4^2$$

center = (1, 0)
radius = 4

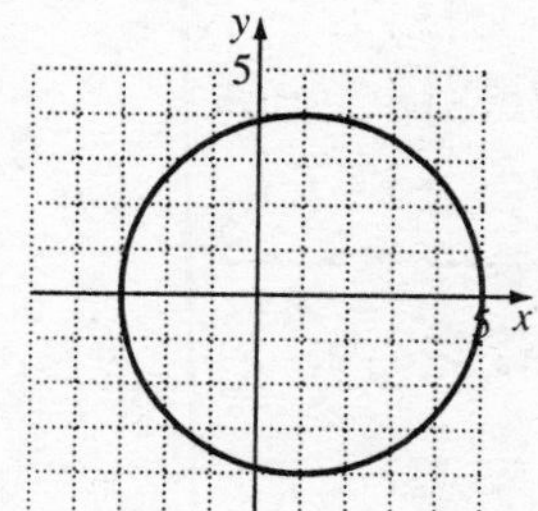

55. a. $m = \dfrac{17-14}{2010-1995} = \dfrac{3}{15} = \dfrac{1}{5}$

b. $m = \dfrac{12-10}{2010-1995} = \dfrac{2}{15}$

c. No, the lines are not parallel since $\dfrac{1}{5} \neq \dfrac{2}{15}$. Since $\dfrac{3}{15} > \dfrac{2}{15}$, the number of women living alone is growing at a faster rate than the number of men living alone, if the projections are correct.

57. a. For the smaller circle, the equation is $(x-0)^2 + (y-0)^2 = 38^2$, or $x^2 + y^2 = 1444$. Thus, the left portion of the inequality can be written as $x^2 + y^2 \geq 1444$.

b. For the larger circle, the equation is $(x-0)^2 + (y-0)^2 = 52^2$, or $x^2 + y^2 = 2704$. Thus, the right portion of the inequailty can be written as $x^2 + y^2 \leq 2704$.

59.–67. Answers may vary.

69.

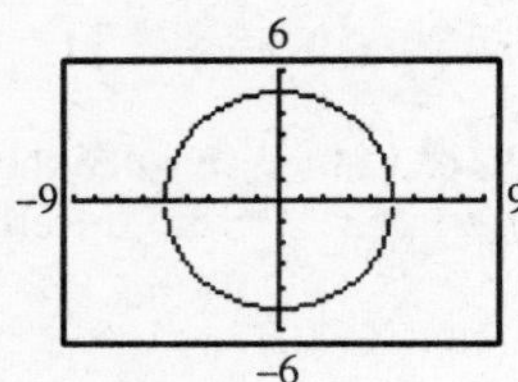

71.

12

–18 18

–12

73. The line passing through (0, 0) and (6, –2) has slope $m = \dfrac{-2-0}{6-0} = \dfrac{-2}{6} = -\dfrac{1}{3}$ and equation $y = -\dfrac{1}{3}x$. The line perpendicular to it has slope 3 and since it passes through (–3, 0), its equation in point-slope form is $y - 0 = 3(x + 3)$ and in slope-intercept form is $y = 3x + 9$.

75. standard form: $(x-3)^2 + (y+5)^2 = r^2$.
Substitute $x = -2$ and $y = 1$:

$$\begin{aligned}(-2-3)^2 + (1+5)^2 &= r^2\\ (-5)^2 + 6^2 &= r^2\\ 25 + 36 &= r^2\\ 61 &= r^2\end{aligned}$$

$$(x-3)^2 + (y+5)^2 = 61$$

general form:

$$\begin{aligned}\left(x^2 - 6x + 9\right) + \left(y^2 + 10y + 25\right) &= 61\\ x^2 + y^2 - 6x + 10y + 34 &= 61\\ x^2 + y^2 - 6x + 10y &= 27\end{aligned}$$

77. Both circles have center (2, –3). The smaller circle has radius 5 and the larger circle has radius 6. The smaller circle is inside of the larger circle. The area between them is given by

$$\begin{aligned}\pi(6)^2 - \pi(5)^2 &= 36\pi - 25\pi\\ &= 11\pi\\ &\approx 34.56 \text{ square units.}\end{aligned}$$

Section 2.3

Check Point Exercises

1. The domain is the set of all first components: {20, 30, 100, 200}. The range is the set of all second components: {157.4, 231.8, 752.6, 1496.6}.

2. a. The relation is not a function since the two ordered pairs (5, 6) and (5, 8) have the same first component but different second components.

b. The relation is a function since two ordered pairs have the same first component and different second components.

3. a. $2x + y = 6$
$y = -2x + 6$
For each value of x, there is one and only one value for y, so the equation defines y as a function of x.

b. $x^2 + y^2 = 1$
$y^2 = 1 - x^2$
$y = \pm\sqrt{1 - x^2}$
Since there are values of x (all values between –1 and 1 exclusive) that give more than one value for y (for example, if $x = 0$, then $y = \pm\sqrt{1 - 0^2} = \pm 1$), the equation does not define y as a function of x.

4. a. $f(-5) = (-5)^2 - 2(-5) + 7$
$= 25 - (-10) + 7$
$= 42$

b. $f(x+4) = (x+4)^2 - 2(x+4) + 7$
$= x^2 + 8x + 16 - 2x - 8 + 7$
$= x^2 + 6x + 15$

c. $f(-x) = (-x)^2 - 2(-x) + 7$
$= x^2 - (-2x) + 7$
$= x^2 + 2x + 7$

5. a. Since $-5 < 0$, we use the first line of the piece wise function:
$f(-5) = (-5)^2 + 3 = 25 + 3 = 28$.

b. Since $6 > 0$, we use the second line of the piece wise function:
$f(6) = 5(6) + 3 = 30 + 3 = 33$.

6. a. The function $f(x) = x^2 + 3x - 17$ contains neither division nor an even root. The domain of f is the set of all real numbers.

b. The denominator equals zero when $x = 7$ or $x = -7$, so we must exclude these values. Thus, the domain of g is $\{x | x \neq -7,\ x \neq 7\}$.

c. Since $h(x) = \sqrt{9x - 27}$ contains an even root, the quantity under the radical must be greater than or equal to 0.
$9x - 27 \geq 0$
$9x \geq 27$
$x \geq 3$
Thus, the domain of h is $\{x | x \geq 3\}$, or the interval $[3, \infty)$.

7. $f(x) = 0.0075x^2 - 0.2672x + 14.8$
$f(50) = 0.0075(50)^2 - 0.2672(50) + 14.8$
$= 20.19$
Since 50 represents the number of years after 1940, this means that in 1990, U.S. automobiles averaged approximately 20.19 miles per gallon of gasoline.

Exercise Set 2.3

1. The relation is a function since no two ordered pairs have the same first component and different second components. The domain is {1, 3, 5} and the range is {2, 4, 5}.

3. The relation is not a function since the two ordered pairs (3, 4) and (3, 5) have the same first component but different second components (the same could be said for the ordered pairs (4, 4) and (4, 5)). The domain is {3, 4} and the range is {4, 5}.

5. The relation is a function since there are no same first components with different second components. The domain is {–3, –2, –1, 0} and the range is {–3, –2, –1, 0}.

7. The relation is not a function since there are ordered pairs with the same first component and different second components. The domain is {1} and the range is {4, 5, 6}.

9. $x + y = 16$
$y = 16 - x$
Since only one value of y can be obtained for each value of x, y is a function of x.

11. $x^2 + y = 16$
$y = 16 - x^2$
Since only one value of y can be obtained for each value of x, y is a function of x.

13. $x^2 + y^2 = 16$
$y^2 = 16 - x^2$
$y = \pm\sqrt{16 - x^2}$
If $x = 0$, $y = \pm 4$.
Since two values, $y = 4$ and $y = -4$, can be obtained for one value of x, y is not a function of x.

15. $x = y^2$
$y = \pm\sqrt{x}$
If $x = 1$, $y = \pm 1$.
Since two values, $y = 1$ and $y = -1$, can be obtained for $x = 1$, y is not a function of x.

17. $y = \sqrt{x+4}$
Since only one value of y can be obtained for each value of x, y is a function of x.

19. $x + y^3 = 8$
$y^3 = 8 - x$
$y = \sqrt[3]{8 - x}$
Since only one value of y can be obtained for each value of x, y is a function of x.

21. **a.** $f(6) = 4(6) + 5 = 29$

b. $f(x + 1) = 4(x + 1) + 5 = 4x + 9$

c. $f(-x) = 4(-x) + 5 = -4x + 5$

23. **a.** $g(-1) = (-1)^2 + 2(-1) + 3$
$= 1 - 2 + 3$
$= 2$

b. $g(x+5) = (x+5)^2 + 2(x+5) + 3$
$= x^2 + 10x + 25 + 2x + 10 + 3$
$= x^2 + 12x + 38$

c. $g(-x) = (-x)^2 + 2(-x) + 3$
$= x^2 - 2x + 3$

25. **a.** $h(2) = 2^4 - 2^2 + 1$
$= 16 - 4 + 1$
$= 13$

b. $h(-1) = (-1)^4 - (-1)^2 + 1$
$= 1 - 1 + 1$
$= 1$

c. $h(-x) = (-x)^4 - (-x)^2 + 1 = x^4 - x^2 + 1$

d. $h(3a) = (3a)^4 - (3a)^2 + 1$
$= 81a^4 - 9a^2 + 1$

27. **a.** $f(-6) = \sqrt{-6+6} + 3 = \sqrt{0} + 3 = 3$

b. $f(10) = \sqrt{10+6} + 3$
$= \sqrt{16} + 3$
$= 4 + 3$
$= 7$

c. $f(x-6) = \sqrt{x-6+6} + 3 = \sqrt{x} + 3$

29. **a.** $f(2) = \dfrac{4(2)^2 - 1}{2^2} = \dfrac{15}{4}$

b. $f(-2) = \dfrac{4(-2)^2 - 1}{(-2)^2} = \dfrac{15}{4}$

c. $f(-x) = \dfrac{4(-x)^2 - 1}{(-x)^2} = \dfrac{4x^2 - 1}{x^2}$

31. **a.** $f(6) = \dfrac{6}{|6|} = 1$

b. $f(-6) = \dfrac{-6}{|-6|} = \dfrac{-6}{6} = -1$

c. $f(r^2) = \dfrac{r^2}{|r^2|} = \dfrac{r^2}{r^2} = 1$

33. a. $f(a) = 4a$

b. $f(a + h) = 4(a + h) = 4a + 4h$

c. $\frac{f(a+h)-f(a)}{h} = \frac{4a+4h-4a}{h}$
$= \frac{4h}{h}$
$= 4, \; h \neq 0$

d. $f(a) + f(h) = 4a + 4h$

35. a. $f(a) = 3a + 7$

b. $f(a + h) = 3(a + h) + 7 = 3a + 3h + 7$

c. $\frac{f(a+h)-f(a)}{h} = \frac{3a+3h+7-(3a+7)}{h}$
$= \frac{3h}{h}$
$= 3, \; h \neq 0$

d. $f(a) + f(h) = 3a + 7 + 3h + 7$
$= 3a + 3h + 14$

37. a. $f(a) = -5a - 3$

b. $f(a + h) = -5(a + h) - 3 = -5a - 5h - 3$

c. $\frac{f(a+h)-f(a)}{h}$
$= \frac{-5a-5h-3-(-5a-3)}{h}$
$= \frac{-5h}{h}$
$= -5, \; h \neq 0$

d. $f(a) + f(h) = (-5a - 3) + (-5h - 3)$
$= -5a - 5h - 6$

39. a. $f(a) = a^2$

b. $f(a+h) = (a+h)^2 = a^2 + 2ah + h^2$

c. $\frac{f(a+h)-f(a)}{h} = \frac{a^2+2ah+h^2-a^2}{h}$
$= \frac{2ah+h^2}{h}$
$= 2a+h, \; h \neq 0$

d. $f(a) + f(h) = a^2 + h^2$

41. a. $f(a) = 6$

b. $f(a + h) = 6$

c. $\frac{f(a+h)-f(a)}{h} = \frac{6-6}{h} = 0, \; h \neq 0$

d. $f(a) + f(h) = 6 + 6 = 12$

43. a. $f(a) = \frac{1}{a}$

b. $f(a+h) = \frac{1}{a+h}$

c. $\frac{f(a+h)-f(a)}{h} = \frac{\frac{1}{a+h}-\frac{1}{a}}{h}$
$= \frac{\frac{a-(a+h)}{a(a+h)}}{h}$
$= \frac{-h}{a(a+h)} \cdot \frac{1}{h}$
$= -\frac{1}{a(a+h)}, \; h \neq 0$

d. $f(a) + f(h) = \frac{1}{a} + \frac{1}{h} = \frac{h+a}{ah}$

45. a. $f(-2) = 3(-2) + 5 = -1$

b. $f(0) = 4(0) + 7 = 7$

c. $f(3) = 4(3) + 7 = 19$

47. a. $g(0) = 0 + 3 = 3$

b. $g(-6) = -(-6 + 3) = -(-3) = 3$

c. $g(-3) = -3 + 3 = 0$

49. **a.** $h(5) = \frac{5^2 - 9}{5 - 3} = \frac{25 - 9}{2} = \frac{16}{2} = 8$

b. $h(0) = \frac{0^2 - 9}{0 - 3} = \frac{-9}{-3} = 3$

c. $h(3) = 6$

51. Since the function is defined and equal to a real number for all real numbers, the domain is $(-\infty, \infty)$.

53. The denominator equals zero when $x = 4$. The domain is $\{x|x \neq 4\}$.

55. Factor the denominator:
$h(x) = \frac{7x}{(x - 4)(x + 4)}$
The denominator equals zero when $x = 4$ or $x = -4$. The domain is $\{x|x \neq -4 \text{ and } x \neq 4\}$.

57. The denominator is zero when $x = -3$ or $x = 7$. The domain is 3 $\{x|x \neq -3 \text{ and } x \neq 7\}$.

59. Factor the denominator.
$H(r) = \frac{4}{(r + 8)(r + 3)}$
The denominator equals zero when $r = -8$ or $r = -3$. The domain is $\{x|x \neq -8 \text{ and } x \neq -3\}$.

61. The denominator is never equal to zero. Since the function is defined and equal to a real number for all real numbers, the domain is $(-\infty, \infty)$.

63. We want $\sqrt{x - 3}$ to equal a real number.
$x - 3 \geq 0$
$x \geq 3$
The domain is $[3, \infty)$.

65. We want $\sqrt{x - 3}$ to equal a positive real number.
$x - 3 > 0$
$x > 3$
The domain is $(3, \infty)$.

67. We want $\sqrt{5x + 35}$ to equal a real number.
$5x + 35 \geq 0$
$5x \geq -35$
$x \geq -7$
The domain is $[-7, \infty)$.

69. We want $\sqrt{24 - 2x}$ to equal a real number.
$24 - 2x \geq 0$
$-2x \geq -24$
$x \leq 12$
The domain is $(-\infty, 12]$.

71. We want $\sqrt{x^2 - 5x - 14}$ to equal a real number.
$x^2 - 5x - 14 \geq 0$
Solve $x^2 - 5x - 14 = 0$
$(x + 2)(x - 7) = 0$
$x = -2$ or $x = 7$
The test intervals are $(-\infty, -2)$, $(-2, 7)$, $(7, \infty)$. Using a representative number from each test interval, the solution is $(-\infty, -2]$ or $[7, \infty)$.

73. Answers may vary.

75. $f(16) = 0.07(16) + 4.1 = 5.22$
There were 5.22 million women enrolled in U.S. colleges in the year 2000.

77. $f(20) - g(20)$
$= (0.07(20) + 4.1) - (0.01(20) + 3.9)$
$= 5.5 - 4.1$
$= 1.4$
There will be 1.4 million more women than men enrolled in U.S. colleges in the year 2004.

79. $f(0) = 6.5(0) + 200 = 200$
There were 200 thousand lawyers in the United States in 1951.

81. $f(50) = 26.2(50) - 252 = 1058$
There will be 1058 thousand or 1,058,000 lawyers in the United States in the year 2001.

83. $f(0) = 1.5(0) + 7 = 7$
$f(2) = 1.5(2) + 7 = 10$
$f(4) = 1.5(4) + 7 = 13$
$f(6) = 1.5(6) + 7 = 16$
$f(0) = 7$ represents the point (0, 7) on the graph. It means that the average infant girl weighs 7 pounds at birth.
$f(2) = 10$ represents the point (2, 10) on the graph. It means that an average infant girl weighs 10 pounds at age 2 months.
$f(4) = 13$ represents the point (4, 13) on the graph. It means that an average infant girl weighs 13 pounds at age 4 months.
$f(6) = 16$ represents the point (6, 16) on the graph. It means that an average infant girl weighs 16 pounds at age 6 months.

85. $f(10) = 0.89(10)^2 - 1.93(10) + 3306.27$
$= 3375.97$
In 1984, 3375.97 calories per person were consumed each day in the United States.

87. $f(15) - f(10) = 3477.57 - 3375.97 = 101.6$
Between 1984 and 1989, the number of calories per person consumed each day in the United States increased by 101.6.

89. **a.** $f(15) = 0.0005(15)^2 + 0.025(15) + 8.8 = 9.3$
In 1955, an average of 10.3 thousand miles were driven per car in the United States each year.

b. $f(50) = 0.0202(50)^2 - 1.58(50) + 39.2 = 10.7$
In 1990, an average of 10.7 thousand miles were driven per car in the United States each year.

91. $V(x) = 17,900 - 2100x$
$V(4) = 17,900 - 2100(4) = 9500$
The value of the car after 4 years is $9500.

93.–97. Answers may vary.

99.

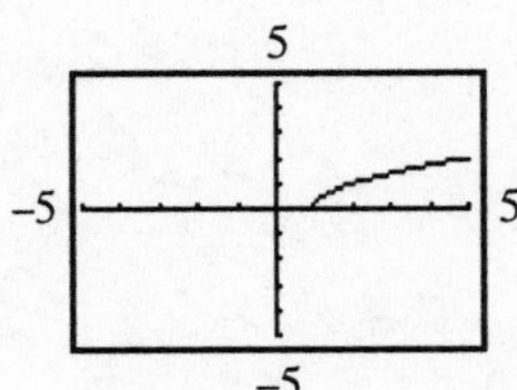

The domain is $[1, \infty)$. Algebraically, $\sqrt{x-1}$ must equal a real number.
$x - 1 \geq 0$
$x \geq 1$

101. 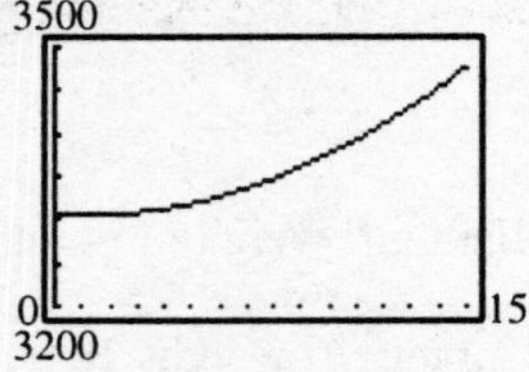

The domain is $(-\infty, 5]$. Algebraically, $\sqrt{15-3x}$ must equal a real number.

$15-3x \geq 0$
$-3x \geq -15$
$x \leq 5$

103. Answers may vary.

105. Answers may vary.

Section 2.4

Check Point Exercises

1.

x	$f(x)=x^2-2$	(x, y) or $(x, f(x))$
-3	$f(-3)=(-3)^2-2=7$	$(-3, 7)$
-2	$f(-2)=(-2)^2-2=2$	$(-2, 2)$
-1	$f(-1)=(-1)^2-2=-1$	$(-1, -1)$
0	$f(0)=0^2-2=-2$	$(0, -2)$
1	$f(1)=1^2-2=-1$	$(1, -1)$
2	$f(2)=2^2-2=2$	$(2, 2)$
3	$f(3)=3^2-2=7$	$(3, 7)$

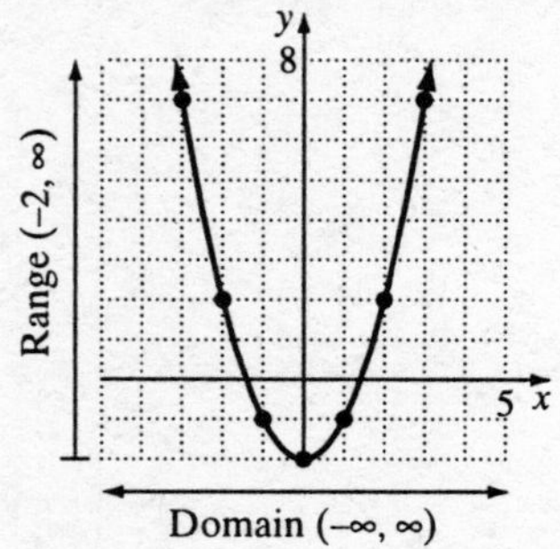

2. $f(4)=1$
domain: $[0, 6)$
range: $(-2, 2]$

3. y is a function of x for the graphs in (a) and (b).

4. The function is increasing on the interval $(-\infty, -1)$, decreasing on the interval $(-1, 1)$, and increasing on the interval $(1, \infty)$.

5. a. $f(-x) = (-x)^2 + 6 = x^2 + 6 = f(x)$
The function is even.

b. $g(-x) = 7(-x)^3 - (-x) = -7x^3 + x = -f(x)$
The function is odd.

c. $h(-x) = (-x)^5 + 1 = -x^5 + 1$
The function is neither even nor odd.

6. a. f is increasing on the interval (0, 3). The concentration of the drug in the body increases during the first three hours after an injection.

b. f is decreasing on the interval (3, 13). The concentration of the drug in the body decreases between the third and thirteenth hours after injection.

c. The drug's maximum concentration is 0.05 milligrams per 100 milliliters at 3 hours after the injection.

d. By the end of the 13 hours, there is no more of the drug in the body.

Exercise Set 2.4

1. (–3, 11), (–2, 6), (–1, 3), (0, 2), (1, 3), (2, 6), (3, 11)

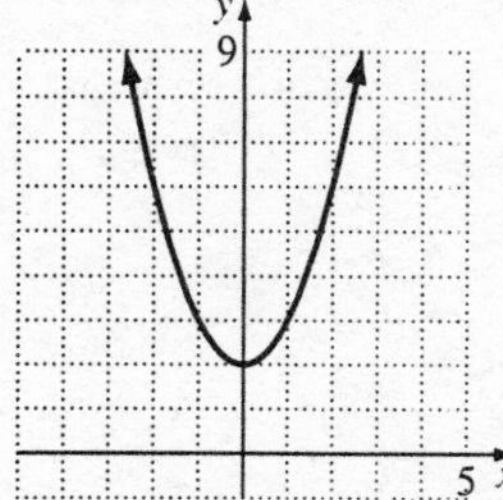

domain: $(-\infty, \infty)$
range: $[2, \infty)$

3. (0, –1), (1, 0), (4, 1), (9, 2)

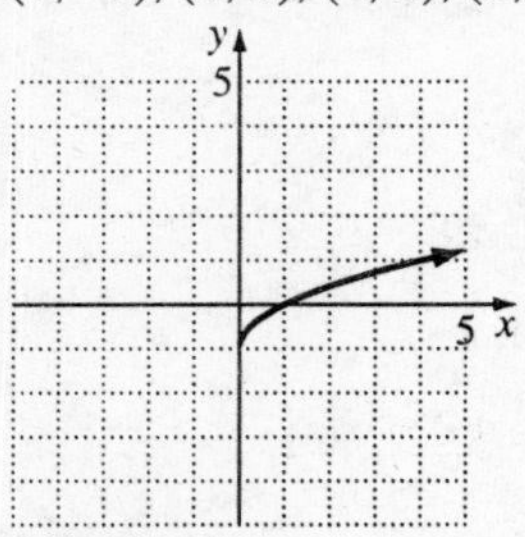

domain: [0, ∞)
range: [–1, ∞)

5. (1, 0), (2, 1), (5, 2), (10, 3)

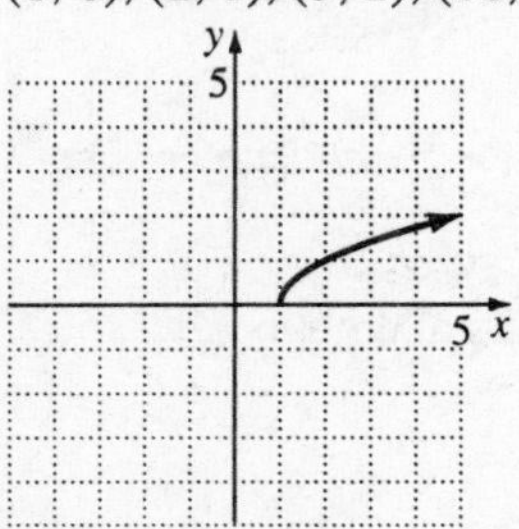

domain: [1, ∞)
range: [0, ∞)

7. (–3, 2), (–2, 1), (–1, 0), (0, –1), (1, 0), (2, 1), (3, 2)

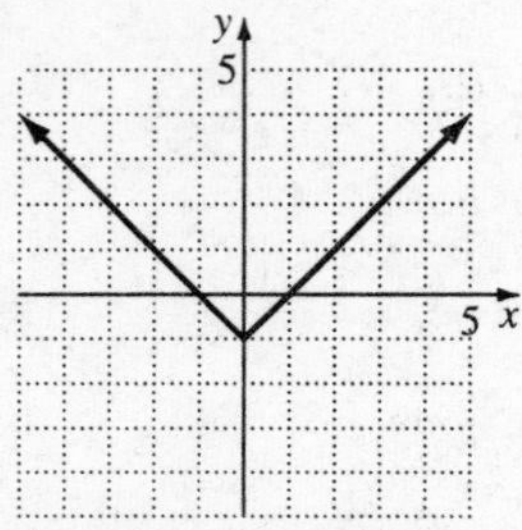

domain: (–∞, ∞)
range: [–1, ∞)

9. (–3, 4), (–2, 3), (–1, 2), (0, 1), (1, 0), (2, 1), (3, 2)

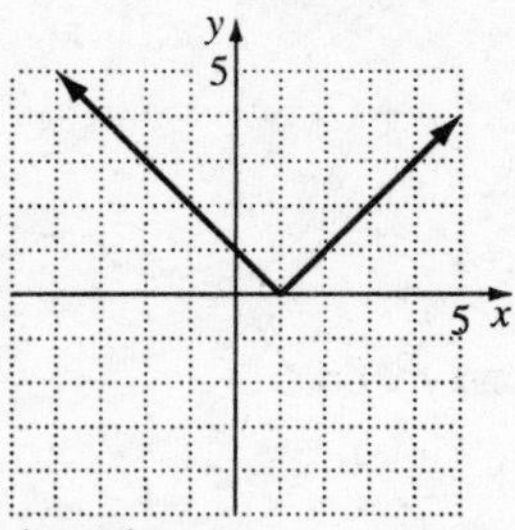

domain: (–∞, ∞)
range: [0, ∞)

11. (–3, 5), (–2, 5), (–1, 5), (0, 5), (1, 5), (2, 5), (3, 5)

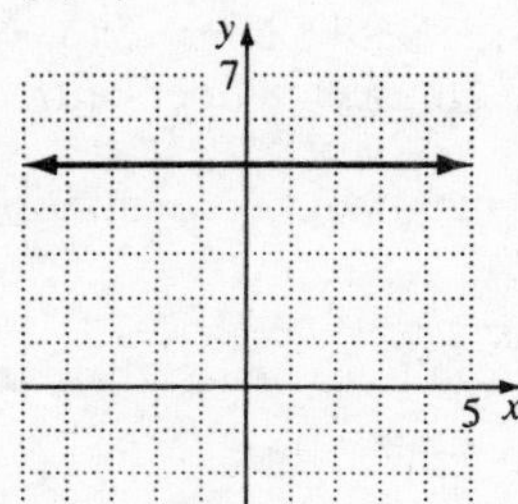

domain: (–∞, ∞)
range: {5}

13. (–2, –10), (–1, –3), (0, –2), (1, –1), (2, 6)

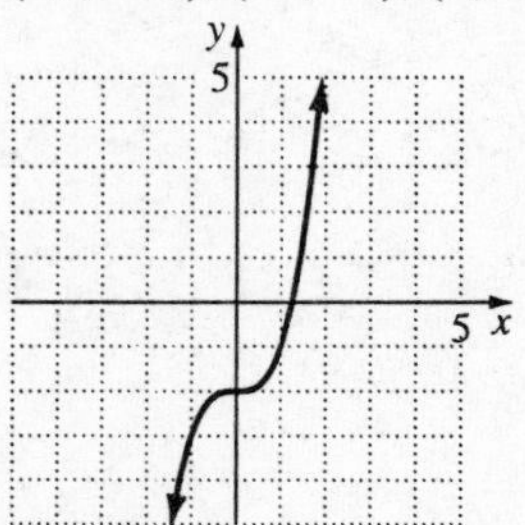

domain: (–∞, ∞)
range: (–∞, ∞)

15. **a.** domain: (–∞, ∞)

b. range: [–4, ∞)

c. x-intercepts: –3 and 1

d. y-intercept: –3

17. a. domain: $(-\infty, \infty)$

b. range: $[1, \infty)$

c. x-intercept: none

d. y-intercept: 1

e. $f(-1) = 2$ and $f(3) = 4$

19. a. domain: $[0, 5)$

b. range: $[-1, 5)$

c. x-intercept: 2

d. y-intercept: -1

e. $f(3) = 1$

21. a. domain: $[0, \infty)$

b. range: $[1, \infty)$

c. x-intercept: none

d. y-intercept: 1

e. $f(4) = 3$

23. a. domain: $[-2, 6]$

b. range: $[-2, 6]$

c. x-intercept: 4

d. y-intercept: 4

e. $f(-1) = 5$

25. a. domain: $(-\infty, \infty)$

b. range: $(-\infty, -2]$

c. x-intercept: none

d. y-intercept: -2

e. $f(-4) = -5$ and $f(4) = -2$

27. a. domain: $(-\infty, \infty)$

b. range: $(0, \infty)$

c. x-intercept: none

d. y-intercept: 1

29. a. domain: $\{-5, -2, 0, 1, 3\}$

b. range: $\{2\}$

c. x-intercept: none

d. y-intercept: 2

31. function

33. function

35. not a function

37. function

39. a. increasing: $(-1, \infty)$

b. decreasing: $(-\infty, -1)$

c. constant: none

41. a. increasing: $(0, \infty)$

b. decreasing: none

c. constant: none

43. a. increasing: none

b. decreasing: $(-2, 6)$

c. constant: none

45. a. increasing: $(-\infty, -1)$

b. decreasing: none

c. constant: $(-1, \infty)$

47. **a.** increasing: $(-\infty, 0)$ or $(1.5, 3)$

b. decreasing: $(0, 1.5)$ or $(3, \infty)$

c. constant: none

49. **a.** increasing: $(-2, 4)$

b. decreasing: none

c. constant: $(-\infty, -2)$ or $(4, \infty)$

51. $f(x) = x^3 + x$
$f(-x) = (-x)^3 + (-x)$
$f(-x) = -x^3 - x = -(x^3 + x)$
$f(-x) = -f(x)$, odd function

53. $g(x) = x^2 + x$
$g(-x) = (-x)^2 + (-x)$
$g(-x) = x^2 - x$, neither

55. $h(x) = x^2 - x^4$
$h(-x) = (-x)^2 - (-x)^4$
$h(-x) = x^2 - x^4$
$h(-x) = h(x)$, even function

57. $f(x) = x^2 - x^4 + 1$
$f(-x) = (-x)^2 - (-x)^4 + 1$
$f(-x) = x^2 - x^4 + 1$
$f(-x) = f(x)$, even function

59. $f(x) = \frac{1}{5}x^6 - 3x^2$
$f(-x) = \frac{1}{5}(-x)^6 - 3(-x)^2$
$f(-x) = \frac{1}{5}x^6 - 3x^2$
$f(-x) = f(x)$, even function

61. $f(x) = x\sqrt{1-x^2}$
$f(-x) = -x\sqrt{1-(-x)^2}$
$f(-x) = -x\sqrt{1-x^2}$
$= -\left(x\sqrt{1-x^2}\right)$
$f(-x) = -f(x)$, odd function

63. The graph is symmetric with respect to the y-axis. The function is even.

65. The graph is symmetric with respect to the origin. The function is odd.

67. identity function

69. square root function

71. standard cubic function

73. $f(1.06) = 1$

75. $f\left(\frac{1}{3}\right) = 0$

77. $f(-2.3) = -3$

79. $f(1989) \approx 294$ billion dollars. This is the maximum function value.

81. Defense spending is increasing from 1988 to 1989, from 1991 to 1992 and from 1996 to 1997.

83. **a.** Increasing: $(45, 74)$
Decreasing: $(16, 45)$
The number of accidents occurring per 50 million miles driven increases with age starting at age 45, while it decreases with age starting at age 16.

b. $x = 45$ and $f(45) = 190$
The fewest number of accidents per 50 million miles driven occurs at age 45.

c. $f(16) = f(74) = 526.4$ so the range is $[190, 526.4]$.
Between the ages of 16 and 74, the number of accidents per 50 million miles driven is between 190 and 526.4.

85.

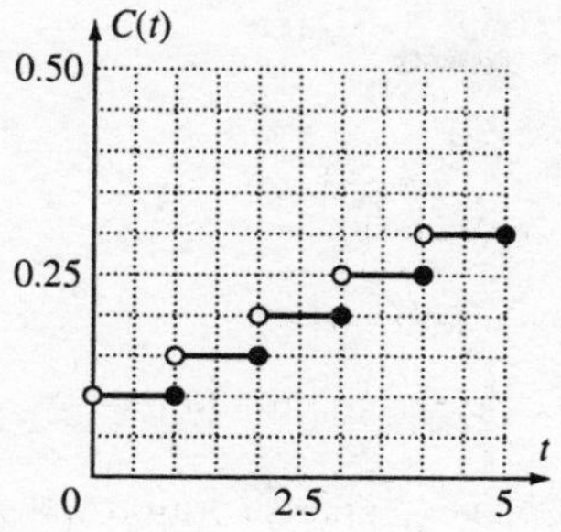

87.–95. Answers may vary.

97.

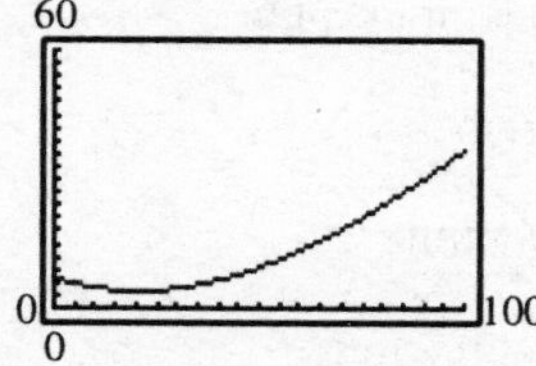

b. The number of doctor visits decreases during childhood and then increases as you get older.

c. The minimum is (20.29, 3.99), which means that the minimum number of doctor visits, about 4, occurs at around age 20.

99.

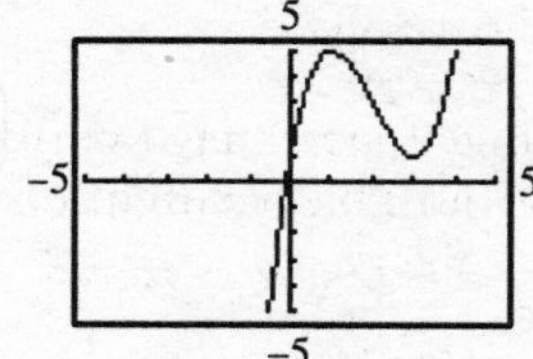

Increasing: $(-\infty,\ 1)$ or $(3,\ \infty)$
Decreasing: $(1, 3)$

101.

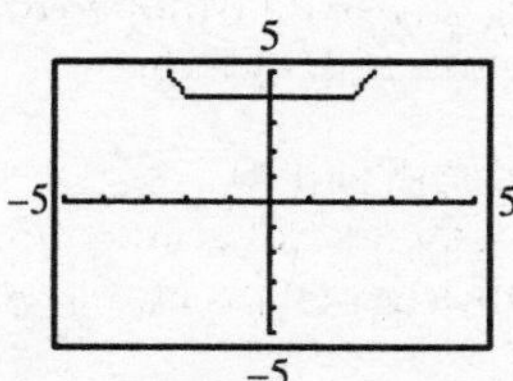

Increasing: $(2,\ \infty)$
Decreasing: $(-\infty,\ -2)$
Constant: $(-2, 2)$

103.

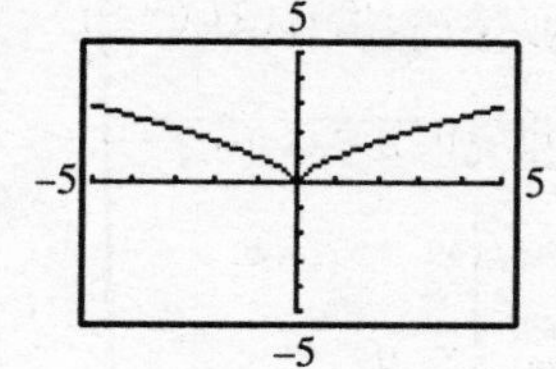

Increasing: $(0,\ \infty)$
Decreasing: $(-\infty,\ 0)$

105. a.

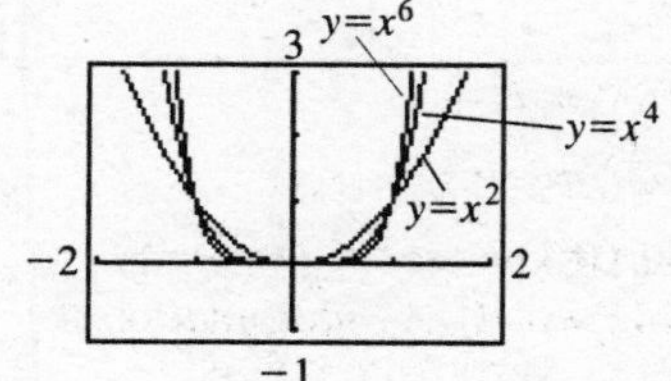

b.

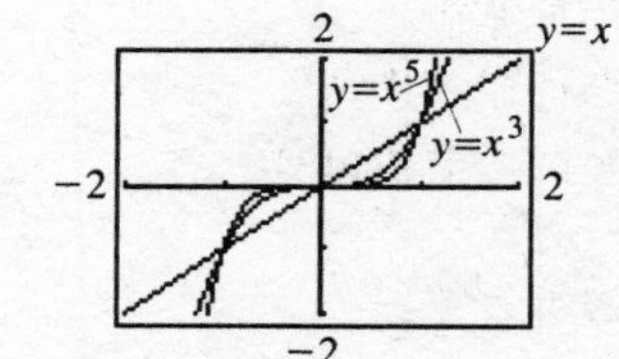

c. Increasing: $(0, \infty)$
Decreasing: $(-\infty, 0)$

d. $f(x) = x^n$ is increasing from $(-\infty, \infty)$ when n is odd.

e.

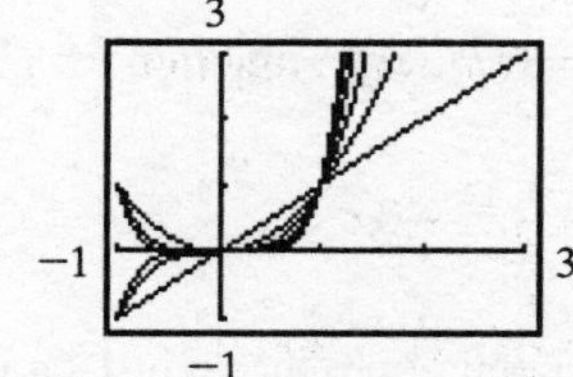

As n increases the steepness increases.

107. Answers may vary.

109. Answers may vary.

111.

Weight at least	Cost
0 oz.	\$0.33
1	0.55
2	0.77
3	0.99
4	1.21

Section 2.5

Check Point Exercises

1. Shift up vertically 3 units.

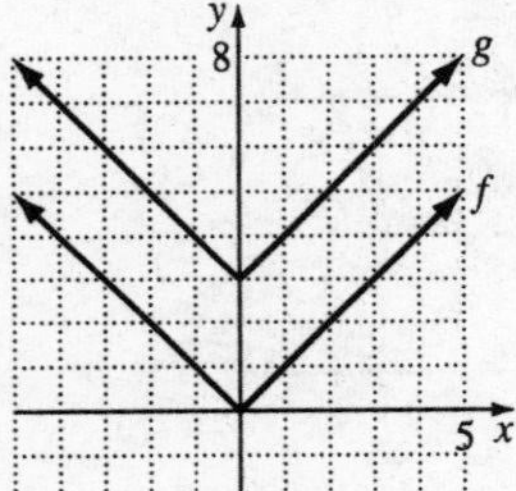

2. Shift horizontally to the right 4 units.

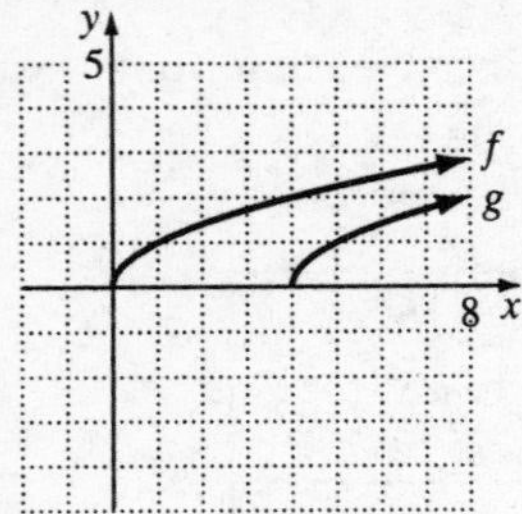

3. Shift horizontally to the right 1 unit and vertically down 2 units.

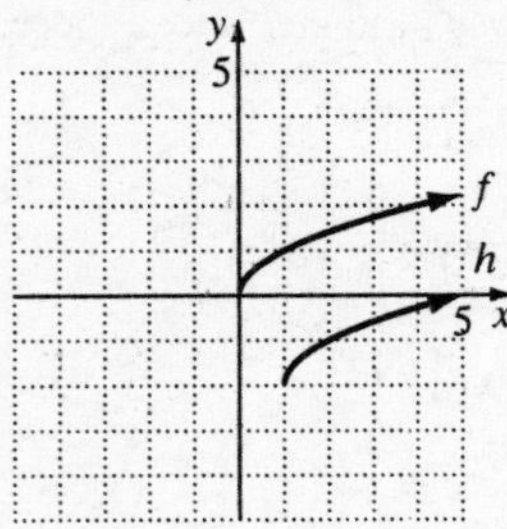

4. Reflect about the x-axis.

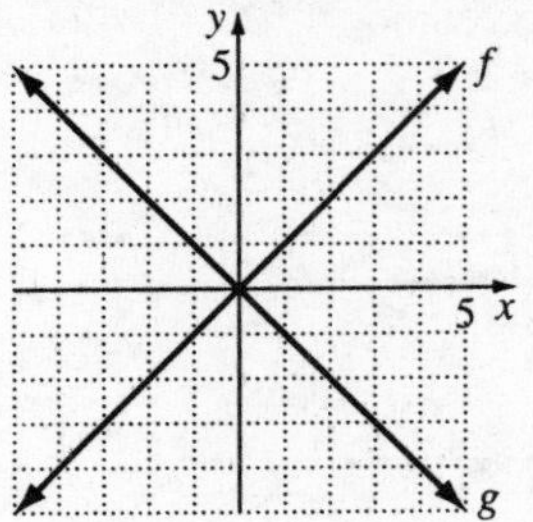

5. Reflect about the y-axis.

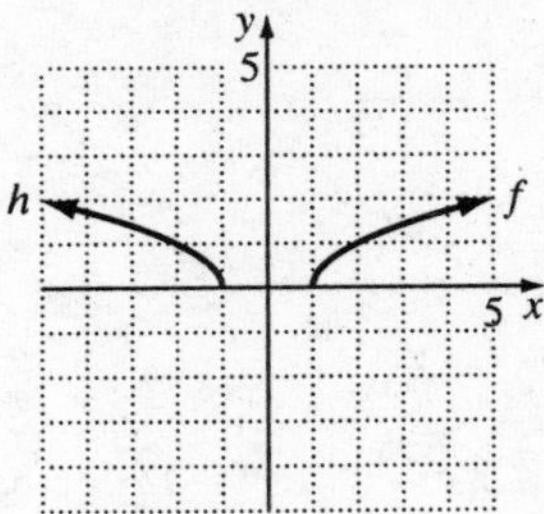

6. Vertically stretch the graph.

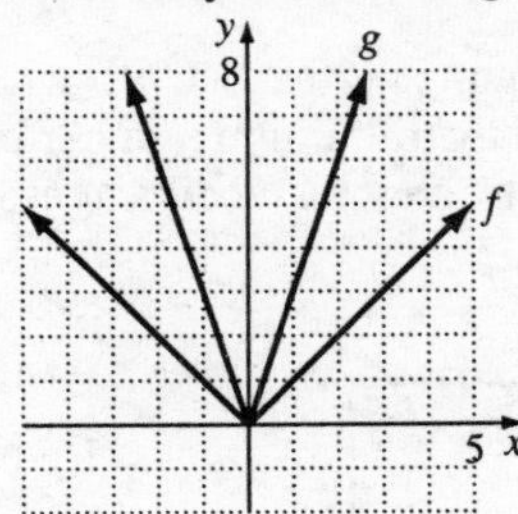

7. Vertically shrink the graph.

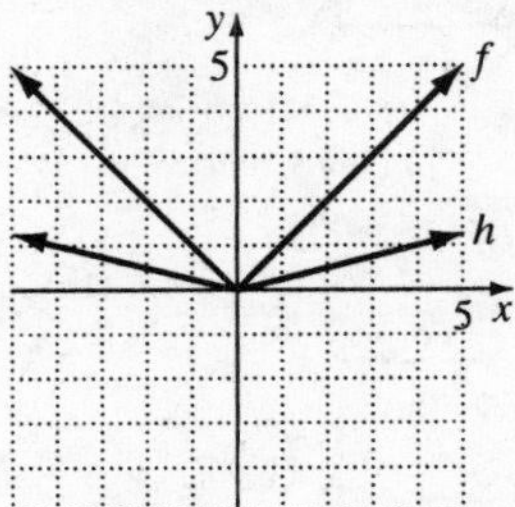

8. Shift horizontally to the right 2 units, reflect across the x-axis, and shift vertically up 3 units.

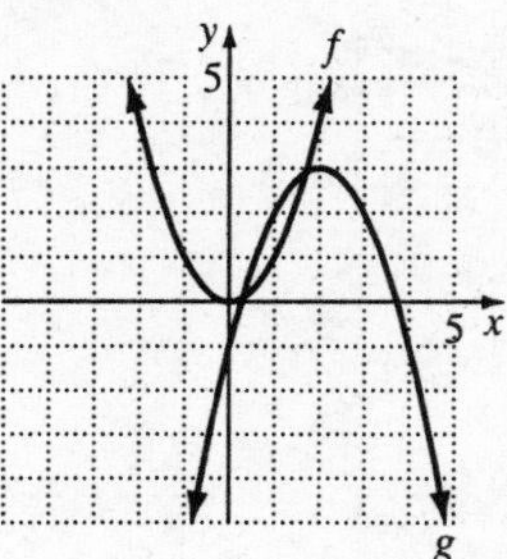

9. a. $(f+g)(x) = f(x)+g(x)$
$= 3x^2+4x-1+2x+7$
$(f+g)(x) = 3x^2+6x+6$

b. $(f+g)(4) = 3(4)^2+6(4)+6 = 78$

10. a. $(f+g)(x) = f(x)+g(x)$
$= \sqrt{x-3}+\sqrt{x+1}$

b. Domain of f:
$x-3 \ge 0$
$x \ge 3$
$[3, \infty)$
Domain of g:
$x+1 \ge 0$
$x \ge -1$
$[-1, \infty)$
The domain of $f+g$ is the set of all real numbers that are common to the domain of f and the domain of g. Thus, the domain of $f+g$ is $[3, \infty)$.

11. a. $(f-g)(x) = f(x)-g(x)$
$= x-5-(x^2-1)$
$= x-5-x^2-1$
$= -x^2+x-4$

b. $(fg)(x) = (x-5)(x^2-1)$
$= x(x^2-1)-5(x^2-1)$
$= x^3-x-5x^2+5$
$= x^3-5x^2-x+5$

c. $\left(\frac{f}{g}\right)(x) = \frac{f(x)}{g(x)}$
$= \frac{x-5}{x^2-1},\ x \ne \pm 1$

Exercise Set 2.5

1.

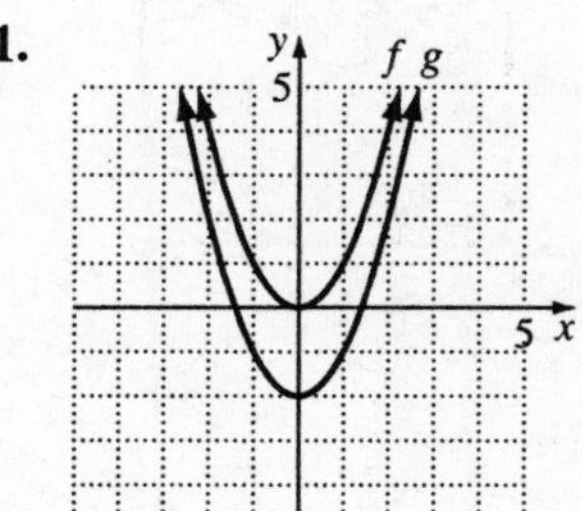

3.

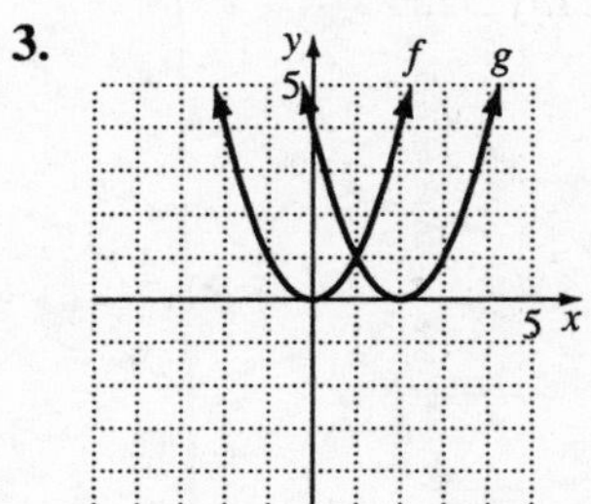

5.

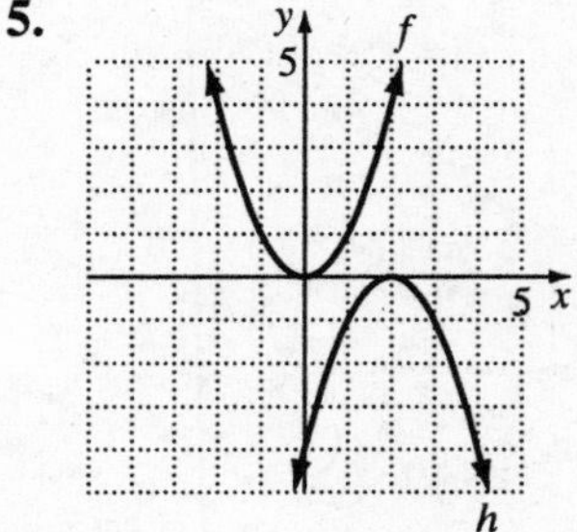

7.

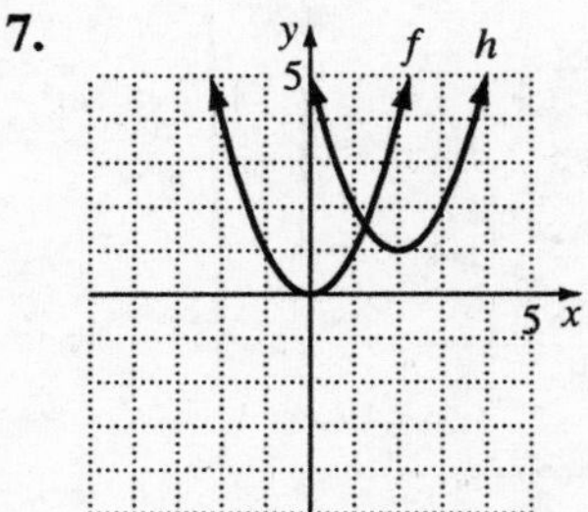

9.

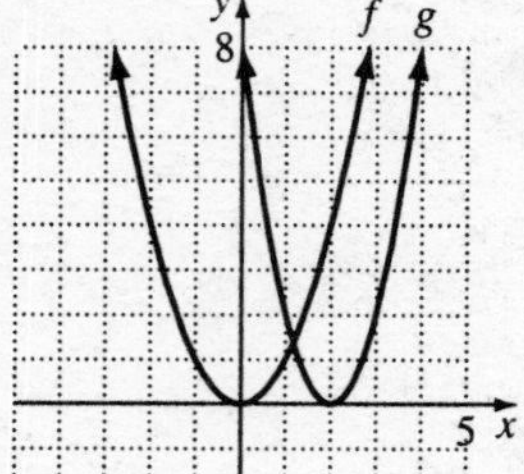

11.

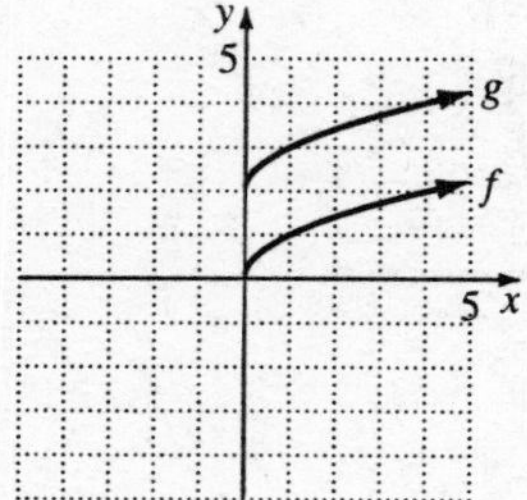

13.

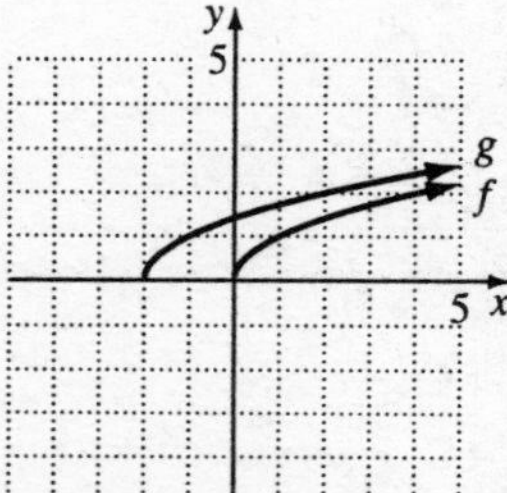

15.

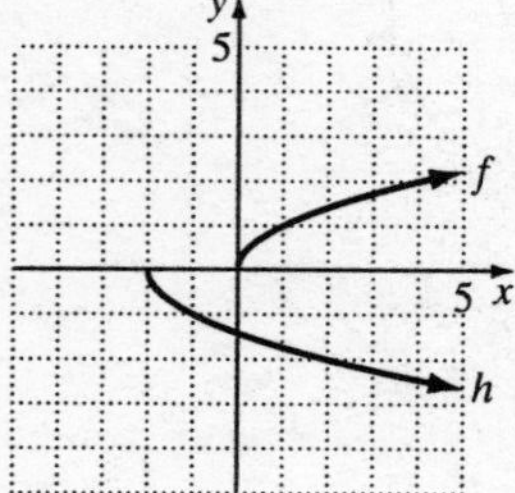

17.

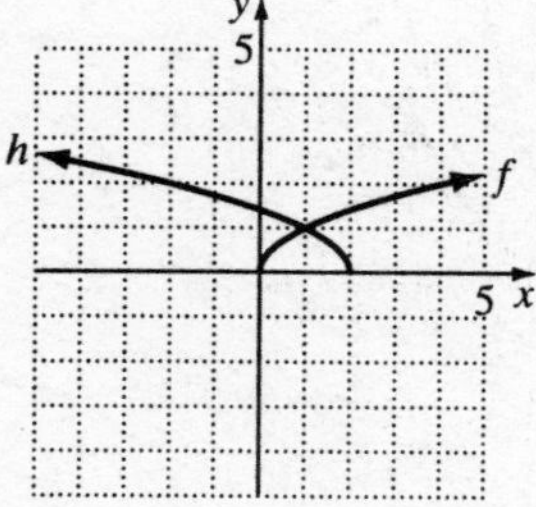

19.

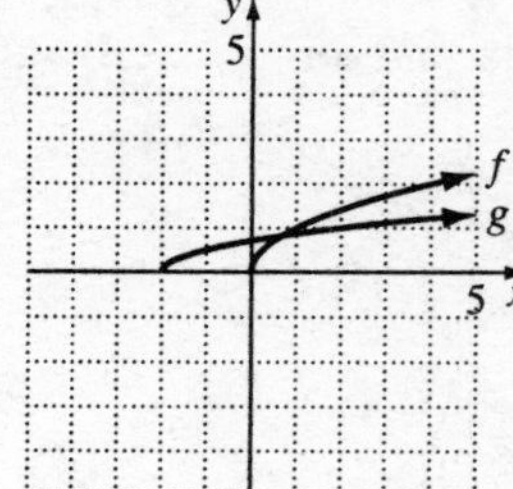

21.

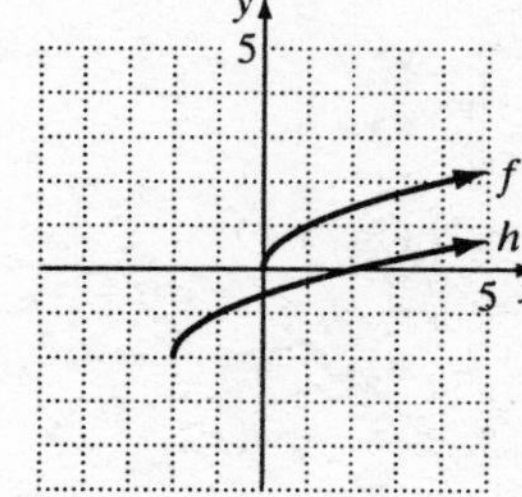

23.

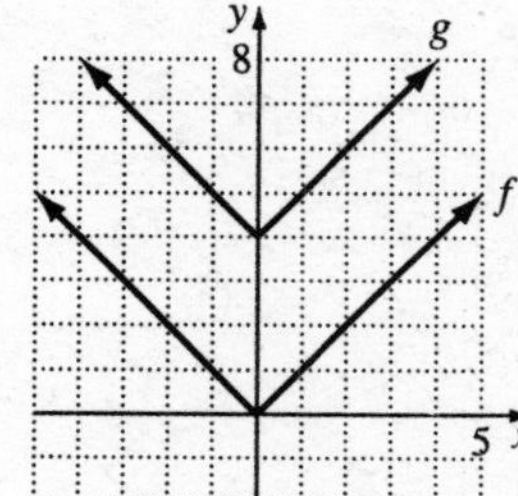

25.

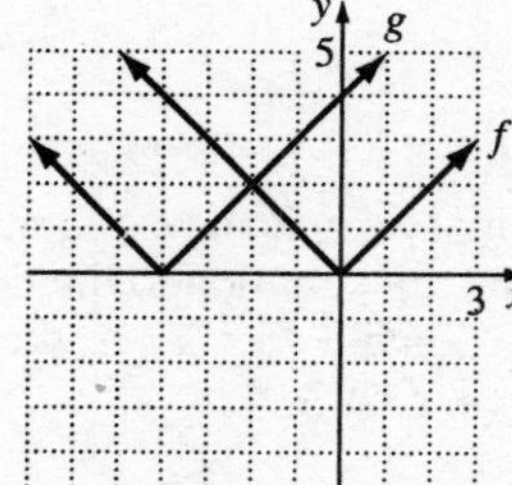

27.

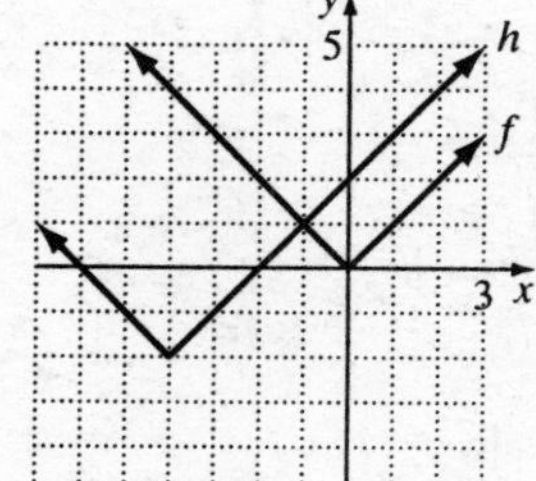

29.

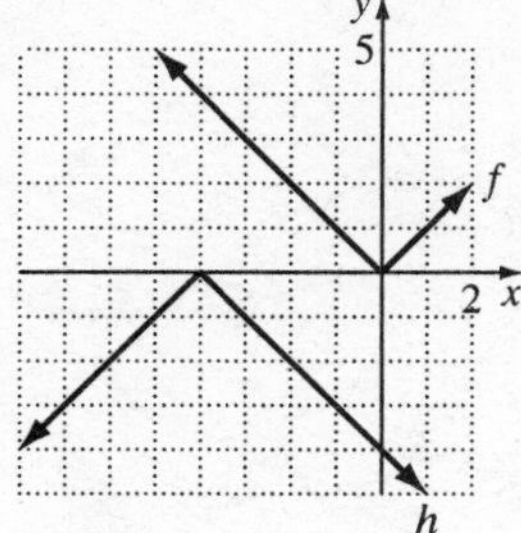

31.

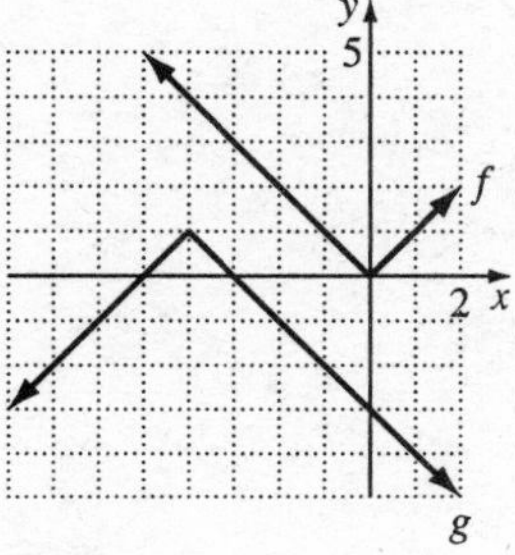

33.

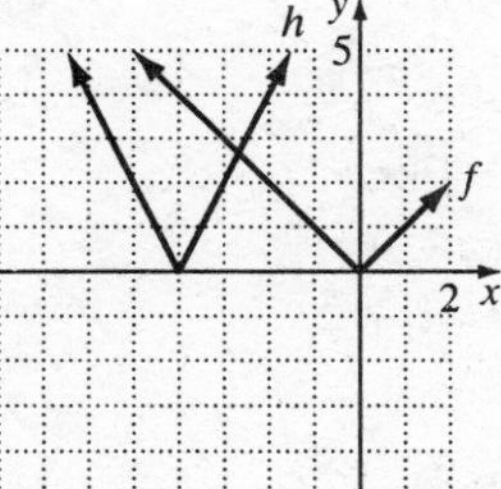

35.

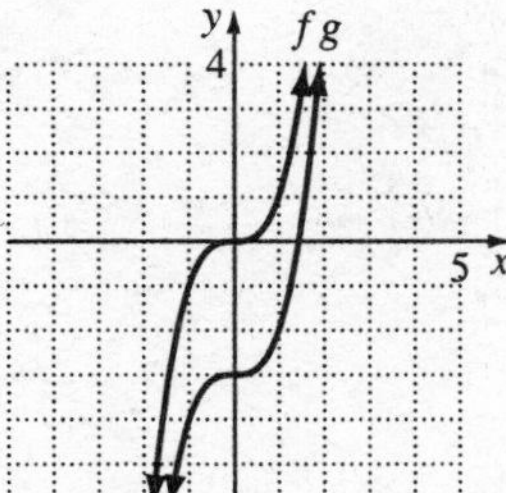

37.

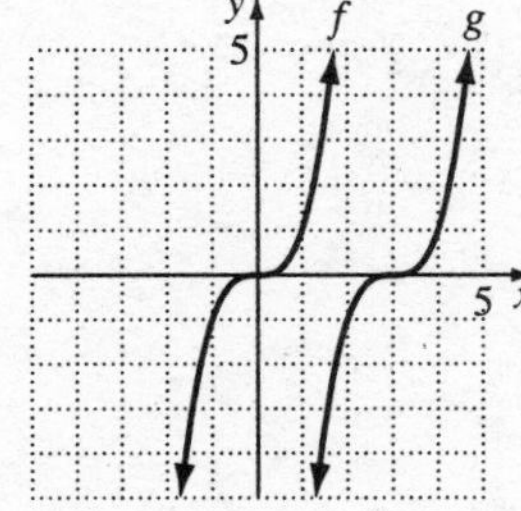

39.

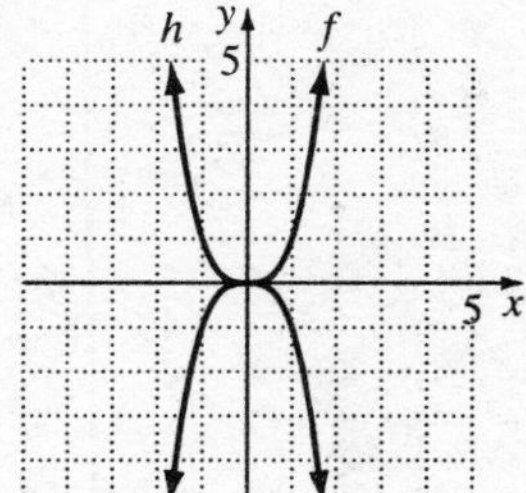

41.

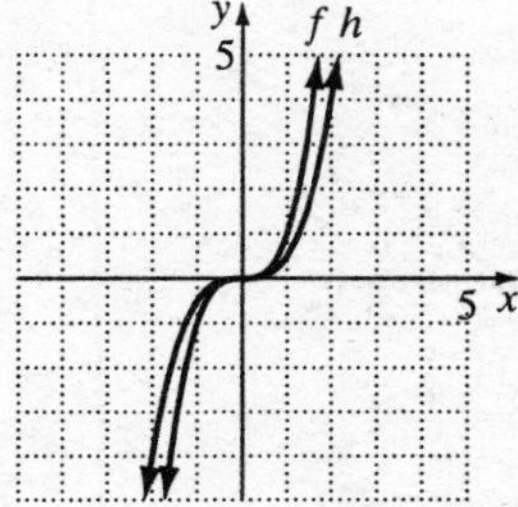

43.

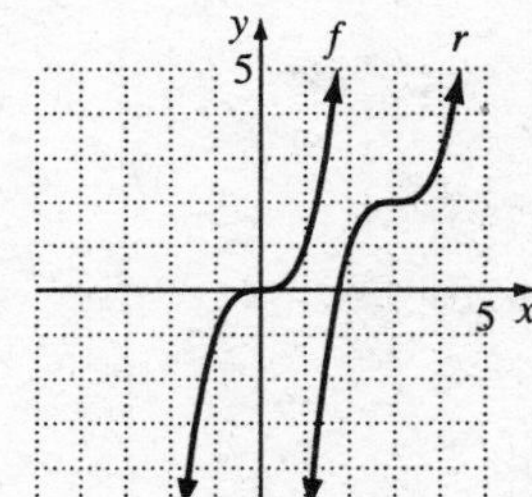

45.

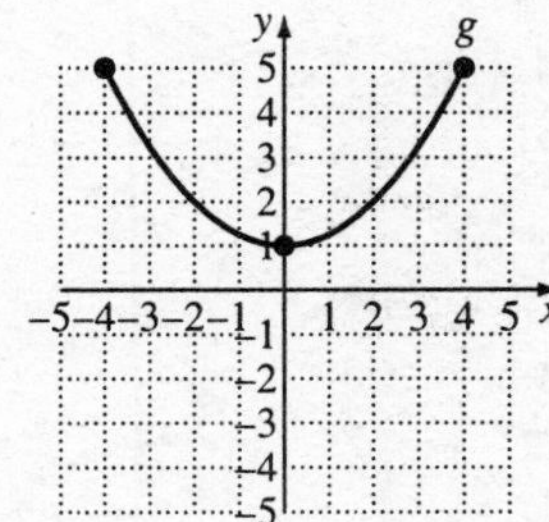

47.

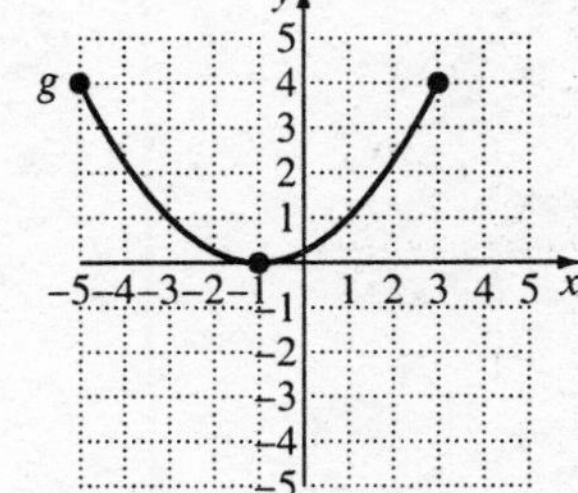

49.

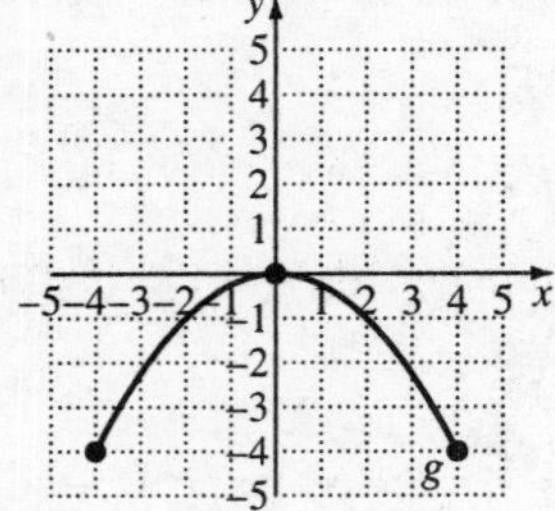

51.

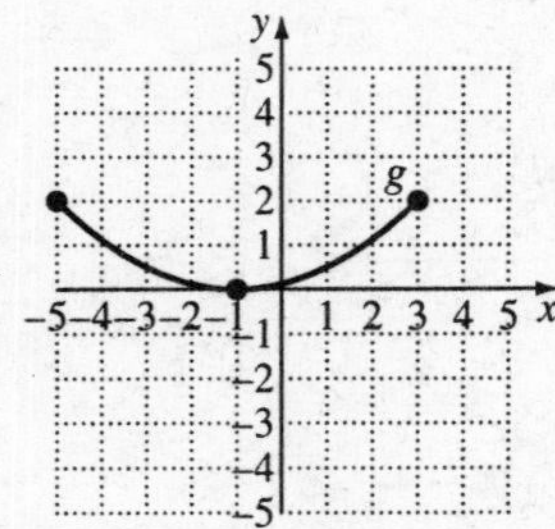

53. a. $(f+g)(x) = 2x^2 + 3x + 2$

b. $(f+g)(4) = 2(4)^2 + 3(4) + 2$
$= 32 + 12 + 2$
$= 46$

55. a. $(f+g)(x) = \sqrt{x-6} + \sqrt{x+2}$

b. Domain: $[6, \infty)$.

57. $(f+g)(x) = 3x + 2$
Domain: $(-\infty, \infty)$
$(f-g)(x) = f(x) - g(x)$
$= (2x+3) - (x-1)$
$= x + 4$
Domain: $(-\infty, \infty)$
$(fg)(x) = f(x) \cdot g(x)$
$= (2x+3) \cdot (x-1)$
$= 2x^2 + x - 3$
Domain: $(-\infty, \infty)$
$\left(\frac{f}{g}\right)(x) = \frac{f(x)}{g(x)} = \frac{2x+3}{x-1}$
Domain: $\{x | x \neq 1\}$

59. $(f+g)(x) = 3x^2 + x - 5$
Domain: $(-\infty, \infty)$
$(f-g)(x) = -3x^2 + x - 5$
Domain: $(-\infty, \infty)$
$(fg)(x) = (x-5)(3x^2) = 3x^3 - 15x^2$
Domain: $(-\infty, \infty)$
$\left(\frac{f}{g}\right)(x) = \frac{x-5}{3x^2}$
Domain: $\{x | x \neq 0\}$

61. $(f+g)(x) = 2x^2 - 2$
Domain: $(-\infty, \infty)$
$(f-g)(x) = 2x^2 - 2x - 4$
Domain: $(-\infty, \infty)$
$(fg)(x) = (2x^2 - x - 3)(x+1)$
$= 2x^3 + x^2 - 4x - 3$
Domain: $(-\infty, \infty)$
$\left(\frac{f}{g}\right)(x) = \frac{2x^2 - x - 3}{x+1}$
$= \frac{(2x-3)(x+1)}{(x+1)} = 2x - 3$
Domain: $\{x | x \neq -1\}$

63. $(f+g)(x) = \sqrt{x} + x - 4$
Domain: $[0, \infty)$
$(f-g)(x) = \sqrt{x} - x + 4$
Domain: $[0, \infty)$
$(fg)(x) = \sqrt{x}(x-4)$
Domain: $[0, \infty)$
$\left(\frac{f}{g}\right)(x) = \frac{\sqrt{x}}{x-4}$
Domain: $\{x | x \geq 0 \text{ and } x \neq 4\}$

65. $(f+g)(x) = 2 + \frac{1}{x} + \frac{1}{x} = 2 + \frac{2}{x} = \frac{2x+2}{x}$

Domain: $\{x | x \neq 0\}$

$(f-g)(x) = 2 + \frac{1}{x} - \frac{1}{x} = 2$

Domain: $\{x | x \neq 0\}$

$(fg)(x) = \left(2 + \frac{1}{x}\right) \cdot \frac{1}{x} = \frac{2}{x} + \frac{1}{x^2} = \frac{2x+1}{x^2}$

Domain: $\{x | x \neq 0\}$

$\left(\frac{f}{g}\right)(x) = \frac{2+\frac{1}{x}}{\frac{1}{x}} = \left(2 + \frac{1}{x}\right) \cdot x = 2x+1$

Domain: $\{x | x \neq 0\}$

67. $(f+g)(x) = \sqrt{x+4} + \sqrt{x-1}$

Domain: $[1, \infty)$

$(f-g)(x) = \sqrt{x+4} - \sqrt{x-1}$

Domain: $[1, \infty)$

$(fg)(x) = \sqrt{x+4} \cdot \sqrt{x-1} = \sqrt{x^2+3x-4}$

Domain: $[1, \infty)$

$\left(\frac{f}{g}\right)(x) = \frac{\sqrt{x+4}}{\sqrt{x-1}}$

Domain: $(1, \infty)$

69. $f + g$ represents the total world population in year x.

71. $f(2000) \approx 1.5$ billion people
$g(2000) \approx 6$ billion people
$(f+g)(2000) = f(2000) + g(2000)$
$\approx 1.5 + 6.0$
$= 7.5$ billion people.

73. $(R-C)(20,000)$
$= 65(20,000) - (600,000 + 45(20,000))$
$= -200,000$
The company lost \$200,000 since costs exceeded revenues.
$(R-C)(30,000)$
$= 65(30,000) - (600,000 + 45(30,000))$
$= 0$
The company broke even since revenues equaled cost.
$(R-C)(40,000)$
$= 65(40,000) - (600,000 + 45(40,000))$
$= 200,000$
The company made a profit of \$200,000.

75.

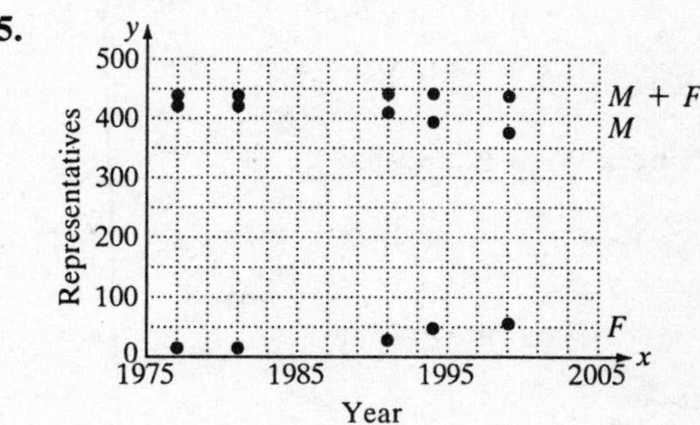

$f(x) = 435$
There is a total of 435 members of the House of Representatives.

77.–83. Answers may vary.

85. a.

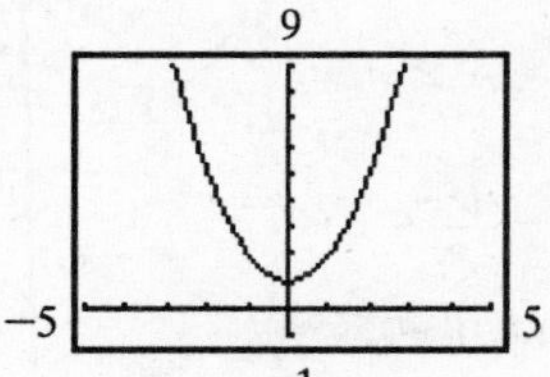

b.

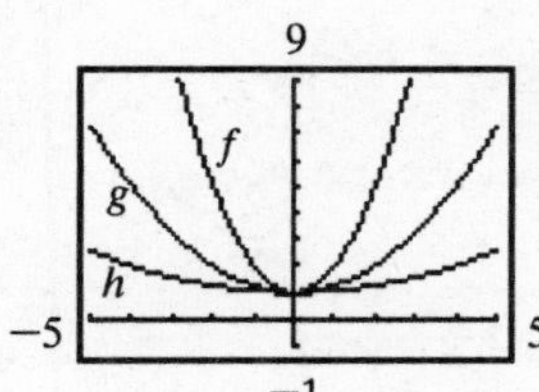

c. Answers may vary.

d. Answers may vary.

e. Answers may vary.

87. $g(x) = -(x+4)^2$

89. $g(x) = -\sqrt{x-2}+2$

91. $(-a, b)$

93. $(a+3, b)$

Section 2.6

Check Point Exercises

1. a. $(f \circ g)(x) = f(g(x)) = 5g(x)+6$
$= 5(x^2-1)+6$
$= 5x^2-5+6$
$= 5x^2+1$

b. $(g \circ f)(x) = g(f(x)) = (f(x))^2-1$
$= (5x+6)^2-1$
$= 25x^2+60x+36-1$
$= 25x^2+60x+35$

2. $f(g(x)) = 7g(x) = 7\left(\frac{x}{7}\right) = x$

$g(f(x)) = \frac{f(x)}{7} = \frac{7x}{7} = x$

f and g are inverses.

3. $f(g(x)) = 4g(x)-7$
$= 4\left(\frac{x+7}{4}\right)-7$
$= x+7-7$
$= x$

$g(f(x)) = \frac{f(x)+7}{4}$
$= \frac{4x-7+7}{4}$
$= \frac{4x}{4}$
$= x$

f and g are inverses.

4. $f(x) = 2x+7$
$y = 2x+7$
$x = 2y+7$
$x-7 = 2y$
$\frac{x-7}{2} = y$
$f^{-1}(x) = \frac{x-7}{2}$

5. $f(x) = 4x^3-1$
$y = 4x^3-1$
$x = 4y^3-1$
$x+1 = 4y^3$
$\frac{x+1}{4} = y^3$
$\sqrt[3]{\frac{x+1}{4}} = y$
$f^{-1}(x) = \sqrt[3]{\frac{x+1}{4}}$

6. **(b)** and **(c)** have inverse functions.

7.

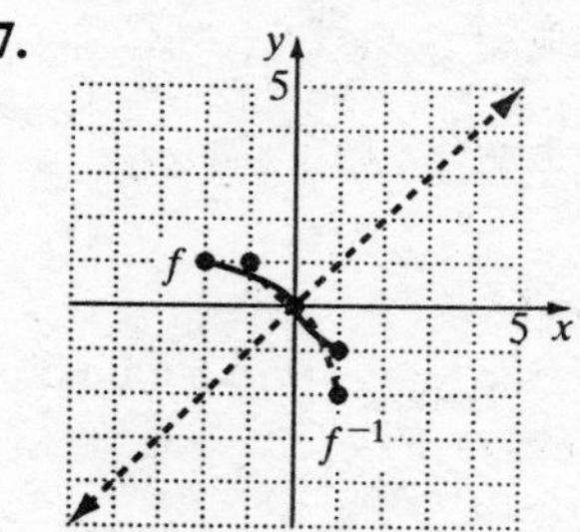

Exercise Set 2.6

1. $f(x) = 2x$; $g(x) = x+7$

a. $(f \circ g)(x) = 2(x+7) = 2x+14$

b. $(g \circ f)(x) = 2x+7$

c. $(f \circ g)(2) = 2(2)+14 = 18$

3. $f(x) = x+4$; $g(x) = 2x+1$

a. $(f \circ g)(x) = (2x+1)+4 = 2x+5$

b. $(g \circ f)(x) = 2(x+4)+1 = 2x+9$

c. $(f \circ g)(2) = 2(2)+5 = 9$

5. $f(x) = 4x - 3;\ g(x) = 5x^2 - 2$

a. $(f \circ g)(x) = 4(5x^2 - 2) - 3 = 20x^2 - 11$

b. $(g \circ f)(x) = 5(4x - 3)^2 - 2 = 5(16x^2 - 24x + 9) - 2 = 80x^2 - 120x + 43$

c. $(f \circ g)(2) = 20(2)^2 - 11 = 69$

7. $f(x) = x^2 + 2;\ g(x) = x^2 - 2$

a. $(f \circ g)(x) = (x^2 - 2)^2 + 2 = x^4 - 4x^2 + 4 + 2 = x^4 - 4x^2 + 6$

b. $(g \circ f)(x) = (x^2 + 2)^2 - 2 = x^4 + 4x^2 + 4 - 2 = x^4 + 4x^2 + 2$

c. $(f \circ g)(2) = 2^4 - 4(2)^2 + 6 = 6$

9. $f(x) = \sqrt{x};\ g(x) = x - 1$

a. $(f \circ g)(x) = \sqrt{x - 1}$

b. $(g \circ f)(x) = \sqrt{x} - 1$

c. $(f \circ g)(2) = \sqrt{2 - 1} = \sqrt{1} = 1$

11. $f(x) = 2x - 3;\ g(x) = \dfrac{x + 3}{2}$

a. $(f \circ g)(x) = 2\left(\dfrac{x + 3}{2}\right) - 3 = x + 3 - 3 = x$

b. $(g \circ f)(x) = \dfrac{(2x - 3) + 3}{2} = \dfrac{2x}{2} = x$

c. $(f \circ g)(2) = 2$

13. $f(x) = \dfrac{1}{x};\ g(x) = \dfrac{1}{x}$

a. $(f \circ g)(x) = \dfrac{1}{\frac{1}{x}} = 1 \cdot \dfrac{x}{1} = x$

b. $(g \circ f)(x) = \dfrac{1}{\frac{1}{x}} = 1 \cdot \dfrac{x}{1} = x$

c. $(f \circ g)(2) = 2$

15. $f(x) = 4x;\ g(x) = \dfrac{x}{4}$

$f(g(x)) = 4\left(\dfrac{x}{4}\right) = x$

$g(f(x)) = \dfrac{4x}{4} = x$

f and *g* are inverses.

17. $f(x) = 3x + 8;\ g(x) = \dfrac{x - 8}{3}$

$f(g(x)) = 3\left(\dfrac{x - 8}{3}\right) + 8 = x - 8 + 8 = x$

$g(f(x)) = \dfrac{(3x + 8) - 8}{3} = \dfrac{3x}{3} = x$

f and *g* are inverses.

19. $f(x) = 5x - 9;\ g(x) = \dfrac{x + 5}{9}$

$f(g(x)) = 5\left(\dfrac{x + 5}{9}\right) - 9 = \dfrac{5x + 25}{9} - 9 = \dfrac{5x - 56}{9}$

$g(f(x)) = \dfrac{5x - 9 + 5}{9} = \dfrac{5x - 4}{9}$

f and *g* are not inverses.

21. $f(x)=\frac{3}{x-4};\ g(x)=\frac{3}{x}+4$

$$f(g(x))=\frac{3}{\frac{3}{x}+4-4}=\frac{3}{\frac{3}{x}}=x$$

$$\begin{aligned}g(f(x))&=\frac{3}{\frac{3}{x-4}}+4\\&=3\cdot\left(\frac{x-4}{3}\right)+4\\&=x-4+4\\&=x\end{aligned}$$

f and *g* are inverses.

23. $f(x)=-x; g(x)=-x$

$$f(g(x))=-(-x)=x$$
$$g(f(x))=-(-x)=x$$

f and *g* are inverses.

25. a.
$$\begin{aligned}f(x)&=x+3\\y&=x+3\\x&=y+3\\y&=x-3\\f^{-1}(x)&=x-3\end{aligned}$$

b. $f(f^{-1}(x))=x-3+3=x$

$f^{-1}(f(x))=x+3-3=x$

27. a.
$$\begin{aligned}f(x)&=2x\\y&=2x\\x&=2y\\y&=\frac{x}{2}\\f^{-1}(x)&=\frac{x}{2}\end{aligned}$$

b. $f(f^{-1}(x))=2\left(\frac{x}{2}\right)=x$

$f^{-1}(f(x))=\frac{2x}{2}=x$

29. a.
$$\begin{aligned}f(x)&=2x+3\\y&=2x+3\\x&=2y+3\\x-3&=2y\\y&=\frac{x-3}{2}\\f^{-1}(x)&=\frac{x-3}{2}\end{aligned}$$

b.
$$\begin{aligned}f(f^{-1}(x))&=2\left(\frac{x-3}{2}\right)+3\\&=x-3+3\\&=x\end{aligned}$$

$$f^{-1}(f(x))=\frac{2x+3-3}{2}=\frac{2x}{2}=x$$

31. a.
$$\begin{aligned}f(x)&=x^3+2\\y&=x^3+2\\x&=y^3+2\\x-2&=y^3\\y&=\sqrt[3]{x-2}\\f^{-1}(x)&=\sqrt[3]{x-2}\end{aligned}$$

b.
$$\begin{aligned}f(f^{-1}(x))&=\left(\sqrt[3]{x-2}\right)^3+2\\&=x-2+2\\&=x\end{aligned}$$

$$f^{-1}(f(x))=\sqrt[3]{x^3+2-2}=\sqrt[3]{x^3}=x$$

33. a.
$$\begin{aligned}f(x)&=(x+2)^3\\y&=(x+2)^3\\x&=(y+2)^3\\\sqrt[3]{x}&=y+2\\y&=\sqrt[3]{x}-2\\f^{-1}(x)&=\sqrt[3]{x}-2\end{aligned}$$

b. $f(f^{-1}(x))=\left(\sqrt[3]{x}-2+2\right)^3=\left(\sqrt[3]{x}\right)^3=x$

$$\begin{aligned}f^{-1}(f(x))&=\sqrt[3]{(x+2)^3}-2\\&=x+2-2\\&=x\end{aligned}$$

35. a.
$$\begin{aligned} f(x) &= \frac{1}{x} \\ y &= \frac{1}{x} \\ x &= \frac{1}{y} \\ xy &= 1 \\ y &= \frac{1}{x} \\ f^{-1}(x) &= \frac{1}{x} \end{aligned}$$

b.
$$f(f^{-1}(x)) = \frac{1}{\frac{1}{x}} = x$$
$$f^{-1}(f(x)) = \frac{1}{\frac{1}{x}} = x$$

37. a.
$$\begin{aligned} f(x) &= \sqrt{x} \\ y &= \sqrt{x} \\ x &= \sqrt{y} \\ y &= x^2 \\ f^{-1}(x) &= x^2, \quad x \ge 0 \end{aligned}$$

b. $f(f^{-1}(x)) = \sqrt{x^2} = |x| = x$ for $x \ge 0$.
$$f^{-1}(f(x)) = (\sqrt{x})^2 = x$$

39. a.
$$\begin{aligned} f(x) &= x^2 + 1, \text{ for } x \ge 0 \\ y &= x^2 + 1 \\ x &= y^2 + 1, \text{ for } y \ge 0 \\ x - 1 &= y^2 \\ y &= \sqrt{x-1} \text{ since } y \ge 0 \\ f^{-1}(x) &= \sqrt{x-1} \end{aligned}$$

b.
$$\begin{aligned} f(f^{-1}(x)) &= (\sqrt{x-1})^2 + 1 \\ &= x - 1 + 1 \\ &= x \end{aligned}$$
$f^{-1}(f(x)) = \sqrt{x^2 + 1 - 1} = \sqrt{x^2} = x$
for $x \ge 0$.

41. a.
$$\begin{aligned} f(x) &= \frac{2x+1}{x-3} \\ y &= \frac{2x+1}{x-3} \\ x &= \frac{2y+1}{y-3} \\ x(y-3) &= 2y + 1 \\ xy - 3x &= 2y + 1 \\ xy - 2y &= 3x + 1 \\ y(x-2) &= 3x + 1 \\ y &= \frac{3x+1}{x-2} \\ f^{-1}(x) &= \frac{3x+1}{x-2} \end{aligned}$$

b.
$$\begin{aligned} f(f^{-1}(x)) &= \frac{2\left(\frac{3x+1}{x-2}\right)+1}{\frac{3x+1}{x-2} - 3} \\ &= \frac{2(3x+1)+x-2}{3x+1-3(x-2)} = \frac{6x+2+x-2}{3x+1-3x+6} \\ &= \frac{7x}{7} = x \end{aligned}$$
$$\begin{aligned} f^{-1}(f(x)) &= \frac{3\left(\frac{2x+1}{x-3}\right)+1}{\frac{2x+1}{x-3} - 2} \\ &= \frac{3(2x+1)+x-3}{2x+1-2(x-3)} \\ &= \frac{6x+3+x-3}{2x+1-2x+6} = \frac{7x}{7} = x \end{aligned}$$

43. a.
$$\begin{aligned} f(x) &= \sqrt[3]{x-4} + 3 \\ y &= \sqrt[3]{x-4} + 3 \\ x &= \sqrt[3]{y-4} + 3 \\ x - 3 &= \sqrt[3]{y-4} \\ (x-3)^3 &= y - 4 \\ y &= (x-3)^3 + 4 \\ f^{-1}(x) &= (x-3)^3 + 4 \end{aligned}$$

b.
$$\begin{aligned} f(f^{-1}(x)) &= \sqrt[3]{(x-3)^3 + 4 - 4} + 3 \\ &= \sqrt[3]{(x-3)^3} + 3 \\ &= x - 3 + 3 = x \end{aligned}$$
$$f^{-1}(f(x)) = \left(\sqrt[3]{x-4} + 3 - 3\right)^3 + 4$$
$$= \left(\sqrt[3]{x-4}\right)^3 + 4 = x - 4 + 4 = x$$

45. The function is not one-to-one, so it does not have an inverse function.

47. The function is not one-to-one, so it does not have an inverse function.

49. The function is one-to-one, so it does have an inverse function.

51.

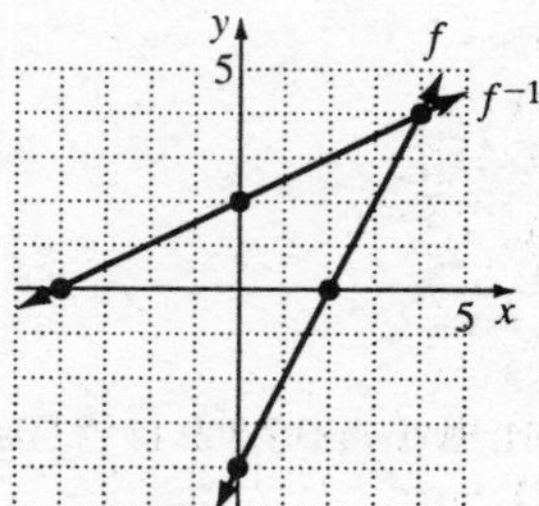

53.

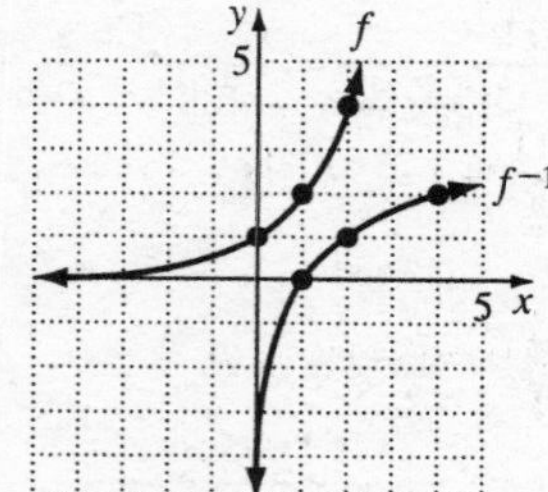

55. a. f gives the price of the computer after a \$400 discount. g gives the price of the computer after a 25% discount.

b. $(f \circ g)(x) = 0.75x - 400$
This models the price of a computer after first a 25% discount and then a \$400 discount.

c. $(g \circ f)(x) = 0.75(x - 400)$
This models the price of a computer after first a \$400 discount and then a 25% discount.

d. The function $f \circ g$ models the greater discount, since the 25% discount is taken on the regular price first.

e.
$$f(x) = x - 400$$
$$y = x - 400$$
$$x = y - 400$$
$$y = x + 400$$
$$f^{-1}(x) = x + 400$$
If x is the discount price of the computer, then $f^{-1}(x)$ is the regular price.

57. a. f is a one-to-one function.

b. $f^{-1}(0.25)$ is the number of people in a room for a 25% probability of two people sharing a birthday. $f^{-1}(0.5)$ is the number of people in a room for a 50% probability of two people sharing a birthday. $f^{-1}(0.7)$ is the number of people in a room for a 70% probability of two people sharing a birthday.

59. No. The graph does not pass the horizontal line test, so it is not one-to-one. This means that the average age at which U.S. women marry has been the same during more than one year.

61.–67. Answers may vary.

69.

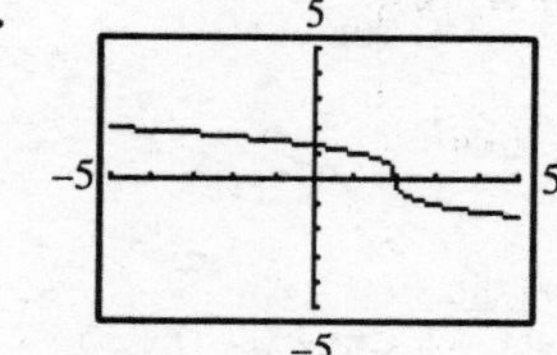

one-to-one

71.

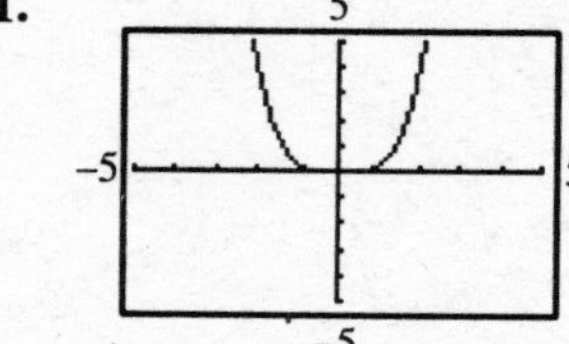

not one-to-one

73.

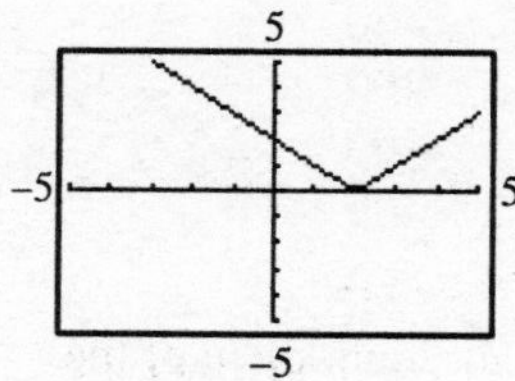

not one-to-one

75.

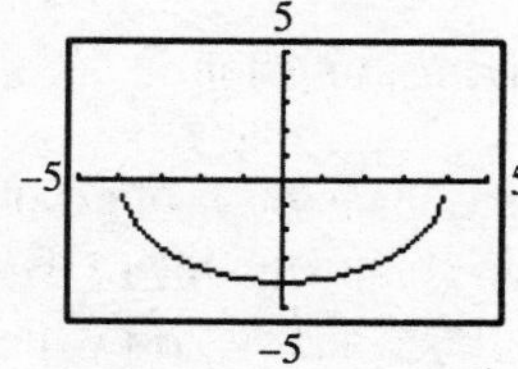

not one-to-one

77.

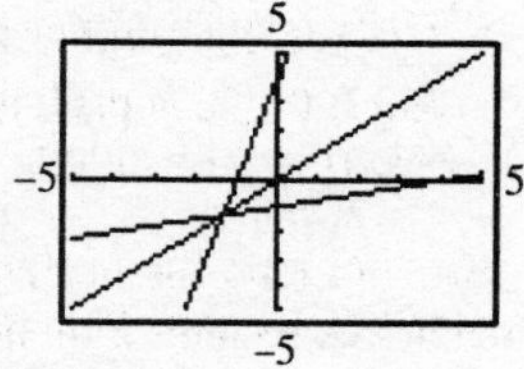

f and g are inverses.

79.

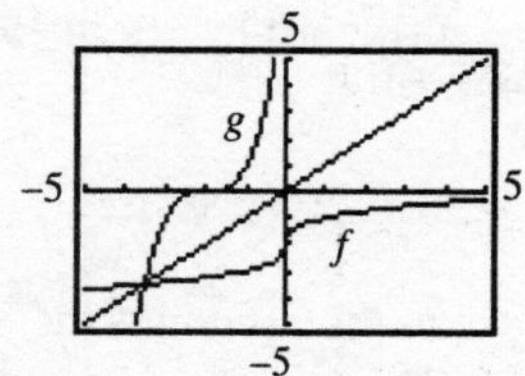

f and g are inverses.

81. Answers may vary.

83.

$$f(x) = \frac{3x-2}{5x-3}$$
$$y = \frac{3x-2}{5x-3}$$
$$x = \frac{3y-2}{5y-3}$$
$$x(5y-3) = 3y-2$$
$$5xy - 3x = 3y - 2$$
$$5xy - 3y = 3x - 2$$
$$y(5x-3) = 3x-2$$
$$y = \frac{3x-2}{5x-3}$$
$$f^{-1}(x) = \frac{3x-2}{5x-3}$$

Note: An alternative approach is to show that $(f \circ f)(x) = x$.

Review Exercises

1. $m = \frac{1-2}{5-3} = \frac{-1}{2} = -\frac{1}{2}$; falls

2. $m = \frac{-4-(-2)}{-3-(-1)} = \frac{-2}{-2} = 1$; rises

3. $m = \frac{\frac{1}{4}-\frac{1}{4}}{6-(-3)} = \frac{0}{9} = 0$; horizontal

4. $m = \frac{10-5}{-2-(-2)} = \frac{5}{0}$ undefined; vertical

5. point-slope form: $y - 2 = -6(x + 3)$
slope-intercept form: $y = -6x - 16$

6. $m = \frac{2-6}{-1-1} = \frac{-4}{-2} = 2$
point-slope form: $y - 6 = 2(x - 1)$
or $y - 2 = 2(x + 1)$
slope-intercept form: $y = 2x + 4$

7. slope: $\frac{2}{5}$; y-intercept: -1

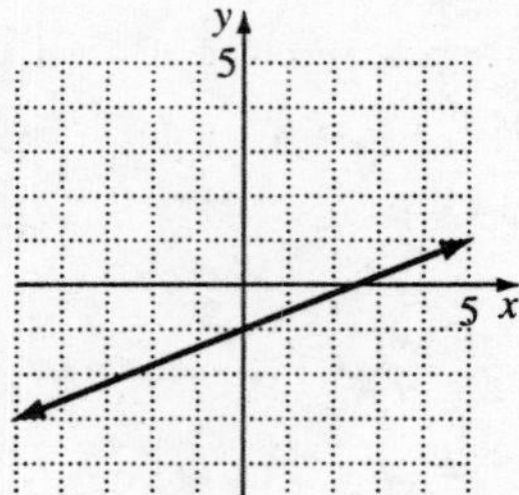

8. slope: -4; y-intercept: 5

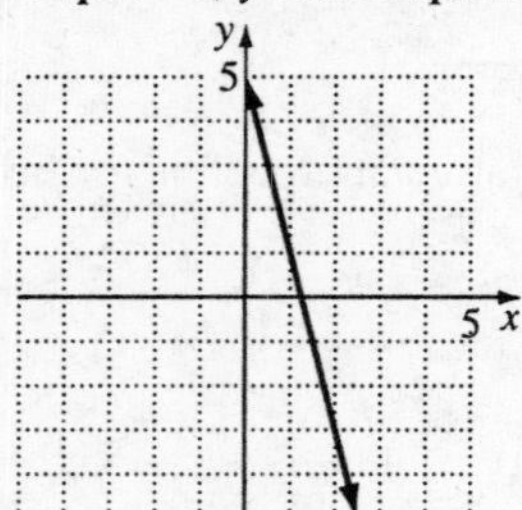

9. $2x + 3y + 6 = 0$

$$3y = -2x - 6$$
$$y = -\frac{2}{3}x - 2$$

slope: $-\frac{2}{3}$; y-intercept: -2

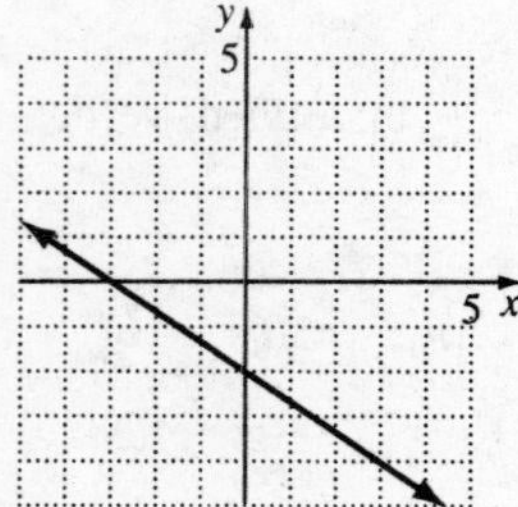

10. $2y - 8 = 0$

$$2y = 8$$
$$y = 4$$

slope: 0; y-intercept: 4

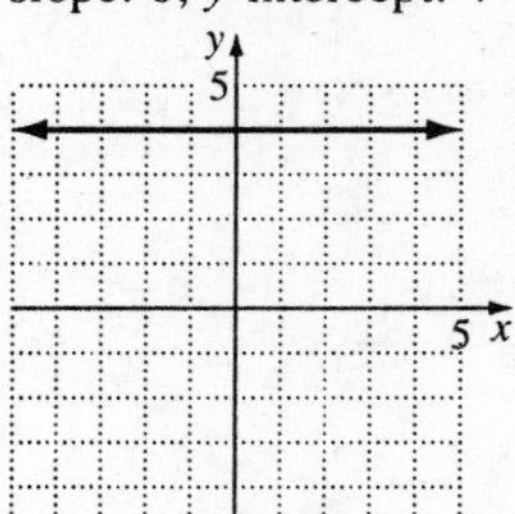

11. a. $m = \frac{12.1 - 16}{30 - 0} = \frac{-3.9}{30} = -0.13$

$y - 16 = -0.13(x - 0)$

or $y - 12.1 = -0.13(x - 30)$

b. $y = -0.13x + 16$

c. In 1970: $y = -0.13(70) + 16$

$y = 6.9$

The average surfboard length in 1970 was 6.9 feet.

In 1980: $y = -0.13(80) + 16$

$y = 5.6$

The average surfboard length in 1980 was 5.6 feet.

d. In 2000: $y = -0.13(100) + 16$

$y = 3$

In 2000, the equation predicts the surfboard length to be 3 feet, which is not reasonable.

12. a. Answers may vary.

b. Answers may vary.

c. Answers may vary.

13. $3x + y - 9 = 0$

$$y = -3x + 9$$

$m = -3$

point-slope form: $y + 7 = -3(x - 4)$

slope-intercept form: $y = -3x + 12 - 7$

$$y = -3x + 5$$

14. perpendicular to $y = \frac{1}{3}x + 4$
$m = -3$
point-slope form:
$y - 6 = -3(x + 3)$
slope-intercept form:
$y = -3x - 9 + 6$
$y = -3x - 3$

15. $x^2 + y^2 = 3^2$
$x^2 + y^2 = 9$

16. $(x - (-2))^2 + (y - 4)^2 = 6^2$
$(x + 2)^2 + (y - 4)^2 = 36$

17. center: (0, 0); radius: 1

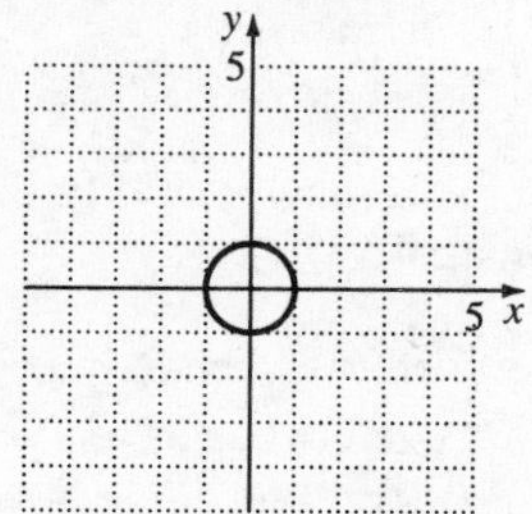

18. center: (–2, 3); radius: 3

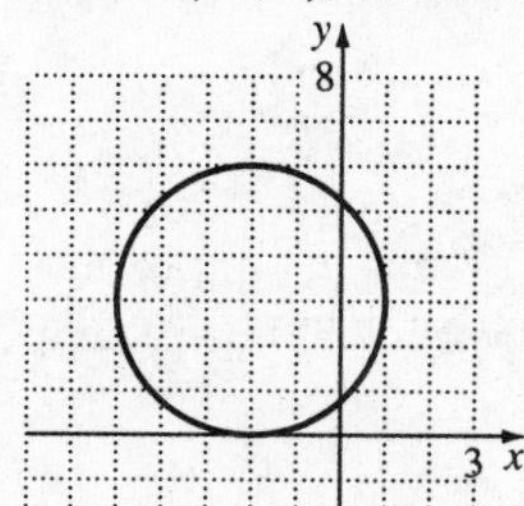

19.
$$x^2 + y^2 - 4x + 2y - 4 = 0$$
$$x^2 - 4x + y^2 + 2y = 4$$
$$(x^2 - 4x + 4) + (y^2 + 2y + 1) = 4 + 4 + 1$$
$$(x - 2)^2 + (y + 1)^2 = 9$$
center: (2, –1); radius: 3

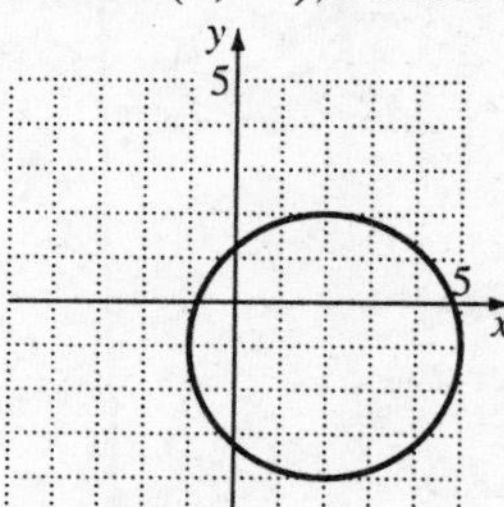

20. function
domain: {2, 3, 5}
range: {7}

21. function
domain: {1, 2, 13}
range: {10, 500, π}

22. not a function
domain: {12, 14}
range: {13, 15, 19}

23. $2x + y = 8$
$y = -2x + 8$
Since only one value of y can be obtained for each value of x, y is a function of x.

24. $3x^2 + y = 14$
$y = -3x^2 + 14$
Since only one value of y can be obtained for each value of x, y is a function of x.

25. $2x + y^2 = 6$
$y^2 = -2x + 6$
$y = \pm\sqrt{-2x + 6}$
Since more than one value of y can be obtained from some values of x, y is not a function of x.

26. $f(x) = 5 - 7x$

a. $f(4) = 5 - 7(4) = -23$

b. $f(x+3) = 5 - 7(x+3)$
$= 5 - 7x - 21$
$= -7x - 16$

c. $f(-x) = 5 - 7(-x) = 5 + 7x$

27. $g(x) = 3x^2 - 5x + 2$

a. $g(0) = 3(0)^2 - 5(0) + 2 = 2$

b. $g(-2) = 3(-2)^2 - 5(-2) + 2$
$= 12 + 10 + 2$
$= 24$

c. $g(x-1) = 3(x-1)^2 - 5(x-1) + 2$
$= 3(x^2 - 2x + 1) - 5x + 5 + 2$
$= 3x^2 - 11x + 10$

d. $g(-x) = 3(-x)^2 - 5(-x) + 2$
$= 3x^2 + 5x + 2$

28. $f(x) = 4x - 3$

a. $f(a) = 4a - 3$

b. $f(a+h) = 4(a+h) - 3 = 4a + 4h - 3$

c.
$$\frac{f(a+h) - f(a)}{h}$$
$$= \frac{(4a + 4h - 3) - (4a - 3)}{h}$$
$$= \frac{4h}{h} = 4,\ h \neq 0$$

d. $f(a) + f(h) = 4a - 3 + 4h - 3$
$= 4a + 4h - 6$

29. a. $g(13) = \sqrt{13 - 4} = \sqrt{9} = 3$

b. $g(0) = 4 - 0 = 4$

c. $g(-3) = 4 - (-3) = 7$

30. a. $f(-2) = \dfrac{(-2)^2 - 1}{-2 - 1} = \dfrac{3}{-3} = -1$

b. $f(1) = 12$

c. $f(2) = \dfrac{2^2 - 1}{2 - 1} = \dfrac{3}{1} = 3$

31. domain: $(-\infty, \infty)$

32. The denominator is zero when $x = 7$. The domain is $\{x | x \neq 7\}$.

33. We want $\sqrt{8 - 2x}$ to equal a real number.
$8 - 2x \geq 0$
$-2x \geq -8$
$x \leq 4$
The domain is $(-\infty, 4]$.

34. The denominator is zero when $x = 1$ or $x = -1$. The domain is $\{x | x \neq -1 \text{ and } x \neq 1\}$.

35. The denominator is zero when $x = 5$. We also want $\sqrt{x - 2}$ to equal a real number.
$x - 2 \geq 0$
$x \geq 2$
The domain is: $\{x | x \geq 2 \text{ and } x \neq 5\}$.

36. $f(6) = -0.46(6)^2 + 3.66(6) + 20.08 = 25.48$
In 1996, there were 25.48 million participants in the Federal Food Stamp program.

37. Ordered pairs: (–1, 9), (0, 4), (1, 1), (2, 0), (3, 1), (4, 4).

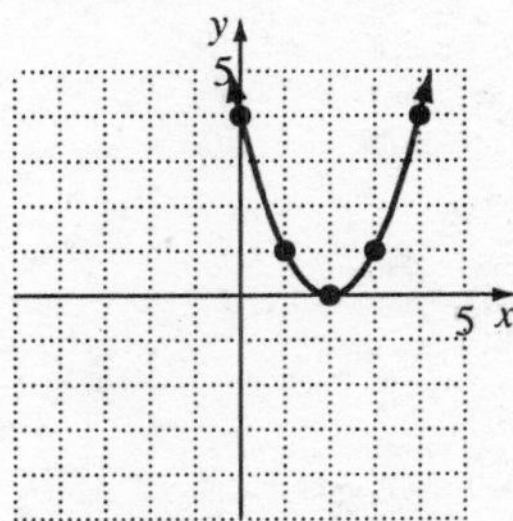

domain: $(-\infty, \infty)$
range: $[0, \infty)$

38. Ordered pairs: (–1, 3), (0, 2), (1, 1), (2, 0), (3, 1), (4, 2).

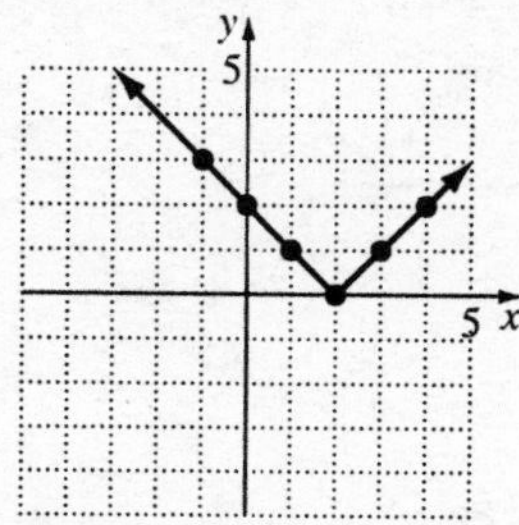

domain: $(-\infty, \infty)$
range: $[0, \infty)$

39. **a.** domain: [–3, 5)

b. range: [–5, 0]

c. x-intercept: –3

d. y-intercept: –2

e. increasing: (–2, 0) or (3, 5)
decreasing: (–3, – 2) or (0, 3)

f. $f(-2) = -3$ and $f(3) = -5$

40. **a.** domain: $(-\infty, \infty)$

b. range: $(-\infty, \infty)$

c. x-intercepts: –2 and 3

d. y-intercept: 3

e. increasing: (–5, 0)
decreasing: $(-\infty, -5)$ or $(0, \infty)$

f. $f(-2) = 0$ and $f(6) = -3$

41. **a.** domain: $(-\infty, \infty)$

b. range: [–2, 2]

c. x-intercept: 0

d. y-intercept: 0

e. increasing: (–2, 2)
constant: $(-\infty, -2)$ or $(2, \infty)$

f. $f(-9) = -2$ and $f(14) = 2$

42. not a function

43. function

44. function

45. not a function

46.
$$\begin{aligned} f(x) &= x^3 - 5x \\ f(-x) &= (-x)^3 - 5(-x) \\ &= -x^3 + 5x \\ &= -f(x) \end{aligned}$$

The function is odd. The function is symmetric with respect to the origin.

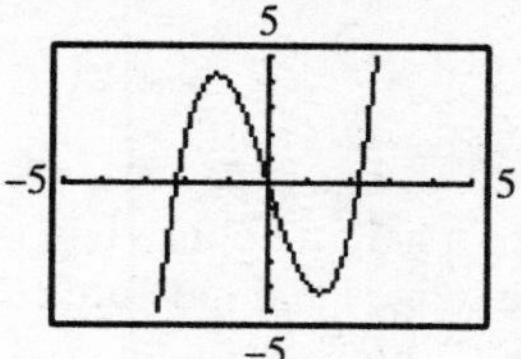

47.
$$\begin{aligned} f(x) &= x^4 - 2x^2 + 1 \\ f(-x) &= (-x)^4 - 2(-x)^2 + 1 \\ &= x^4 - 2x^2 + 1 \\ &= f(x) \end{aligned}$$

The function is even. The function is symmetric with respect to the y-axis.

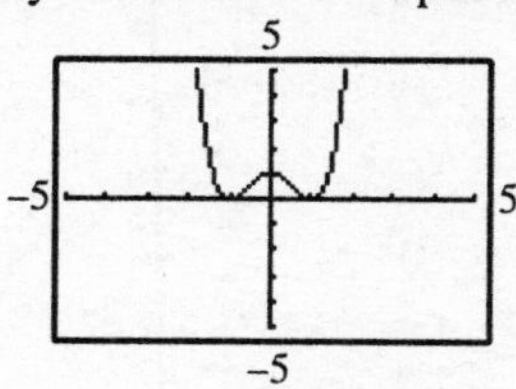

48. $f(x) = 2x\sqrt{1-x^2}$

$f(-x) = 2(-x)\sqrt{1-(-x)^2}$

$= -2x\sqrt{1-x^2}$

$= -f(x)$

The function is odd. The function is symmetric with respect to the origin.

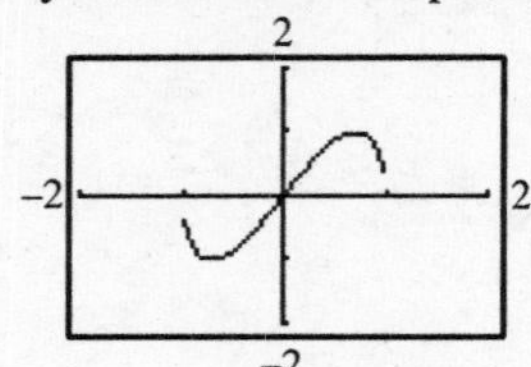

49. a. Yes, the vulture's height is a function of time since the graph passes the vertical line test.

b. Decreasing: (3, 12)
The vulture descended.

c. Constant: (0, 3) and (12, 17)
The vulture's height held steady during the first 3 seconds and the vulture was on the ground for 5 seconds.

d. Increasing: (17, 30)
The vulture was ascending.

50.

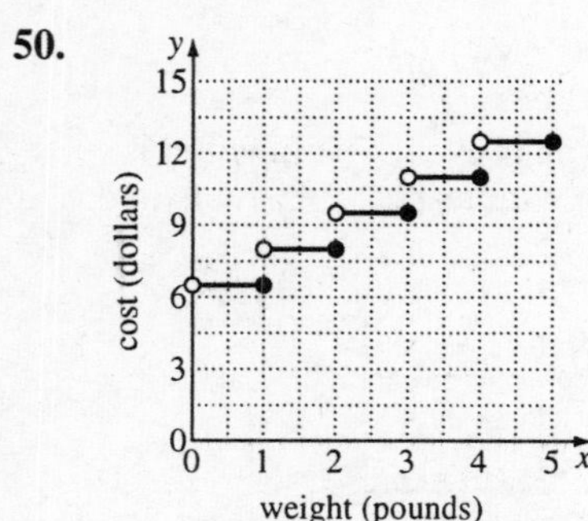

51.

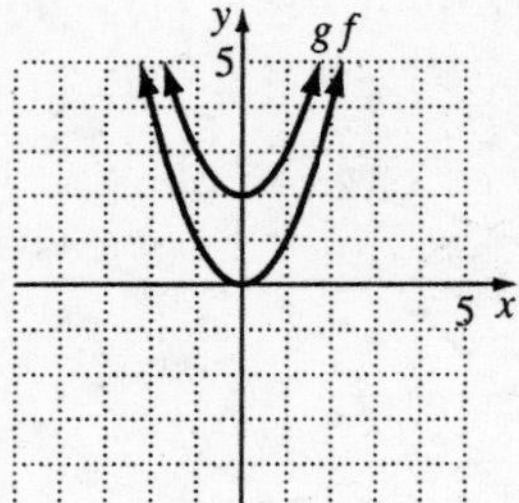

52.

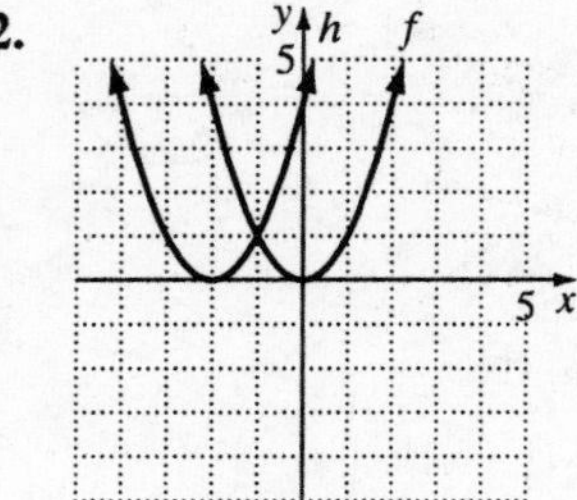

53.

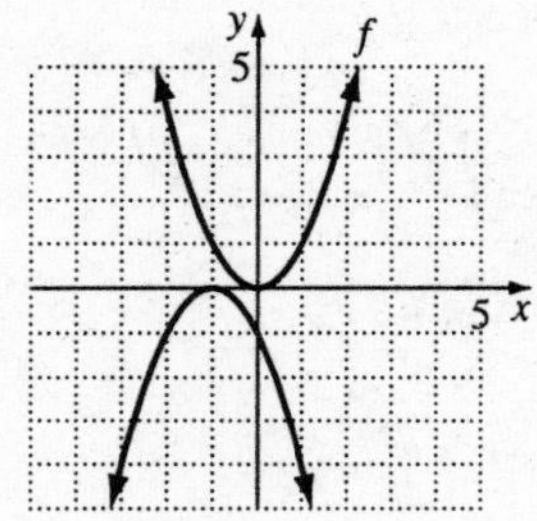

54.

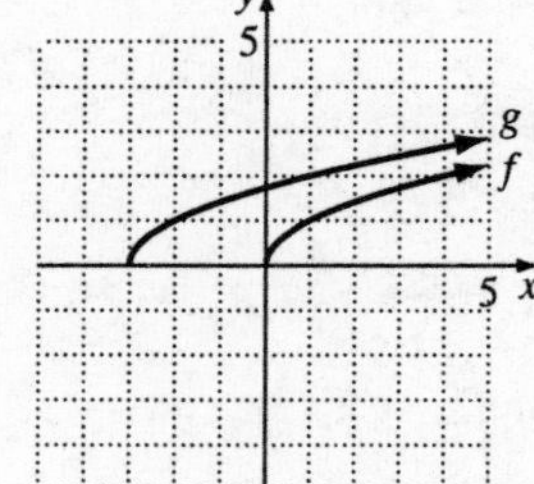

55.

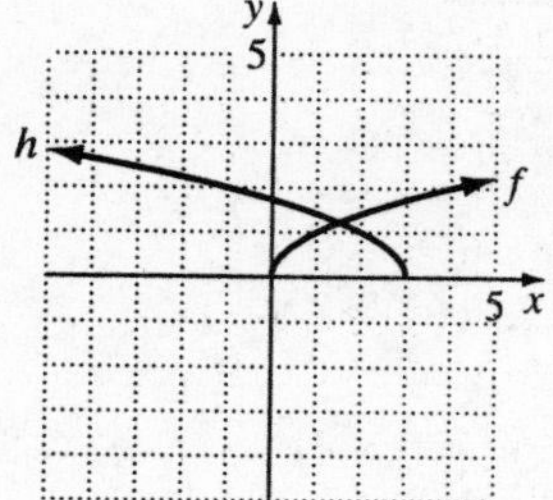

56.

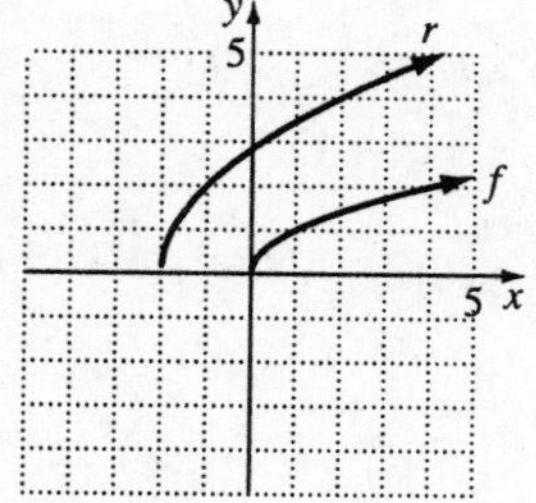

57.

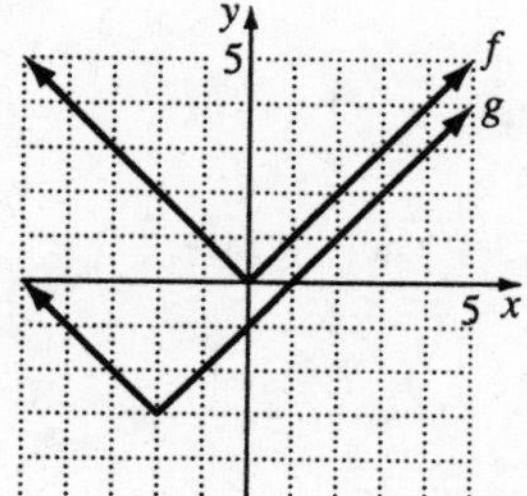

58.

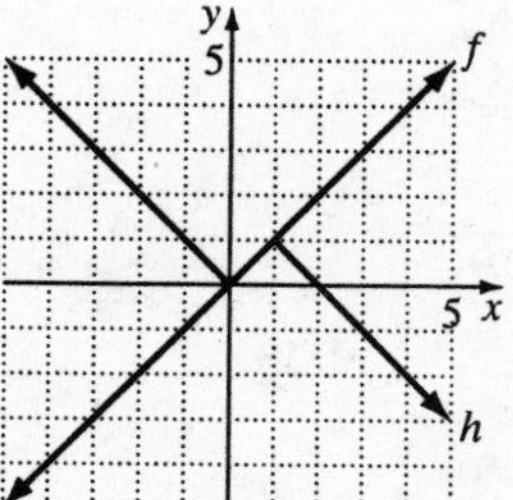

59.

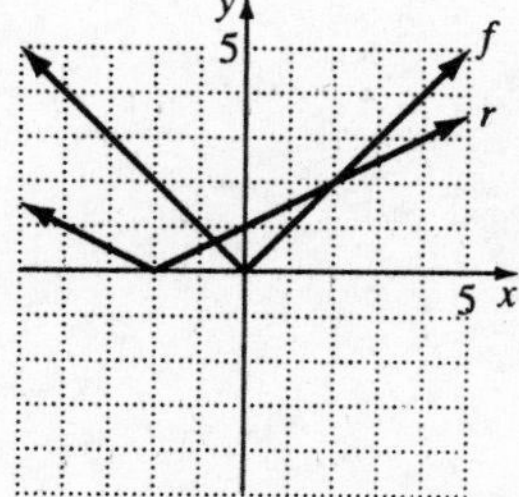

60.

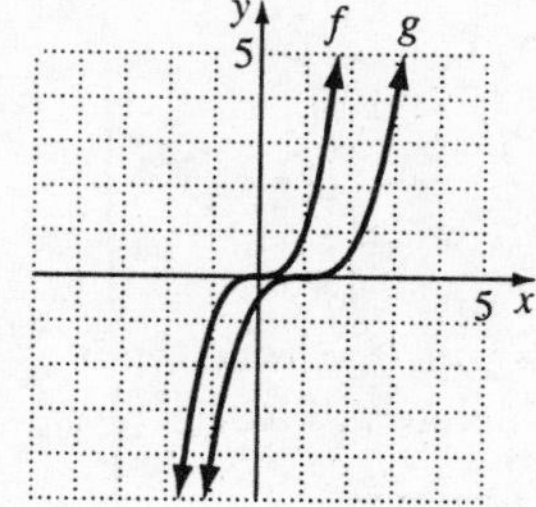

61.

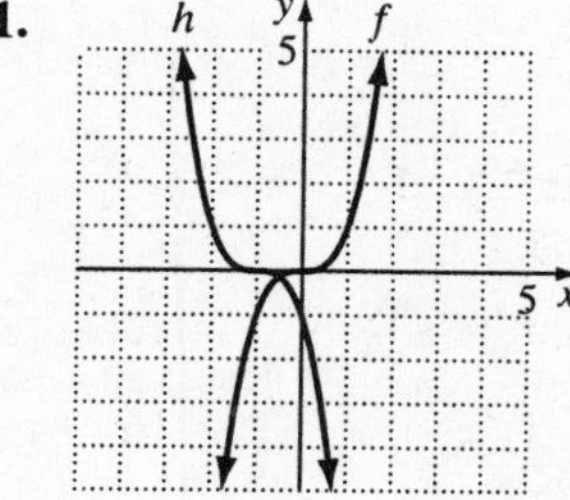

62.

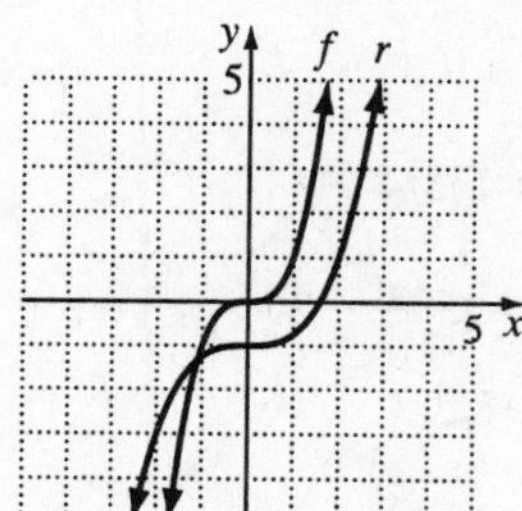

63.

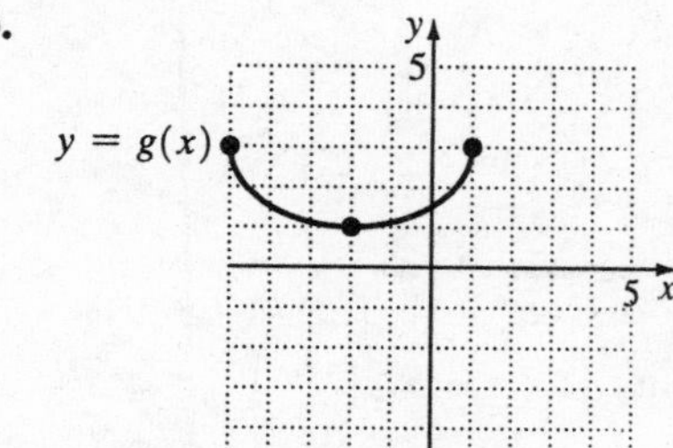

64.

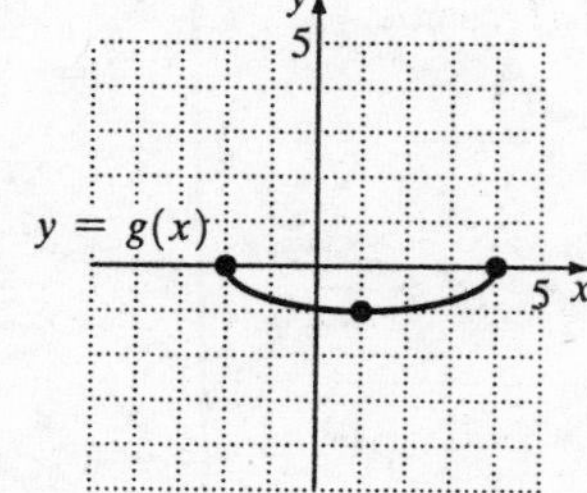

65.

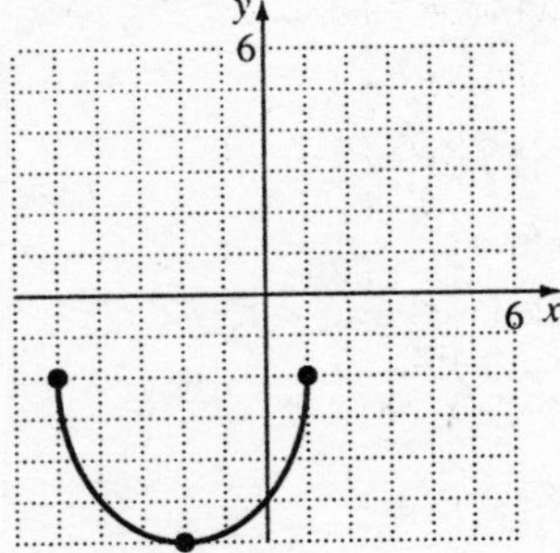

66. $f(x) = 3x - 1;\ g(x) = x - 5$
$(f + g)(x) = 4x - 6$
Domain: $(-\infty, \infty)$
$(f - g)(x) = (3x - 1) - (x - 5) = 2x + 4$
Domain: $(-\infty, \infty)$
$(fg)(x) = (3x - 1)(x - 5) = 3x^2 - 16x + 5$
Domain: $(-\infty, \infty)$
$\left(\frac{f}{g}\right)(x) = \frac{3x - 1}{x - 5}$
Domain: $\{x|x \neq 5\}$

67. $f(x) = x^2 + x + 1;\ g(x) = x^2 - 1$
$(f + g)(x) = 2x^2 + x$
Domain: $(-\infty, \infty)$
$(f - g)(x) = (x^2 + x + 1) - (x^2 - 1) = x + 2$
Domain: $(-\infty, \infty)$
$(fg)(x) = (x^2 + x + 1)(x^2 - 1)$
$= x^4 + x^3 - x - 1$
$\left(\frac{f}{g}\right)(x) = \frac{x^2 + x + 1}{x^2 - 1}$
Domain: $\{x|x \neq -1 \text{ and } x \neq 1\}$

68. $f(x) = \sqrt{x + 7};\ g(x) = \sqrt{x - 2}$
$(f + g)(x) = \sqrt{x + 7} + \sqrt{x - 2}$
Domain: $[2, \infty)$
$(f - g)(x) = \sqrt{x + 7} - \sqrt{x - 2}$
Domain: $[2, \infty)$
$(fg)(x) = \sqrt{x + 7} \cdot \sqrt{x - 2}$
$= \sqrt{x^2 + 5x - 14}$
Domain: $[2, \infty)$
$\left(\frac{f}{g}\right)(x) = \frac{\sqrt{x + 7}}{\sqrt{x - 2}}$
Domain: $(2, \infty)$

69. $f(x) = x^2 + 3;\ g(x) = 4x - 1$

a. $(f \circ g)(x) = (4x - 1)^2 + 3$
$= 16x^2 - 8x + 4$

b. $(g \circ f)(x) = 4(x^2 + 3) - 1$
$= 4x^2 + 11$

c. $(f \circ g)(3) = 16(3)^2 - 8(3) + 4 = 124$

70. $f(x) = \sqrt{x};\ g(x) = x + 1$

a. $(f \circ g)(x) = \sqrt{x + 1}$

b. $(g \circ f)(x) = \sqrt{x} + 1$

c. $(f \circ g)(3) = \sqrt{3 + 1} = \sqrt{4} = 2$

71. $f(x) = \frac{3}{5}x + \frac{1}{2};\ g(x) = \frac{5}{3}x - 2$
$f(g(x)) = \frac{3}{5}\left(\frac{5}{3}x - 2\right) + \frac{1}{2}$
$= x - \frac{6}{5} + \frac{1}{2}$
$= x - \frac{7}{10}$
$g(f(x)) = \frac{5}{3}\left(\frac{3}{5}x + \frac{1}{2}\right) - 2$
$= x + \frac{5}{6} - 2$
$= x - \frac{7}{6}$
f and g are not inverses.

72. $f(x) = 2 - 5x;\ g(x) = \dfrac{2-x}{5}$

$$\begin{aligned} f(g(x)) &= 2 - 5\left(\frac{2-x}{5}\right) \\ &= 2 - (2 - x) \\ &= x \end{aligned}$$

$$g(f(x)) = \frac{2-(2-5x)}{5} = \frac{5x}{5} = x$$

f and g are inverses.

73. a.

$$\begin{aligned} f(x) &= 4x - 3 \\ y &= 4x - 3 \\ x &= 4y - 3 \\ y &= \frac{x+3}{4} \\ f^{-1}(x) &= \frac{x+3}{4} \end{aligned}$$

b.

$$\begin{aligned} f(f^{-1}(x)) &= 4\left(\frac{x+3}{4}\right) - 3 \\ &= x + 3 - 3 \\ &= x \end{aligned}$$

$$f^{-1}(f(x)) = \frac{(4x-3)+3}{4} = \frac{4x}{4} = x$$

74. a.

$$\begin{aligned} f(x) &= \sqrt{x+2} \\ y &= \sqrt{x+2} \\ x &= \sqrt{y+2} \\ x^2 &= y + 2 \\ y &= x^2 - 2 \\ f^{-1}(x) &= x^2 - 2 \text{ for } x \ge 0 \end{aligned}$$

b.

$$\begin{aligned} f(f^{-1}(x)) &= \sqrt{x^2 - 2 + 2} \\ &= \sqrt{x^2} \\ &= |x| \\ &= x \text{ for } x \ge 0 \end{aligned}$$

$$\begin{aligned} f^{-1}(f(x)) &= \left(\sqrt{x+2}\right)^2 - 2 \\ &= x + 2 - 2 \\ &= x \end{aligned}$$

75. a.

$$\begin{aligned} f(x) &= 8x^3 + 1 \\ y &= 8x^3 + 1 \\ x &= 8y^3 + 1 \\ \frac{x-1}{8} &= y^3 \\ y &= \sqrt[3]{\frac{x-1}{8}} \\ f^{-1}(x) &= \sqrt[3]{\frac{x-1}{8}} \end{aligned}$$

b.

$$\begin{aligned} f(f^{-1}(x)) &= 8\left(\sqrt[3]{\frac{x-1}{8}}\right)^3 + 1 \\ &= 8\left(\frac{x-1}{8}\right) + 1 \\ &= x - 1 + 1 \\ &= x \end{aligned}$$

$$\begin{aligned} f^{-1}(f(x)) &= \sqrt[3]{\frac{8x^3 + 1 - 1}{8}} \\ &= \sqrt[3]{\frac{8x^3}{8}} \\ &= \sqrt[3]{x^3} \\ &= x \end{aligned}$$

76. The inverse function exists.

77. The inverse function does not exist since it does not pass the horizontal line test.

78. The inverse function exists.

79. The inverse function does not exist since it does not pass the horizontal line test.

80.

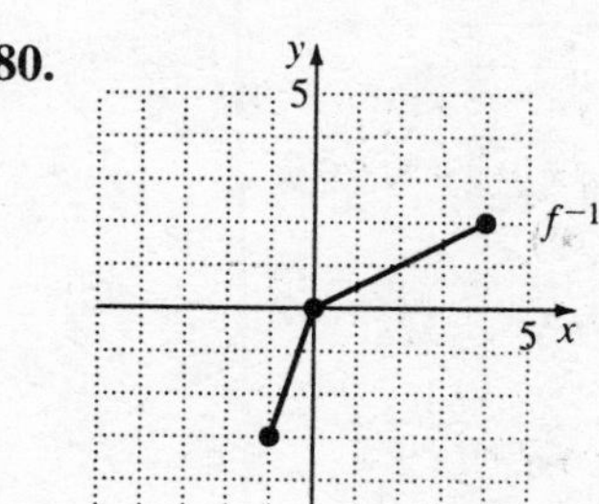

Chapter 2 Test

1. $m = \frac{-8-1}{-1-2} = \frac{-9}{-3} = 3$
point-slope form: $y - 1 = 3(x - 2)$
or $y + 8 = 3(x + 1)$
slope-intercept form: $y = 3x - 5$

2. $y = -\frac{1}{4}x + 5$ so $m = 4$
point-slope form: $y - 6 = 4(x + 4)$
slope-intercept form: $y = 4x + 22$

3. a. (4, 401.1); (9, 475.6)
$m = \frac{475.6 - 401.1}{9-4} = \frac{74.5}{5} = 14.9$
point-slope form:
$y - 401.1 = 14.9(x - 4)$ or
$y - 475.6 = 14.9(x - 9)$
slope-intercept form: $y = 14.9x + 341.5$

b. When $x = 20$,
$y = 14.9(20) + 341.5 = 639.5$
The predicted average weekly earnings for U.S. workers in 2005 is $639.50

4.
$$x^2 + y^2 + 4x - 6y - 3 = 0$$
$$(x^2 + 4x + 4) + (y^2 - 6y + 9) = 3 + 4 + 9$$
$$(x+2)^2 + (y-3)^2 = 16$$
center: (–2, 3); radius: 4

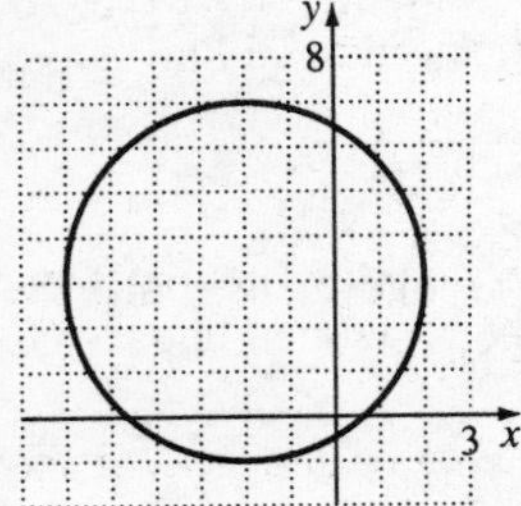

5. (b), (c), and (d) are not functions.

6.
$$f(x) = x^2 - 2x + 5$$
$$f(x-1) = (x-1)^2 - 2(x-1) + 5$$
$$= x^2 - 2x + 1 - 2x + 2 + 5$$
$$= x^2 - 4x + 8$$

7. $g(-1) = 3 - (-1) = 4$
$g(7) = \sqrt{7-3} = \sqrt{4} = 2$

8. We want $\sqrt{12-3x}$ to equal a real number.
$12 - 3x \geq 0$
$-3x \geq -12$
$x \leq 4$
domain: $(-\infty, 4]$

9. $f(10) = 0.79(10)^2 - 2(10) - 4$
$= 79 - 20 - 4$
$= 55$
There are 55 board feet in a 16-foot log whose average diameter is 10 inches.

10. a. $f(4) - f(-3) = 3 - (-2) = 5$

b. domain: (–5, 6]

c. range: [–4, 5]

d. increasing: (–1, 2)

e. decreasing: (–5, –1) or (2, 6)

f. *x*-intercepts: –4, 1, and 5.

g. *y*-intercept: –3

11. $f(x) = x^4 - x^2$
$f(-x) = (-x)^4 - (-x)^2 = x^4 - x^2 = f(x)$
$f(-x) = f(x)$, so the function $f(x)$ is even and is symmetric with respect to the *y*-axis. The graph in the figure is symmetric with respect to the origin.

12. The graph of *f* is shifted 3 to the right to obtain the graph of *g*. Then the graph of *g* is stretched by a factor of 2 and reflected about the *x*-axis to obtain the graph of *h*.

13. 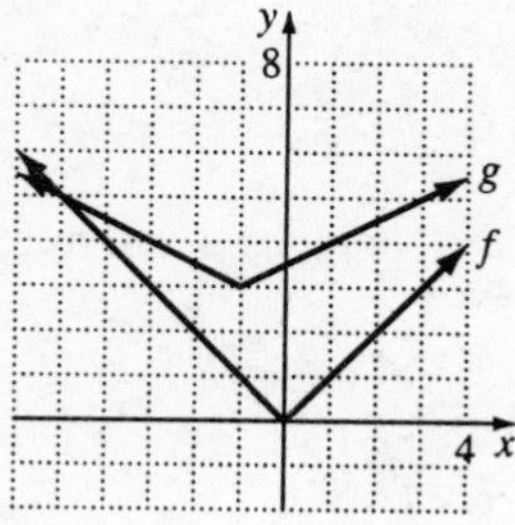

14. $(f-g)(x) = (x^2+3x-4)-(5x-2)$
$= x^2-2x-2$

15. $\left(\frac{f}{g}\right)(x) = \frac{x^2+3x-4}{5x-2}$

domain: $\left\{x \middle| x \neq \frac{2}{5}\right\}$

16. $(f \circ g)(x) = (5x-2)^2+3(5x-2)-4$
$= 25x^2-20x+4+15x-6-4$
$= 25x^2-5x-6$

17. $(g \circ f)(x) = 5(x^2+3x-4)-2$
$= 5x^2+15x-22$

18. $g(2) = 5(2)-2 = 8$
$f(g(2)) = f(8)$
$= 8^2+3(8)-4$
$= 64+24-4$
$= 84$

19. $f(x) = \sqrt{x-2}$
$y = \sqrt{x-2}$
$x = \sqrt{y-2}$
$x^2 = y-2$
$y = x^2+2$
$f^{-1}(x) = x^2+2 \text{ for } x \geq 0$
$f(f^{-1}(x)) = \sqrt{x^2+2-2}$
$= \sqrt{x^2}$
$= |x|$
$= x \text{ for } x \geq 0$
$f^{-1}(f(x)) = \left(\sqrt{x-2}\right)^2+2$
$= x-2+2$
$= x$

20. a. The graph of f passes the horizontal line test.

b. $f(80) = 2000$

c. $f^{-1}(2000)$ is the income, in thousands of dollars, for those who give \$2000 to charity.

21. 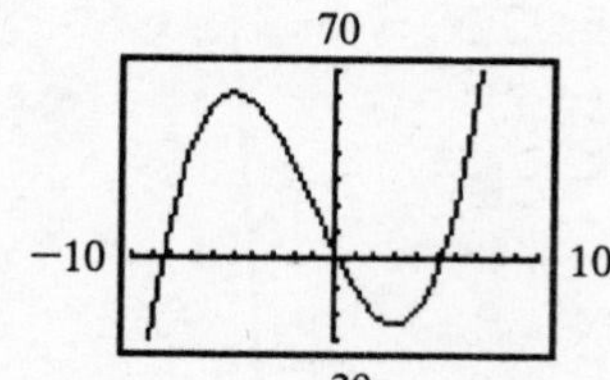

a. f is not one-to-one since it fails the horizontal line test.

b. f is neither even or odd since it shows no y-axis symmetry or symmetry about the origin.

c. range: $[-\infty, \infty)$

d. increasing: $(-\infty, -5)$ or $(3, \infty)$

e. decreasing: $(-5, 3)$

Cumulative Review Exercises (Chapters P–2)

1. $\dfrac{4x^2y}{2x^5y^{-3}} = \dfrac{2y^4}{x^3}$

2. $\dfrac{5}{4\sqrt{2}} = \dfrac{5}{4\sqrt{2}} \cdot \dfrac{\sqrt{2}}{\sqrt{2}} = \dfrac{5\sqrt{2}}{8}$

3. $x^3 - 4x^2 + 2x - 8 = x^2(x-4) + 2(x-4)$
$= (x-4)(x^2+2)$

4. $\dfrac{x-3}{x+4} + \dfrac{x}{x-2} = \dfrac{(x-3)(x-2) + x(x+4)}{(x+4)(x-2)}$
$= \dfrac{x^2 - 5x + 6 + x^2 + 4x}{(x+4)(x-2)}$
$= \dfrac{2x^2 - x + 6}{(x+4)(x-2)}$

5. $\dfrac{4+\frac{2}{x}}{4-\frac{2}{x}} = \dfrac{\left(4+\frac{2}{x}\right)\cdot x}{\left(4-\frac{2}{x}\right)\cdot x}$
$= \dfrac{4x+2}{4x-2}$
$= \dfrac{2(2x+1)}{2(2x-1)}$
$= \dfrac{2x+1}{2x-1}$

6. $(x+3)(x-4) = 8$
$x^2 - x - 12 = 8$
$x^2 - x - 20 = 0$
$(x+4)(x-5) = 0$
$x + 4 = 0$ or $x - 5 = 0$
$x = -4$ or $x = 5$

7. $3(4x-1) = 4 - 6(x-3)$
$12x - 3 = 4 - 6x + 18$
$18x = 25$
$x = \dfrac{25}{18}$

8. $\sqrt{x} + 2 = x$
$\sqrt{x} = x - 2$
$(\sqrt{x})^2 = (x-2)^2$
$x = x^2 - 4x + 4$
$0 = x^2 - 5x + 4$
$0 = (x-1)(x-4)$
$x - 1 = 0$ or $x - 4 = 0$
$x = 1$ or $x = 4$
A check of the solutions shows that $x = 1$ is an extraneous solution. The only solution is $x = 4$.

9. $x^{2/3} - x^{1/3} - 6 = 0$
Let $u = x^{1/3}$. Then $u^2 = x^{2/3}$.
$u^2 - u - 6 = 0$
$(u+2)(u-3) = 0$
$u = -2$ or $u = 3$
$x^{1/3} = -2$ or $x^{1/3} = 3$
$x = (-2)^3$ or $x = 3^3$
$x = -8$ or $x = 27$

10. $\dfrac{x}{2} - 3 \le \dfrac{x}{4} + 2$
$4\cdot\left(\dfrac{x}{2} - 3\right) \le 4\cdot\left(\dfrac{x}{4} + 2\right)$
$2x - 12 \le x + 8$
$x \le 20;$
The solution set is $(-\infty, 20]$.

11.

$$\frac{x+3}{x-2} \le 2$$

$$\frac{x+3}{x-2} - 2 \le 0$$

$$\frac{x+3-2(x-2)}{x-2} \le 0$$

$$\frac{-x+7}{x-2} \le 0$$

Critical numbers:

$-x+7=0 \quad x-2=0$

$x=7 \qquad x=2$

0 1 2 3 4 5 6 7 8 9 10

Test Interval	Representative Number	Substitute into $\frac{x+3}{x-2} \le 2$	Conclusion
$(-\infty,\ 2)$	0	$\frac{0+3}{0-2} \overset{?}{\le} 2$ $-\frac{3}{2} \le 2$ True	$(-\infty,\ 2)$ belongs to the solution set.
$(2, 7)$	3	$\frac{3+3}{3-2} \overset{?}{\le} 2$ $6 \le 2$ False	$(2, 7)$ does not belong to the solution set.
$(7,\ \infty)$	8	$\frac{8+3}{8-2} \overset{?}{\le} 2$ $\frac{11}{6} \le 2$ True	$(7,\ \infty)$ belongs to the solution set.

Solution: $(-\infty,\ 2)$ or $[7,\ \infty)$

12. $y = -\frac{1}{4}x + \frac{1}{3}$, so $m = 4$.

point-slope form: $y - 5 = 4(x + 2)$

slope-intercept form: $y = 4x + 13$

13.

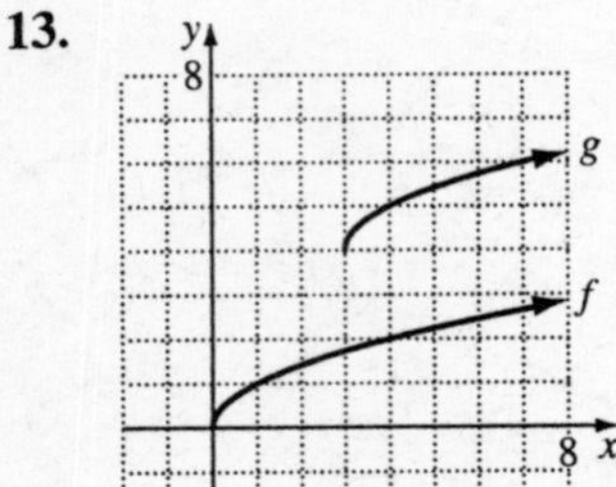

14.
$$f(x) = 2 + \sqrt{x-3}$$
$$y = 2 + \sqrt{x-3}$$
$$x = 2 + \sqrt{y-3}$$
$$x - 2 = \sqrt{y-3}$$
$$(x-2)^2 = y - 3$$
$$y = (x-2)^2 + 3$$
$$f^{-1}(x) = (x-2)^2 + 3$$

15.
$$f(x) = 3 - x^2$$
$$f(x-2) = 3 - (x-2)^2$$
$$= 3 - (x^2 - 4x + 4)$$
$$= 3 - x^2 + 4x - 4$$
$$= -x^2 + 4x - 1$$

16.
$$G = \frac{a}{1-r}$$
$$G - Gr = a$$
$$Gr = G - a$$
$$r = \frac{G-a}{G}$$

17. width = w
length = $2w + 2$
$$2(2w + 2) + 2w = 22$$
$$4w + 4 + 2w = 22$$
$$6w = 18$$
$$w = 3$$
$$2w + 2 = 8$$
The garden is 3 feet by 8 feet.

18. New wage
= Old wage + (Percent raise) × (Old wage)
Let x = your salary prior to the raise (old wage)
$$19{,}610 = x + 0.06x$$
$$19{,}610 = 1.06x$$
$$x = \frac{19{,}610}{1.06}$$
$$x = 18{,}500$$
Your salary prior to the raise was $18,500.

19. Let x = your score on the final.
Then,
$$\frac{61 + 95 + 71 + 83 + 80 + x + x}{7} = 80$$
$$\frac{390 + 2x}{7} = 80$$
$$390 + 2x = 560$$
$$2x = 170$$
$$x = 85$$
You must make an 85 on the final exam to have an average score of 80.

20.
$$f(x) = -16x^2 + 80x$$
$$f(3) = -16(3)^2 + 80(3)$$
$$= -144 + 240$$
$$= 96$$
A rock thrown with an initial velocity of 80 feet per second will have a height of 96 feet at a time of 3 seconds after it was thrown.

Chapter 3

Section 3.1

Check Point Exercises

1. $f(x) = -(x-1)^2 + 4$
   The vertex is (1, 4).
   $0 = -(x-1)^2 + 4$
   $(x-1)^2 = 4$
   $x - 1 = \pm 2$
   $x = 3$ or $x = -1$
   The x-intercepts are 3 and -1.
   $f(0) = -(0-1)^2 + 4 = 3$
   The y-intercept is 3.

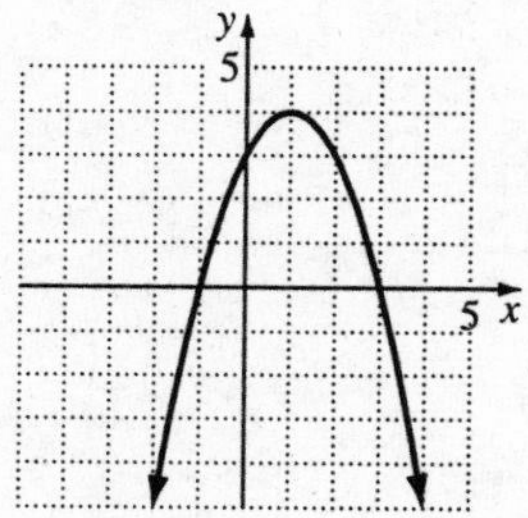

2. $f(x) = (x-2)^2 + 1$
   The vertex is (2, 1).
   $0 = (x-2)^2 + 1$
   $(x-2)^2 = -1$
   No x-intercepts.
   $f(0) = (0-2)^2 + 1 = 5$
   The y-intercept is 5.

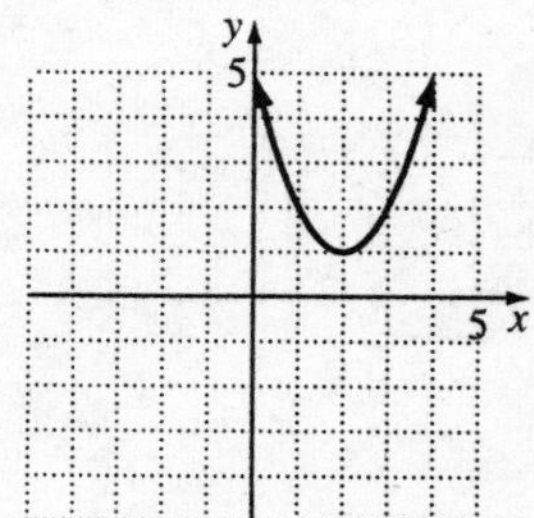

3. $f(x) = x^2 - 2x - 3$
   $x = -\frac{b}{2a} = -\frac{-2}{2} = 1$
   $f(1) = 1^2 - 2(1) - 3 = -4$
   $x^2 - 2x - 3 = 0$
   $(x-3)(x+1) = 0$
   $x = 3$ or $x = -1$
   The x-intercepts are 3 and -1.
   $f(0) = 0^2 - 2(0) - 3 = -3$
   The y-intercept is -3.

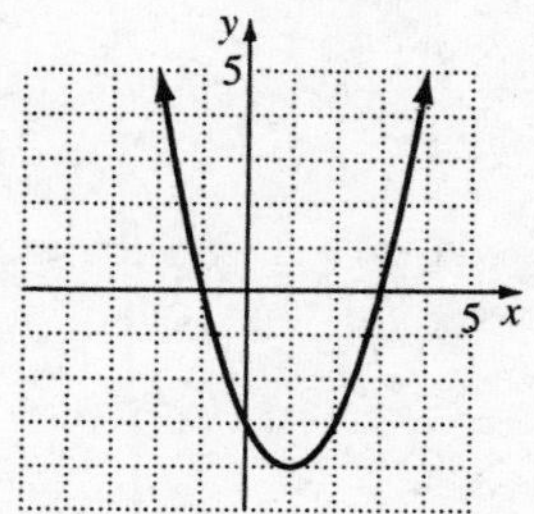

4. $x = -\frac{b}{2a} = -\frac{-36}{2(0.4)} = 45$
   $f(45) = 0.4(45)^2 - 36(45) + 1000 = 190$
   The age of a driver having the least number of accidents is 45. The minimum number of accidents is 190 per 50 million miles driven.

Exercise Set 3.1

1. vertex: (1, 1)
   $h(x) = (x-1)^2 + 1$

3. vertex: (1, –1)
   $j(x) = (x-1)^2 - 1$

5. The graph is $f(x) = x^2$ translated down one.
   $h(x) = x^2 - 1$

7. The point (1, 0) is on the graph and $g(1) = 0$. $g(x) = x^2 - 2x + 1$

9. $f(x) = 2(x - 3)^2 + 1$
$h = 3, k = 1$
The vertex is at (3, 1).

11. $f(x) = -2(x + 1)^2 + 5$
$h = -1, k = 5$
The vertex is at (–1, 5).

13. $f(x) = 2x^2 - 8x + 3$
$x = \frac{-b}{2a} = \frac{8}{4} = 2$
$f(2) = 2(2)^2 - 8(2) + 3$
$= 8 - 16 + 3 = -5$
The vertex is at (2, –5).

15. $f(x) = -x^2 - 2x + 8$
$x = \frac{-b}{2a} = \frac{2}{-2} = -1$
$f(-1) = -(-1)^2 - 2(-1) + 8$
$= -1 + 2 + 8 = 9$
The vertex is at (–1, 9).

17. $f(x) = (x-4)^2 - 1$
vertex: (4, –1)
x-intercepts:
$0 = (x-4)^2 - 1$
$1 = (x-4)^2$
$\pm 1 = x - 4$
$x = 3$ or $x = 5$
y-intercept:
$f(0) = (0-4)^2 - 1 = 15$
The axis of symmetry is $x = 4$.

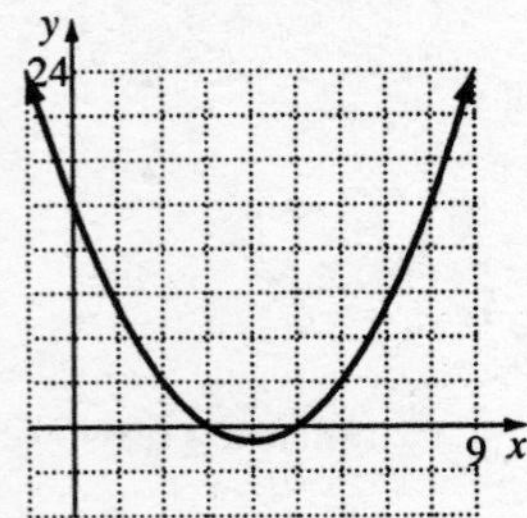

19. $f(x) = (x-1)^2 + 2$
vertex: (1, 2)
x-intercepts:
$0 = (x-1)^2 + 2$
$(x-1)^2 = -2$
$x - 1 = \pm\sqrt{-2}$
$x = 1 \pm i\sqrt{2}$
No x-intercepts.
y-intercept:
$f(0) = (0-1)^2 + 2 = 3$
The axis of symmetry is $x = 1$.

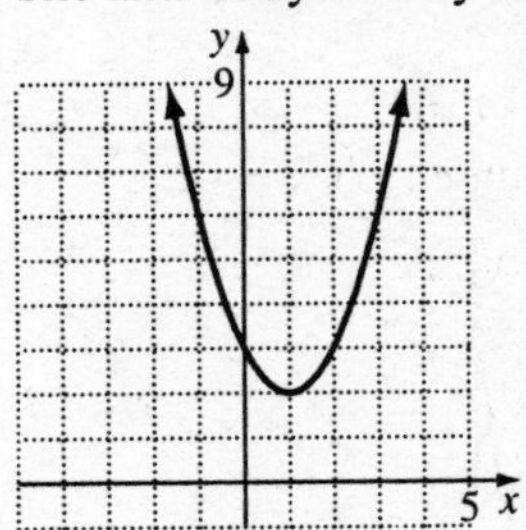

21. $y - 1 = (x-3)^2$
$y = (x-3)^2 + 1$
vertex: (3, 1)
x-intercepts:
$0 = (x-3)^2 + 1$
$(x-3)^2 = -1$
$x - 3 = \pm i$
$x = 3 \pm i$
No x-intercepts.
y-intercept: 10
$y = (0-3)^2 + 1 = 10$
The axis of symmetry is $x = 3$.

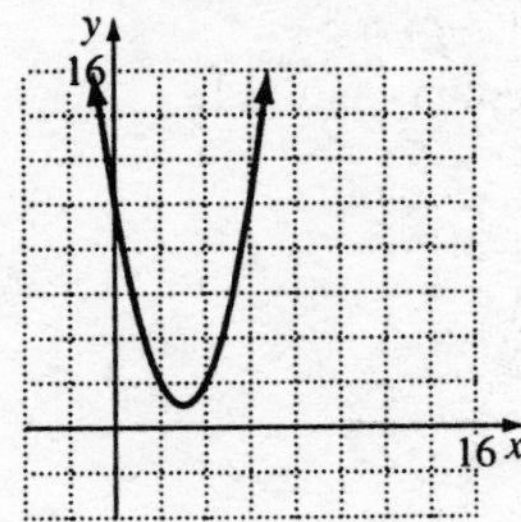

23. $y = 2(x+2)^2 - 1$

vertex: (–2, –1)

x-intercepts:

$0 = 2(x+2)^2 - 1$

$2(x+2)^2 = 1$

$(x+2)^2 = \frac{1}{2}$

$x + 2 = \pm\frac{1}{\sqrt{2}}$

$x = -2 \pm \frac{1}{\sqrt{2}} = -2 \pm \frac{\sqrt{2}}{2}$

y-intercept:

$y = 2(0+2)^2 - 1 = 7$

The axis of symmetry is $x = -2$.

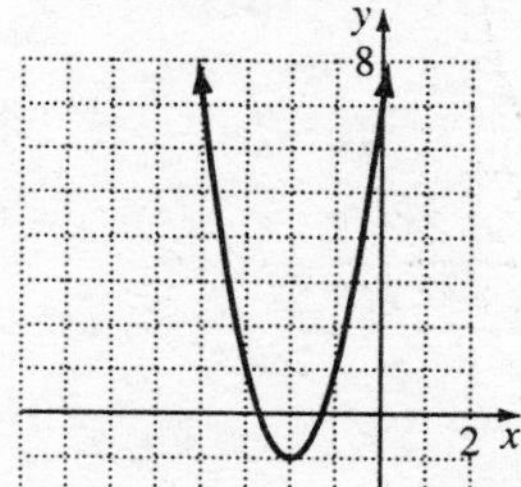

25. $f(x) = 4 - (x-1)^2$

$f(x) = -(x-1)^2 + 4$

vertex: (1, 4)

x-intercepts:

$0 = -(x-1)^2 + 4$

$(x-1)^2 = 4$

$x - 1 = \pm 2$

$x = -1$ or $x = 3$

y-intercept:

$f(x) = -(0-1)^2 + 4 = 3$

The axis of symmetry is $x = 1$.

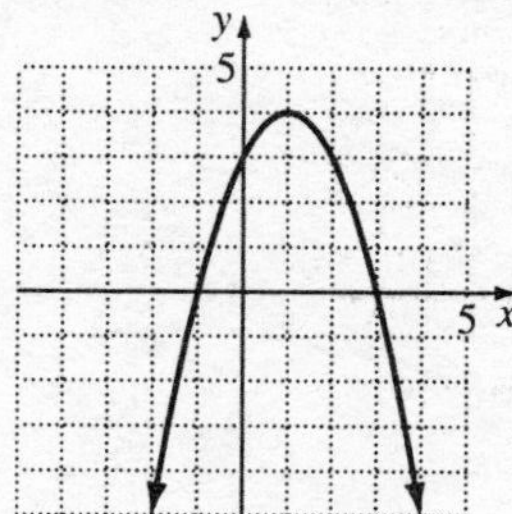

27. $f(x) = x^2 - 2x - 3$

$f(x) = \left(x^2 - 2x + 1\right) - 3 - 1$

$f(x) = (x-1)^2 - 4$

vertex: (1, –4)

x-intercepts:

$0 = (x-1)^2 - 4$

$(x-1)^2 = 4$

$x - 1 = \pm 2$

$x = -1$ or $x = 3$

y-intercept: –3

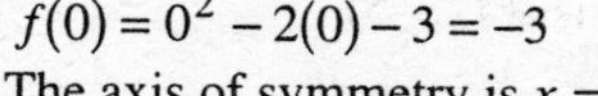

$f(0) = 0^2 - 2(0) - 3 = -3$

The axis of symmetry is $x = 1$.

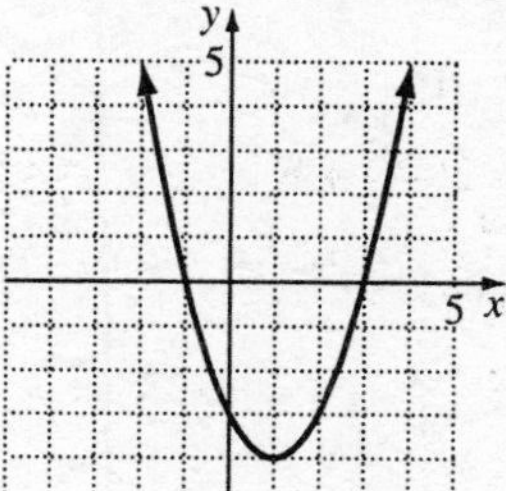

29. $f(x) = x^2 + 3x - 10$

$f(x) = \left(x^2 + 3x + \frac{9}{4}\right) - 10 - \frac{9}{4}$

$f(x) = \left(x + \frac{3}{2}\right)^2 - \frac{49}{4}$

vertex: $\left(-\frac{3}{2}, -\frac{49}{4}\right)$

x-intercepts:

$0 = \left(x + \frac{3}{2}\right)^2 - \frac{49}{4}$

$\left(x + \frac{3}{2}\right)^2 = \frac{49}{4}$

$x + \frac{3}{2} = \pm\frac{7}{2}$

$x = -\frac{3}{2} \pm \frac{7}{2}$

$x = 2$ or $x = -5$

y-intercept:

$f(x) = 0^2 + 3(0) - 10 = -10$

The axis of symmetry is $x = -\frac{3}{2}$.

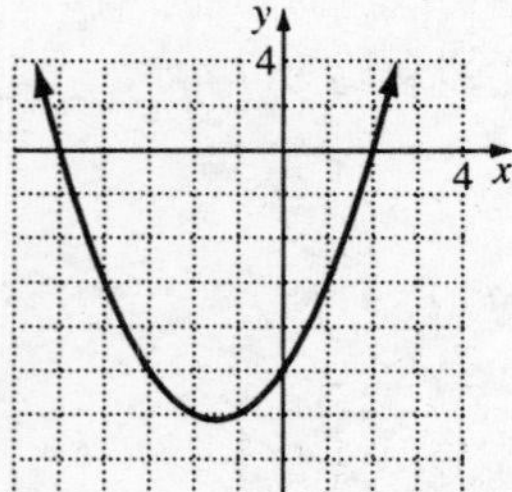

31. $y = 2x - x^2 + 3$

$y = -x^2 + 2x + 3$

$y = -\left(x^2 - 2x + 1\right) + 3 + 1$

$y = -(x - 1)^2 + 4$

vertex: (1, 4)

x-intercepts:

$0 = -(x - 1)^2 + 4$

$(x - 1)^2 = 4$

$x - 1 = \pm 2$

$x = -1$ or $x = 3$

y-intercept:

$f(0) = 2(0) - (0)^2 + 3 = 3$

The axis of symmetry is $x = 1$.

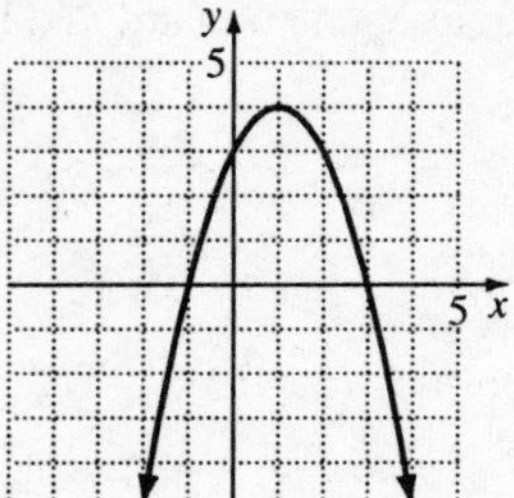

33. $y = 2x - x^2 - 2$

$y = -x^2 + 2x - 2$

$y = -\left(x^2 - 2x + 1\right) - 2 + 1$

$y = -(x - 1)^2 - 1$

vertex: (1, –1)

x-intercepts:

$0 = -(x - 1)^2 - 1$

$(x - 1)^2 = -1$

$x - 1 = \pm i$

$x = 1 \pm i$

No x-intercepts.

y-intercept:

$y = 2(0) - (0)^2 - 2 = -2$

The axis of symmetry is $x = 1$.

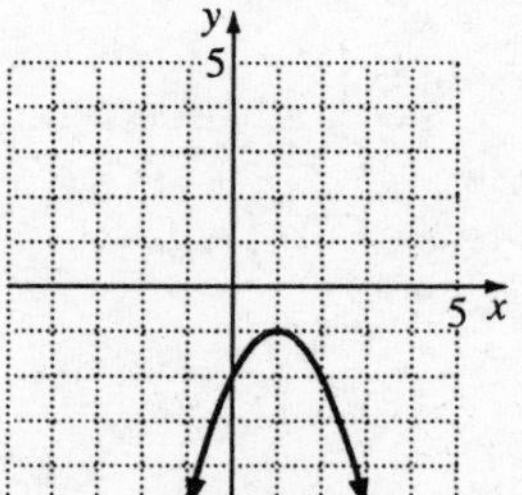

35. $f(x) = 3x^2 - 12x - 1$

$a = 3$. The parabola opens upward and has a minimum value.

$$x = \frac{-b}{2a} = \frac{12}{6} = 2$$

$$f(2) = 3(2)^2 - 12(2) - 1$$
$$= 12 - 24 - 1 = -13$$

The minimum point is $(2, -13)$.

37. $f(x) = -4x^2 + 8x - 3$

$a = -4$. The parabola opens downward and has a maximum value.

$$x = \frac{-b}{2a} = \frac{-8}{-8} = 1$$

$$f(1) = -4(1)^2 + 8(1) - 3$$
$$= -4 + 8 - 3 = 1$$

The maximum point is $(1, 1)$.

39. $f(x) = 5x^2 - 5x$

$a = 5$. The parabola opens upward and has a minimum value.

$$x = \frac{-b}{2a} = \frac{5}{10} = \frac{1}{2}$$

$$f\left(\frac{1}{2}\right) = 5\left(\frac{1}{2}\right)^2 - 5\left(\frac{1}{2}\right)$$
$$= \frac{5}{4} - \frac{5}{2} = \frac{5}{4} - \frac{10}{4} = \frac{-5}{4}$$

The minimum point is $\left(\frac{1}{2}, \frac{-5}{4}\right)$.

41. $c(t) = -3.1t^2 + 51.4t + 4024.5$

$a = -3.1$, $b = 51.4$

$$x = -\frac{b}{2a} = -\frac{51.4}{-6.2} \approx 8.3 \text{ years}$$

$1960 + 8.3 = 1968.3 \Rightarrow 1968$

Year: 1968

$$c(8.3) = -3.1(8.3)^2 + 51.4(8.3) + 4021.5$$
$$= +213.559 + 426.62 + 4024.5$$
$$= 4237.561 \approx 4238$$

The consumption is 4238 cigarettes per person.

43. $y = -16x^2 + 64x + 80$

$$x = \frac{-b}{2a} = \frac{-64}{-32} = 2$$

$$y = -16(2)^2 + 64(2) + 80$$
$$= -64 + 128 + 80 = 144$$

The maximum height of 144 feet is reached in 2 seconds.

45. The maximum point on the graph appears to be about 2100 in 1994. Hence, the vertex is approximately (9, 2100).

47. $A(x) = x(120 - 2x)$

$$= 12x - 2x^2$$

$a = -2$, $b = 120$

$$x = \frac{-b}{2a} = \frac{-120}{-4} = 30$$

$$\text{length} = 120 - 2x = 120 - 2(30)$$
$$= 120 - 60 = 60$$

width: 30 ft

length: 60 ft

$$A(30) = 120(30) - 2(30)^2$$
$$= 1800$$

The maximum area is 1800 ft^2.

49.–55. Answers may vary.

57. $y = 2x^2 - 82x + 720$

a.

20

−20 20

−20

You can only see a little of the parabola.

b. $a = 2$; $b = -82$

$$x = -\frac{b}{2a} = -\frac{-82}{4} = 20.5$$

$$y = 2(20.5)^2 - 82(20.5) + 720$$
$$= 840.5 - 1681 + 720$$
$$= -120.5$$

vertex: $(20.5, -120.5)$

c. Answers may vary.

d. Answers may vary.

59. $y = -4x^2 + 20x + 160$

$x = \dfrac{-b}{2a} = \dfrac{-20}{-8} = 2.5$

$y = -4(2.5)^2 + 20(2.5) + 160$
$= -2.5 + 50 + 160 = 185$

The vertex is at (2.5, 185).

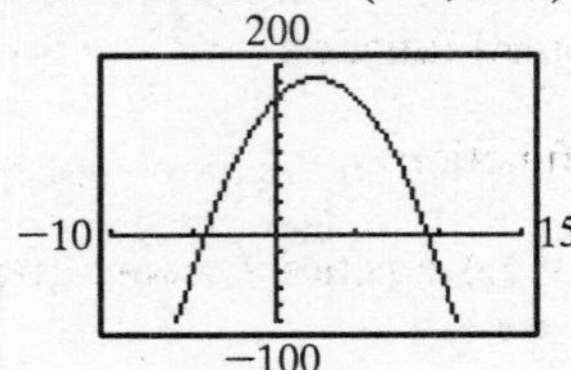

61. $y = 0.01x^2 + 0.6x + 100$

$x = \dfrac{-b}{2a} = \dfrac{-0.6}{0.02} = -30$

$y = 0.01(-30)^2 + 0.6(-30) + 100$
$= 9 - 18 + 100 = 91$

The vertex is at (−30, 91).

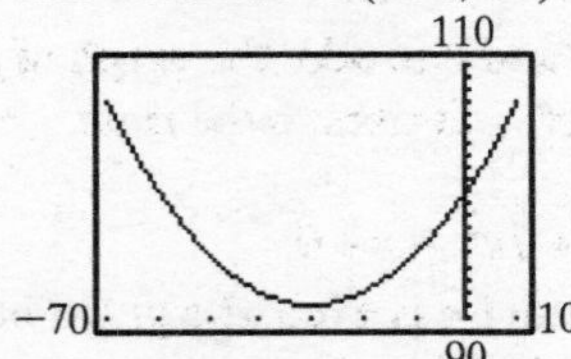

63. $y = 0.011x^2 - 0.097x + 4.1$

6

0 20

3

vertex: about (4.41, 3.89)
The minimum number of people in the U.S. holding more than one job was 3.89 million in 1974.

65. **a.** True; all quadratic functions have a minimum value or a maximum value.

b. False;
$f(x) = 2(x-5)^2 - 1$
vertex = (5, −1)

c. False;
$f(x) = -2(x+4)^2 - 8$
The parabola is opening concave downward, with a vertex below the x-axis, at (−4, −8). No x-intercepts exist.

d. False;
$f(x) = -x^2 + x + 1$

$x = -\dfrac{b}{2a} = -\dfrac{1}{2(-1)} = \dfrac{1}{2}$

$f\left(\dfrac{1}{2}\right) = -\left(\dfrac{1}{2}\right)^2 + \left(\dfrac{1}{2}\right) + 1 = \dfrac{3}{2} - \dfrac{1}{4} = \dfrac{5}{4}$

Maximum value of y is $\dfrac{5}{4}$.

(a) is true.

67. $f(x) = 3(x+2)^2 - 5$; (−1, −2)
axis: $x = -2$
(−1, −2) is one unit right of (−2, −2). One unit left of (−2, −2) is (−3, −2).
point: (−3, −2)

69. $3x + 4y = 100$

$4y = 1000 - 3x$

$y = 250 - 0.75x$

$A(x) = x(250 - 0.75x)$
$= 250x - 0.75x^2$

$x = \dfrac{-b}{2a} = \dfrac{-250}{-1.5} = 166\dfrac{2}{3}$

$y = 250 - 0.75\left(166\dfrac{2}{3}\right) = 125$

The dimensions are $x = 166\dfrac{2}{3}$ ft, $y = 125$ ft.

The maximum area is about 20,833 ft^2.

Section 3.2

Check Point Exercises

1. Since n is even and $a_n > 0$, the graph rises to the left and to the right.

2. Since n is odd and the leading coefficient is negative, the function falls to the right. Since the ratio cannot be negative, the model won't be appropriate.

3. The graph does not show the function's end behavior. Since $a_n > 0$ and n is odd, the graph should fall to the left.

4. $f(x) = x^3 + 2x^2 - 4x - 8$
$0 = x^2(x+2) - 4(x+2)$
$0 = (x+2)(x^2 - 4)$
$0 = (x+2)^2(x-2)$
$x = 2$ or $x = -2$
The zeros are 2 and –2.

5. $f(x) = x^4 - 4x^2$
$x^4 - 4x^2 = 0$
$x^2(x^2 - 4) = 0$
$x^2(x+2)(x-2) = 0$
$x = 0$ or $x = -2$ or $x = 2$
The zeros are 0, –2, and 2.

6. $f(x) = x^3 - 3x^2$
Since $a_n > 0$ and n is odd, the graph falls to the left and rises to the right.
$x^3 - 3x^2 = 0$
$x^2(x-3) = 0$
$x = 0$ or $x = 3$
The x-intercepts are 0 and 3.
$f(0) = 0^3 - 3(0)^2 = 0$
The y-intercept is 0.
$f(-x) = (-x)^3 - 3(-x)^2 = -x^3 - 3x^2$
No symmetry.

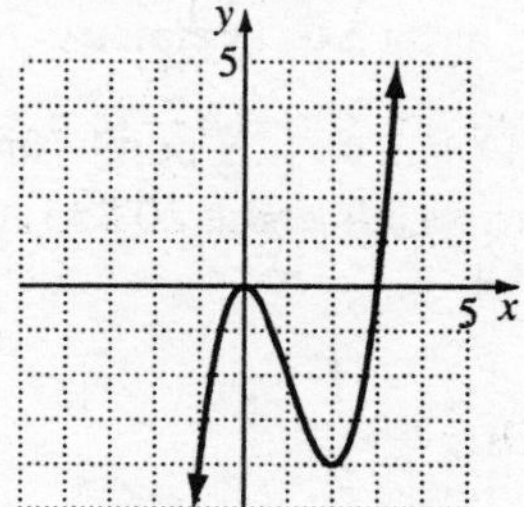

Exercise Set 3.2

1. polynomial function;
degree: 3

3. polynomial function;
degree: 5

5. not a polynomial function

7. not a polynomial function

9. not a polynomial function

11. polynomial function

13. Not a polynomial function because graph is not continuous.

15. (c)

17. (b)

19. (a)

21. $f(x) = 5x^3 + 7x^2 - x + 9$
Since $a_n > 0$ and n is odd, the graph of $f(x)$ falls to the left and rises to the right.

23. $f(x) = 5x^4 + 7x^2 - x + 9$
Since $a_n > 0$ and n is even, the graph of $f(x)$ rises to the left and to the right.

25. $f(x) = -5x^4 + 7x^2 - x + 9$
Since $a_n < 0$ and n is even, the graph of $f(x)$ falls to the left and to the right.

27. $f(x) = 2(x-5)(x+4)^2$
x = 5 has multiplicity 1;
The graph crosses the x-axis.
$x = -4$ has multiplicity 2;
The graph touches the x-axis and turns around.

29. $f(x) = 4(x-3)(x+6)^3$
x = 3 has multiplicity 1;
The graph crosses the x-axis.
$x = -6$ has multiplicity 3;
The graph crosses the x-axis.

31. $f(x) = x^3 - 2x^2 + x$
$= x(x^2 - 2x + 1)$
$= x(x-1)^2$
$x = 0$ has multiplicity 1;
The graph crosses the x-axis.
$x = 1$ has multiplicity 2;
The graph touches the x-axis and turns around.

33. $f(x) = x^3 + 7x^2 - 4x - 28$
$= x^2(x+7) - 4(x+7)$
$= (x^2 - 4)(x+7)$
$= (x-2)(x+2)(x+7)$
$x = 2$, $x = -2$ and $x = -7$ have multiplicity 1;
The graph crosses the x-axis.

35. $f(x) = x^3 + 2x^2 - x - 2$

a. Since $a_n > 0$ and n is odd, $f(x)$ rises to the right and falls to the left.

b.
$$x^3 + 2x^2 - x - 2 = 0$$
$$x^2(x+2) - (x+2) = 0$$
$$(x+2)(x^2 - 1) = 0$$
$$(x+2)(x-1)(x+1) = 0$$
$x = -2$, $x = 1$, $x = -1$
The zeros at –2, –1, and 1 have odd multiplicity so $f(x)$ crosses the x-axis at these points.

c. $f(0) = (0)^3 + 2(0)^2 - 0 - 2$
$= -2$
The y-intercept is –2.

d. $f(-x) = (-x) + 2(-x)^2 - (-x) - 2$
$= -x^3 + 2x^2 + x - 2$
$-f(x) = -x^3 - 2x^2 + x + 2$
The graph has neither origin symmetry or y-axis symmetry.

e. The graph has 2 turning points and $2 \le 3 - 1$.

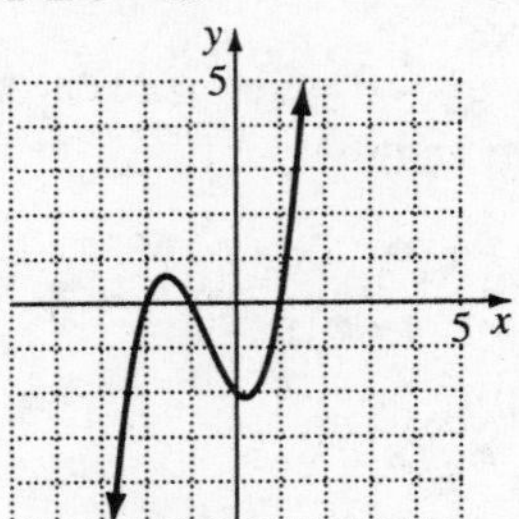

37. $f(x) = x^4 - 9x^2$

a. Since $a_n > 0$ and n is even, $f(x)$ rises to the left and the right.

b.
$$x^4 - 9x^2 = 0$$
$$x^2(x^2 - 9) = 0$$
$$x^2(x-3)(x+3) = 0$$
$x = 0$, $x = 3$, $x = -3$

The zeros at –3 and 3 have odd multiplicity, so $f(x)$ crosses the x-axis at these points. The root at 0 has even multiplicity, so $f(x)$ touches the x-axis at 0.

c. $f(0) = (0)^4 - 9(0)^2 = 0$
The y-intercept is 0.

d. $f(-x) = x^4 - 9x^2$
$f(-x) = f(x)$
The graph has y-axis symmetry.

e. The graph has 3 turning points and $3 \le 4 - 1$.

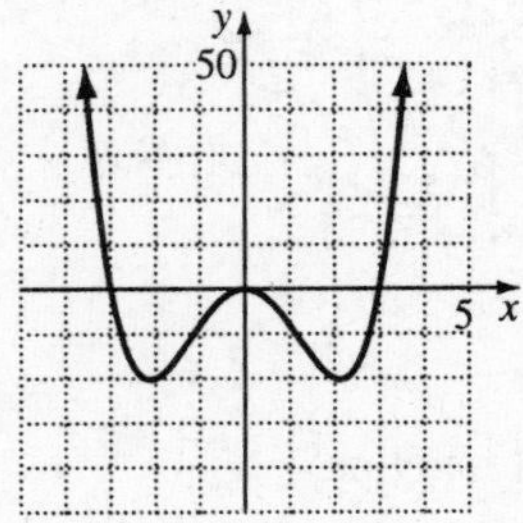

39. $f(x) = -x^4 + 16x^2$

a. Since $a_n < 0$ and n is even, $f(x)$ falls to the left and the right.

b. $-x^4 + 16x^2 = 0$
$x^2(-x^2 + 16) = 0$
$x^2(4 - x)(4 + x) = 0$
$x = 0, x = 4, x = -4$
The zeros at –4 and 4 have odd multi-- plicity, so $f(x)$ crosses the x-axis at these points. The root at 0 has even multi- plicity, so $f(x)$ touches the x-axis at 0.

c. $f(0) = (0)^4 - 9(0)^2 = 0$
The y-intercept is 0.

d. $f(-x) = -x^4 + 16x^2$
$f(-x) = f(x)$
The graph has y-axis symmetry.

e. The graph has 3 turning points and $3 \le 4 - 1$.

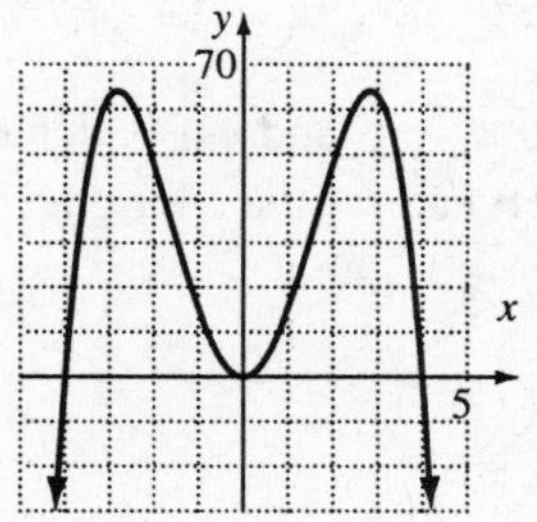

41. $f(x) = x^4 - 2x^3 + x^2$

a. Since $a_n > 0$ and n is even, $f(x)$ rises to the left and the right.

b. $x^4 - 2x^3 + x^2 = 0$
$x^2(x^2 - 2x + 1) = 0$
$x^2(x - 1)(x - 1) = 0$
$x = 0, x = 1$
The zeros at 1 and 0 have even multiplicity, so $f(x)$ touches the x-axis at 0 and 1.

c. $f(0) = (0)^4 - 2(0)^3 + (0)^2 = 0$
The y-intercept is 0.

d. $f(-x) = x^4 + 2x^3 + x^2$
The graph has neither y-axis nor origin symmetry.

e. The graph has 3 turning points and $3 \le 4 - 1$.

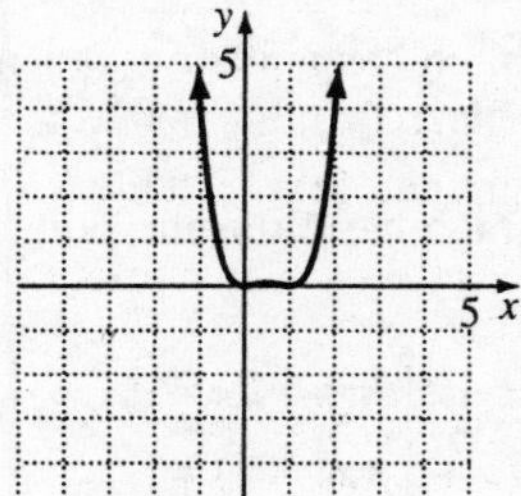

43. $f(x) = -2x^4 + 4x^3$

a. Since $a_n < 0$ and n is even, $f(x)$ falls to the left and the right.

b. $-2x^4 + 4x^3 = 0$
$x^3(-2x + 4) = 0$
$x = 0, x = 2$
The zeros at 0 and 1 have odd multiplicity, so $f(x)$ crosses the x-axis at these points. At 0 the multiplicity is greater than 1, so the function will also flatten out.

c. $f(0) = -2(0)^4 + 4(0)^3 = 0$
The y-intercept is 0.

d. $f(-x) = -2x^4 - 4x^3$
The graph has neither y-axis nor origin symmetry.

e. The graph has 1 turning point and $1 \le 4 - 1$.

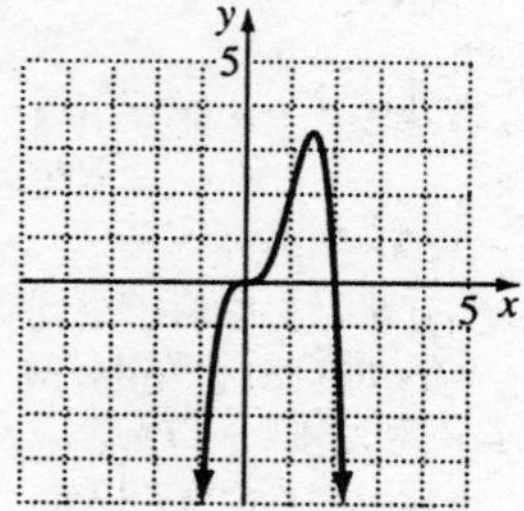

45. $f(x) = 6x^3 - 9x - x^5$

a. Since $a_n < 0$ and n is odd, $f(x)$ rises to the left and falls to the right.

b. $-x^5 + 6x^3 - 9x = 0$
$-x\left(x^4 - 6x^2 + 9\right) = 0$
$-x\left(x^2 - 3\right)\left(x^2 - 3\right) = 0$
$x = 0,\ x = \pm\sqrt{3}$

The root at 0 has odd multiplicity so $f(x)$ crosses the x-axis at (0, 0). The zeros at $-\sqrt{3}$ and $\sqrt{3}$ have even multiplicity so $f(x)$ touches the x-axis at $\sqrt{3}$ and $-\sqrt{3}$.

c. $f(0) = -(0)^5 + 6(0)^3 - 9(0) = 0$
The y-intercept is 0.

d. $f(-x) = x^5 - 6x^3 + 9x$
$f(-x) = -f(x)$
The graph has origin symmetry.

e. The graph has 4 turning point and $4 \le 5 - 1$.

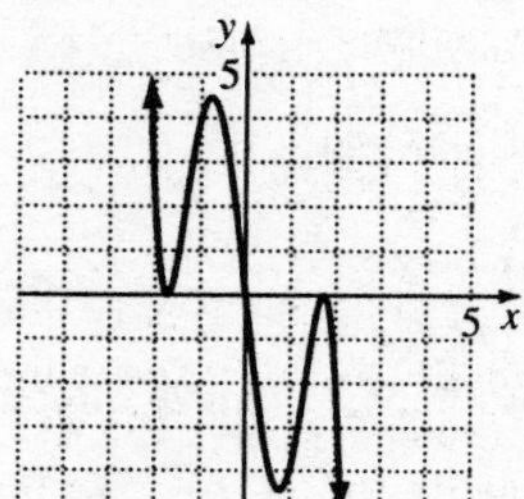

47. $f(x) = 3x^2 - x^3$

a. Since $a_n < 0$ and n is odd, $f(x)$ rises to the left and falls to the right.

b. $-x^3 + 3x^2 = 0$
$-x^2(x - 3) = 0$
$x = 0, x = 3$
The zero at 3 has odd multiplicity so $f(x)$ crosses the x-axis at that point. The root at 0 has even multiplicity so $f(x)$ touches the axis at (0, 0).

c. $f(0) = -(0)^3 + 3(0)^2 = 0$
The y-intercept is 0.

d. $f(-x) = x^3 + 3x^2$
The graph has neither y-axis nor origin symmetry.

e. The graph has 2 turning point and $2 \le 3 - 1$.

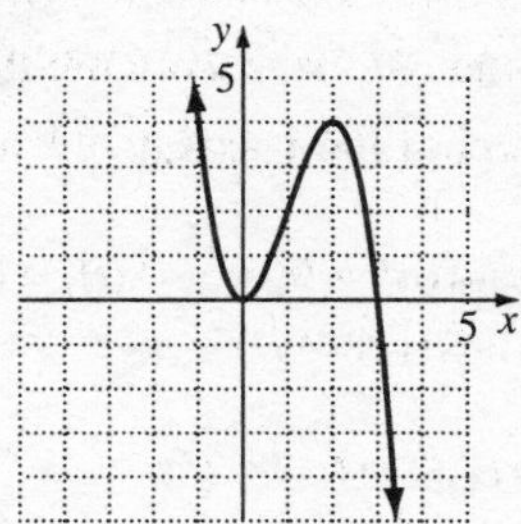

49. $f(x) = -3(x-1)^2\left(x^2-4\right)$

a. Since $a_n < 0$ and n is even, $f(x)$ falls to the left and the right.

b. $-3(x-1)^2\left(x^2-4\right) = 0$

$x = 1, x = -2, x = 2$

The zeros at –2 and 2 have odd multiplicity, so $f(x)$ crosses the x-axis at these points. The root at 1 has even multiplicity, so $f(x)$ touches the x-axis at (1, 0).

c. $f(0) = -3(0-1)^2(0^2-4)^3$

$= -3(1)(-4) = 12$

The y-intercept is 12.

d. $f(-x) = -3(-x-1)^2\left(x^2-4\right)$

The graph has neither x-axis nor origin symmetry.

e. The graph has 3 turning point and $3 \le 4 - 1$.

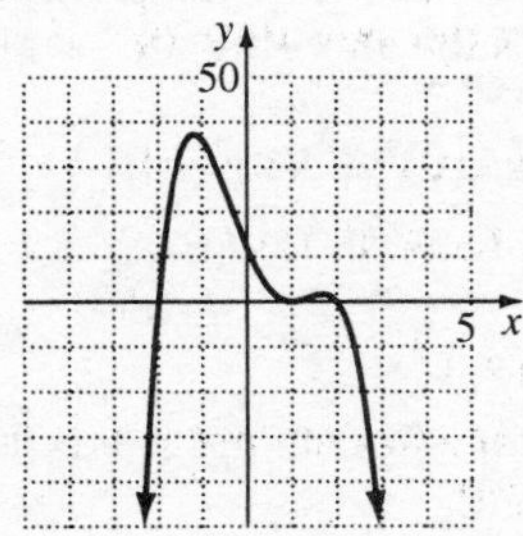

51. a. Leading coefficient test suggests the elk population will decline and eventually will die off.

b.

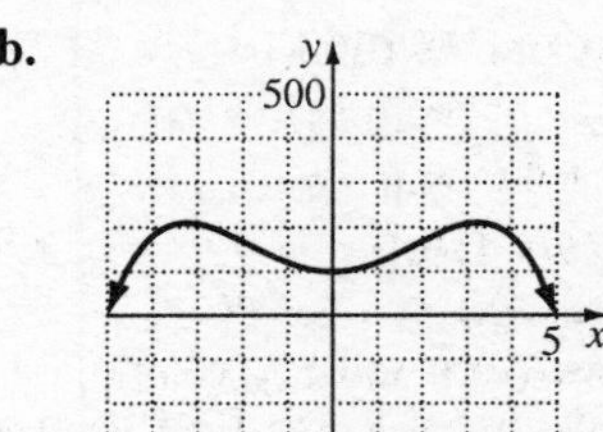

c.

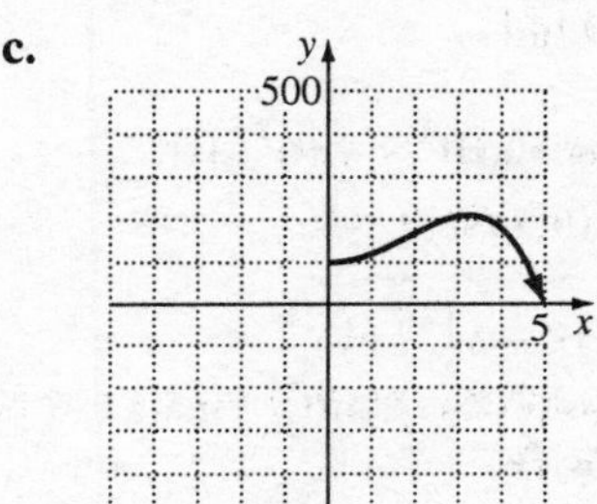

The population reaches extinction at the end of 5 years.

53. a. $F(x) = -0.87x^3 + 0.35x^2 + 81.62x + 7684.94$

$2005 - 1987 = 18$

$$\begin{aligned} F(18) &= -0.87(18)^3 + 0.35(18)^2 + 81.62(18) + 7684.94 \\ &= -5073.84 + 113.4 + 1469.16 + 7684.94 \\ &= 4193.66 \end{aligned}$$

There are about 4194 larcency thefts.

b. No. Since $a_n < 0$ and n is odd, the graph of $F(x)$ falls to the right. Eventually the function would predict a negative number of larcency thefts, which is impossible.

55. $H(x) = -0.001183x^4 + 0.05495x^3$
$-0.8523x^2 + 9.054x + 6.748$

a. $H(10) = -0.001183(10)^4$
$+0.05495(10)^3 - 0.8523(10)^2$
$+9.054(10) + 6.748$
$= -11.83 + 54.95 - 85.23$
$+90.54 + 6.748$
$= 55.178$ years

b. No. $a_n < 0$ and n is even; the graph falls to the right and would eventually give $H(x) < x$.

57.–71. Answers may vary.

73.

400

−20 10

−200

75.

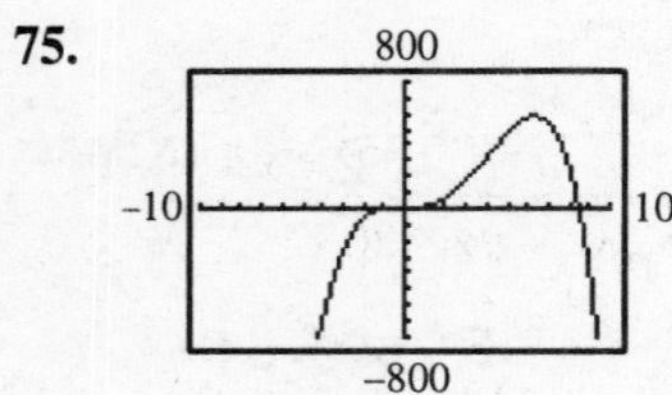

77.

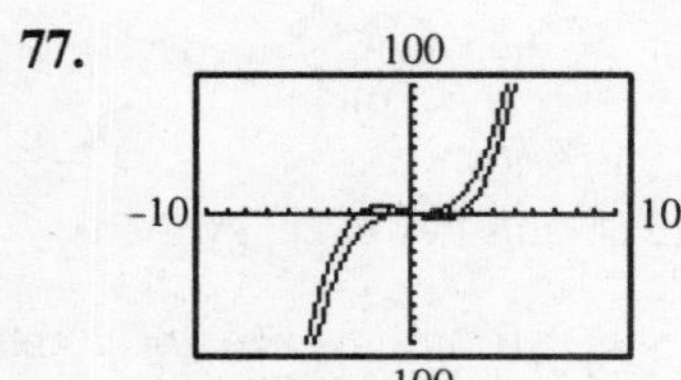

79. a. False; $f(x)$ falls to the left and rises to the right.

b. False

c. True; There are many 3rd degree polynomials with the same three x-intercepts.

d. False; a function with origin symmetry either falls to the left and rises to the right, or rises to the left and falls to the right.

(c) is true.

81. Answers may vary.

Section 3.3

Check Point Exercises

1.
$$\begin{array}{r} x+5 \\ x+9\overline{)x^2+14x+45} \\ \underline{x^2+9x} \\ 5x+45 \\ \underline{5x+45} \\ 0 \end{array}$$

The answer is $x + 5$.

2.
$$\begin{array}{r} 2x^2+3x-2 \\ x-3\overline{)2x^3-3x^2-11x+7} \\ \underline{2x^3-6x^2} \\ 3x^2-11x \\ \underline{3x^2-9x} \\ -2x+7 \\ \underline{-2x+6} \\ 1 \end{array}$$

The answer is $2x^2 + 3x - 2 + \dfrac{1}{x-3}$.

3.
$$\begin{array}{r} 2x^2+7x+14 \\ x^2-2x\overline{)2x^4+3x^3+0x^2-7x-10} \\ \underline{2x^4-4x^3} \\ 7x^3+0x^2 \\ \underline{7x^3-14x^2} \\ 14x^2-7x \\ \underline{14x^2-28x} \\ 21x-10 \end{array}$$

The answer is $2x^2 + 7x + 14 + \dfrac{21x-10}{x^2-2x}$.

4.

$$\begin{array}{r|rrrr} -2 & 1 & 0 & -7 & -6 \\ & & -2 & 4 & 6 \\ \hline & 1 & -2 & -3 & 0 \end{array}$$

The answer is $x^2 - 2x - 3$.

5.

$$\begin{array}{r|rrrr} -4 & 3 & 4 & -5 & 3 \\ & & -12 & 32 & -108 \\ \hline & 3 & -8 & 27 & -105 \end{array}$$

$f(-4) = -105$

6.

$$\begin{array}{r|rrrr} -1 & 15 & 14 & -3 & -2 \\ & & -15 & 1 & 2 \\ \hline & 15 & -1 & -2 & 0 \end{array}$$

$$15x^2 - x - 2 = 0$$
$$(3x+1)(5x-2) = 0$$
$$x = -\frac{1}{3} \quad \text{or} \quad x = \frac{2}{5}$$

The solution set is $\left\{-1, -\frac{1}{3}, \frac{2}{5}\right\}$.

Exercise Set 3.3

1.

$$\begin{array}{r} x+3 \\ x+5\overline{)x^2+8x+15} \\ \underline{x^2+5x} \\ 3x+15 \\ \underline{3x+15} \\ 0 \end{array}$$

The answer is $x + 3$.

3.

$$\begin{array}{r} x^2+3x+1 \\ x+2\overline{)x^3+5x^2+7x+2} \\ \underline{x^3+2x^2} \\ 3x^2+7x \\ \underline{3x^2+6x} \\ x+2 \\ \underline{x+2} \\ 0 \end{array}$$

The answer is $x^2 + 3x + 1$.

5.

$$\begin{array}{r} 2x^2+3x+5 \\ 3x-1\overline{)6x^3+7x^2+12x-5} \\ \underline{6x^3-2x^2} \\ 9x^2+12x \\ \underline{9x^2-3x} \\ 15x-5 \\ \underline{15x-5} \\ 0 \end{array}$$

The answer is $2x^2 + 3x + 5$.

7.

$$\begin{array}{r} 4x+3+\frac{2}{3x-2} \\ 3x-2\overline{)12x^2+x-4} \\ \underline{12x^2-8x} \\ 9x-4 \\ \underline{9x-6} \\ 2 \end{array}$$

The answer is $4x + 3 + \frac{2}{3x-2}$.

9.

$$\begin{array}{r} 2x^2+x+6-\frac{38}{x+3} \\ x+3\overline{)2x^3+7x^2+9x-20} \\ \underline{2x^3+6x^2} \\ x^2+9x \\ \underline{x^2+3x} \\ 6x-20 \\ \underline{6x+18} \\ -38 \end{array}$$

The answer is $2x^2 + x + 6 - \frac{38}{x+3}$.

11.

$$\begin{array}{r}
4x^3+16x^2+60x+246+\dfrac{984}{x-4} \\
x-4\overline{)4x^4-4x^2+6x} \\
\underline{4x^4-16x^3} \\
16x^3-\ \ 4x^2 \\
\underline{16x^3-64x^2} \\
60x^2+\ \ 6x \\
\underline{60x^2-240x} \\
246x \\
\underline{246x-984} \\
984
\end{array}$$

The answer is
$4x^3+16x^2+60x+246+\dfrac{984}{x-4}$.

13.

$$\begin{array}{r}
2x+5 \\
3x^2-x-3\overline{)6x^3+13x^2-11x-15} \\
\underline{6x^3-2x^2-6x} \\
15x^2-5x-15 \\
\underline{15x^2-5x-15} \\
0
\end{array}$$

The answer is $2x+5$.

15.

$$\begin{array}{r}
6x^2+3x-1 \\
3x^2+1\overline{)18x^4+9x^3+3x^2} \\
\underline{18x^4+6x^2} \\
9x^3-3x^2 \\
\underline{9x^3+3x} \\
-3x^2-3x \\
\underline{-3x^2-1} \\
-3x+1
\end{array}$$

The answer is $6x^2+3x-1-\dfrac{3x-1}{3x^2+1}$.

17. $\left(2x^2+x-10\right)\div(x-2)$

$$\begin{array}{r|rrr}
2 & 2 & 1 & -10 \\
 & & 4 & 10 \\
\hline
 & 2 & 5 & 0
\end{array}$$

The answer is $2x+5$.

19. $\left(3x^2+7x-20\right)\div(x+5)$

$$\begin{array}{r|rrr}
-5 & 3 & 7 & -20 \\
 & & -15 & 40 \\
\hline
 & 3 & -8 & 20
\end{array}$$

The answer is $3x-8+\dfrac{20}{x+5}$.

21. $\left(4x^3-3x^2+3x-1\right)\div(x-1)$

$$\begin{array}{r|rrrr}
1 & 4 & -3 & 3 & -1 \\
 & & 4 & 1 & 4 \\
\hline
 & 4 & 1 & 4 & 3
\end{array}$$

The answer is $4x^2+x+4+\dfrac{3}{x-1}$.

23. $\left(6x^5-2x^3+4x^2-3x+1\right)\div(x-2)$

$$\begin{array}{r|rrrrrr}
2 & 6 & 0 & -2 & 4 & -3 & 1 \\
 & & 12 & 24 & 44 & 96 & 186 \\
\hline
 & 6 & 12 & 22 & 48 & 93 & 187
\end{array}$$

The answer is
$6x^4+12x^3+22x^2+48x+93+\dfrac{187}{x-2}$.

25. $\left(x^2-5x-5x^3+x^4\right)\div(5+x)\Rightarrow$
$\left(x^4-5x^3+x^2-5x\right)\div(x+5)$

–5	1	–5	1	–5	0
		–5	50	–255	1300
	1	–10	51	–260	1300

The answer is
$x^3-10x^2+51x-260+\dfrac{1300}{x+5}$.

27. $\dfrac{x^5+x^3-2}{x-1}$

1	1	0	1	0	0	–2
		1	1	2	2	2
	1	1	2	2	2	0

The answer is $x^4+x^3+2x^2+2x+2$.

29. $\dfrac{x^4-256}{x-4}$

4	1	0	0	0	–256
		4	16	64	256
	1	4	16	64	0

The answer is $x^3+4x^2+16x+64$.

31. $\dfrac{2x^5-3x^4+x^3-x^2+2x-1}{x+2}$

–2	2	–3	1	–1	2	–1
		–4	14	–30	62	–128
	2	–7	15	–31	64	–129

The answswer is
$2x^4-7x^3+15x^2-31x+64-\dfrac{129}{x+2}$.

33. $f(x)=2x^3-11x^2+7x-5$

4	2	–11	7	–5
		8	–12	–20
	2	–3	–5	–25

$f(4)=-25$

35. $f(x)=7x^4-3x^3+6x+9$

–5	7	–3	0	6	9
		–35	190	–950	4720
	7	–38	190	–944	4729

$f(-5)=4729$

37. Dividend: x^3-4x^2+x+6
Divisor: $x+1$

–1	1	–4	1	6
		–1	5	–6
	1	–5	6	0

The answer is x^2-5x+6.

$(x+1)(x^2-5x+6)=0$
$(x+1)(x-2)(x-3)=0$
$x=-1,\ x=2,\ x=3$
The solution set is $\{-1, 2, 3\}$.

39. $2x^3-5x^2+x+2=0$

2	2	–5	1	2
		4	–2	–2
	2	–1	–1	0

$(x-2)(2x^2-x-1)=0$
$(x-2)(2x+1)(x-1)=0$
$x=2,\ x=-\frac{1}{2},\ x=1$

The solution set is $\left\{-\frac{1}{2}, 1, 2\right\}$.

41. $12x^3+16x^2-5x-3=0$

$$\begin{array}{r|rrrr} -\frac{3}{2} & 12 & 16 & -5 & -3 \\ & & -18 & 3 & 3 \\ \hline & 12 & -2 & -2 & 0 \end{array}$$

$\left(x+\frac{3}{2}\right)(12x^2-2x-2)=0$

$\left(x+\frac{3}{2}\right)2\left(6x^2-x-1\right)=0$

$\left(x+\frac{3}{2}\right)2(3x+1)(2x-1)=0$

$x=-\frac{3}{2},\ x=-\frac{1}{3},\ x=\frac{1}{2}$

The solution set is $\left\{-\frac{3}{2}, -\frac{1}{3}, \frac{1}{2}\right\}$.

43.
$$\begin{array}{r} x^3+5x^2-9x-45 \\ 2x+5\overline{)2x^4+15x^3+7x^2-135x-225} \\ \underline{2x^4+5x^3} \\ 10x^3+7x^2 \\ \underline{10x^3+25x^2} \\ -18x^2-135x \\ \underline{-18x^2-45x} \\ -90x-225 \\ \underline{-90x-225} \end{array}$$

Width: $x^3+5x^2-9x-45$

45. a.
$$\begin{array}{r} 1+\frac{5}{x+20} \\ x+20\overline{)x+25} \\ \underline{x+20} \\ 5 \end{array}$$

b.

x	0	5	10	25	50	75
$\frac{x+25}{x+20}$	1.25	1.2	1.17	1.11	1.07	1.05

c. Answers may vary.

47.–53. Answers may vary.

55.

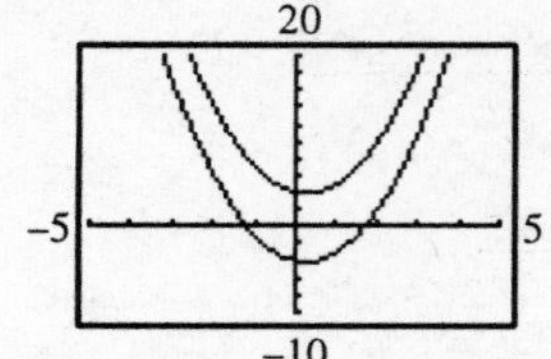

The division is not correct.

$$\begin{array}{r|rrrr} 1 & 2 & -3 & -3 & 4 \\ & & 2 & -1 & -4 \\ \hline & 2 & -1 & -4 & 0 \end{array}$$

Quotient: $2x^2-x-4$

57.

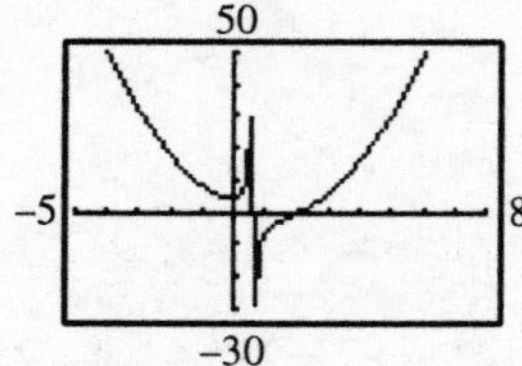

The division is correct.

59.
$$\begin{array}{r} 5x^2+2x-4 \\ 4x+3\overline{)20x^3+23x^2-10x+k} \\ \underline{20x^3+15x^2} \\ 8x^2-10 \\ \underline{8x^2+6x} \\ -16x+k \\ \underline{-16x-12} \end{array}$$

To get a remainder of zero, k must equal −12.
$k=-12$

61.
$$\begin{array}{r} x^{2n} - x^n + 1 \\ x^n + 1 \overline{\big) x^{3n} \qquad\qquad + 1} \\ \underline{x^{3n} + x^{2n}} \qquad\qquad \\ -x^{2n} \qquad\qquad \\ \underline{-x^{2n} - x^n} \qquad \\ x^n + 1 \\ \underline{x^n + 1} \\ 0 \end{array}$$

Section 3.4

Check Point Exercises

1. p: $\pm 1, \pm 2, \pm 3, \pm 6$
q: ± 1
$\frac{p}{q}$: $\pm 1, \pm 2, \pm 3, \pm 6$
are the possible rational zeros.

2. p: $\pm 1, \pm 3$
q: $\pm 1, \pm 2, \pm 4$
$\frac{p}{q}$: $\pm 1, \pm 3, \pm \frac{1}{2}, \pm \frac{1}{4}, \pm \frac{3}{2}, \pm \frac{3}{4}$
are the possible rational zeros.

3. $\pm 1, \pm 2, \pm 4, \pm 5, \pm 10, \pm 20$ are possible rational zeros

$$\begin{array}{r|rrrr} 1 & 1 & 8 & 11 & -20 \\ & & 1 & 9 & 20 \\ \hline & 1 & 9 & 20 & 0 \end{array}$$

1 is a zero.
$x^2 + 9x + 20 = 0$
$(x + 4)(x + 5) = 0$
$x = -4$ or $x = -5$
The solution set is $\{1, -4, -5\}$.

4. $\pm 1, \pm 13$ are possible rational zeros.

$$\begin{array}{r|rrrrr} 1 & 1 & -6 & 22 & -30 & 13 \\ & & 1 & -5 & 17 & -13 \\ \hline & 1 & -5 & 17 & -13 & 0 \end{array}$$

1 is a zero.

$$\begin{array}{r|rrrr} 1 & 1 & 5 & 17 & -13 \\ & & 1 & -4 & 13 \\ \hline & 1 & -4 & 13 & 0 \end{array}$$

1 is a double root.
$x^2 - 4x + 13 = 0$
$x = \frac{4 \pm \sqrt{16 - 52}}{2} = \frac{4 \pm \sqrt{-36}}{2} = 2 + 3i$
The solution set is $\{1, 2 + 3i, 2 - 3i\}$.

5. $f(x) = x^4 - 14x^3 + 71x^2 - 154x + 120$
$f(x) = x^4 + 14x^3 + 71x^2 + 154x + 120$
Since $f(x)$ has 4 changes of sign, there are 4, 2, or 0 positive real zeros.
Since $f(-x)$ has no changes of sign, there are no negative real zeros.

Exercise Set 3.4

1. $f(x) = x^3 + x^2 - 4x - 4$
p: $\pm 1, \pm 2, \pm 4$
q: ± 1
$\frac{p}{q}$: $\pm 1, \pm 2, \pm 4$

3. $f(x) = 3x^4 - 11x^3 - x^2 + 19x + 6$
p: $\pm 1, \pm 2, \pm 3, \pm 6$
q: $\pm 1, \pm 3$
$\frac{p}{q}$: $\pm 1, \pm 2, \pm 3, \pm 6, \pm \frac{1}{3}, \pm \frac{2}{3}$

5. $f(x) = 4x^4 - x^3 + 5x^2 - 2x - 6$
p: ±1, ±2, ±3, ±6
q: ±1, ±2, ±4
$\frac{p}{q}: \pm 1, \pm 2, \pm 3, \pm 6, \pm\frac{1}{2}, \pm\frac{1}{4}, \pm\frac{3}{2}, \pm\frac{3}{4}$

7. $f(x) = x^5 - x^4 - 7x^3 + 7x^2 - 12x - 12$
p: ±1, ±2, ±3 ±4 ±6 ±12
q: ±1
$\frac{p}{q}$: ±1, ±2, ±3 ±4 ±6 ±12

9. $f(x) = x^3 + x^2 - 4x - 4$

a. p: ±1, ±2, ±4
q: ±1
$\frac{p}{q}$: ±1, ±2, ±4

b.

2	1	1	–4	–4
		2	6	4
	1	3	2	0

2 is a zero.

c. $x^3 + x^2 - 4x - 4 = 0$
$(x-2)(x^2 + 3x + 2) = 0$
$(x-2)(x+2)(x+1) = 0$

$x - 2 = 0 \quad x + 2 = 0 \quad x + 1 = 0$
$x = 2,\ x = -2,\ x = -1$
The solution set is {2, –2, –1}.

11. $f(x) = 2x^3 - 3x^2 - 11x + 6$

a. p: ±1, ±2, ±3, ±6
q: ±1, ±2
$\frac{p}{q}: \pm 1, \pm 2, \pm 3, \pm 6, \pm\frac{1}{2}, \pm\frac{3}{2}$

b.

3	2	–3	–11	6
		6	9	–6
	2	3	–2	0

3 is a zero.

c. $2x^3 - 3x^2 - 11x + 6 = 0$
$(x-3)(2x^2 + 3x - 2) = 0$
$(x-3)(2x-1)(x+2) = 0$
$x = 3,\ x = \frac{1}{2},\ x = -2$
The solution set is $\left\{3, \frac{1}{2}, -2\right\}$.

13. $f(x) = 3x^3 + 7x^2 - 22x - 8$

a. p: ±1, ±2, ±4, ±8
q: ±1, ±3
$\frac{p}{q}: \pm 1, \pm 2, \pm 4, \pm 8, \pm\frac{1}{3}, \pm\frac{2}{3}, \pm\frac{4}{3}, \pm\frac{8}{3}$

b.

4	3	7	–22	–8
		12	76	216
	3	19	54	208

4 is not a zero.

2	3	7	–22	–8
		6	26	8
	3	13	4	0

2 is a zero.

c. $3x^3 + 7x^2 - 22x - 8 = 0$
$(x-2)(3x^2 + 13x + 4) = 0$
$(x-2)(3x+1)(x+4) = 0$
$x = 2,\ x = -\frac{1}{3},\ x = -4$
The solution set is $\left\{2, -\frac{1}{3}, -4\right\}$.

15. $x^3 - 2x^2 - 11x + 12 = 0$

a. $p: \pm 1, \pm 2, \pm 3, \pm 4, \pm 6, \pm 12$
$q: \pm 1$
$\frac{p}{q}: \pm 1, \pm 2, \pm 3, \pm 4, \pm 6, \pm 12$

b.

$$\begin{array}{r|rrrr} 3 & 1 & -2 & -11 & 12 \\ & & 3 & 3 & -24 \\ \hline & 1 & 1 & -8 & -12 \end{array}$$

3 is not a zero.

$$\begin{array}{r|rrrr} 4 & 1 & -2 & -11 & 12 \\ & & 4 & 8 & -12 \\ \hline & 1 & 2 & -3 & 0 \end{array}$$

4 is a zero.

c. $x^3 - 2x^2 - 11x + 12$
$(x-4)(x^2 + 2x - 3) = 0$
$(x-4)(x+3)(x-1) = 0$
$x - 4 = 0 \quad x + 3 = 0 \quad x - 1 = 0$
$x = 4 \qquad x = -3 \qquad x = 1$
The solution set is $\{-3, 1, 4\}$.

17. $x^3 - 10x - 12 = 0$

a. $p: \pm 1, \pm 2, \pm 3, \pm 4, \pm 6, \pm 12$
$q: \pm 1$
$\frac{p}{q}: \pm 1, \pm 2, \pm 3, \pm 4, \pm 6, \pm 12$

b.

$$\begin{array}{r|rrrr} -2 & 1 & 0 & -10 & -12 \\ & & -2 & 4 & 12 \\ \hline & 1 & -2 & -6 & 0 \end{array}$$

-2 is a zero.

c. $x^3 - 10x - 12 = 0$
$(x+2)(x^2 - 2x - 6) = 0$

$$x = \frac{2 \pm \sqrt{4+24}}{2} = \frac{2 \pm \sqrt{28}}{2} = \frac{2 \pm 2\sqrt{7}}{2} = 1 \pm \sqrt{7}$$

The solution set is $\{-2, 1+\sqrt{7}, 1-\sqrt{7}\}$.

19. $6x^3 + 25x^2 - 24x + 5 = 0$

a. $p: \pm 1, \pm 5$
$q: \pm 1, \pm 2, \pm 3, \pm 6$
$\frac{p}{q}: \pm 1, \pm 5, \pm \frac{1}{2}, \pm \frac{5}{2}, \pm \frac{1}{3}, \pm \frac{5}{3}, \pm \frac{1}{6}, \pm \frac{5}{6}$

b.

$$\begin{array}{r|rrrr} -5 & 6 & 25 & -24 & 5 \\ & & -30 & 25 & -5 \\ \hline & 6 & -5 & 1 & 0 \end{array}$$

-5 is a zero.

c. $6x^3 + 25x^2 - 24x + 5 = 0$
$(x+5)(6x^2 - 5x + 1) = 0$
$(x+5)(2x-1)(3x-1) = 0$
$x + 5 = 0 \quad 2x - 1 = 0 \quad 3x - 1 = 0$
$x = -5, \qquad x = \frac{1}{2}, \qquad x = \frac{1}{3}$

The solution set is $\left\{-5, \frac{1}{2}, \frac{1}{3}\right\}$.

21. $x^4 - 2x^3 - 5x^2 + 8x + 4 = 0$

a. $p: \pm 1, \pm 2, \pm 4$
$q: \pm 1$
$\frac{p}{q}: \pm 1, \pm 2, \pm 4$

b.

$$\begin{array}{r|rrrrr} 2 & 1 & -2 & -5 & 8 & 4 \\ & & 2 & 0 & -10 & -4 \\ \hline & 1 & 0 & -5 & -2 & 0 \end{array}$$

2 is a zero.

c. $x^4 - 2x^3 - 5x^2 + 8x + 4 = 0$
$(x-2)(x^3 - 5x - 2) = 0$

$$\begin{array}{r|rrrr} -2 & 1 & 0 & -5 & -2 \\ & & -2 & 4 & 2 \\ \hline & 1 & -2 & -1 & 0 \end{array}$$

-2 is a zero of $x^3 - 5x - 2 = 0$.

$(x-2)(x+2)(x^2 - 2x - 1) = 0$

$$x = \frac{2 \pm \sqrt{4+4}}{2} = \frac{2 \pm \sqrt{8}}{2} = \frac{2 \pm 2\sqrt{2}}{2}$$
$$= 1 \pm \sqrt{2}$$

The solution set is
$\{-2, 2, 1+\sqrt{2}, 1-\sqrt{2}\}$.

23. $f(x) = x^3 + 2x^2 + 5x + 4$
Since $f(x)$ has no sign variations, no positive real roots exist.
$f(-x) = -x^3 + 2x^2 - 5x + 4$
Since $f(-x)$ has 3 sign variations, 3 or 1 negative real roots exist.

25. $f(x) = 5x^3 - 3x^2 + 3x - 1$
Since $f(x)$ has 3 sign variations, 3 or 1 positive real roots exist.
$f(-x) = -5x^3 - 3x^2 - 3x - 1$
Since $f(-x)$ has no sign variations, no negative real roots exist.

27. $f(x) = 2x^4 - 5x^3 - x^2 - 6x + 4$
Since $f(x)$ has 2 sign variations, 2 or 0 positive real roots exist.
$f(-x) = 2x^4 + 5x^3 - x^2 + 6x + 4$
Since $f(-x)$ has 2 sign variations, 2 or 0 negative real roots exist.

29. $f(x) = x^3 - 4x^2 - 7x + 10$
$p: \pm 1, \pm 2, \pm 5, \pm 10$
$q: \pm 1$
$\frac{p}{q}: \pm 1, \pm 2, \pm 5, \pm 10$
Since $f(x)$ has 2 sign variations, 0 or 2 positive real zeros exist.
$f(-x) = -x^3 - 4x^2 + 7x + 10$
Since $f(-x)$ has 1 sign variation, exactly one negative real zeros exists.

$$\begin{array}{r|rrrr} -2 & 1 & -4 & -7 & 10 \\ & & -2 & 12 & -10 \\ \hline & 1 & -6 & 5 & 0 \end{array}$$

-2 is a zero.

$f(x) = (x+2)(x^2 - 6x + 5)$
$= (x+2)(x-5)(x-1)$
$x = -2, x = 5, x = 1$
The solution set is $\{-2, 5, 1\}$.

31. $2x^3 - x^2 - 9x - 4 = 0$

p: $\pm 1, \pm 2, \pm 4$

q: $\pm 1, \pm 2$

$\frac{p}{q}$: $\pm 1, \pm 2, \pm 4 \pm \frac{1}{2}$

1 positive real root exists.

$f(-x) = -2x^3 - x^2 + 9x - 4$ 2 or no negative real roots exist.

$$\begin{array}{r|rrrr} -\frac{1}{2} & 2 & -1 & -9 & -4 \\ & & -1 & 1 & 4 \\ \hline & 2 & -2 & -8 & 0 \end{array}$$

$-\frac{1}{2}$ is a root.

$$\left(x + \frac{1}{2}\right)\left(2x^2 - 2x - 8\right) = 0$$

$$2\left(x + \frac{1}{2}\right)\left(x^2 - x - 4\right) = 0$$

$$x = \frac{1 \pm \sqrt{1 + 16}}{2} = \frac{1 \pm \sqrt{17}}{2}$$

The solution set is

$$\left\{-\frac{1}{2}, \frac{1 + \sqrt{17}}{2}, \frac{1 - \sqrt{17}}{2}\right\}.$$

33. $x^4 - 3x^3 - 20x^2 - 24x - 8 = 0$

p: $\pm 1, \pm 2, \pm 4, \pm 8$

q: ± 1

$\frac{p}{q}$: $\pm 1, \pm 2, \pm 4 \pm 8$

1 positive real root exists.

3 or 1 negative real roots exist.

$$\begin{array}{r|rrrrr} -1 & 1 & -3 & -20 & -24 & -8 \\ & & -1 & 4 & 16 & 8 \\ \hline & 1 & -4 & -16 & -8 & 0 \end{array}$$

$$(x + 1)\left(x^3 - 4x^2 - 16x - 8\right) = 0$$

$$\begin{array}{r|rrrr} -2 & 1 & -4 & -16 & -8 \\ & & -2 & 12 & 8 \\ \hline & 1 & -6 & -4 & 0 \end{array}$$

$$(x + 1)(x + 2)\left(x^2 - 6x - 4\right) = 0$$

$$x = \frac{6 \pm \sqrt{36 + 16}}{2} = \frac{6 \pm \sqrt{52}}{2}$$

$$= \frac{6 \pm 2\sqrt{13}}{2} = \frac{3 \pm \sqrt{13}}{2}$$

The solution set is

$$\left\{-1, -2, 3 \pm \sqrt{13}, 3 - \sqrt{13}\right\}.$$

35. $f(x) = 3x^4 - 11x^3 - x^2 + 19x + 6$

p: $\pm 1, \pm 2, \pm 3, \pm 6$

q: $\pm 1, \pm 3$

$\frac{p}{q}$: $\pm 1, \pm 2, \pm 3, \pm 6, \pm \frac{1}{3}, \pm \frac{2}{3}$

2 or no positive real zeros exists.

$f(-x) = 3x^4 + 11x^3 - x^2 - 19x + 6$

2 or no negative real zeros exist.

$$\begin{array}{r|rrrrr} -1 & 3 & -11 & -1 & 19 & 6 \\ & & -3 & 14 & -13 & -6 \\ \hline & 3 & -14 & 13 & 6 & 0 \end{array}$$

$$f(x) = (x + 1)\left(3x^3 - 14x^2 + 13x + 6\right)$$

$$\begin{array}{r|rrrr} 2 & 3 & -14 & 13 & 6 \\ & & 6 & -16 & -6 \\ \hline & 3 & -8 & -3 & 0 \end{array}$$

$$f(x) = (x + 1)(x - 2)\left(3x^2 - 8x - 3\right)$$

$$= (x + 1)(x - 2)(3x + 1)(x - 3)$$

$$x = -1,\ x = 2\ x = -\frac{1}{3},\ x = 3$$

The solution set is $\left\{-1, 2, -\frac{1}{3}, 3\right\}$.

37. $4x^4 - x^3 + 5x^2 - 2x - 6 = 0$
p: $\pm 1, \pm 2, \pm 3, \pm 6$
q: $\pm 1, \pm 2, \pm 4$
$\frac{p}{q}$: $\pm 1, \pm 2, \pm 3, \pm 6, \pm\frac{1}{2}, \pm\frac{3}{2}, \pm\frac{1}{4}, \pm\frac{3}{4}$
3 or 1 positive real roots exists.
1 negative real root exists.

1	4	−1	5	−2	−6
		4	3	8	6
	4	3	8	6	0

$(x-1)(4x^3 + 3x^2 + 8x + 6) = 0$
$4x^3 + 3x^2 + 8x + 6 = 0$ has no positive real roots.

$-\frac{3}{4}$	4	3	8	6
		−3	0	−6
	4	0	8	0

$(x-1)\left(x+\frac{3}{4}\right)(4x^2+8) = 0$
$4(x-1)\left(x+\frac{3}{4}\right)(x^2+2) = 0$
$x^2 + 2 = 0$
$x^2 = -2$
$x = \pm i\sqrt{2}$
The solution set is $\left\{1, -\frac{3}{4}, i\sqrt{2}, -i\sqrt{2}\right\}$.

39. $2x^5 + 7x^4 - 18x^2 - 8x + 8 = 0$
p: $\pm 1, \pm 2, \pm 4, \pm 8$
q: $\pm 1, \pm 2$
$\frac{p}{q}$: $\pm 1, \pm 2, \pm 4, \pm 8, \pm\frac{1}{2}$
2 or no positive real roots exists.
3 or 1 negative real root exist.

−2	2	7	0	−18	−8	8
		−4	−6	12	12	−8
	2	3	−6	−6	4	0

$(x+2)(2x^4 + 3x^3 - 6x^2 - 6x + 4) = 0$
$4x^3 + 3x^2 + 8x + 6 = 0$ has no positive real roots.

−2	2	3	−6	−6	4
		−4	2	8	−4
	2	−1	−4	2	0

$(x+2)^2(2x^3 - x^2 - 4x + 2)$

$\frac{1}{2}$	2	−1	−4	2
		1	0	2
	2	0	−4	0

$(x+2)^2\left(x-\frac{1}{2}\right)(2x^2-4) = 0$
$2(x+2)^2\left(x-\frac{1}{2}\right)(x^2-2) = 0$
$x^2 - 2 = 0$
$x^2 = 2$
$x = \pm\sqrt{2}$
The solution set is $\left\{-2, \frac{1}{2}, \sqrt{2}, -\sqrt{2}\right\}$.

41. a. $f(x) = 6.2$
$x = 3,\ x \approx 4.2$

b. degree: 4
leading coefficient: negative

43. $14W^3 - 17W^2 - 16W + 34 = 211$
$14W^3 - 17W^2 - 16W - 177 = 0$
p: $\pm 1, \pm 3, \pm 59, \pm 177$
q: $\pm 1, \pm 2, \pm 7, \pm 14$

3	14	−17	−16	−177
		42	75	177
	14	25	59	0

$(x-3)(14x^2 + 25x + 59) = 0$
$b^2 - 4ac = 625 - 3304 < 0$
$W = 3$ mm
The abdominal width is 3 millimeters.

45. $V = lwh$
$72 = (h + 7)(2h)(h)$
$72 = 2h^2(h + 7)$
$2h^3 + 14h^2 - 72 = 0$
$h^3 + 7h^2 - 36 = 0$

2	1	7	0	−36
		2	18	36
	1	9	18	0

$(h-2)(h^2 + 9h + 18) = 0$
$(h-2)(h+3)(h+6) = 0$
$h = 2\ \ h = -3\ \ h = -6$
$h = -3$ and $h = -6$ do not make sense.
$h = 2$
$h + 7 = 9$
$2h = 4$
The dimensions are 2 in. by 9 in. by 4 in.

47.–53. Answers may vary.

55. $6x^3 - 19x^2 + 16x - 4 = 0$
p: $\pm 1, \pm 2, \pm 4$
q: $\pm 1, \pm 2, \pm 3, \pm 6$
$\frac{p}{q}: \pm 1, \pm 2, \pm 4, \pm \frac{1}{2}, \pm \frac{1}{3}, \pm \frac{2}{3}, \pm \frac{4}{3}, \pm \frac{1}{6}$

From the graph, we see that the solutions are $\frac{1}{2}, \frac{2}{3}$ and 2.

57. $4x^4 + 4x^3 + 7x^2 - x - 2 = 0$
p: $\pm 1, \pm 2$
q: $\pm 1, \pm 2, \pm 4$
$\frac{p}{q}: \pm 1, \pm 2, \pm \frac{1}{2}, \pm \frac{1}{4}$

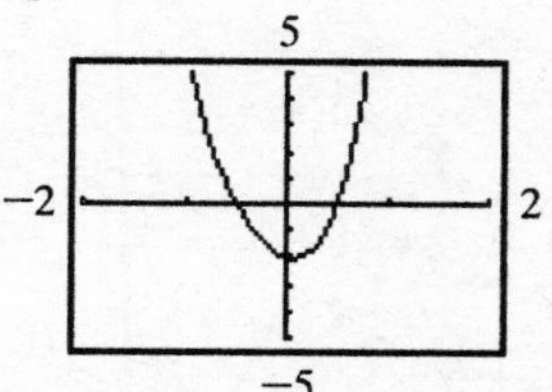

From the graph, we see that the solutions are $-\frac{1}{2}$ and $\frac{1}{2}$.

59. $f(x) = x^5 - x^4 + x^3 - x^2 + x - 8$
$f(x)$ has 5 sign variations, so either 5, 3, or 1 positive real roots exist.
$f(-x) = -x^5 - x^4 - x^3 - x^2 - x - 8$
$f(-x)$ has no sign variations, so no negative real roots exist.

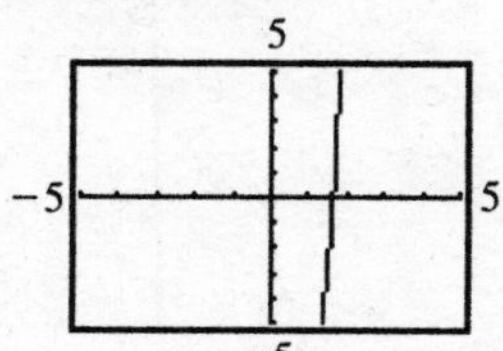

61. a. False; the equation has 0 sign variations, so no positive roots exist.

b. False; Descartes's Rule gives the possible number of roots.

c. False; Every polynomial equation of degree 3 has at least one real root.

d. True

(d) is true.

63. $(2x+1)(x+5)(x+2)-3x(x+5)=208$

$\left(2x^2+11x+5\right)(x+2)-3x^2-15x=208$

$2x^3+4x^2+11x^2+22x+5x$
$+10-3x^2-15x=208$

$2x^3+15x^2+27x-3x^2-15x-198=0$

$2x^3+12x^2+12x-198=0$

$2\left(x^3+6x^2+6x-99\right)=0$

3	1	6	6	–99
		3	27	99
	1	9	33	0

$x^2+9x+33=0$

$b^2-4ac=-51$

$x=3$ in.

Section 3.5

Check Point Exercises

1.

–7	2	11	–7	–6
		–14	21	–98
	2	–3	14	–104

The signs alternate.

2	2	11	–7	–6
		4	30	46
	2	15	23	40

All the numbers are nonnegative. Thus, –7 is a lower bound and 2 is an upper bound.

2. $f(-3)=3(-3)^3-10(-3)+9=-42$

$f(-2)=3(-2)^3-10(-2)+9=5$

The sign change shows there is a zero between –3 and –2.

3. $(x-2+i)(x-2-i)=x^2-2x-ix-2x+4$
$+2i+ix-2i-i^2=x^2-4x+5$

$$\begin{array}{r} x^2-4x-21 \\ x^2-4x+5\overline{\big)\,x^4-8x^3+0x^2+64x-105} \\ \underline{x^4-4x^3+5x^2} \\ -4x^3-5x^2+64x \\ \underline{-4x^3+16x^2-20x} \\ -21x^2+84x-105 \\ \underline{-21x^2+84x-105} \\ 0 \end{array}$$

$x^2-4x-21=0$

$(x-7)(x+3)=0$

$x=7$ or $x=-3$

The solution set is $\{-3,7,2+i,2-i\}$.

4. a. $x^4-4x^2-5=\left(x^2-5\right)\left(x^2+1\right)$

b. $\left(x+\sqrt{5}\right)\left(x-\sqrt{5}\right)\left(x^2+1\right)$

c $\left(x+\sqrt{5}\right)\left(x-\sqrt{5}\right)(x+i)(x-i)$

5. $(x+3)(x-i)(x+i)=(x+3)(x^2+1)$

$f(x)=a_n(x+3)(x^2+1)$

$f(1)=a_n(1+3)(1^2+1)=8a_n=8$

$a_n=1$

$f(x)=(x+3)(x^2+1)$ or x^3+3x^2+x+3

Exercise Set 3.5

1. $x^4-5x^3+11x^2+33x-18=0$

–4	1	–5	11	33	–18
		–4	36	–188	620
	1	–9	47	–155	602

Since signs alternate, –4 is a lower bound.

7	1	−5	11	33	−18
		7	14	175	1456
	1	2	25	208	1438

Since no sign is negative, 7 is an upper bound.

3. $2x^3 + 5x^2 - 8x - 7 = 0$

−4	2	5	−8	7
		−8	12	−16
	2	−3	4	−9

Since signs alternate, −4 is a lower bound.

2	2	5	−8	7
		4	18	20
	2	9	10	27

Since no sign is negative, 2 is an upper bound.

5. $x^4 + 3x^3 + 2x^2 - 5x + 12 = 0$

a. p: ±1, ±2, ±3, ±4, ±6, ±12
q: ±1
$\frac{p}{q}: \pm 1, \pm 2, \pm 3, \pm 4, +6, \pm 12$

b.

1	1	3	2	−5	12
		1	4	6	1
	1	4	6	1	13

1 is not a root.
1 is an upper bound.

c. Eliminate all positive possible rational roots.

d.

−3	1	3	2	−5	12
		−3	0	−6	33
	1	0	2	−11	45

−3 is not a root.
−3 is a lower bound.

e. Eliminate −3, −4, −6 and −12.

7. $f(x) = x^3 - x - 1$
$f(1) = -1$
$f(2) = 5$
$f(1.3) = -0.103$
$f(1.4) = 0.344$
$f(1.35) = 0.11038$
To the nearest tenth, the zero is 1.3.

9. $f(x) = 2x^4 - 4x^2 + 1$
$f(-1) = -1$
$f(0) = 1$
$f(-0.5) = 0.125$
$f(-0.6) = -0.1808$
$f(-0.55) = -0.027$
To the nearest tenth, the zero is −0.5.

11. $f(x) = x^3 + x^2 - 2x + 1$
$f(-3) = -11$
$f(-2) = 1$
$f(-2.2) = -0.408$
$f(-2.1) = 0.349$
$f(-2.15) = -0.0159$
To the nearest tenth, the zero is −2.1.

13. $f(x) = 3x^3 - 10x + 9$
$f(-3) = -42$
$f(-2) = 5$
$f(-2.1) = 2.217$
$f(-2.2) = -0.944$
$f(-2.15) = 0.68488$
To the nearest tenth, the zero is −2.2.

15. $x = -2i$, so $x = 2i$ also.
$(x + 2i)(x - 2i) = x^2 + 4$

$$\begin{array}{r} x - 2 \\ x^2 + 4 \overline{\smash{)}\, x^3 + 4x - 2x^2 - 8} \\ \underline{x^3 + 4x} \qquad\qquad \\ -2x^2 - 8 \\ \underline{-2x^2 - 8} \\ 0 \end{array}$$

$x - 2 = 0$
$x = 2$
Solution: $\{-2i, 2i, 2\}$

17. $x = (1 + i)$, so $x = (1 - i)$ also.
$(x - 1 - i)(x - 1 + i)$
$= x^2 - x + ix - x + 1 - i - ix + i - i^2$
$= x^2 - 2x + 2$

$$\begin{array}{r|l} & 3x - 1 \\ \hline x^2 - 2x + 2 & 3x^3 - 7x^2 + 8x - 2 \\ & \underline{3x^3 - 6x^2 + 6x} \\ & -x^2 + 2x - 2 \\ & \underline{-x^2 + 2x - 2} \\ & 0 \end{array}$$

$3x - 1 = 0$
$x = \frac{1}{3}$
Solution: $\left\{1 - i, 1 + i, \frac{1}{3}\right\}$

19. $x = 2 - i$, so $x = 2 + i$ also.
$(x - 2 + i)(x - 2 - i)$
$= x^2 - 2x - ix - 2x + 4 + 2i + ix - 2i - i^2$
$= x^2 - 4x + 5$

$$\begin{array}{r|l} & x^2 + 4x + 5 \\ \hline x^2 - 4x + 5 & x^4 + 0x^3 - 6x^2 + 0x + 25 \\ & \underline{x^4 - 4x^3 + 5x^2} \\ & 4x^3 - 11x^2 + 0x \\ & \underline{4x^3 - 16x^2 + 20x} \\ & 5x^2 - 20x + 25 \\ & \underline{5x^2 - 20x + 25} \\ & 0 \end{array}$$

$x^2 + 4x + 5 = 0$
$x = \frac{-4 \pm \sqrt{16 - 4(5)}}{2} = \frac{-4 \pm \sqrt{-4}}{2}$
$= \frac{-4 \pm 2i}{2} = -2 \pm i$
The solution set is
$\{2 - i, 2 + i, -2 + i, -2 - i\}$,

21. $x = 2 - i$, so $x = 2 + i$ also.
$(x - 2 + i)(x - 2 - i)$
$= x^2 - 2x - xi - 2x + 4 + 2i + ix - 2i - i^2$
$= x^2 - 4x + 5$

$$\begin{array}{r|l} & x^2 - 4x + 5 \\ \hline x^2 - 4x + 5 & x^4 - 8x^3 + 0x^2 + 64x - 105 \\ & \underline{x^4 - 4x^3 + 5x^2} \\ & -4x^3 - 5x^2 + 64x \\ & \underline{-4x^3 + 16x^2 - 20x} \\ & -21x^2 + 84x - 105 \\ & \underline{-21x^2 + 84x - 105} \\ & 0 \end{array}$$

$x^2 - 4x - 21 = 0$
$(x - 7)(x + 3) = 0$
$x = 7, x = -3$
The solution set is $\{2 + i, 2 - i, -3, 7\}$.

23. $x^4 - x^2 - 20$

a. $\left(x^2 - 5\right)\left(x^2 + 4\right)$

b. $\left(x + \sqrt{5}\right)\left(x - \sqrt{5}\right)\left(x^2 + 4\right)$

c. $\left(x + \sqrt{5}\right)\left(x - \sqrt{5}\right)(x + 2i)(x - 2i)$

25. $x^4 + x^2 - 6$

a. $\left(x^2 - 2\right)\left(x^2 + 3\right)$

b. $\left(x + \sqrt{2}\right)\left(x - \sqrt{2}\right)\left(x^2 + 3\right)$

c. $\left(x + \sqrt{2}\right)\left(x - \sqrt{2}\right)\left(x + i\sqrt{3}\right)\left(x - i\sqrt{3}\right)$

27. $x^4 - 2x^3 + x^2 - 8x - 12$

a.
$$\begin{array}{r} x^2 - 2x - 3 \\ x^2 + 4 \overline{\big)\, x^4 - 2x^3 + x^2 + 8x - 12} \\ \underline{x^4 \qquad\;\; - 4x^2 \qquad\qquad} \\ -2x^3 - 3x^2 + 8x \qquad \\ \underline{-2x^3 \qquad\quad - 8x} \qquad \\ -3x^2 \quad - 12 \\ \underline{-3x^2 \quad - 12} \end{array}$$

$\left(x^2 - 2x - 3\right)\left(x^2 + 4\right)$

$(x-3)(x+1)\left(x^2+4\right)$

b. $(x-3)(x+1)\left(x^2+4\right)$

c. $(x-3)(x+1)(x+2i)(x-2i)$

29. $(x-1)(x+5i)(x-5i)$

$= (x-1)\left(x^2+25\right)$

$= x^3 + 25x - x^2 - 25$

$= x^3 - x^2 + 25x - 25$

$f(x) = a_n\left(x^3 - x^2 + 25x - 25\right)$

$f(-1) = a_n(-1-1-25-25)$

$-104 = a_n(-52)$

$a_n = 2$

$f(x) = 2\left(x^3 - x^2 + 25x - 25\right)$

$f(x) = 2x^3 - 2x^2 + 50x - 50$

31. $(x+5)(x-4-3i)(x-4+3i)$

$= (x+5)\left(x^2 - 4x + 3ix - 4x + 16 - 12i\right.$

$\left.-3ix + 12i - 9i^2\right)$

$= (x+5)\left(x^2 - 8x + 25\right)$

$= \left(x^3 - 8x^2 + 25x + 5x^2 - 40x + 125\right)$

$= x^3 - 3x^2 - 15x + 125$

$f(x) = a_n(x^3 - 3x^2 - 15x + 125)$

$f(2) = a_n\left(2^3 - 3(2)^2 - 15(2) + 125\right)$

$91 = a_n(91)$

$a_n = 1$

$f(x) = 1\left(x^3 - 3x^2 - 15x + 125\right)$

$f(x) = x^3 - 3x^2 - 15x + 125$

33. $(x-i)(x+i)(x-3i)(x+3i)$

$= \left(x^2 - i^2\right)\left(x^2 - 9i^2\right)$

$= \left(x^2 + 1\right)\left(x^2 + 9\right)$

$= x^4 + 10x^2 + 9$

$f(x) = a_n(x^4 + 10x^2 + 9)$

$f(-1) = a_n((-1)^4 + 10(-1)^2 + 9)$

$20 = a_n(20)$

$a_n = 1$

$f(x) = x^4 + 10x^2 + 9$

35. $(x+2)(x-5)(x-3+2i)(x-3-2i)$

$= \left(x^2 - 3x - 10\right)$

$\left(x^2 - 3x - 2ix - 3x + 9 + 6i + 2ix - 6i - 4i\right)$

$= \left(x^2 - 3x - 10\right)\left(x^2 - 6x + 13\right)$

$= x^4 - 6x + 13x^2 - 3x^3 + 18x^2$

$- 39x - 10x^2 + 60x - 130$

$= x^4 - 9x^3 + 21x^2 + 21x - 130$

$f(x) = a_n\left(x^4 - 9x^3 + 21x^2 + 21x - 130\right)$

$f(1) = a_n(1 - 9 + 21 + 21 - 130)$

$-96 = a_n(-96)$

$a_n = 1$

$f(x) = x^4 - 9x^3 + 21x^2 + 21x - 130$

37. $f(x) = x^3 - x^2 + 25x - 25$

p: ±1, ±5, ±25

q: ±1

$\frac{p}{q}: \pm 1, \pm 5, \pm 25$

$$\begin{array}{r|rrrr} 1 & 1 & -1 & 25 & -25 \\ & & 1 & 0 & 25 \\ \hline & 1 & 0 & 25 & 0 \end{array}$$

$x = 1$

$x^2 + 25 = 0$

$x^2 = -25$

$x = \pm\sqrt{-25} = \pm 5i$

$f(x) = (x - 1)(x - 5i)(x + 5i)$

39. $f(x) = x^3 - 8x^2 + 25x - 26$

p: ±1, ±2, ±13, ±26

q: ±1

p: ±1, ±2, ±13, ±26

q:

$$\begin{array}{r|rrrr} 2 & 1 & -8 & 25 & -26 \\ & & 2 & -12 & 26 \\ \hline & 1 & -6 & 13 & 0 \end{array}$$

$x = 2$

$x^2 - 6x + 13 = 0$

$x = \dfrac{6 \pm \sqrt{36 - 52}}{2} = \dfrac{6 \pm \sqrt{-16}}{2}$

$= \dfrac{6 \pm 4i}{2} = 3 \pm 2i$

$f(x) = (x - 2)(x - 3 + 2i)(x - 3 - 2i)$

41. $f(x) = x^4 + 37x^2 + 36$

$x^4 + 37x^2 + 36 = 0$

$\left(x^2 + 36\right)\left(x^2 + 1\right) = 0$

$x^2 = -36 \qquad x^2 = -1$

$x = \pm 6i \qquad x = \pm i$

$f(x) = (x - 6i)(x + 6i)(x - i)(x + i)$

43. $f(x) = 16x^4 + 36x^3 + 16x^2 + x - 30$

p: ±1, ±2, ±3, ±5, ±6, ±10, ±15, ±30

q: ±1, ±2, ±4, ±8, ±16

$\frac{p}{q}$: ±1, ±2, ±3, ±5, ±6, ±10, ±15, ±30,

$\pm\frac{1}{2}, \pm\frac{3}{2}, \pm\frac{5}{2}, \pm\frac{15}{2}, \pm\frac{1}{4}, \pm\frac{3}{4}, \pm\frac{5}{4},$

$\pm\frac{15}{4}, \pm\frac{30}{4}, \pm\frac{1}{8}, \pm\frac{3}{8}, \pm\frac{5}{8}, \pm\frac{15}{8},$

$\pm\frac{30}{8}, \pm\frac{1}{16}, \pm\frac{3}{16}, \pm\frac{5}{16}, \pm\frac{15}{16}$

$$\begin{array}{r|rrrrr} -2 & 16 & 36 & 16 & 1 & -30 \\ & & -32 & -8 & -16 & 30 \\ \hline & 16 & 4 & 8 & -15 & 0 \end{array}$$

$x = -2$

$0 = 16x^3 + 4x^2 + 8x - 15$

$$\begin{array}{r|rrrr} \frac{3}{4} & 16 & 4 & 8 & -15 \\ & & 12 & 12 & 15 \\ \hline & 16 & 16 & 20 & 0 \end{array}$$

$x = \frac{3}{4}$

$16x^2 + 16x + 20 = 0$

$x = \dfrac{-16 \pm \sqrt{-1024}}{32} = \dfrac{-16 \pm 32i}{32}$

$x = -\frac{1}{2} \pm i$

$f(x)$

$= (x + 2)(4x - 3)(2x + 1 - 2i)(2x + 1 + 2i)$

45. about 2.5 years

47. Answers may vary.

49. $27x + 163 = 458$
$27x = 295$
$x = 10.9$
According to the linear model, spending will reach \$458 billion, 10.9 or almost 11 years after 1995, just before 2006.

$1.2x^2 + 15.2x + 181.4 = 458$

$1.2x^2 + 15.2x - 276.6 = 0$

$$x = \frac{-15.2 \pm \sqrt{231.04 + 1327.68}}{2.4}$$

$$\approx \frac{-15.2 \pm 39.48}{2.4}$$

$x \approx -22.78$ or $x \approx 10.12$

According to quadratic model, spending will reach \$458 billion 10.12 years after 1995, in 2005.

$0.08x^3 - 0.06x^2 + 20.08x$
$+178.32 = 458$

$0.08x^3 - 0.06x^2 + 20.08x$
$-279.68 = 0$

$0.08(10.1)^3 - 0.06(10.1)^2 +$
$20.08(10.1) - 279.68$
$= -0.56852$

$0.08(10.2)^3 - 0.06(10.2)^2 +$
$20.08(10.2) - 279.68$
$= 3.79$

There is a solution between 10.1 and 10.2. According to the third-degree polynomial model, spending will reach \$458 billion, just over 10 years after 1995, in 2005.
The third-degree polynomial model is best.

51.–53. Answers may vary.

55. $f(x) = 2x^3 + x^2 - 14x - 7$

−3	2	1	−14	−7
		−6	15	−3
	2	−5	1	−10

3	2	1	−14	−7
		6	21	21
	2	7	7	14

−3 is a lower bound; 3 is an upper bound.

57. $f(x) = -0.00002x^3 + 0.008x^2 - 0.3x + 6.95$

a. $f(x) = -0.00002x^3 + 0.008x^2 - 0.3x + 6.95$

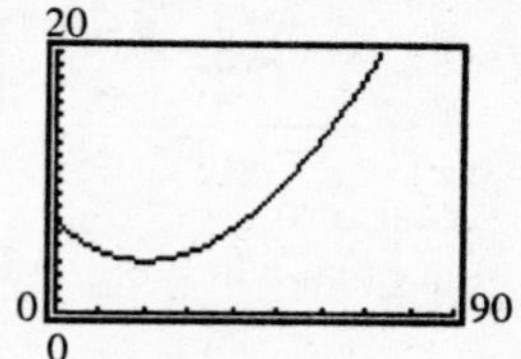

The graph suggests that people visit a physician more often as they age.

b. $f(x) = -0.00002x^3 + 0.008x^2 - 0.3x + 6.95$
$13.43 = -0.00002x^3 + 0.008x^2 - 0.3x + 6.95$
$0 = -0.00002x^3 + 0.008x^2 - 0.3x - 6.48$
$x = 60 \Rightarrow$ 60 years of age

c. Use Trace to find the value of the function at $y = 13.43$.

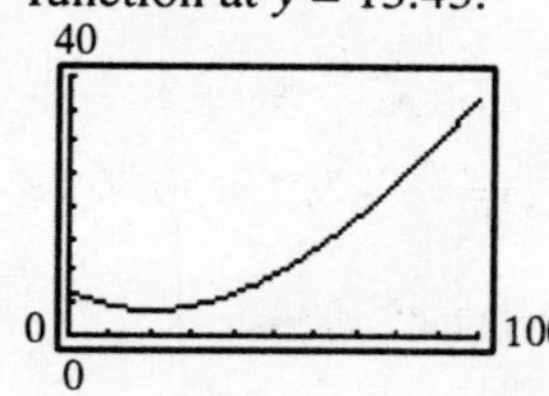

59. $f(x) = 3x^5 - 2x^4 + 6x^3 - 4x^2 - 24x + 16$

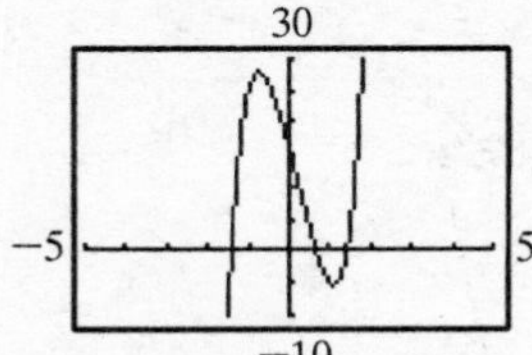

3 real zeros
2 nonreal complex zeros

61. $f(x) = x^6 - 64$

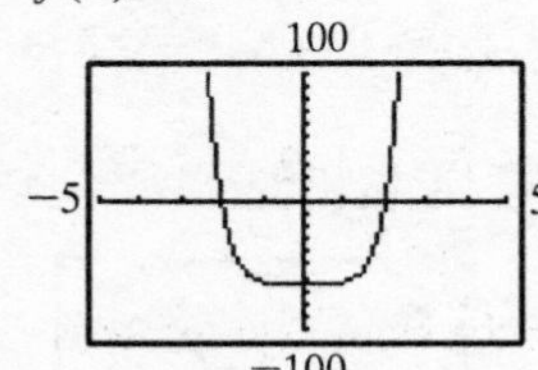

2 real zeros
4 nonreal complex zeros

63. Because the polynomial has no obvious changes of direction but the graph is obviously not linear, the smallest degree is 3.

65.–67. Answers may vary.

Section 3.6

Check Point Exercises

1. a. $x - 5 = 0$
$x = 5$
$\{x|x \neq 5\}$

b. $x^2 - 25 = 0$
$x^2 = 25$
$x = \pm 5$
$\{x|x \neq 5, x \neq 5\}$

c. The denominator cannot equal zero. All real numbers.

2. a. $x^2 - 1 = 0$
$x^2 = 1$
$x = 1, \; x = -1$

b. $g(x) = \dfrac{x-1}{x^2-1} = \dfrac{x-1}{(x-1)(x+1)} = \dfrac{1}{x+1}$
$x = -1$

c. The denominator cannot equal zero. No vertical asymptotes

3. a. Since $n = m$, $y = \dfrac{9}{3} = 3$ is a horizontal asymptote.

b. Since $n < m$, $y = 0$ is a horizontal asymptote.

c. Since $n > m$, there is no horizontal asymptote.

4. $f(x) = \dfrac{3x}{x-2}$
$f(-x) = \dfrac{3(-x)}{-x-2} = \dfrac{3x}{x+2}$
no symmetry
$f(0) = \dfrac{3(0)}{0-2} = 0$
The y-intercept is 0.
$3x = 0$
$x = 0$
The x-intercept is 0.
Vertical asymptote:
$x - 2 = 0$
$x = 2$
Horizontal asymptote:
$y = \dfrac{3}{1} = 3$

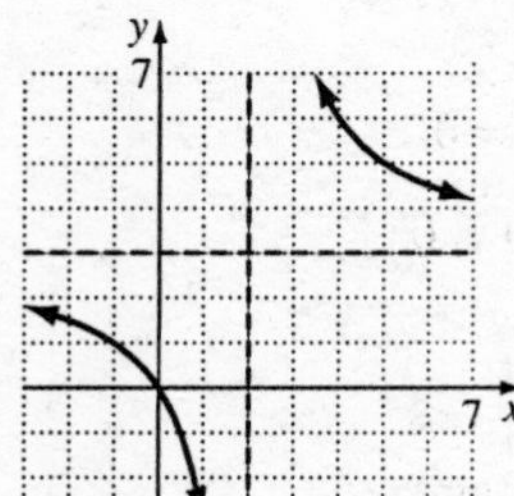

5. $f(x)=\dfrac{2x^2}{x^2-9}$

$f(-x)=\dfrac{2(-x)^2}{(-x)^2-9}=\dfrac{2x^2}{x^2-9}=f(x)$

The y-axis symmetry.

$f(0)=\dfrac{2(0)^2}{0^2-9}=0$

The y-intercept is 0.

$2x^2=0$

$x=0$

The x-intercept is 0.

vertical asymptotes:

$x^2-9=0$

$x=3,\ x=-3$

horizontal asymptote:

$y=\dfrac{2}{1}=2$

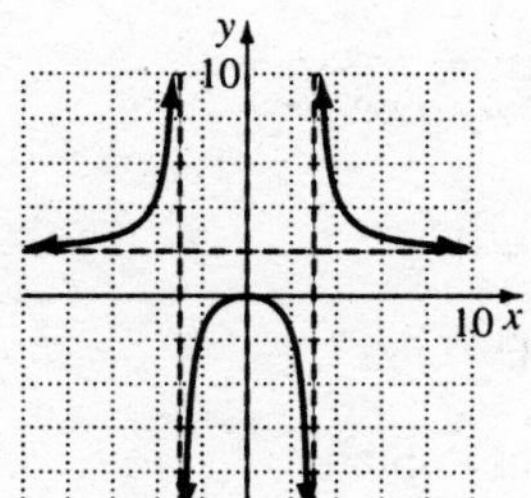

6. $f(x)=\dfrac{x^4}{x^2+2}$

$f(-x)=\dfrac{(-x)^4}{(-x)^2+2}=\dfrac{x^4}{x^2+2}=f(x)$

y-axis symmetry

$f(0)=\dfrac{0^4}{0^2+2}=0$

The y-intercept is 0.

$x^4=0$

$x=0$

The x-intercept is 0.

vertical asymptotes:

$x^2+2=0$

$x^2=-2$

no vertical asymptotes

horizontal asymptote:

Since $n>m$, there is no horizontal asymptote.

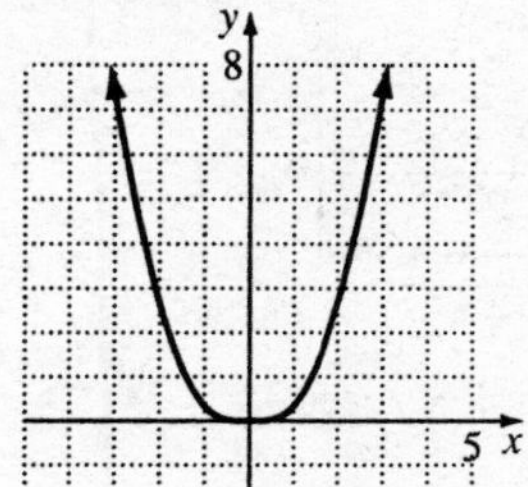

7.

$$\begin{array}{r|rrr} 2 & 2 & -5 & 7 \\ & & 4 & -2 \\ \hline & 2 & -1 & 5 \end{array}$$

the equation of the slant asymptote is $y=2x-1$.

8. a. $\overline{C}(1000)=\dfrac{30(1000)+300{,}000}{1000}=\$330$

When 1000 pairs of shoes are produced, it costs \$330 to produce each pair.

$\overline{C}(10{,}000)=\dfrac{30(10{,}000)+300{,}000}{10{,}000}=\$60$

When 10,000 pairs of shoes are produced, it costs \$60 to produce each pair.

$\overline{C}(100{,}000)=\dfrac{30(100{,}000)+300{,}000}{100{,}000}=\$33$

When 100,000 pairs of shoes are produced, it cost \$33 to produce each pair.

These are the average costs per pair of shoes for producing 1000, 10,000, and 100,000 pairs per week.

b. horizontal asymptote:

$y=\dfrac{30}{1}=30$

The cost per pair of shoes approaches \$30 as more shoes are produced.

Exercise Set 3.6

1. $f(x) = \dfrac{5x}{x-4}$
$\{x | x \neq 4\}$

3. $g(x) = \dfrac{3x^2}{(x-5)(x+4)}$
$\{x | x \neq 5, x \neq -4\}$

5. $h(x) = \dfrac{x+7}{x^2-49}$
$x^2 - 49 = (x-7)(x+7)$
$\{x | x \neq 7, x \neq -7\}$

7. $f(x) = \dfrac{x+7}{x^2+49}$
all real numbers

9. $-\infty$

11. $-\infty$

13. 0

15. $+\infty$

17. $-\infty$

19. 1

21. $f(x) = \dfrac{x}{x+4}$
$x + 4 = 0$
$x = -4$
vertical asymptote: $x = 0,\ x - -4$

23. $g(x) = \dfrac{x+3}{x(x+4)}$
$x(x+4) = 0$
$x = 0, x = -4$
vertical asymptotes: $x = 0,\ x = -4$

25. $h(x) = \dfrac{x}{x(x+4)} = \dfrac{1}{x+4}$
$x + 4 = 0$
$x = -4$
vertical asymptote: $x = -4$

27. $r(x) = \dfrac{x}{x^2+4}$
$x^2 + 4$ has no real zeros
There are no vertical asymptotes.

29. $f(x) = \dfrac{12x}{3x^2+1}$
$n < m$
horizontal asymptote: $y = 0$

31. $g(x) = \dfrac{12x^2}{3x^2+1}$
$n = m,$
horizontal asymptote: $y = \dfrac{12}{3} = 4$

33. $h(x) = \dfrac{12x^3}{3x^2+1}$
$n > m$
no horizontal asymptote

35. $f(x) = \dfrac{-2x+1}{3x+5}$
$n = m$
horizontal asymptote: $y = -\dfrac{2}{3}$

37. $f(x)=\dfrac{4x}{x-2}$

$f(-x)=\dfrac{4(-x)}{(-x)-2}=\dfrac{4x}{x+2}$

$f(-x)\neq f(x), f(-x)\neq -f(x)$

no symmetry

y-intercept: $y=\dfrac{4(0)}{0-2}=0$

x-intercept: $4x=0$

$x=0$

vertical asymptote:

$x-2=0$

$x=2$

horizontal asymptote:

$n=m$, so $y=\dfrac{4}{1}=4$

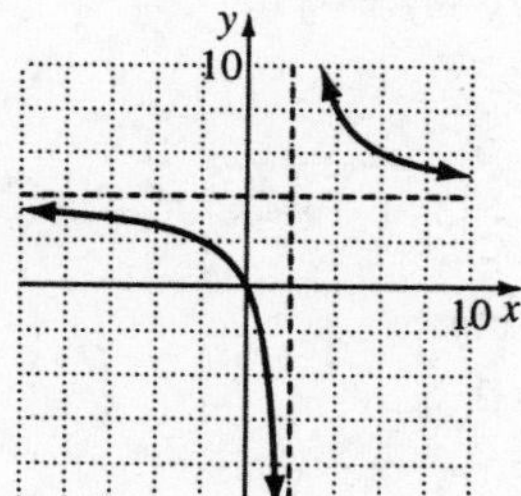

39. $f(x)=\dfrac{2x}{x^2-4}$

$f(-x)=\dfrac{2(-x)}{(-x)^2-4}=-\dfrac{2x}{x^2-4}=-f(x)$

Origin symmetry

y-intercept: $\dfrac{2(0)}{0^2-4}=\dfrac{0}{-4}=0$

x-intercept:

$2x=0$

$x=0$

vertical asymptotes:

$x^2-4=0$

$x=\pm 2$

horizontal asymptote:

$n<m$ so $y=0$

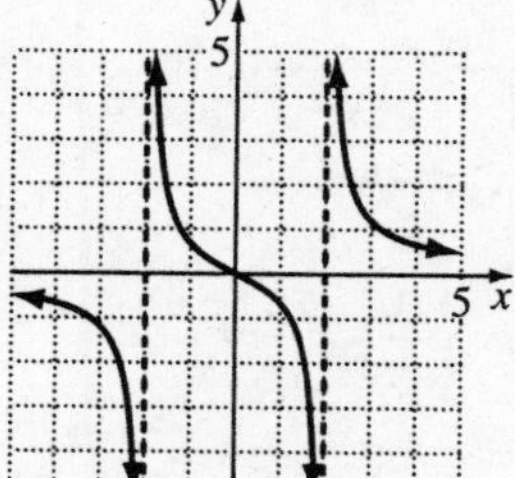

41. $f(x)=\dfrac{2x^2}{x^2-1}$

$f(-x)=\dfrac{2(-x)^2}{(-x)^2-1}=\dfrac{2x^2}{x^2-1}=f(x)$

y-axis symmetry

y-intercept: $y=\dfrac{2(0)^2}{0^2-1}=\dfrac{0}{1}=0$

x-intercept:

$2x^2=0$

$x=0$

vertical asymptote:

$x^2-1=0$

$x^2=1$

$x=\pm 1$

horizontal asymptote:

$n=m$, so $y=\dfrac{2}{1}=2$

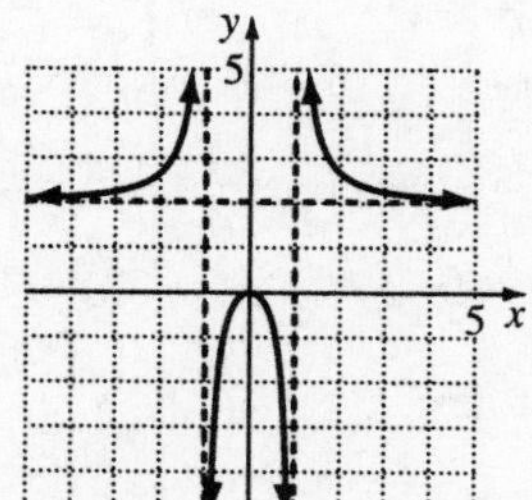

43. $f(x) = \frac{-x}{x+1}$

$f(-x) = \frac{-(-x)}{(-x)+1} = \frac{x}{-x+1}$

$f(-x) \neq f(x), f(-x) \neq -f(x)$

no symmetry

y-intercept: $y = \frac{-(0)}{0+1} = \frac{0}{1} = 0$

x-intercept:

$-x = 0$

$x = 0$

vertical asymptote:

$x + 1 = 0$

$x = -1$

horizontal asymptote:

$n = m$, so $y = \frac{-1}{1} = -1$

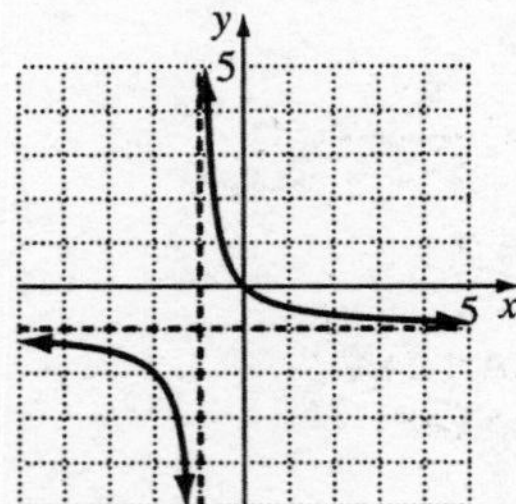

45. $f(x) = -\frac{1}{x^2 - 4}$

$f(-x) = -\frac{1}{(-x)^2 - 4} = -\frac{1}{x^2 - 4} = f(x)$

y-axis symmetry

y-intercept: $y = -\frac{1}{0^2 - 4} = \frac{1}{4}$

x-intercept: $-1 \neq 0$

no x-intercept

vertical asymptotes:

$x^2 - 4 = 0$

$x^2 = 4$

$x = \pm 2$

horizontal asymptote:

$n < m$ or $y = 0$

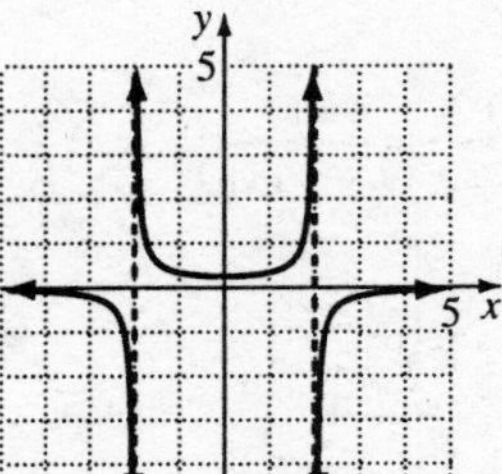

47. $f(x) = \frac{2}{x^2 + x - 2}$

$f(-x) = -\frac{2}{(-x)^2 - x - 2} = \frac{2}{x^2 - x - 2}$

$f(-x) \neq f(x), f(-x) \neq -f(x)$

no symmetry

y-intercept: $y = \frac{2}{0^2 + 0 - 2} = \frac{2}{-2} = -1$

x-intercept: none

vertical asymptotes:

$x^2 + x - 2 = 0$

$(x+2)(x-1) = 0$

$x = -2, x = 1$

horizontal asymptote:

$n < m$ so $y = 0$

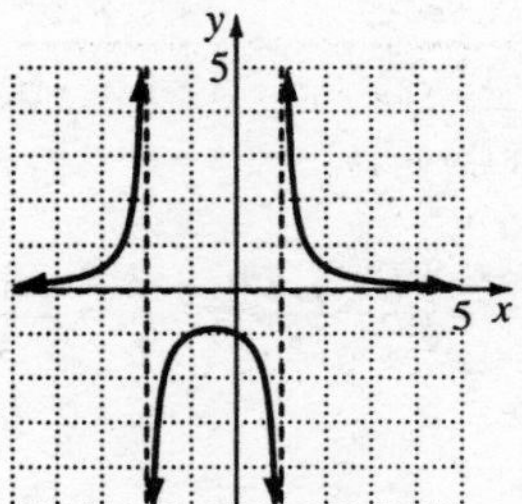

49. $f(x) = \dfrac{2x^2}{x^2+4}$

$f(-x) = \dfrac{2(-x)^2}{(-x)^2+4} = \dfrac{2x^2}{x^2+4} = f(x)$

y axis symmetry

y-intercept: $y = \dfrac{2(0)^2}{0^2+4} = 0$

x-intercept: $2x^2 = 0$

$x = 0$

vertical asymptote: none

horizontal asymptote:

$n = m$, so $y = \dfrac{2}{1} = 2$

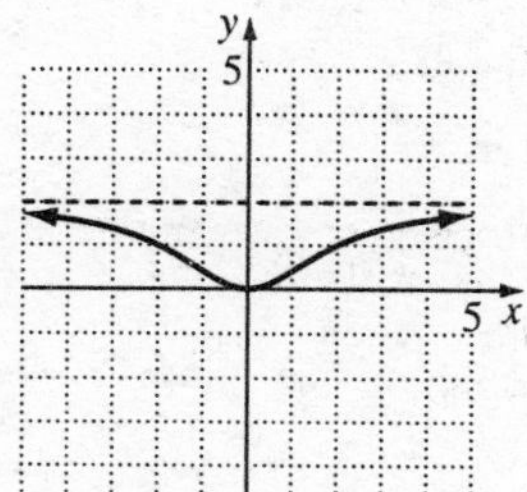

51. $f(x) = \dfrac{x+2}{x^2+x-6}$

$f(-x) = \dfrac{-x+2}{(-x)^2-(-x)-6} = \dfrac{-x+2}{x^2+x-6}$

$f(-x) \neq f(x), f(-x) \neq -f(x)$

no symmetry

y-intercept: $y = \dfrac{0+2}{0^2+0-6} = -\dfrac{2}{6} = -\dfrac{1}{3}$

x-intercept:

$x+2=0$

$x=-2$

vertical asymptotes:

$x^2+x-6=0$

$(x+3)(x-2)$

$x=-3, x=2$

horizontal asymptote:

$n < m$, so $y = 0$

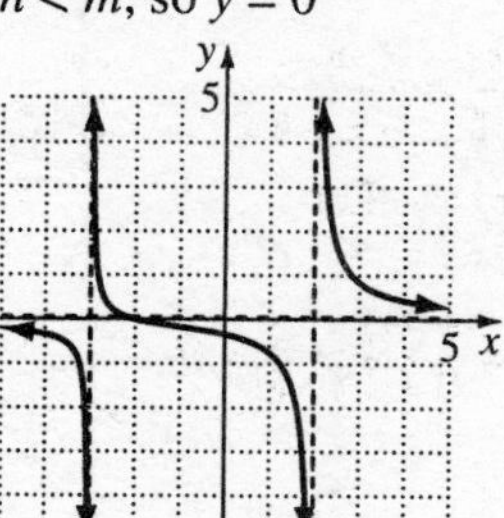

53. $f(x) = \dfrac{x^4}{x^2+2}$

$f(-x) = \dfrac{(-x)^4}{(-x)^2+2} = \dfrac{x^4}{x^2+2} = f(x)$

y-axis symmetry

y-intercept: $y = \dfrac{0^4}{0^2+2} = 0$

x-intercept: $x^4 = 0$

$x = 0$

vertical asymptote: none

horizontal asymptote:

$n > m$, so none

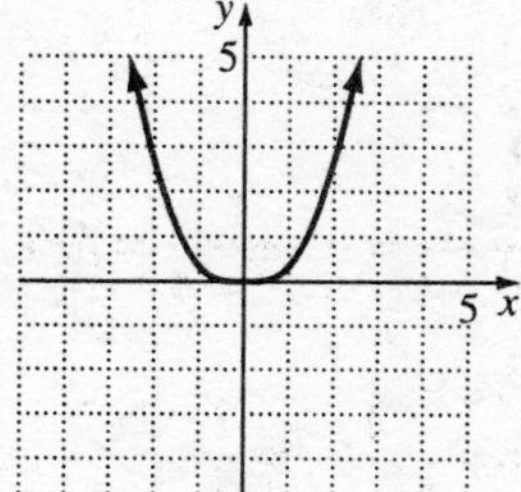

55. $f(x)=\dfrac{x^2+x-12}{x^2-4}$

$f(-x)=\dfrac{(-x)^2-x-12}{(-x)^2-4}=\dfrac{x^2-x-12}{x^2-4}$

$f(-x)\neq f(x), f(-x)\neq -f(x)$

no symmetry

y-intercept: $y=\dfrac{0^2+0-12}{0^2-4}=3$

x-intercept: $x^2+x-12=0$

$(x-3)(x+4)=0$

$x=3, x=-4$

vertical asymptotes:

$x^2-4=0$

$(x-2)(x+2)=0$

$x=2, x=-2$

horizontal asymptote:

$n=m$, so $y=\dfrac{1}{1}=1$

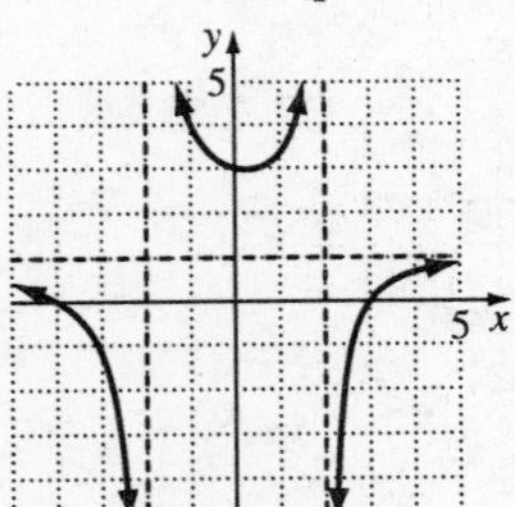

57. $f(x)=\dfrac{3x^2+x-4}{2x^2-5x}$

$f(-x)=\dfrac{3(-x)^2-x-4}{2(-x)^2+5x}=\dfrac{3x^2-x-4}{2x^2+5x}$

$f(-x)\neq f(x), f(-x)\neq -f(x)$

no symmetry

y-intercept: $y=\dfrac{3(0)^2+0-4}{2(0)^2-5(0)}=\dfrac{-4}{0}$

no y-intercept

x-intercepts:

$3x^2+x-4=0$

$(3x+4)(x-1)=0$

$3x+4=0 \quad x-1=0$

$3x=-4$

$x=-\dfrac{4}{3}, x=1$

vertical asymptotes:

$2x^2-5x=0$

$x(2x-5)=0$

$x=0, 2x=5$

$x=\dfrac{5}{2}$

horizontal asymptote:

$n=m$, so $y=\dfrac{3}{2}$

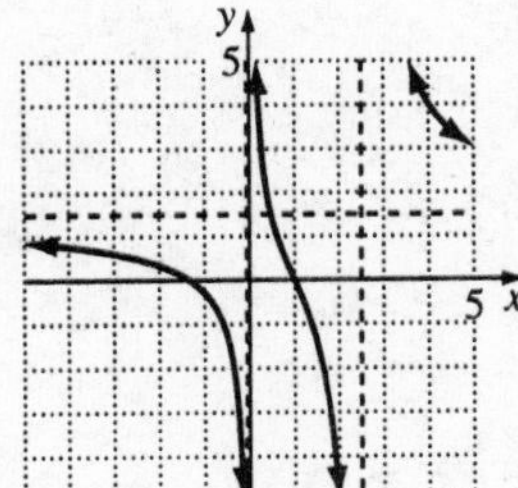

59. a. Slant asymptote:

$f(x)=x-\dfrac{1}{x}$

$y=x$

b. $f(x)=\dfrac{x^2-1}{x}$

$f(-x)=\dfrac{(-x)^2-1}{(-x)}=\dfrac{x^2-1}{-x}=-f(x)$

Origin symmetry

y-intercept: $y=\dfrac{0^2-1}{0}=\dfrac{-1}{0}$

no y-intercept

x-intercepts:

$x^2-1=0$

$x=\pm 1$

vertical asymptote: $x=0$

horizontal asymptote:

$n<m$, so none exist.

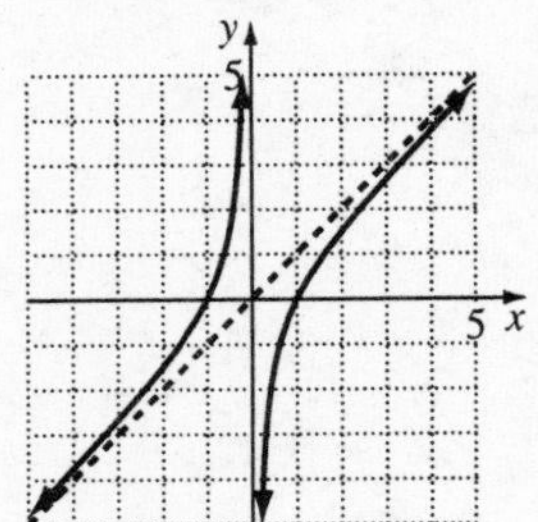

61. a. Slant asymptote:

$$f(x) = x + \frac{1}{x}$$

$$y = x$$

b. $f(x) = \dfrac{x^2 + 1}{x}$

$$f(-x) = \frac{(-x)^2 + 1}{-x} = \frac{x^2 + 1}{-x} = -f(x)$$

Origin symmetry

y-intercept: $y = \dfrac{0^2 + 1}{0} = \dfrac{1}{0}$

no y-intercept

x-intercept:

$x^2 + 1 = 0$

$x^2 = -1$

no x-intercept

vertical asymptote: $x = 0$

horizontal asymptote:

$n > m$, so none exist.

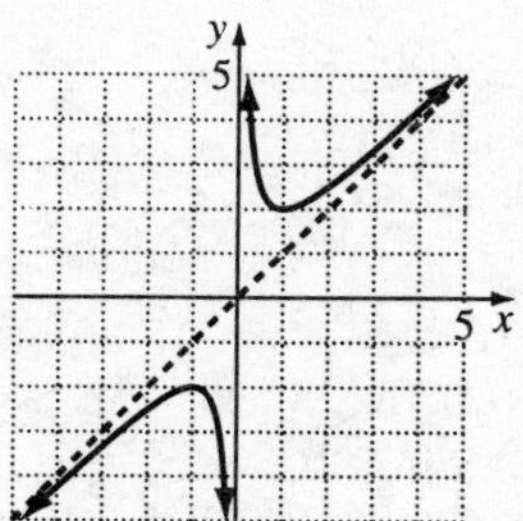

63. a. Slant asymptote:

$$f(x) = x + 4 + \frac{6}{x - 3}$$

$$y = x + 4$$

b. $f(x) = \dfrac{x^2 + x - 6}{x - 3}$

$$f(-x) = \frac{(-x)^2 + (-x) - 6}{-x - 3} = \frac{x^2 - x - 6}{-x - 3}$$

$f(-x) \neq g(x)$, $g(-x) \neq -g(x)$

No symmetry

y-intercept: $y = \dfrac{0^2 + 0 - 6}{0 - 3} = \dfrac{-6}{-3} = 2$

x-intercept:

$x^2 + x - 6 = 0$

$(x + 3)(x - 2) = 0$

$x = -3$ and $x = 2$

vertical asymptote:

$x - 3 = 0$

$x = 3$

horizontal asymptote:

$n > m$, so none exist.

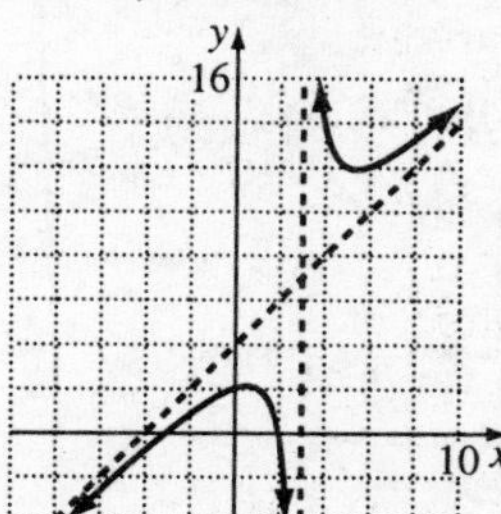

65. $f(x)=\dfrac{x^3+1}{x^2+2x}$

a. slant asymptote:

$$\begin{array}{r} x-2 \\ x^2+2x\overline{)x^3 \qquad +1} \\ \underline{x^3+2x^2} \\ -2x^2 \\ \underline{-2x^2+4x} \\ -4x+1 \end{array}$$

$y=x-2$

b.

$f(-x)=\dfrac{(-x)^3+1}{(-x)^2+2(-x)}=\dfrac{-x^3+1}{x^2-2x}$

$f(-x)\neq f(x),\quad f(-x)\neq -f(x)$

no symmetry

y-intercept: $y=\dfrac{0^3+1}{0^2+2(0)}=\dfrac{1}{0}$

no y-intercept

x-intercept: $x^3+1=0$

$x^3=-1$

$x=-1$

vertical asymptotes:

$x^2+2x=0$

$x(x+2)=0$

$x=0,\ x=-2$

horizontal asymptote:

$n>m$, so none

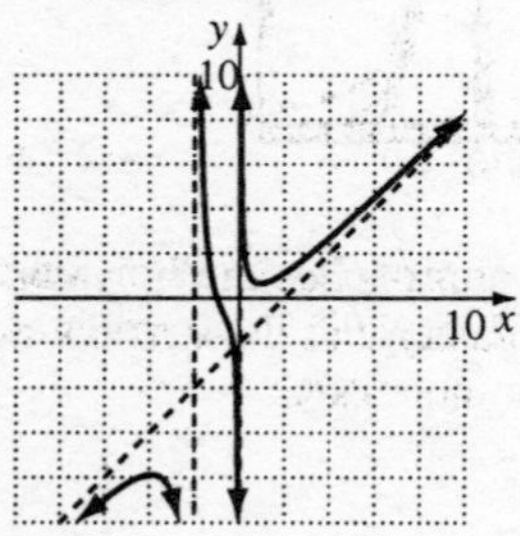

67. a. $\overline{C}(x)=\dfrac{20(x)+20,000}{x}$

$\overline{C}(100)=\dfrac{20(100)+20,000}{100}=\$220$

$\overline{C}(1000)=\dfrac{20(1000)+20,000}{1000}=\$40$

$\overline{C}(10,000)=\dfrac{20(10,000)+20,000}{10,000}$

$=\$22$

$\overline{C}(100,000)=\dfrac{20(100,000)+20,000}{100,000}$

$=\$20.20$

b. $n=m$, so $y=\dfrac{20}{1}=20$ is the horizontal asymptote.

\$20 is the minimum average cost of producing a canoe. As more canoes are manufactured, the average cost approaches \$20.

69. a. $C(p)=\dfrac{60,000p}{100-p}$

$C(85)-C(80)$

$=\dfrac{60,000(85)}{100-85}-\dfrac{60,000(80)}{100-80}$

$=\$100,000$

b. No; the model indicates that no amount of money can remove 100% of the pollutants since $C(p)$ increases without bound as p approaches 100.

71. a. $F(t) = \dfrac{80}{t^2 + t + 1}$

$F(0) = \dfrac{80}{0^2 + 4(0) + 1} = 80$

When the dessert is placed in the icebox, its temperature is 80°F.

b. $F(1) = \dfrac{80}{1^2 + 4(1) + 1} = \dfrac{80}{6} \approx 13.3°\text{F}$

$F(2) = \dfrac{80}{2^2 + 4(2) + 1} = \dfrac{80}{13} \approx 6.2°\text{F}$

$F(3) = \dfrac{80}{3^2 + 4(3) + 1} = \dfrac{80}{22} \approx 3.6°\text{F}$

$F(4) = \dfrac{80}{4^2 + 4(4) + 1} = \dfrac{80}{33} \approx 2.4°\text{F}$

$F(5) = \dfrac{80}{5^2 + 4(5) + 1} = \dfrac{80}{46} \approx 1.7°\text{F}$

c. $n < m$, so $y = 0$.
The temperature will approach but not reach 0°F.

d.

y: 100, 80, 60, 40, 20; t: 0, 1, 2, 3, 4, 5

73. a. after 1 day: 35 words
after 5 days: about 12 words
after 15 days: about 7 words

b. $N(t) = \dfrac{5t + 30}{t}, \ t \geq 1$

$N(1) = \dfrac{5 + 30}{t} = 35$ words

This is the same as the estimate for the graph.

$N(5) = \dfrac{25 + 30}{5} = 11$ words

This is a little less than the estimate from the graph.

$N(15) = 7$ words
This is the same as the estimate from the graph.

c. The graph indicates that the students will remember 5 words over a long period of time.

d. $n = m$, so $y = \dfrac{5}{1} = 5$

The horizontal asymptote indicates that the students will remember 5 words over a long period of time.

75.–83. Answers may very.

85.

100; 0, 5; 0

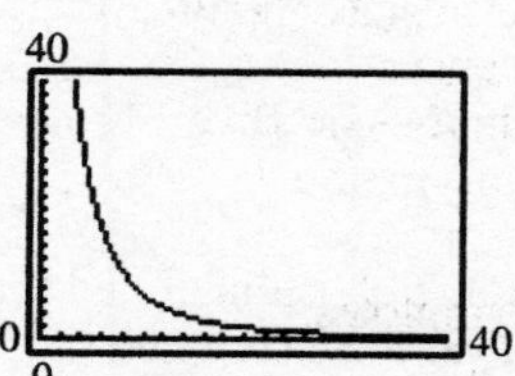

87.

2; −3, 3; 0

The graph approaches the horizontal asymptote faster and the vertical asymptote slower as n increases.

89. $f(x) = \dfrac{x^2 - 4x + 3}{x - 2}$

$g(x) = \dfrac{x^2 - 5x + 6}{x - 2}$

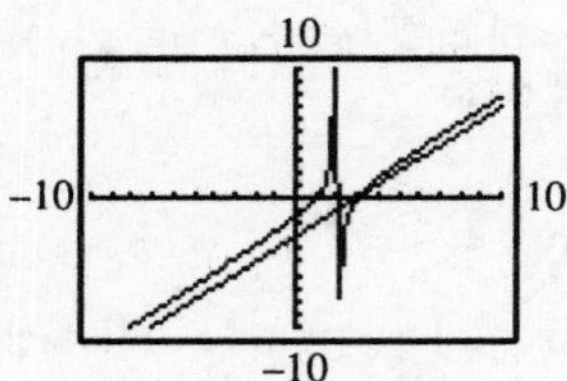

$g(x)$ is the graph of a line where $f(x)$ is the graph of a rational function with a slant asymptote.
In $g(x)$, $x - 2$ is a factor of $x^2 - 5x + 6$.

91. **a.** False

b. False; the graph of a rational function may not have a y-intercept when the y-axis is a vertical asymptote.

c. False; the graph can have 1 or no horizontal asymptotes.

d. True; the function is undefined for x values at a vertical asymptote.

(d) is true.

93.–95. Answers may very.

Section 3.7

Check Point Exercises

1. **a.** $L = kN$

b. $L = 4N$

c. $L = 4(17) = 68$

Sain's moustache grew to 68 inches.

2. **a.** $W = kL$

b. $75 = k(6)$

$k = \dfrac{75}{6}$

c. $W = kL$

$W = \left(\dfrac{75}{6}\right)L = \dfrac{75L}{6}$

d. $W = \dfrac{75(16)}{6} = 200$

A 16-foot canoe weighs 200 pounds.

3. $P = kD$

$25 = k(60)$

$k = \dfrac{25}{60} = \dfrac{5}{12}$

$P = \dfrac{5}{12}D$

$P = \dfrac{5}{12}(330) = 137.5$

The pressure will be 137.5 pounds per square inch.

4. $d = kv^2$

$200 = k(60)^2$

$k = \dfrac{200}{3600} = \dfrac{1}{18}$

$d = \dfrac{1}{18}v^2$

$d = \dfrac{1}{18}(100)^2 \approx 556$

About 556 feet are required.

5. $P = \dfrac{k}{v}$

$12 = \dfrac{k}{8}$

$k = 96$

$P = \dfrac{96}{v}$

$p = \dfrac{96}{22} \approx 4.36$

The new pressure is about 4.36 pounds per square inch.

6. $M = \frac{kP}{W}$

$32 = \frac{k16}{4}$

$k = 8$

$M = \frac{8P}{W}$

$M = \frac{8(24)}{8} = 24$

It will take 24 minutes.

7. $V = khr^2$

$120\pi = k(10)(6)^2$

$k = \frac{120\pi}{360} = \frac{\pi}{3}$

$V = \frac{\pi hr^2}{3}$

$V = \frac{\pi(2)(12)^2}{3} = 96\pi$

The volume of the cone is 96π cubic feet.

Exercise Set 3.7

1. $g = kh$

3. $a = kb^2$

5. $r = \frac{k}{t}$

7. $a = \frac{k}{b^3}$

9. $r = \frac{ks}{v}$

11. $s = kgt^2$

13. $y = kx$

$75 = k \cdot 3$

$k = 25$

15. $y = kx^2$

$45 = k \cdot 3^2$

$9k = 45$

$k = 5$

17. $W = \frac{k}{r}$

$500 = \frac{k}{10}$

$k = 5000$

19. $A = \frac{kB}{C}$

$9 = \frac{k \cdot 12}{4}$

$k = 9 \cdot \frac{4}{12}$

$k = 3$

21. $a = kbc$

$72 = k \cdot 18 \cdot 2$

$36k = 72$

$k = 2$

23. $y = kx$

$35 = k \cdot 5$

$k = 7$

$y = 7x$

$y = 7 \cdot 12$

$y = 84$

25. $y = \frac{k}{x}$

$10 = \frac{k}{5}$

$k = 50$

$y = \frac{50}{x}$

$y = \frac{50}{2}$

$y = 25$

27. $y = \frac{kx}{z^2}$
$20 = \frac{k \cdot 50}{5^2} = \frac{50k}{25} = 2k$
$20 = 2k$
$k = 10$
$y = \frac{10x}{z^2}$
$y = \frac{10 \cdot 3}{6^2} = \frac{30}{36} = \frac{5}{6}$
$y = \frac{5}{6}$

29. $y = hxz$
$25 = k \cdot 2 \cdot 5$
$k = \frac{25}{10} = 2.5$
$y = 2.5xz$
$y = 2.5(8)(12)$
$y = 240$

31. **a.** $L = kW$

b. $L = 0.02\text{W}$

c. $L = 0.02(52)$
$= 1.04$
Your fingernail length will be 1.04 inches.

33. $C = kM$
$400 = k \cdot 3000$
$k = \frac{400}{3000} = \frac{2}{15}$
$C = \frac{2}{15}M$
$C = \frac{2}{15} \cdot 450 = 60$
The cost is \$60.

35. $s = kM$
$1502.2 = k(2.03)$
$k = 740$
$s = 740M$
$s = 740(3.3)$
$= 2442$
The Blackbird's speed is 2442 miles per hour.

37. $W = kh^3$
$170 = k \cdot 70^3$
$343,000k = 170$
$k = \frac{17}{34,300}$
$W = \frac{17}{34,300}h^3$
$W = \frac{17}{34,300}(107)^3$
$W \approx 607$
Mr. Wadlow weighed approximately 607 pounds.

39. $t = \frac{k}{r}$
$1.5 = \frac{k}{20}$
$k = 30$
$t = \frac{30}{r}$
$t = \frac{30}{60} = 0.5$
It will take half an hour.

41. $v = \frac{k}{p}$
$32 = \frac{k}{8}$
$k = 256$
$v = \frac{256}{p}$
$40 = \frac{256}{p}$
$40p = 256$
$p = 6.4$
The pressure is 6.4 pounds.

43. $$i = \frac{kw}{h}$$
$$21 = \frac{k \cdot 150}{70}$$
$$1470 = 150k$$
$$k = 9.8$$
$$i = \frac{9.8w}{h}$$
$$i = \frac{9.8(240)}{74} \approx 31.78$$
index: about 32
This person is not in the desirable range.

45. $$I = \frac{k}{d^2}$$
$$25 = \frac{k}{4^2}$$
$$k = 400$$
$$I = \frac{400}{d^2}$$
$$I = \frac{400}{6^2} \approx 11.11$$
The illumination is about 11.11 foot-candles.

47. $$e = kmv^2$$
$$36 = k \cdot 8 \cdot 3^2$$
$$72k = 36$$
$$k = 0.5$$
$$e = 0.5mv^2$$
$$e = 0.5(4)6^2 = 72$$
The kinetic energy is 72 ergs.

49. $$\frac{c}{p} = \frac{kp_1 \cdot p_2}{d^2}$$
$$158,233 = \frac{k(2538)(1818)}{(108)^2}$$
$$k \approx 400$$
$$c = \frac{(400)(1225)(2970)}{(3403)^2}$$
$$c \approx 126$$
About 126 phone calls per day are made.

51.–57. Answers may vary.

59. $$p = kv^2$$
$$p = k(2v)^2$$
$$p = k \cdot 4v^2$$
$$p = 4kv^2$$
The destructive power is four times as much.

61. $$h = \frac{kv^2}{r}$$
$$3h = \frac{3kv^2}{r} = \frac{kv^2}{\frac{r}{3}}$$
Reduce the resistance by a factor of $\frac{1}{3}$.

Review Exercises

1. $f(x) = -2(x-1)^2 + 3$

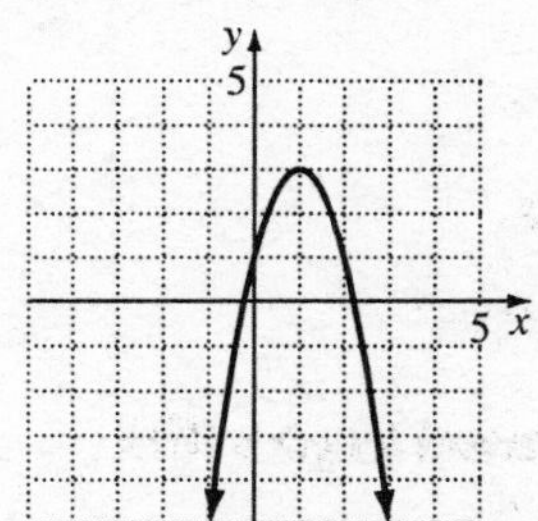

axis of symmetry: $x = 1$

2. $g(x) = (x+4)^2 - 2$

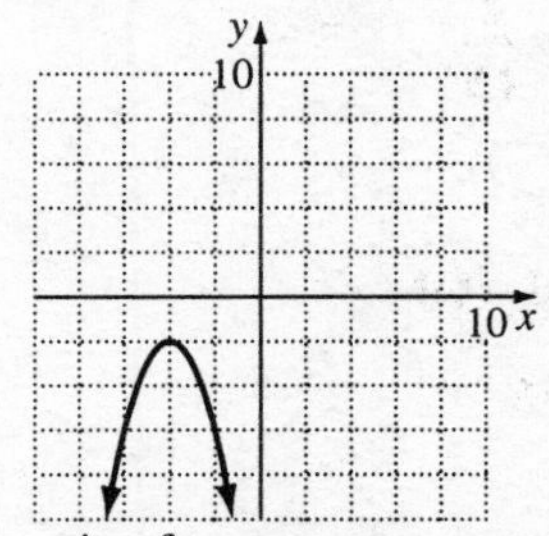

axis of symmetry: $x = -4$

3. $f(x) = -x^2 + 2x + 3$
$= -\left(x^2 - 2x + 1\right) + 3 + 1$
$f(x) = -(x-1)^2 + 4$

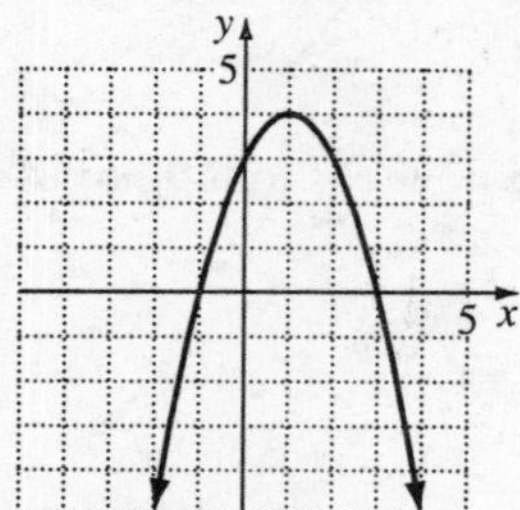

axis of symmetry: $x = 1$

4. $f(x) = 2x^2 - 4x - 6$
$f(x) = 2\left(x^2 - 2x + 1\right) - 6 - 2$
$2(x-1)^2 - 8$

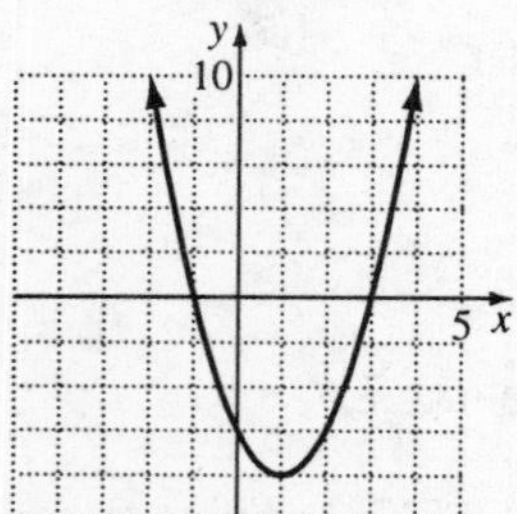

axis of symmetry: $x = 1$

5. $f(x) = 104.5x^2 - 1501.5x + 6016$
$x = \frac{1501.5}{209} \approx 7.2$
7.2 hours of sleep
$f(7.2) = 104.5(7.2)^2 - 1501.5(7.2) \approx 622$
622 is the minimum death rate.

6. $s(t) = -16t^2 + 64t + 80$
$t = -\frac{b}{2a} = -\frac{64}{2(-16)} = 2$
It reaches its maximum height after 2 seconds.
$s(2) = -16(2)^2 + 64(2) + 80 = 144$
The maximum height is 144 feet.

7. $f(x) = -x^3 + 12x^2 - x$
The graph rises to the left and falls to the right and goes through the origin, so graph (c) is the best match.

8. $g(x) = x^6 - 6x^4 + 9x^2$
The graph rises to the left and rises to the right, so graph (b) is the best match.

9. $h(x) = x^5 - 5x^3 + 4x$
The graph falls to the left and rises to the right and crosses the y-axis at zero, so graph (a) is the best match.

10. $r(x) = x^3 + 1$
$r(x)$ falls to the left and rises to the right and does not go through the origin, so graph (d) is the best match.

11. $f(x) = -0.0013x^3 + 0.78x^2 - 1.43x + 18.1$
Because the degree is odd and the leading coefficient is negative, the graph falls to the right. Therefore, the model indicates that the percentage of families below the poverty level will eventually be negative, which is impossible.

12. $N(t) = -\frac{3}{4}t^4 + 3t^3 + 5$
Since the degree is even and the leading coefficient is negative, the graph falls to the right. Therefore, the model indicates a patient will eventually have a negative number of viral bodies, which is impossible.

13. $f(x) = -2(x-1)(x+2)^2(x+5)^3$
$x = 1$, multiplicity 1, the graph crosses the x-axis
$x = -2$, multiplicity 2, the graph touches the x-axis
$x = -5$, multiplicity 5, the graph crosses the x-axis

14. $f(x) = x^3 - 5x^2 - 25x + 125$
$= x^2(x-5) - 25(x-5)$
$= (x^2 - 25)(x-5)$
$= (x+5)(x-5)^2$
$x = -5$, multiplicity 1, the graph crosses the x-axis
$x = 5$, multiplicity 2, the graph touches the x-axis

15. $f(x) = x^3 - x^2 - 9x + 9$

a. Since n is odd and $a_n > 0$, the graph falls to the left and rises to the right.

b. $f(-x) = (-x)^3 - (-x)^2 - 9(-x) + 9$
$= -x^3 - x^2 + 9x + 9$
$f(-x) \neq f(x), f(-x) \neq -f(x)$
no symmetry

c. $f(x) = (x-3)(x+3)(x-1)$
zeros: 3, – 3, 1

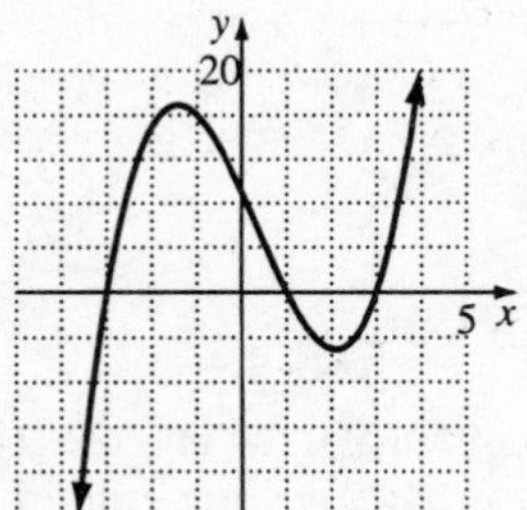

16. $f(x) = 4x - x^3$

a. Since n is odd and $a_n < 0$, the graph rises to the left and falls to the right.

b. $f(-x) = -4x + x^3$
$f(-x) = -f(x)$
origin symmetry

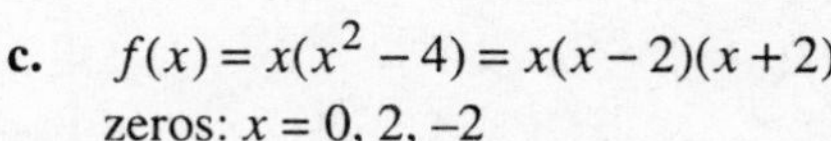

c. $f(x) = x(x^2 - 4) = x(x-2)(x+2)$
zeros: $x = 0, 2, -2$

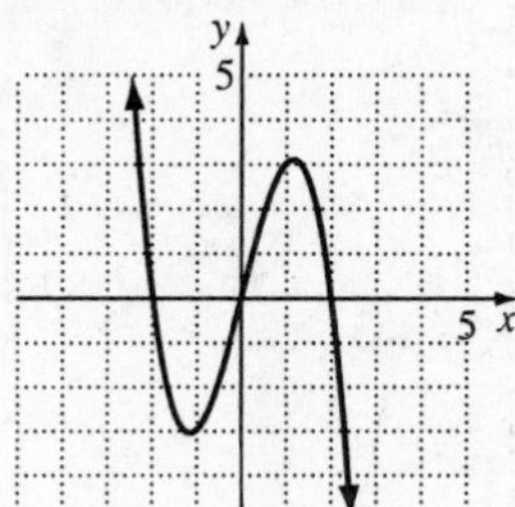

17. $f(x) = 2x^3 + 3x^2 - 8x - 12$

a. Since h is odd and $a_n > 0$, the graph falls to the left and rises to the right.

b. $f(-x) = -2x^3 + 3x^2 + 8x - 12$
$f(-x) \neq f(x),\ f(-x) = -f(x)$
no symmetry

c. $f(x) = (x-2)(x+2)(2x+3)$
zeros: $x = 2, -2, -\frac{3}{2}$

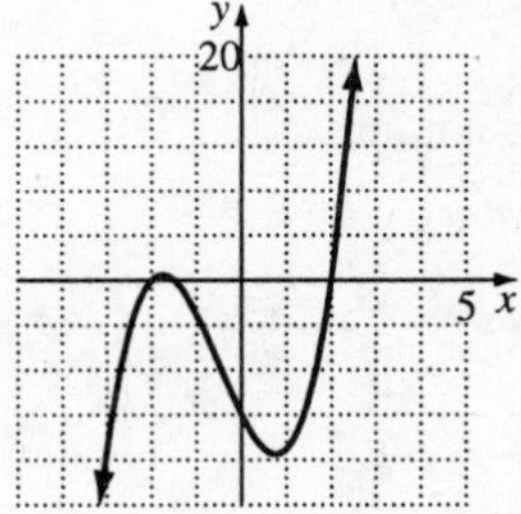

18. $g(x) = -x^4 + 25x^2$

a. The graph falls to the left and to the right.

b. $f(-x) = -(-x)^4 + 25(-x)^2$
$= -x^4 + 25x^2 = f(x)$
y-axis symmetry

c. $-x^4 + 25x^2 = 0$
$-x^2\left(x^2 - 25\right) = 0$
$-x^2(x-5)(x+5) = 0$
zeros: $x = -5, 0, 5$

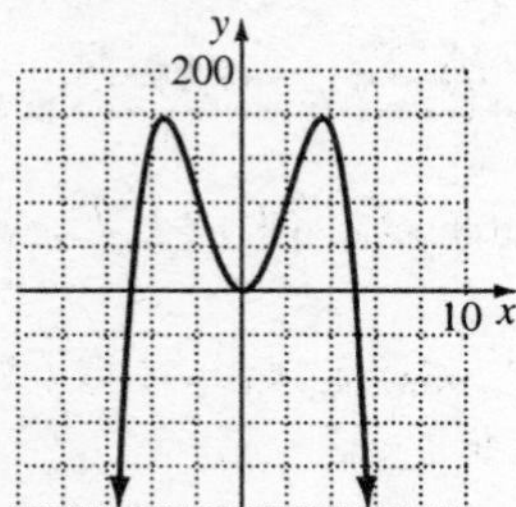

19. $f(x) = -x^4 + 6x^3 - 9x^2$

a. The graph falls to the left and to the right.

b. $f(-x) = -(-x)^4 + 6(-x)^3 - 9(-x)$
$= -x^4 - 6x^3 - 9x^2 f(-x) \neq f(x)$
$f(-x) \neq -f(x)$
no symmetry

c. $= -x^2\left(x^2 - 6x + 9\right) = 0$
$-x^2(x-3)(x-3) = 0$
zeros: $x = 0, 3$

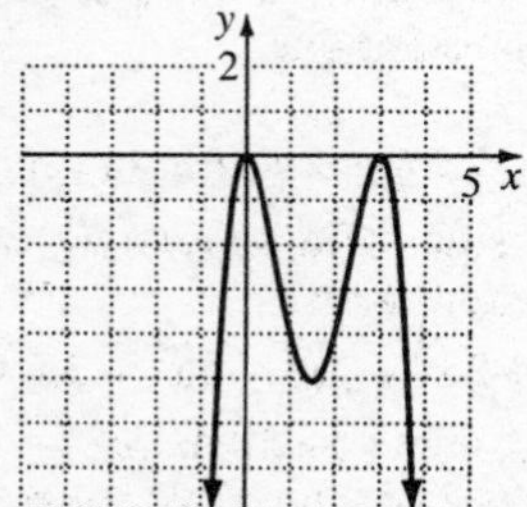

20. $f(x) = 3x^4 - 15x^3$

a. The graph rises to the left and to the right.

b. $f(-x) = 3(-x)^4 - 15(-x)^2 = 3x^4 + 15x^3$
$f(-x) \neq f(x),\ f(-x) \neq -f(x)$
no symmetry

c $3x^4 - 15x^3 = 0$
$3x^3(x-5) = 0$
zeros: $x = 0, 5$

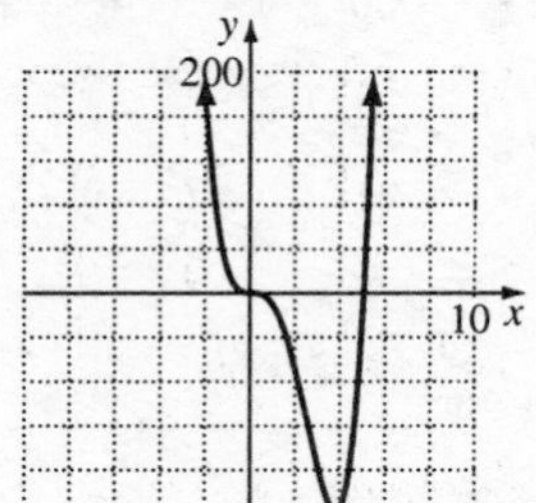

21. $x+1 \overline{\big) 4x^3 - 3x^2 - 2x + 1}$ with quotient $4x^2 - 7x + 5$

$$\begin{array}{r} 4x^3 + 4x^2 \\ \hline -7x^2 - 2x \\ -7x^2 - 7x \\ \hline 5x + 1 \\ 5x + 5 \\ \hline -4 \end{array}$$

Quotient: $4x^2 - 7x + 5 - \dfrac{4}{x+1}$

22. $5x-3 \overline{\big) 10x^3 - 26x^2 + 17x - 13}$ with quotient $2x^2 - 4x + 1$

$$\begin{array}{r} 10x^3 + 6x^2 \\ \hline -20x^2 + 17x \\ -20x^2 + 12x \\ \hline 5x - 13 \\ 5x - 3 \\ \hline -10 \end{array}$$

Quotient: $2x^2 - 4x + 1 - \dfrac{10}{5x-3}$

23.
$$\begin{array}{r} 2x^2+3x-1 \\ 2x^2+1\overline{)4x^4+6x^3+3x-1} \\ \underline{4x^2+2x^2} \\ 6x^3-2x^2+3x \\ \underline{6x^2+3x} \\ -2x^2-1 \\ \underline{-2x^2-1} \\ 0 \end{array}$$

24. $(3x^4+11x^3-20x^3+7x+35)\div(x+5)$

–5	3	11	–20	7	35
		–15	20	0	–35
	3	–4	0	7	0

Quotient: $3x^3-4x^2+7$

25. $(3x^4-2x^2-10x)\div(x-2)$

2	3	0	–2	–10	0
		6	12	20	20
	3	6	10	10	20

Quotient: $3x^3+6x^2+10x+10+\dfrac{20}{x-2}$

26. $f(x)=2x^3-7x^2+9x-3$

–13	2	–7	9	–3
		–26	429	–5694
	2	–33	438	–5697

Quotient: $f(-13)=-5697$

27. $f(x)=2x^3+x^2-13x+6$

2	2	1	–13	6
		4	10	–6
	2	5	–3	0

$$f(x)=(x-2)(2x^2+5x-3)$$
$$=(x-2)(2x-1)(x+3)$$

Zeros: $x=2,\dfrac{1}{2},-3$

28. $x^3-17x+4=0$

4	1	0	–17	4
		4	16	–4
	1	4	–1	0

$(x-4)\left(x^2+4x-1\right)=0$

$$x=\frac{-4\pm\sqrt{16+4}}{2}=\frac{-4\pm2\sqrt{5}}{2}=-2\pm\sqrt{5}$$

The solution set is $\left\{4,-2\pm\sqrt{5},-2-\sqrt{5}\right\}$.

29. $f(x)=x^4-6x^3+14x^2-14x+5$

p: $\pm1,\pm5$

q: ±1

$\dfrac{p}{q}$: $\pm1,\pm5$

30. $f(x)=3x^5-2x^4-15x^3+10x^2+12x-8$

p: $\pm1,\pm2,\pm4,\pm8$

q: $\pm1,\pm3$

$\dfrac{p}{q}$: $\pm1,\pm2,\pm4,\pm8,\pm\dfrac{8}{3},\pm\dfrac{4}{3},\pm\dfrac{2}{3},\pm\dfrac{1}{3}$

31. $f(x)=3x^4-2x^3-8x+5$

$f(x)$ has 2 sign variations, so $f(x)=0$ has 2 or 0 positive solutions.

$f(-x)=3x^4+2x^3+x+5$

$f(-x)$ has no sign variations, so $f(x)=0$ has no negative solutions.

32. $f(x)=2x^5-3x^3-5x^2+3x-1$

$f(x)$ has 3 sign variations, so $f(x)=0$ has 3 or 1 positive real roots.

$f(-x)=-2x^5+3x^3-5x^2-3x-1$

$f(-x)$ has 2 sign variations, so $f(x)=0$ has 2 or 0 negative solutions.

33. $f(x) = f(-x) = 2x^4 + 6x^2 + 8$
No sign variations exist for either $f(x)$ or $f(-x)$, so no real roots exist.

34. $f(x) = x^3 + 3x^2 - 4$

a. $p: \pm 1, \pm 2, \pm 4$
$q: \pm 1$
$\frac{p}{q}: \pm 1, \pm 2, \pm 4$

b. 1 sign variation ⇒ 1 positive real zero
$f(-x) = -x^3 + 3x^2 - 4$
2 sign variations ⇒ 2 or no negative real zeros

c.

1	1	3	0	−4
		1	4	−4
	1	4	4	0

1 is a zero.

d. $(x-1)(x^2 + 4x + 4) = 0$
$(x-1)(x+2)^2 = 0$
$x = 1$ or $x = -2$
The solution set is $\{1, -2\}$.

35. $f(x) = 6x^3 + x^2 - 4x + 1$

a. $p: \pm 1$
$q: \pm 1, \pm 2, \pm 3, \pm 6$
$\frac{p}{q}: \pm 1, \pm\frac{1}{2}, \pm\frac{1}{3}, \pm\frac{1}{6}$

b. $f(x) = 6x^3 + x^2 - 4x + 1$
2 sign variations ⇒ 2 or 0 positive real zeros.
$f(-x) = -6x^3 + x^2 + 4x + 1$
1 sign variation ⇒ 1 negative real zero.

c.

−1	6	1	−4	1
		−6	5	−1
	6	−5	1	0

−1 is a zero.

d. $6x^3 + x^2 - 4x + 1 = 0$
$(x+1)(6x^2 - 5x + 1) = 0$
$(x+1)(3x-1)(2x-1) = 0$
$x = -1$ or $x = \frac{1}{3}$ or $x = \frac{1}{2}$
The solution set is $\left\{-1, \frac{1}{3}, \frac{1}{2}\right\}$.

36. $f(x) = 8x^3 - 36x^2 + 46x - 15$

a. $p: \pm 1, \pm 3, \pm 5, \pm 15$
$q: \pm 1, \pm 2, \pm 4, \pm 8$
$\frac{p}{q}: \pm 1, \pm 3, \pm 5, \pm 15, \pm\frac{1}{2}, \pm\frac{1}{4}, \pm\frac{1}{8}, \pm\frac{3}{2}, \pm\frac{3}{4}, \pm\frac{3}{8}, \pm\frac{5}{2}, \pm\frac{5}{4}, \pm\frac{5}{8}, \pm\frac{15}{2}, \pm\frac{15}{4}, \pm\frac{15}{8}$

b. $f(x) = 8x^3 - 36x^2 + 46x - 15$
3 sign variations ⇒ 3 or 1 positive real solutions.
$f(-x) = -8x^3 - 36x^2 - 46x - 15$
0 sign variations ⇒ no negative real solutions.

c.

$\frac{1}{2}$	8	−36	46	−15
		4	−16	15
	8	−32	30	0

$\frac{1}{2}$ is a zero.

d. $8x^3-36x^2+46x-15=0$

$\left(x-\frac{1}{2}\right)(8x^2-32x+30)=0$

$2\left(x-\frac{1}{2}\right)(4x-16x+15)=0$

$2\left(x-\frac{1}{2}\right)(2x-5)(2x-3)=0$

$x=\frac{1}{2}$ or $x=\frac{5}{2}$ or $x=\frac{3}{2}$

The solution set is $\left\{\frac{1}{2}, \frac{3}{2}, \frac{5}{2}\right\}$.

37. $f(x)=x^4-x^3-7x^2+x+6$

a. p: ±1, ±2, ±3, ±6
q: ±1
$\frac{p}{q}$: ± 1, ± 2, ± 3, ± 6

b. $f(x)=x^4-x^3-7x^2+x+6$
2 sign variations ⇒ 2 or zero positive real solutions.
$f(-x)=x^4+x^3-7x^2-x+6$
2 sign variations ⇒ 2 or zero negative real solutions.

c.

–2	1	–1	–7	1	6
		–2	6	2	–6
	1	–3	–1	3	0

–2 is a zero.

d.
$$x^4-x^3-7x^2+x+6=0$$
$$(x+2)(x^3-3x^2-x+3)=0$$
$$(x+2)[x^2(x-3)-(x-3)]=0$$
$$(x+2)(x-3)(x^2-1)=0$$
$$(x+2)(x-3)(x-1)(x+1)=0$$
$x=-2$ or $x=3$ or $x=1$ or $x=-1$
The solution set is {–2, –1, 1, 3}.

38. $4x^4+7x^2-2=0$

a. p: ± 1, ± 2
q: ± 1, ± 2, ± 4
$\frac{p}{q}$: ± 1, ± 2, $\pm\frac{1}{2}$, $\pm\frac{1}{4}$

b. 1 sign variation ⇒ 1 positive real root
$f(-x)=4x^4+7x^2-2$
1 sign variation ⇒ 1 negative real root

c.

$\frac{1}{2}$	4	0	7	0	–2
		2	1	4	2
	4	2	8	4	0

$(2x-1)(4x^3+2x^2+8x+4)=0$

$\frac{1}{2}$ is a zero.

d.

$-\frac{1}{2}$	4	2	8	4
		–2	0	–4
	4	0	8	0

$(2x-1)(2x+1)(4x^2+8)=0$
$4(2x-1)(2x+1)(x^2+2)=0$
$x^2=-2$
$x=\pm i\sqrt{2}$

The solution set is $\left\{\frac{1}{2}, -\frac{1}{2}, i\sqrt{2}, -i\sqrt{2}\right\}$.

39. $f(x) = 2x^4 + x^3 - 9x^2 - 4x + 4$

a. $p: \pm 1, \pm 2, \pm 4$
$q: \pm 1, \pm 2$
$\frac{p}{q} = \pm 1, \pm 2, \pm 4, \pm \frac{1}{2}$

b. 2 sign variations ⇒ 2 or no positive zeros
$f(-x) = 2x^4 - x^3 - 9x^2 + 4x + 4$
2 sign variations ⇒ 2 or no negative zeros

c.

2	2	1	−9	−4	4
		4	10	2	−4
	2	5	1	−2	0

2 is a zero.

d. $f(x) = (x-2)(2x^3 + 5x^2 + x - 2)$

−2	2	5	1	−2
		−4	−2	2
	2	1	−1	0

$f(x) = (x-2)(x+2)(2x^2 + x - 1)$
$= (x-2)(x+2)(2x-1)(x+1)$
$x = 2, -2, \frac{1}{2}, -1$

The solution set is $\left\{2, -2, \frac{1}{2}, -1\right\}$.

40. $2x^4 - 7x^3 - 5x^2 + 28x - 12 = 0$

−2	2	−7	−5	28	−12
		−4	22	−34	12
	2	−11	17	−6	0

−2 is a root and a lower bound.

6	2	−7	−5	28	−12
		12	30	150	1068
	2	5	25	178	1056

6 is an upper bound, but not a zero.
$p: \pm 1, \pm 2, \pm 3, \pm 4, +6, \pm 12$
$q: \pm 1, \pm 2$
$\frac{p}{q}: \pm 1, \pm 2, \pm 3, \pm 4, \pm 6, \pm 12, \pm\frac{1}{2}, \pm\frac{3}{2}$

Possible roots are: $\pm 1, \pm 2, 3, 4, \pm\frac{1}{2}, \pm\frac{3}{2}$

41. $2x^4 - x^3 - 5x^2 + 10x + 12 = 0$

a. $p: \pm 1, \pm 2, \pm 3, \pm 4, \pm 6, \pm 12$
$q: \pm 1, \pm 2$
$\frac{p}{q}: \pm 1, \pm 2, \pm 3, \pm 4, \pm 6, \pm 12, \pm\frac{1}{2}, \pm\frac{3}{2}$

b.

2	2	−1	−5	10	12
		4	6	2	24
	2	3	1	12	36

2 is not a root but is an upper bound.

c.

−2	2	−1	−5	10	12
		−4	10	−10	0
	2	−5	5	0	12

−2 is not a root but is a lower bound.

d. Possible roots are ± 1, $\pm\frac{1}{2}$, and $\pm\frac{3}{2}$.

42. $f(x) = x^3 - 2x - 1$
$f(1) = (1)^3 - 2(1) - 1 = -2$
$f(2) = (2)^3 - 2(2) - 1 = 3$
Continue to use the Intermediate Value Theorem:
$f(1.5) = -0.625$
$f(1.6) = -0.104$
$f(1.7) = 0.513$
$f(1.65) = 0.192125$
$x \approx 1.6$

43. $f(x) = 3x^3 + 2x^2 - 8x + 7$
$f(-3) = 3(-3)^3 + 2(-3)^2 - 8(-3) + 7 = -32$
$f(-2) = 3(-2)^3 + 2(-2)^2 - 8(-2) + 7 = 7$
Continue to use the Intermediate Value Theorem:
$f(-2.4) = -3.752$
$f(-2.3) = -0.521$
$f(-2.2) = 2.336$
$f(-2.25) = 0.953125$
$x \approx -2.3$

44. $(x - 6 - 5i)(x - 6 + 5i)$
$= x^2 - 6x - 6x + 36 - 25i^2$
$= x^2 - 12x + 61$

$$\begin{array}{r} 4x+1 \\ x^2-12x+61 \overline{\smash{\big)}\, 4x^3 - 47x^2 + 232x + 61} \\ \underline{4x^3 - 48x^2 + 244x} \\ x^2 - 12x + 61 \\ \underline{x^2 - 12x + 61} \\ 0 \end{array}$$

$4x + 1 = 0$
$x = -\frac{1}{4}$

The solution set is $\left\{-\frac{1}{4},\ 6 \pm 5i,\ 6 - 5i\right\}$.

45. $(x - 1 + 3i)(x - 1 - 3i) = x^2 - 2x + 1 - 9i^2$
$= x^2 - 2x + 10$

$$\begin{array}{r} x^2-2x+2 \\ x^2-2x+10 \overline{\smash{\big)}\, x^4 - 4x^3 + 16x^2 - 24x + 20} \\ \underline{x^4 - 2x^3 + 10x^2} \\ -2x^3 + 6x^2 - 24x \\ \underline{-2x^3 + 4x^2 - 20x} \\ 2x^2 - 4x + 20 \\ \underline{2x^2 - 4x + 20} \\ 0 \end{array}$$

$x^2 - 2x + 2 = 0$
$x = \frac{2 \pm \sqrt{4 - 4(1)(2)}}{2}$
$x = \frac{2 \pm 2i}{2} = 1 \pm i$
The solution set is
$\{1 + 3i, 1 - 3i, 1 + i, 1 - i\}$.

46. $(x - 4 - 7i)(x - 4 + 7i) = x^2 - 8x + 16 + 49$
$= x^2 - 8x + 65$

$$\begin{array}{r} 2x^2-x-1 \\ x^2-8x+65 \overline{\smash{\big)}\, 2x^4 - 17x^3 + 137x^2 - 57x - 65} \\ \underline{2x^4 - 16x^3 + 130x^2} \\ -x^3 + 7x^2 - 57x \\ \underline{-x^3 + 8x^2 - 65x} \\ -x^2 + 8x - 65 \\ \underline{-x^2 + 8x - 65} \\ 0 \end{array}$$

$2x^2 - x - 1 = 0$
$x = \frac{1 \pm \sqrt{1 - 4(2)(-1)}}{4}$
$x = \frac{1 \pm 3}{4}$
$x = 1, -\frac{1}{2}$

The solution set is $\left\{-\frac{1}{2},\ 1,\ 4 \pm 7i,\ 7i\right\}$.

47. $f(x) = a_n(x - 2)(x - 2 + 3i)(x - 2 - 3i)$
$f(x) = a_n(x - 2)\left(x^2 - 4x + 13\right)$
$f(1) = a_n(1 - 2)\left[1^2 - 4(1) + 13\right]$
$-10 = -10a_n$
$a_n = 1$
$f(x) = 1(x - 2)\left(x^2 - 4x + 13\right)$
$f(x) = x^3 - 4x^2 + 13x - 2x^2 + 8x - 26$
$f(x) = x^3 - 6x^2 + 21x - 26$

48. $f(x) = a_n(x - i)(x + i)(x + 3)^2$
$f(x) = a_n\left(x^2 + 1\right)\left(x^2 + 6x + 9\right)$
$f(-1) = a_n\left[(-1)^2 + 1\right]\left[(-1)^2 + 6(-1) + 9\right]$
$16 = 8a_n$
$a_n = 2$
$f(x) = 2\left(x^2 + 1\right)\left(x^2 + 6x + 9\right)$
$f(x) = 2\left(x^4 + 6x^3 + 9x^2 + x^2 + 6x + 9\right)$
$f(x) = 2x^4 + 12x^3 + 20x^2 + 12x + 18$

49. $f(x) = a_n(x+2)(x-3)(x-1-3i)(x-1+3i)$

$f(x) = a_n\left(x^2 - x - 6\right)\left(x^2 - 2x + 10\right)$

$f(x) = a_n\begin{pmatrix} x^4 - 2x^3 + 10x^2 - x^3 + \\ 2x^2 - 10x - 6x^2 + 12x - 60 \end{pmatrix}$

$f(x) = a_n\left(x^4 - 3x^3 + 6x^2 + 2x - 60\right)$

$f(2) = a_n\left[(2)^4 - 3(2)^3 + 6(2)^2 + 2(2) - 60\right]$

$-40 = -40a_n$

$a_n = 1$

$f(x) = x^4 - 3x^3 + 6x^2 + 2x - 60$

50. $f(x) = 2x^4 + 3x^3 + 3x - 2$

p: ±1, ±2

q: ±1, ±2

$\frac{p}{q}: \pm 1, \pm 2, \pm\frac{1}{2}$

$$\begin{array}{r|rrrrr} -2 & 2 & 3 & 0 & 3 & -2 \\ & & -4 & 2 & -4 & 2 \\ \hline & 2 & -1 & 2 & -1 & 0 \end{array}$$

$2x^4 + 3x^3 + 3x - 2 = 0$

$(x+2)(2x^3 - x^2 + 2x - 1) = 0$

$(x+2)[x^2(2x-1) + (2x-1)] = 0$

$(x+2)(2x-1)(x^2+1) = 0$

$x = -2,\ x = \frac{1}{2}$ or $x = \pm i$

The zeros are $-2, \frac{1}{2}, \pm i$.

$f(x) = (x-i)(x+i)(x+2)\left(x - \frac{1}{2}\right)$

51. $g(x) = x^4 - 6x^3 + x^2 + 24x + 16$

p: ±1, ±2, ±4, ±8, ±16

q: ±1

$\frac{p}{q}: \pm 1, \pm 2, \pm 4, \pm 8, \pm 16$

$$\begin{array}{r|rrrrr} -1 & 1 & -6 & 1 & 24 & 16 \\ & & -1 & 7 & -8 & -16 \\ \hline & 1 & -7 & 8 & 16 & 0 \end{array}$$

$x^4 - 6x^3 + x^2 + 24x + 16 = 0$

$(x+1)(x^3 - 7x^2 + 8x + 16) = 0$

$$\begin{array}{r|rrrr} -1 & 1 & -7 & 8 & 16 \\ & & -1 & 8 & -16 \\ \hline & 1 & -8 & 16 & 0 \end{array}$$

$(x+1)^2(x^2 - 8x + 16) = 0$

$(x+1)^2(x-4)^2 = 0$

$x = -1$ or $x = 4$

$g(x) = (x+1)^2(x-4)^2$

52. 4 real zeros, one with multiplicity two

53. 3 real zeros; 2 nonreal complex zeros

54. 2 real zeros, one with multiplicity two; 2 nonreal complex zeros

55. 1 real zero; 4 nonreal complex zeros

56. $f(x)=\dfrac{2x}{x^2-9}$

Symmetry: $f(-x)=-\dfrac{2x}{x^2-9}=-f(x)$

origin symmetry

x-intercept:

$0=\dfrac{2x}{x^2-9}$

$2x=0$

$x=0$

y-intercept: $y=\dfrac{2(0)}{0^2-9}=0$

Vertical asymptote:

$x^2-9=0$

$(x-3)(x+3)=0$

$x=3$ and $x=-3$

Horizontal asymptote:

$n<m$, so $y=0$

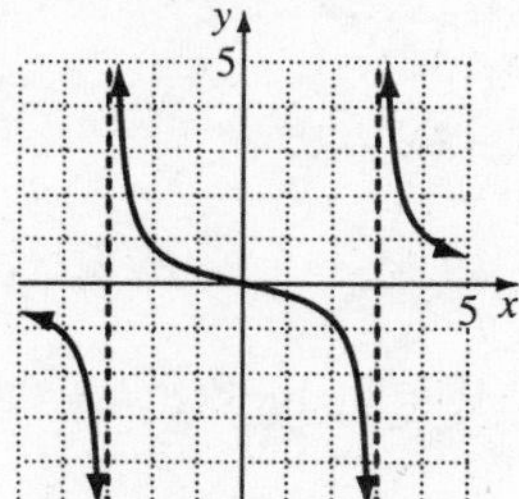

57. $g(x)=\dfrac{2x-4}{x+3}$

Symmetry: $g(-x)=\dfrac{-2x-4}{x+3}$

$g(-x)\neq g(x)$, $g(-x)\neq -g(x)$

No symmetry

x-intercept:

$2x-4=0$

$x=2$

y-intercept: $y=\dfrac{2(0)-4}{(0)+3}=-\dfrac{4}{3}$

Vertical asymptote:

$x+3=0$

$x=-3$

Horizontal asymptote:

$n=m$, so $y=\dfrac{2}{1}=2$

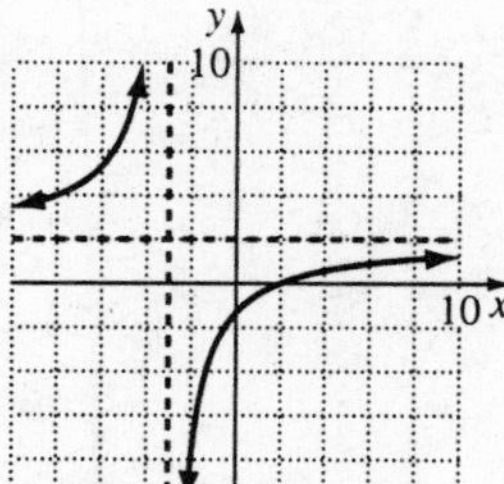

58. $h(x)=\dfrac{x^2-3x-4}{x^2-x-6}$

Symmetry: $h(-x)=\dfrac{x^2+3x-4}{x^2+x-6}$

$h(-x)\neq h(x)$, $h(-x)\neq -h(x)$

No symmetry

x-intercepts:

$x^2-3x-4=0$

$(x-4)(x+1)$

$x=4 \quad x=-1$

y-intercept: $y=\dfrac{0^2-3(0)-4}{0^2-0-6}=\dfrac{2}{3}$

Vertical asymptotes:

$x^2-x-6=0$

$(x-3)(x+2)=0$

$x=3, -2$

Horizontal asymptote:

$n=m$, so $y=\dfrac{1}{1}=1$

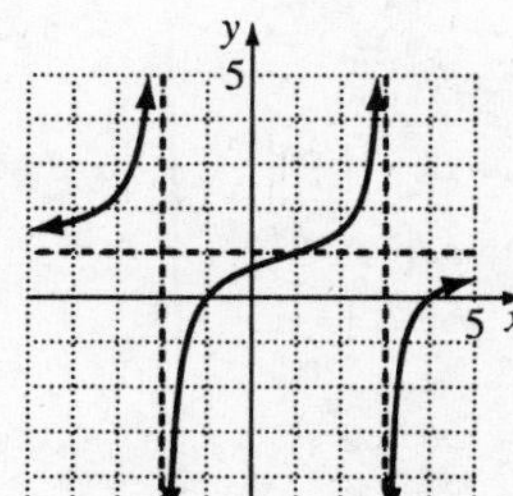

59. $r(x)=\dfrac{x^2+4x+3}{(x+2)^2}$

Symmetry: $r(-x)=\dfrac{x^2-4x+3}{(-x+2)^2}$

$r(-x)\neq r(x),\ r(-x)\neq -r(x)$

No symmetry

x-intercepts:

$x^2+4x+3=0$

$(x+3)(x+1)=0$

$x=-3,-1$

y-intercept: $y=\dfrac{0^2+4(0)+3}{(0+2)^2}=\dfrac{3}{4}$

Vertical asymptote:

$x+2=0$

$x=-2$

Horizontal asymptote:

$n=m$, so $y=\dfrac{1}{1}=1$

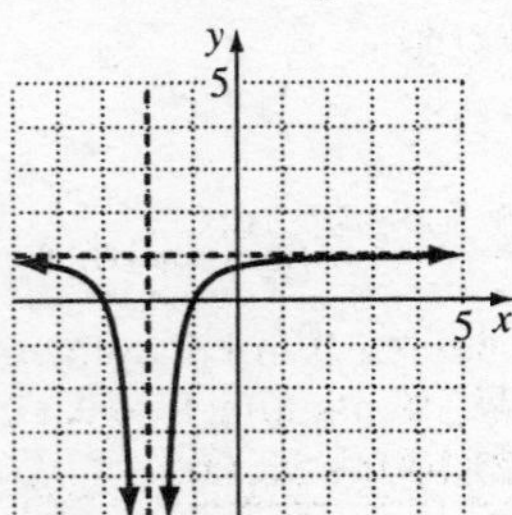

60. $y=\dfrac{x^2}{x+1}$

Symmetry: $f(-x)=\dfrac{x^2}{-x+1}$

$f(-x)\neq f(x),\ f(-x)\neq -f(x)$

No symmetry

x-intercept:

$x^2=0$

$x=0$

y-intercept: $y=\dfrac{0^2}{0+1}=0$

Vertical asymptote:

$x+1=0$

$x=-1$

$n>m$, no horizontal asymptote.

Slant asymptote:

$y=x-1+\dfrac{1}{x+1}$

$y=x-1$

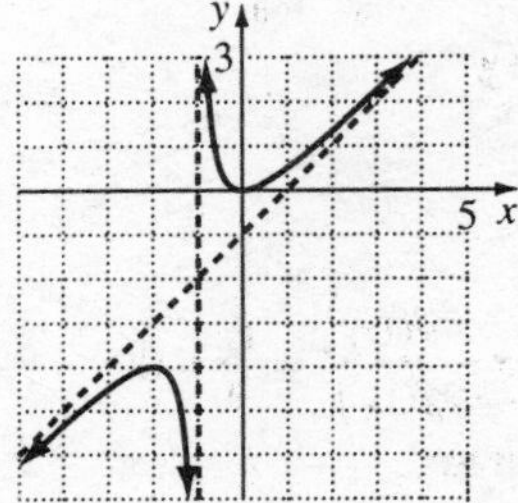

61. $y=\dfrac{x^2+2x-3}{x-3}$

Symmetry: $f(-x)=\dfrac{x^2-2x-3}{-x-3}$

$f(-x)\neq f(x),\ f(-x)\neq -f(x)$

No symmetry

x-intercepts:

$x^2+2x-3=0$

$(x+3)(x-1)=0$

$x=-3,1$

y-intercept: $y=\dfrac{0^2+2(0)-3}{0-3}=\dfrac{-3}{-3}=1$

Vertical asymptote:

$x-3=0$

$x=3$

Horizontal asymptote:

$n>m$, so no horizontal asymptote.

slant asymptote:

$y=x+5+\dfrac{12}{x-3}$

$y=x+5$

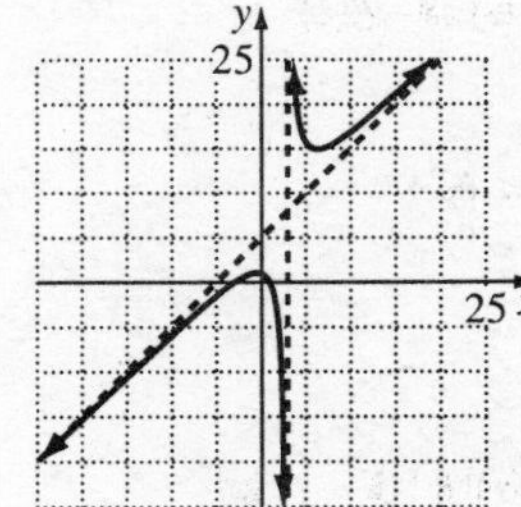

62. $f(x) = \dfrac{-2x^3}{x^2+1}$

Symmetry: $f(-x) = \dfrac{2}{x^2+1} = -f(x)$

Origin symmetry

x-intercept:

$-2x^3 = 0$

$x = 0$

y-intercept: $y = \dfrac{-2(0)^3}{0^2+1} = \dfrac{0}{1} = 0$

Vertical asymptote:

$x^2 + 1 = 0$

$x^2 = -1$

No vertical asymptote.

Horizontal asymptote:

$n > m$, so no horizontal asymptote.

Slant asymptote:

$f(x) = -2x + \dfrac{2x}{x^2+1}$

$y = -2x$

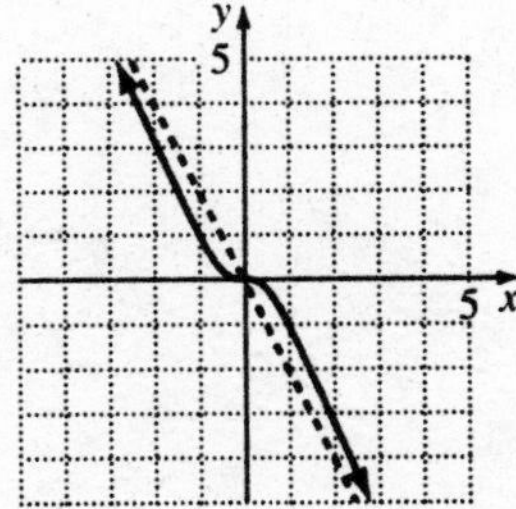

63. $g(x) = \dfrac{4x^2 - 16x + 16}{2x - 3}$

Symmetry: $g(-x) = \dfrac{4x^2 + 16x + 16}{-2x - 3}$

$g(-x) \neq g(x)$, $g(-x) \neq -g(x)$

No symmetry

x-intercept:

$4x^2 - 16x + 16 = 0$

$4(x-2)^2 = 0$

$x = 2$

y-intercept:

$y = \dfrac{4(0)^2 - 16(0) + 16}{2(0) - 3} = -\dfrac{16}{3}$

Vertical asymptote:

$2x - 3 = 0$

$x = \frac{3}{2}$

Horizontal asymptote:

$n > m$, so no horizontal asymptote.

Slant asymptote:

$g(x) = 2x - 5 + \dfrac{1}{2x-3}$

$y = 2x - 5$

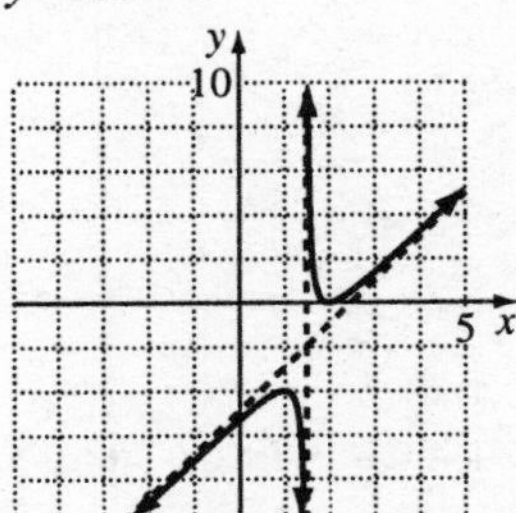

64. $\overline{C}(x) = \dfrac{25x + 50,000}{x}$

a. $\overline{C}(50) = \dfrac{25(50) + 50,000}{50} = 1025$

When 50 calculators are manufactured, it costs \$1025 to manufacture each.

$\overline{C}(100) = \dfrac{25(100) + 50,000}{100} = 525$

When 100 calculators are manufactured, it costs \$525 to manufacture each.

$\overline{C}(1000) = \dfrac{25(1000) + 50,000}{1000} = 75$

When 1,000 calculators are manufactured, it costs \$75 to manufacture each.

$\overline{C}(100,000) = \dfrac{25(100,000) + 50,000}{100,000} = 25.5$

When 100,000 calculators are manufactured, it costs \$25.50 to manufacture each.

b. $n = m$, so $y = \dfrac{25}{1} = 25$ is the horizontal asymptote. Minimum costs will approach \$25.

65. a. $C(90) - C(50) = \frac{200(90)}{100-90} - \frac{200(50)}{100-50}$
$C(90) - C(50) = 1800 - 200$
$C(90) - C(50) = 1600$
The difference in cost of removing 90% versus 50% of the contaminants is 16 million dollars.

b. $x = 100$; No amount of money can remove 100% of the contaminants, since $C(x)$ increases without bound as x approaches 100.

66. $F(x) = \frac{30(4+5x)}{1+0.05x}$
$n = m$, so $y = \frac{150}{0.05} = 3000$
The number of fish available in the pond approaches 3,000,000.

67. $P(x) = \frac{72,900}{100x^2 + 729}$
$n < m$ so $y = 0$
As the number of years of education increases the percentage rate of unemployment approaches zero.

68. Since $C(p)$ increases without bound as P approaches 100, the politician will not be able to keep the promise to seize 100% of illegal drugs as they enter the country.

69. $b = ke$
$98 = k \cdot 1400$
$k = 0.07$
$b = 0.07e$
$b = 0.07(2200) = \$154$

70. $d = kt^2$
$144 = k(3)^2$
$k = 16$
$d = 16t^2$
$d = 16(10)^2 = 1,600$ ft

71. $t = \frac{k}{r}$
$4 = \frac{k}{50}$
$k = 200$
$t = \frac{200}{r}$
$t = \frac{200}{40} = 5$ hours

72. $l = \frac{k}{d^2}$
$28 = \frac{k}{8^2}$
$k = 1792$
$l = \frac{1792}{d^2}$
$l = \frac{1792}{4^2} = 112$ decibels

73. $t = \frac{kc}{w}$
$10 = \frac{k \cdot 30}{6}$
$10 = 5h$
$h = 2$
$t = \frac{2c}{w}$
$t = \frac{2(40)}{5} = 16$ hours

74. $V = khB$
$175 = k \cdot 15 \cdot 35$
$k = \frac{1}{3}$
$V = \frac{1}{3}hB$
$V = \frac{1}{3} \cdot 20 \cdot 120 = 800 \text{ ft}^3$

Chapter 3 Test

1. $f(x) = (x+1)^2 + 4$
vertex: (–1, 4)
axis of symmetry: $x = -1$
x-intercepts:
$(x+1)^2 + 4 = 0$
$x^2 + 2x + 5 = 0$
$x = \frac{-2 \pm \sqrt{4-20}}{2} = -1 \pm 2i$
no x-intercepts
y-intercept:
$f(0) = (0+1)^2 + 4 = 5$

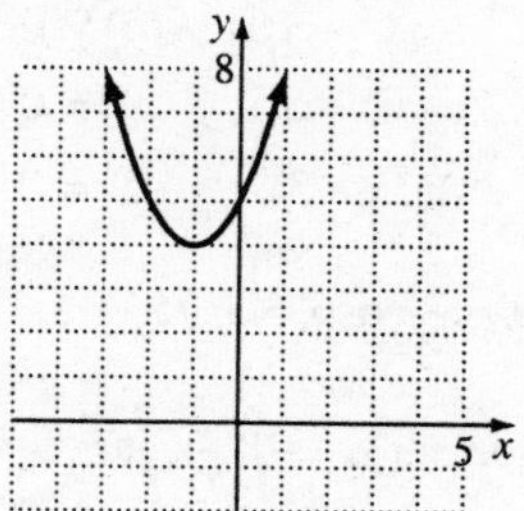

2. $f(x) = x^2 - 2x - 3$
$x = \frac{-b}{2a} = \frac{2}{2} = 1$
$f(1) = 1^2 - 2(1) - 3 = -4$
vertex: (1, –4)
axis of symmetry $x = 1$
x-intercepts:
$x^2 - 2x - 3 = 0$
$(x-3)(x+1) = 0$
$x = 3$ or $x = -1$
y-intercept:
$f(0) = 0^2 - 2(0) - 3 = -3$

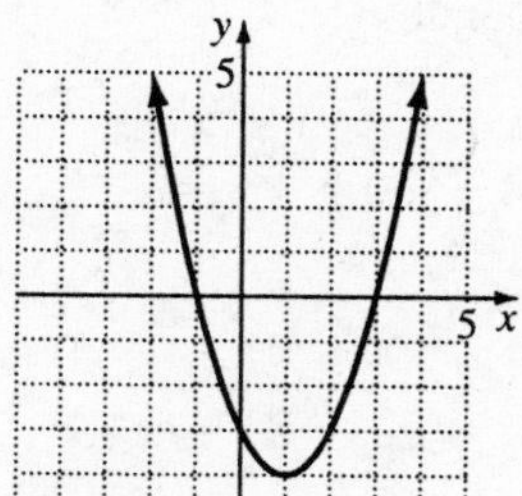

3. $f(x) = -2x^2 - 12x - 16$
Since the coefficient of x^2 is negative, the graph of $f(x)$ opens down and $f(x)$ has a maximum point.
$x = \frac{-b}{2a} = \frac{12}{2(-2)} = -3$
$f(-3) = -2(-3)^2 - 12(-3) - 16$
$= -18 + 36 - 16 = 2$
maximum point: (–3, 2)

4. $f(x) = x^2 + 46x - 360$
$x = -\frac{b}{2a} = \frac{-46}{-2} = 23$
23 VCRs will maximize profit.
$f(23) = -(23)^2 + 46(23) - 360 = 169$
Maximum daily profit = $16,900.

5. **a.** $f(x) = x^3 - 5x^2 - 4x + 20$
$x^3 - 5x^2 - 4x + 20 = 0$
$x^2(x-5) - 4(x-5) = 0$
$(x-5)(x-2)(x+2) = 0$
$x = 5, 2, -2$
The solution set is {5, 2, –2}.

b. The degree of the polynomial is odd and the leading coefficient is positive. Thus the graph falls to the left and rises to the right.

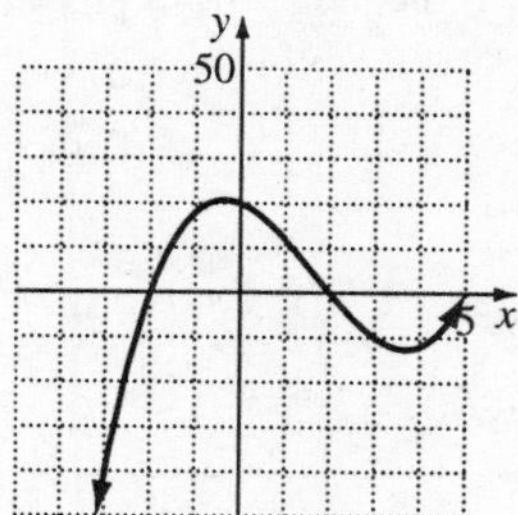

6. $f(x) = x^5 - x$
Since the degree of the polynomial is odd and the leading coefficient is positive, the graph of f should fall to the left and rise to the right. The x-intercepts should be –1 and 1.

7. a. The integral root appears to be 2.

b.

2	6	−19	16	−4
		12	−14	4
	6	−7	2	0

$6x^2 - 7x + 2 = 0$
$(3x - 2)(2x - 1) = 0$
$x = \frac{2}{3}$ or $x = \frac{1}{2}$

The other two roots are $\frac{1}{2}$ and $\frac{2}{3}$.

8. $2x^3 + 11x^2 - 7x - 6 = 0$
p: ±1, ±2, ±3, ±6
q: ±1, ±2
$\frac{p}{q}: \pm 1, \pm 2, \pm 3, \pm 6, \pm\frac{1}{2}, \pm\frac{3}{2}$

9. $f(x) = 3x^5 - 2x^4 - 2x^2 + x - 1$
$f(x)$ has 3 sign variations.
$f(-x) = -3x^5 - 2x^4 - 2x^2 - x - 1$
$f(-x)$ has no sign variations.
There are 3 or 1 positive real solutions and no negative real solutions.

10. $x^3 + 6x^2 - x - 30 = 0$
p: ±1, ±2, ±3, ±5, ±6, ±10, ±15, ±30
q: ±1
$\frac{p}{q}: \pm 1, \pm 2, \pm 3, \pm 5, \pm 6, \pm 10, \pm 15, \pm 30$

−5	1	6	−1	−30
		−5	−5	30
	1	1	−6	0

$x^3 + 6x^2 - x - 30 = 0$
$(x + 5)(x^2 + x - 6) = 0$
$(x + 5)(x + 3)(x - 2) = 0$
$x = -5$ or $x = -3$ or $x = 2$
The solution set is {−5, −3, 2}.

11. $f(x) = 2x^4 - x^3 - 13x^2 + 5x + 15$

a. p: ±1, ±3, ±5, ±15
q: ±1, ±2
$\frac{p}{q}: \pm 1, \pm 3, \pm 5, \pm 15, \pm\frac{1}{2}, \pm\frac{3}{2}, \pm\frac{5}{2}, \pm\frac{15}{2}$

b.

−1	2	−1	−13	5	15
		−2	3	10	−15
	2	−3	−10	15	0

$(x + 1)(2x^3 - 3x^2 - 10x + 15) = 0$
$(x + 1)[x^2(2x - 3) - 5(2x - 3)] = 0$
$(x + 1)(2x - 3)\left(x^2 - 5\right) = 0$

$x = -1$ or $x = \frac{3}{2}$ or $x = \pm\sqrt{5}$

The solution set is $\left\{-1, \frac{3}{2}, \sqrt{5}, -\sqrt{5}\right\}$.

12. $3x^4 + 4x^3 - 7x^2 - 2x - 3 = 0$

−3	3	4	−7	−2	−3
		−9	15	−24	78
	3	−5	8	−26	75

−3 is a lower bound.

2	3	4	−7	−2	−3
		6	20	26	48
	3	10	13	24	45

2 is an upper bound.

13. $(x-1+i)(x-1-i)=x^2-2x+2$

$$\begin{array}{r} x^2-5x+6 \\ x^2-2x+2\overline{)x^4-7x^3+18x^2-22x+12} \\ \underline{x^4-2x^3+2x^2} \\ -5x^3+16x^2-22x \\ \underline{-5x^3+10x^2-10x} \\ 6x^2-12x+12 \\ \underline{6x^2-12x+12} \\ 0 \end{array}$$

$x^2-5x+6=0$
$(x-3)(x-2)=0$
$x=3$ or $x=2$
The solution set is $\{2, 3, 1+i\}$.

14. $f(x)$ has zeros at -2 and 1. The zero at -2 has multiplicity of 2.
$x^3+3x^2-4=(x-1)(x+2)^2$

15. $f(x)=\dfrac{x}{x^2-16}$
domain: $\{x \mid x \neq 4, x \neq -4\}$
Symmetry: $f(-x)=\dfrac{-x}{x^2-16}=-f(x)$
y-axis symmetry
x-intercept: $x=0$
y-intercept: $y=\dfrac{0}{0^2-16}=0$
Vertical asymptotes:
$x^2-16=0$
$(x-4)(x+4)=0$
$x=4, -4$
Horizontal asymptote:
$n<m$, so $y=0$ is the horizontal asymptote.

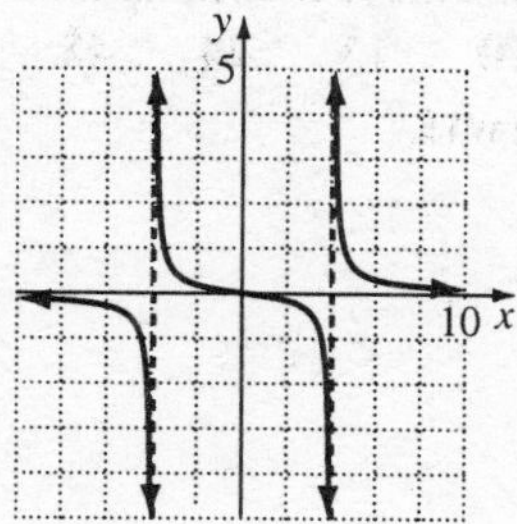

16. $f(x)=\dfrac{x^2-9}{x-2}$
domain: $\{x \mid x \neq 2\}$
Symmetry: $f(-x)=\dfrac{x^2-9}{-x-2}$
$f(-x) \neq f(x), f(-x) \neq -f(x)$
No symmetry
x-intercepts:
$x^2-9=0$
$(x-3)(x+3)=0$
$x=3, -3$
y-intercept: $y=\dfrac{0^2-9}{0-2}=\dfrac{9}{2}$
Vertical asymptote:
$x-2=0$
$x=2$
Horizontal asymptote:
$n>m$, so no horizontal asymptote exists.
Slant asymptote: $f(x)=x+2-\dfrac{5}{x-2}$
$y=x+2$

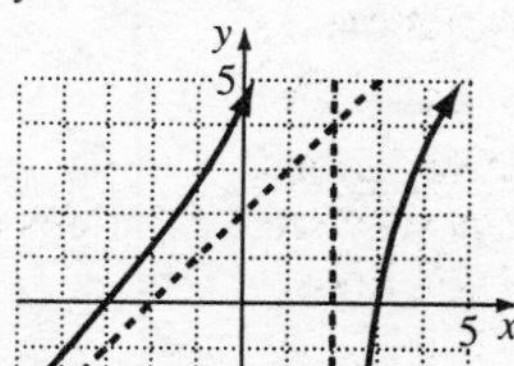

17. $f(x) = \dfrac{x+1}{x^2+2x-3}$

$x^2+2x-3 = (x+3)(x-1)$

domain: $\{x \mid x = -3, x \neq 1\}$

Symmetry: $f(-x) = \dfrac{-x+1}{x^2-2x-3}$

$f(-x) \neq f(x), f(-x) \neq -f(x)$

No symmetry

x-intercept:

$x + 1 = 0$

$x = -1$

y-intercept: $y = \dfrac{0+1}{0^2+2(0)-3} = -\dfrac{1}{3}$

Vertical asymptotes:

$x^2+2x-3 = 0$

$(x+3)(x-1) = 0$

x –3, 1

Horizontal asymptote:

$n < m$, so $y = 0$ is the horizontal asymptote.

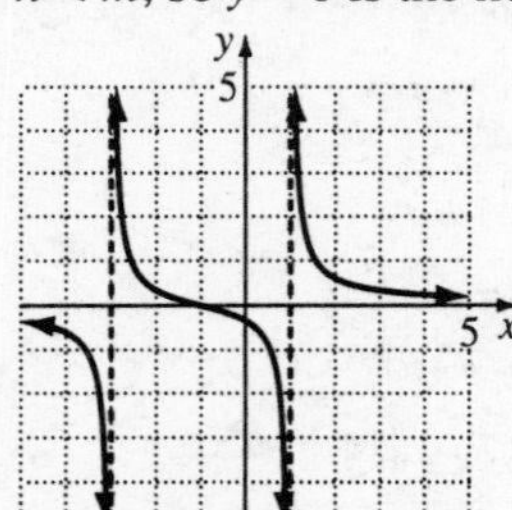

18. $f(x) = \dfrac{4x^2}{x^2+3}$

domain: all real numbers

Symmetry: $f(-x) = \dfrac{4x^2}{x^2+3} = f(x)$

y-axis symmetry

x-intercept:

$4x^2 = 0$

$x = 0$

y-intercept: $y = \dfrac{4(0)^2}{0^2+3} = 0$

Vertical asymptote:

$x^2+3 = 0$

$x^2 = -3$

No vertical asymptote.

Horizontal asymptote:

$n = m$, so $y = \dfrac{4}{1} = 4$ is the horizontal asymptote.

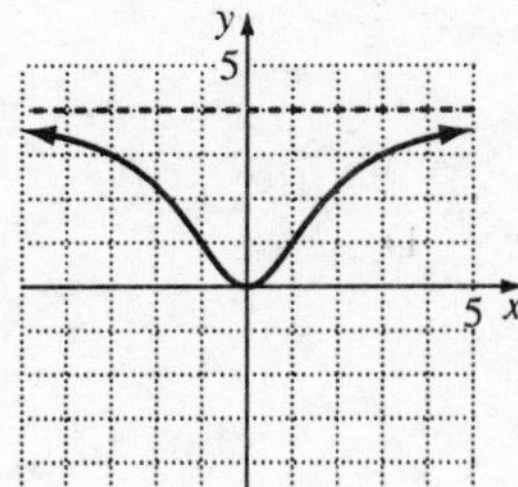

19. a. When $x = 0$, $y = 50$
50 deer were introduced into the habitat.

b. When $x = 10$, $y = 150$
After 10 years, there are 150 deer.

c. $y = 225$
The deer population will approach a maximum of 225 deer.

20. $I = \dfrac{k}{d^2}$

$20 = \dfrac{k}{d^2}$

$k = 4500$

$I = \dfrac{4500}{d^2}$

$I = \dfrac{4500}{10^2} = 45$ foot-candles

Cumulative Review Exercises (Chapters P–3)

1. $\dfrac{1}{2-\sqrt{3}} \cdot \dfrac{2+\sqrt{3}}{2+\sqrt{3}} = \dfrac{2+\sqrt{3}}{4-3} = 2+\sqrt{3}$

2. $3(x^2-3x+1) - 2(3x^2+x-4)$

$= 3x^2 - 9x + 3 - 6x^2 - 2x + 8$

$= -3x^2 - 11x + 11$

3. $3\sqrt{8}+5\sqrt{50}-4\sqrt{32}$
$=3\sqrt{4\cdot 2}+5\sqrt{25\cdot 2}-4\sqrt{16\cdot 2}$
$=3\cdot 2\sqrt{2}+5\cdot 5\sqrt{2}-4\cdot 4\sqrt{2}$
$=6\sqrt{2}+25\sqrt{2}-16\sqrt{2}$
$=15\sqrt{2}$

4. $x^7-x^5=x^5(x^2-1)$
$=x^5(x-1)(x+1)$

5. $|2x-1|=3$
$2x-1=3$
$2x=4$
$x=2$
$2x-1=-3$
$2x=-2$
$x=-1$
The solution set is $\{2, -1\}$.

6. $3x^2-5x+1=0$
$x=\frac{5\pm\sqrt{25-12}}{6}=\frac{5\pm\sqrt{13}}{6}$
The solution set is $\left\{\frac{5+\sqrt{13}}{6}, \frac{5-\sqrt{13}}{6}\right\}$.

7. $9+\frac{3}{x}=\frac{2}{x^2}$
$9x^2+3x=2$
$9x^2+3x-2=0$
$(3x-1)(3x+2)=0$
$3x-1=0 \quad 3x+2=0$
$x=\frac{1}{3}$ or $x=-\frac{2}{3}$
The solution set is $\left\{\frac{1}{3}, -\frac{2}{3}\right\}$.

8. $x^3+2x^2-5x-6=0$
p: ±1, ±2, ±3, ±6
q: ±1
$\frac{p}{q}$: ±1, ±2, ±3, ±6

$$\begin{array}{r|rrrr} -3 & 1 & 2 & -5 & -6 \\ & & -3 & 3 & 6 \\ \hline & 1 & -1 & -2 & 0 \end{array}$$

$x^3+2x^2-5x-6=0$
$(x+3)(x^2-x-2)=0$
$(x+3)(x+1)(x-2)=0$
$x=-3$ or $x=-1$ or $x=2$
The solution set is $\{-3, -1, 2\}$.

9. $|2x-5|>3$
$2x-5>3$
$2x>8$
$x>4$
$2x-5<-3$
$2x<2$
$x<1$
$(-\infty, 1)$ or $(4, \infty)$

10. $3x^2>2x+5$
$3x^2-2x-5>0$
$3x^2-2x-5=0$
$(3x-5)(x+1)=0$
$x=\frac{5}{3}$ or $x=-1$
Test intervals are $(-\infty, -1)$, $\left(-1, \frac{5}{3}\right), \left(\frac{5}{3}, \infty\right)$.
Testing points, the solution is $(-\infty, -1)$ or $\left(\frac{5}{3}, \infty\right)$.

11. $x^2 + y^2 - 2x + 4y - 4 = 0$

$x^2 - 2x + 1 + y^2 + 4y + 4 = 4 + 1 + 4$

$(x-1)^2 + (y+2)^2 = 9$

center: (1, –2)
radius: 3

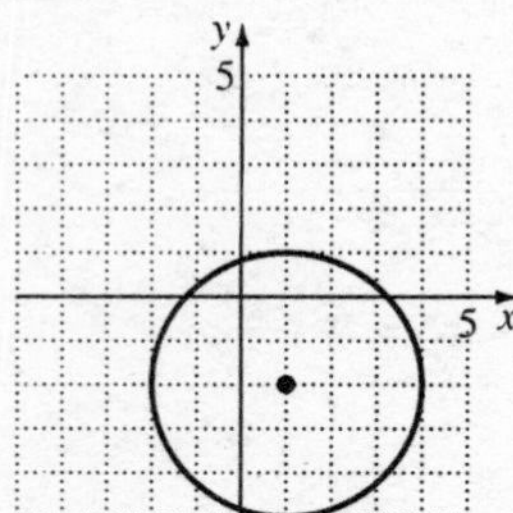

12. $V = C(1-t)$

$\frac{V}{C} = 1 - t$

$\frac{V}{C} - 1 = -t$

$t = 1 - \frac{V}{C}$

13. $f(x) = \sqrt{45 - 9x}$

$45 - 9x \geq 0$
$45 \geq 9x$
$5 \geq x$
Domain: $(-\infty, 5]$

14. $(f - g)(x) = x^2 + 2x - 5 - (4x - 1)$

$= x^2 + 2x - 5 - 4x + 1$

$= x^2 - 2x - 4$

15. $(f \circ g)(x) = (4x-1)^2 + 2(4x-1) - 5$

$= 16x^2 - 8x + 1 + 8x - 2 - 5$

$= 16x^2 - 6$

16. $g(f(-3))$

$f(-3) = (-3)^2 + 2(-3) - 5$

$= 9 - 6 - 5 = -2$

$g(-2) = 4(-2) - 1 = -8 - 1 = -9$

17. $f(x) = x^3 - 4x^2 - x + 4$

a. $x^3 - 4x^2 - x + 4 = 0$

$x^2(x-4) - (x-4) = 0$

$(x^2 - 1)(x - 4) = 0$

$(x-1)(x+1)(x-4) = 0$

$x = -1, 1, 4$

The solution set is $\{-1, 1, 4\}$.

b. The graph falls to the left and rises to the right.

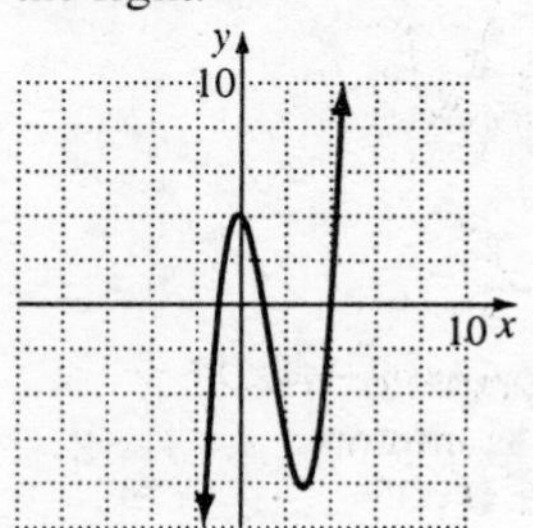

18. $f(x) = x^2 + 2x - 8$

$x = \frac{-b}{2a} = \frac{-2}{2} = -1$

$f(-1) = (-1)^2 + 2(-1) - 8$

$= 1 - 2 - 8 = -9$

vertex: (–1, –9)
x-intercepts:

$x^2 + 2x - 8 = 0$

$(x+4)(x-2) = 0$

$x = -4$ or $x = 2$

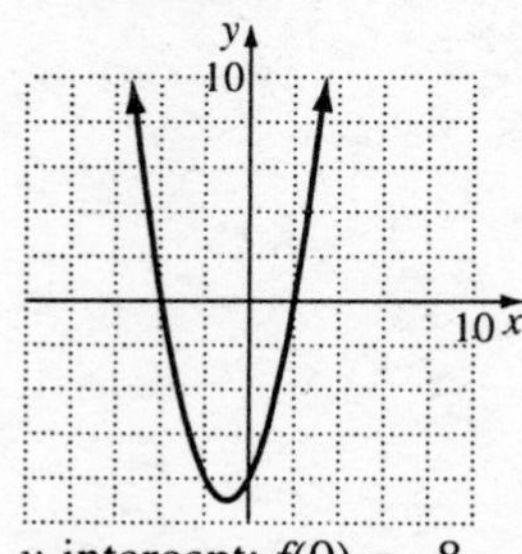

y-intercept: $f(0) = -8$

19. $f(x) = x^2(x-3)$
zeros: $x = 0$ (multiplicity 2) and $x = 3$
y-intercept: $y = 0$
$f(x) = x^3 - 3x^2$
$n = 3,\ a_n = 0$ so the graph falls to the left and rises to the right.

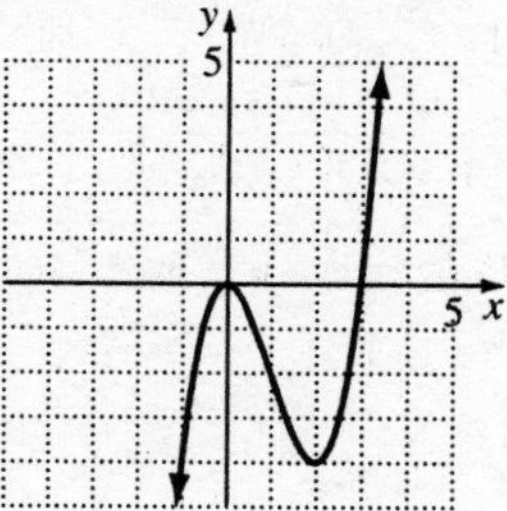

20. $f(x) = \dfrac{x-1}{x-2}$
vertical asymptote: $x = 2$
horizontal asymptote: $y = 1$
x-intercept: $x = 1$
y-intercept: $y = \frac{1}{2}$

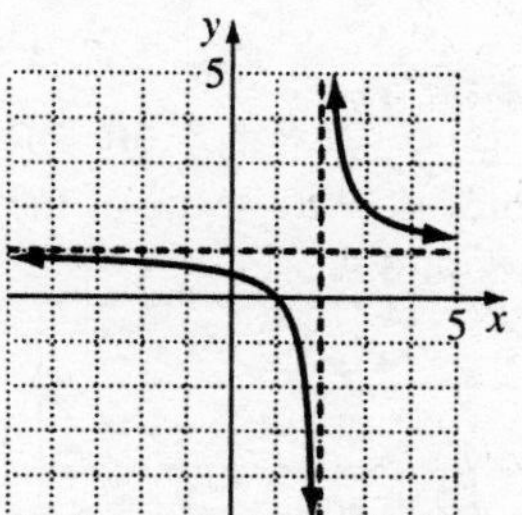

Chapter 4

Section 4.1

Check Point Exercises

1. Substitute 60 for x and evaluate the function at 60. $f(60) = 13.49(0.967)^{-60} - 1 \approx 1$
   Thus, one O-ring is expected to fail at a temperature of 60°F.

2. Begin by setting up a table of coordinates.

x	$f(x) = 3^x$
−3	$f(-3) = 3^{-3} = \frac{1}{27}$
−2	$f(-2) = 3^{-2} = \frac{1}{9}$
−1	$f(-1) = 3^{-1} = \frac{1}{3}$
0	$f(0) = 3^0 = 1$
1	$f(1) = 3^1 = 3$
2	$f(2) = 3^2 = 9$
3	$f(3) = 3^3 = 27$

   Plot these points, connecting them with a continuous curve.

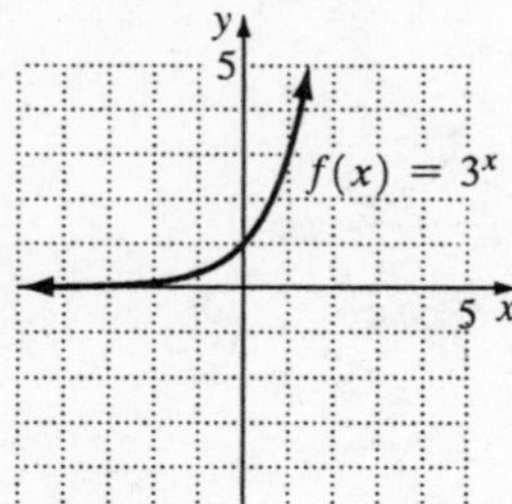

3. Note that the function $g(x) = 3^{x-1}$ has the general form $g(x) = b^{x+c}$ where $c = -1$. Because $c < 0$, we graph $g(x) = 3^{x-1}$ by shifting the graph of $f(x) = 3^x$ one unit to the right. Construct a table showing some of the coordinates for f and g.

x	$f(x) = 3^x$	$g(x) = 3^{x-1}$
−2	$3^{-2} = \frac{1}{9}$	$3^{-2-1} = 3^{-3} = \frac{1}{27}$
−1	$3^{-1} = \frac{1}{3}$	$3^{-1-1} = 3^{-2} = \frac{1}{9}$
0	$3^0 = 1$	$3^{0-1} = 3^{-1} = \frac{1}{3}$
1	$3^1 = 3$	$3^{1-1} = 3^0 = 1$
2	$3^2 = 9$	$3^{2-1} = 3^1 = 3$

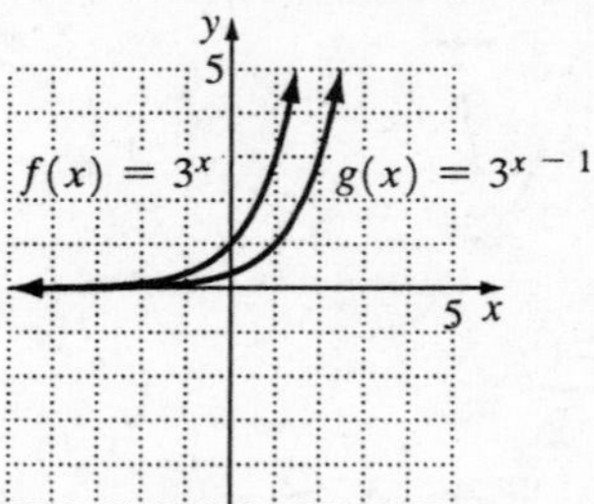

4. Note that the function $g(x) = 2^x + 1$ has the general form $g(x) = b^x + c$ where $c = 1$. Because $c > 0$, we graph $g(x) = 2^x + 1$ by shifting the graph of $f(x) = 2^x$ up one unit. Construct a table showing some of the coordinates for f and g.

x	$f(x) - 2^x$	$g(x) = 2^x + 1$
−2	$2^{-2} = \frac{1}{4}$	$2^{-2} + 1 = \frac{1}{4} + 1 = \frac{5}{4}$
−1	$2^{-1} = \frac{1}{2}$	$2^{-1} + 1 = \frac{1}{2} + 1 = \frac{3}{2}$
0	$2^0 = 1$	$2^0 + 1 = 1 + 1 = 2$
1	$2^1 = 2$	$2^1 + 1 = 2 + 1 = 3$
2	$2^2 = 4$	$2^2 + 1 = 4 + 1 = 5$

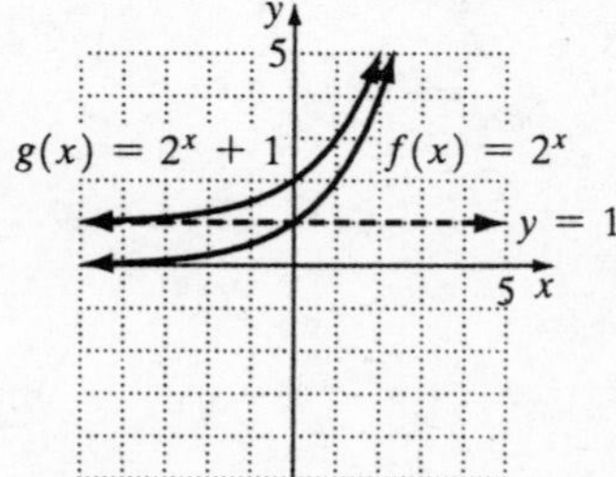

5. Because 2050 is 51 years after 1999, substitute 51 for x.
$f(51) = 6e^{0.013(51)} = 6e^{0.663} \approx 11.64$.
The world population is 2050 will be approximately 11.64 billion.

6. a. $A = 10,000\left(1+\dfrac{0.08}{4}\right)^{4\cdot 5} \approx 14,859.47$
The balance in this account after 5 years is $14,859.47.

b. $A = 10,000e^{0.08(5)} \approx 14,918.25$
The balance in this account after 5 years is $14,918.25.

Exercise Set 4.1

1. $2^{3.4} \approx 10.556$

3. $3^{\sqrt{5}} \approx 11.665$

5. $4^{-1.5} = 0.125$

7. $e^{2.3} \approx 9.974$

9. $e^{-0.95} \approx 0.387$

11.

x	$f(x) = 4^x$
-2	$4^{-2} = \frac{1}{16}$
-1	$4^{-1} = \frac{1}{4}$
0	$4^0 = 1$
1	$4^1 = 4$
2	$4^2 = 16$

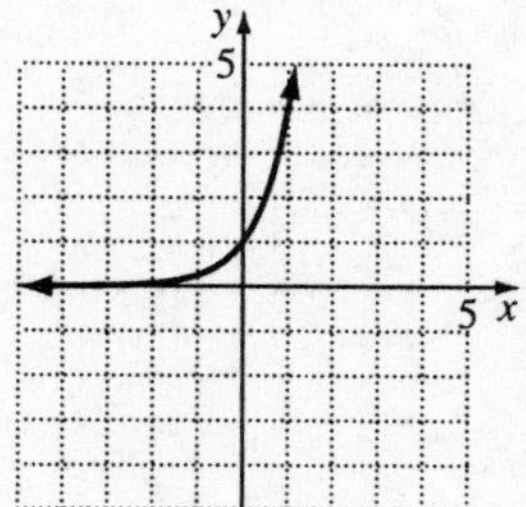

13.

x	$g(x) = \left(\frac{3}{2}\right)^x$
-2	$\left(\frac{3}{2}\right)^{-2} = \frac{4}{9}$
-1	$\left(\frac{3}{2}\right)^{-1} = \frac{2}{3}$
0	$\left(\frac{3}{2}\right)^{0} = 1$
1	$\left(\frac{3}{2}\right)^{1} = \frac{3}{2}$
2	$\left(\frac{3}{2}\right)^{2} = \frac{9}{4}$

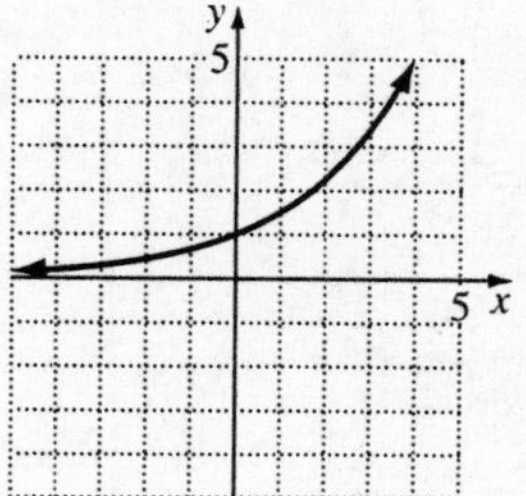

15.

x	$h(x) = \left(\frac{1}{2}\right)^x$
-2	$\left(\frac{1}{2}\right)^{-2} = 4$
-1	$\left(\frac{1}{2}\right)^{-1} = 2$
0	$\left(\frac{1}{2}\right)^{0} = 1$
1	$\left(\frac{1}{2}\right)^{1} = \frac{1}{2}$
2	$\left(\frac{1}{2}\right)^{2} = \frac{1}{4}$

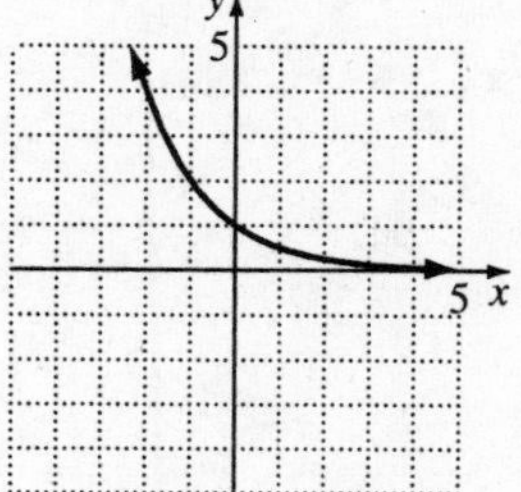

17.

x	$f(x)=(0.6)^x$
−2	$(0.6)^{-2}=2.\overline{7}$
−1	$(0.6)^{-1}=1.\overline{6}$
0	$(0.6)^0=1$
1	$(0.6)^1=0.6$
2	$(0.6)^2=0.36$

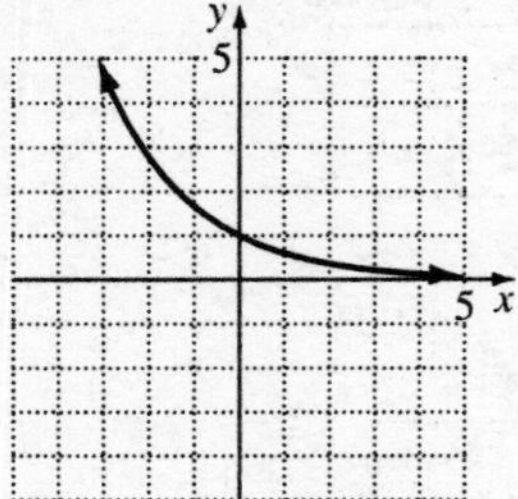

19. This is the graph of $f(x)=3^x$ reflected about the x-axis and about the y-axis, so the function is $H(x)=-3^{-x}$.

21. This is the graph of $f(x)=3^x$ reflected about the x-axis, so the function is $F(x)=-3^x$.

23. This is the graph of $f(x)=3^x$ shifted one unit downward, so the function is $h(x)=3^x-1$.

25. The graph of $g(x)=2^{x+!}$ can be obtained by shifting the graph of $f(x)=2^x$ one unit to the left.

x	$g(x)=2^{x+1}$
−2	$2^{-2+1}=2^{-1}=\frac{1}{2}$
−1	$2^{-1+1}=2^0=1$
0	$2^{0+1}=2^1=2$
1	$2^{1+1}=2^2=4$
2	$2^{2+1}=2^3=8$

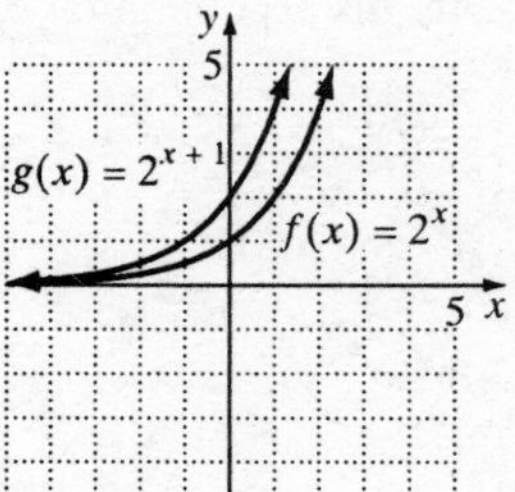

27. The graph of $g(x)=2^x-1$ can be obtained by shifting the graph of $f(x)=2^x$ downward one unit.

x	$g(x)=2^x-1$
−2	$2^{-2}-1=\frac{1}{4}-1=-\frac{3}{4}$
−1	$2^{-1}-1=\frac{1}{2}-1=-\frac{1}{2}$
0	$2^0-1=1-1=0$
1	$2^1-1=2-1=1$
2	$2^2-1=4-1=3$

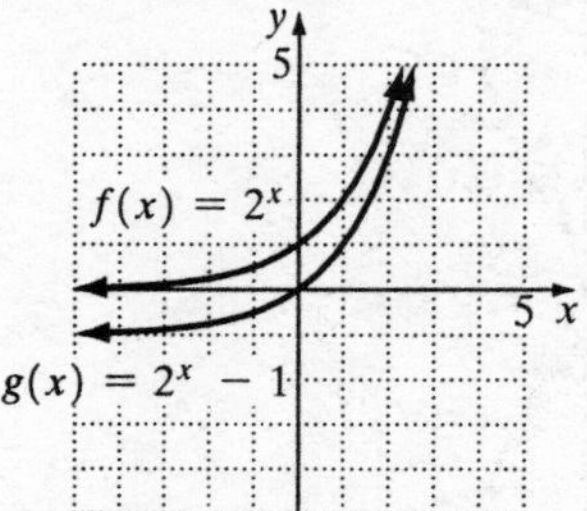

29. The graph of $h(x) = 2^{x+1} - 1$ can be obtained by shifting the graph of $f(x) = 2^x$ one unit to the left and one unit downward.

x	$h(x) = 2^{x+1} - 1$
-2	$2^{-2+1} - 1 = 2^{-1} - 1 = \frac{1}{2} - 1 = -\frac{1}{2}$
-1	$2^{-1+1} - 1 = 2^0 - 1 = 1 - 1 = 0$
0	$2^{0+1} - 1 = 2^1 - 1 = 2 - 1 = 1$
1	$2^{1+1} - 1 = 2^2 - 1 = 4 - 1 = 3$
2	$2^{2+1} - 1 = 2^3 - 1 = 8 - 1 = 7$

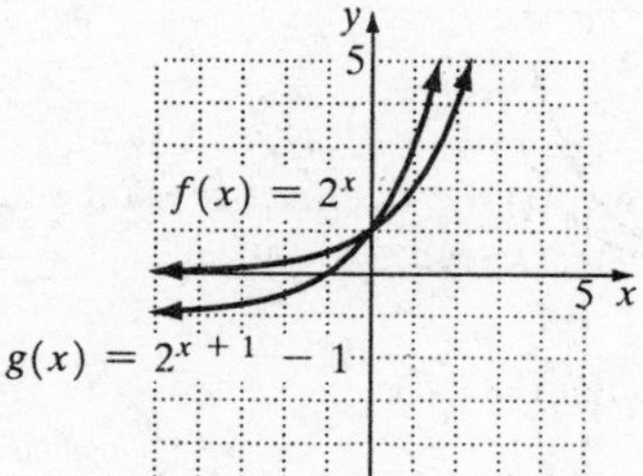

31. The graph of $g(x) = -2^x$ can be obtained by reflecting the graph of $f(x) = 2^x$ about the x-axis.

x	$g(x) = -2^x$
-2	$-2^{-2} = -\frac{1}{4}$
-1	$-2^{-1} = -\frac{1}{2}$
0	$-2^0 = -1$
1	$-2^1 = -2$
2	$-2^2 = -4$

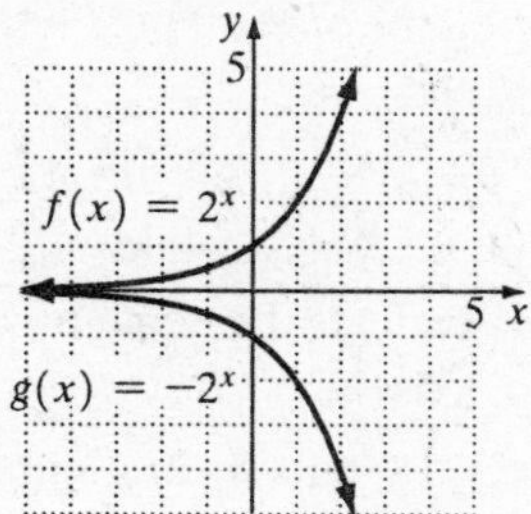

33. The graph of $g(x) = 2 \cdot 2^x$ can be obtained by vertically stretching the graph of $f(x) = 2^x$ by a factor of two.

x	$g(x) = 2 \cdot 2^x$
-2	$2 \cdot 2^{-2} = 2 \cdot \frac{1}{4} = \frac{1}{2}$
-1	$2 \cdot 2^{-1} = 2 \cdot \frac{1}{2} = 1$
0	$2 \cdot 2^0 = 2 \cdot 1 = 2$
1	$2 \cdot 2^1 = 2 \cdot 2 = 4$
2	$2 \cdot 2^2 = 2 \cdot 4 = 8$

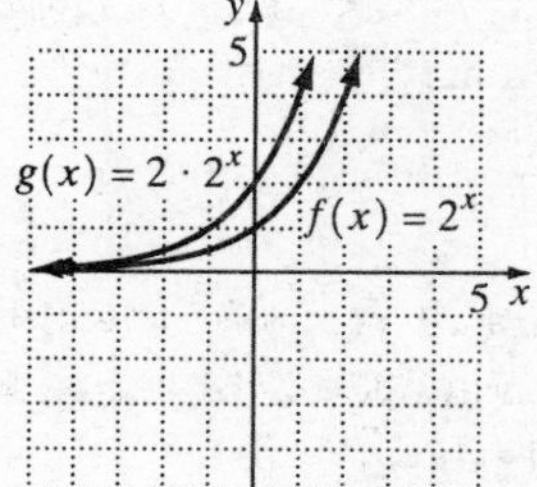

35. a. $A = 10{,}000\left(1 + \frac{0.055}{2}\right)^{2(5)}$
$\approx 13{,}116.51$

b. $A = 10{,}000\left(1 + \frac{0.055}{12}\right)^{12(5)}$
$\approx 13{,}157.04$

c. $A = 10{,}000e^{0.055(5)}$
$\approx 13{,}165.31$

37. $A = 12{,}000\left(1 + \frac{0.07}{12}\right)^{12(3)}$
$\approx 14{,}795.11$ (7% yield)
$A = 12{,}000e^{0.0685(3)}$
$\approx 14{,}737.67$ (6.85% yield)
Investing \$12,000 for 3 years at 7% compounded monthly yields the greatest return.

39. a. $f(0) = 67.38(1.026)^0 = 67.38$
67.38 million

b. $f(27) = 67.38(1.026)^{27}$
≈ 134.7441 million

c. $f(54) = 67.38(1.026)^{254}$
≈ 269.4564 million

d. $f(81) = 67.38(1.026)^{81}$
≈ 538.8492 million

e. The population appears to double every 27 years.

41. $f(25) = \dfrac{0.9}{1+271(0.885)^{25}} \approx 0.0653$
This means that only 6.5% of 25-year-olds have some coronary heart disease.

43. $\$65{,}000(1 + 0.06)^{10} \approx 116{,}405.10$
The house will be worth $116,405.10.

45. $2^{1.7} \approx 3.249009585$
$2^{1.73} \approx 3.317278183$
$2^{1.732} \approx 3.321880096$
$2^{1.73205} \approx 3.321995226$
$2^{1.7320508} \approx 3.321997068$
$2^{\sqrt{3}} \approx 3.321997085$
The closer the exponent is to $\sqrt{3}$, the closer the value is to $2^{\sqrt{3}}$.

47. $f(11) = 24{,}000e^{0.21(11)} \approx 241{,}786.1917$
The number of AIDS cases among IV drug users in 2000 will be about 241,786.

49. a. $24\left(1+\dfrac{0.05}{12}\right)^{12(374)}$
$\approx \$3{,}052{,}428{,}614.31$

b. $24e^{0.05(374)} \approx \$3{,}173{,}350{,}575.95$

51. a. $N(0) = \dfrac{30{,}000}{1+20e^{-1.5(0)}} = 1428.57$
About 1429 people became ill.

b. $N(3) = \dfrac{30{,}000}{1+20e^{-1.5(3)}} \approx 24{,}546.30$
About 24,546 people were ill by the end of the third week.

c. The growth of the epidemic is limited by the size of the population. The horizontal asymptote shows that the epidemic will grow to the limiting size of the population, so that the entire population will eventually become ill.

53.–57. Answers may vary.

59.

When $x = 31$, $y \approx 3.77$. NASA would not have launched the *Challenger*, since nearly 4 O-rings are expected to fail.

61. a. $A = 10{,}000\left(1+\dfrac{0.05}{4}\right)^{4(t)}$

$A = 10{,}000\left(1+\dfrac{0.045}{12}\right)^{12(t)}$

b. 5% compounded quarterly offers the better return.

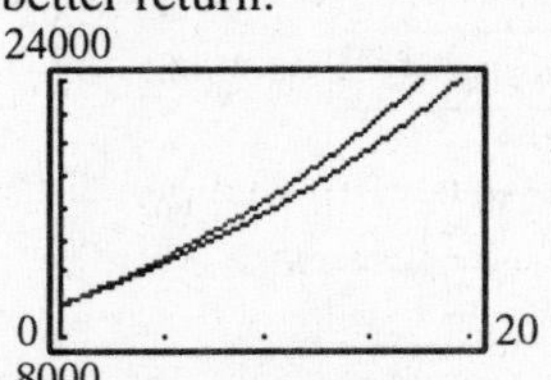

63. a. False; even continuous compounding has a limit on the amount over a fixed interval of time.

b. False; $f(x) = 3^{-x}$ reflects the graph of $y = 3^x$ about the y-axis while $f(x) = -3^x$ reflects the graph of $y = 3^x$ about the x-axis.

c. False; $e \approx 2.718$, but e is irrational.

d. True;
$f(x) = \left(\dfrac{1}{3}\right)^x = \left(3^{-1}\right)^x = (3)^{-x} = g(x).$

(d) is true.

65. $y = 3^x$ is (d). y increases as x increases, but not as quickly as $y = 5^x$. $y = 5^x$ is (c).
$y=\left(\frac{1}{3}\right)^x$ is (a). $y=\left(\frac{1}{3}\right)^x$ is the same as $y = 3^{-x}$, so it is (d) reflected about the y-axis.
$y=\left(\frac{1}{5}\right)^x$ is (b). $y=\left(\frac{1}{5}\right)^x$ is the same as $y = 5^{-x}$, so it is (c) reflected about the y-axis.

Section 4.2

Check Point Exercises

1. a. $3 = \log_7 x$ means $7^3 = x$.

b. $2 = \log_b 25$ means $b^2 = 25$.

c. $\log_4 26 = y$ means $4^y = 26$.

2. a. $2^5 = x$ means $5 = \log_2 x$.

b. $b^3 = 27$ means $3 = \log_b 27$.

c. $e^y = 33$ means $y = \log_e 33$.

3. a. Question: 10 to what power gives 100?
$\log_{10} 100 = 2$ because $10^2 = 100$.

b. Question: 3 to what power gives 3?
$\log_3 3 = 1$ because $3^1 = 3$.

c. Question: 36 to what power gives 6?
$\log_{36} 6 = \frac{1}{2}$ because $36^{1/2} = \sqrt{36} = 6$

4. a. Because $\log_b b = 1$, we conclude $\log_9 9 = 1$.

b. Because $\log_b 1 = 0$, we conclude $\log_8 1 = 0$.

5. a. Because $\log_b b^x = x$, we conclude $\log_7 7^8 = 8$.

b. Because $b^{\log_b x} = x$, we conclude $3^{\log_3 17} = 17$.

6. First, set up a table of coordinates for $f(x) = 3^x$.

x	−2	−1	0	1	2	3
$f(x) = 3^x$	$\frac{1}{9}$	$\frac{1}{3}$	1	3	9	27

Reversing these coordinates gives the coordinates for the inverse function $g(x) = \log_3 x$.

x	$\frac{1}{9}$	$\frac{1}{3}$	1	3	9	27
$g(x) = \log_3 x$	−2	−1	0	1	2	3

The graph of the inverse can also be drawn by reflecting the graph of $f(x) = 3^x$ about the line $y = x$.

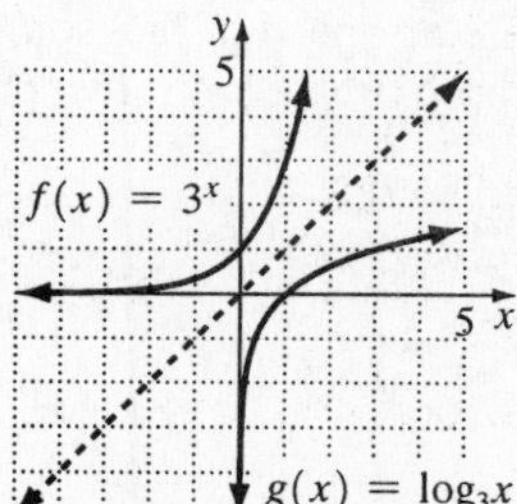

7. The domain of h consists of all x for which $x - 5 > 0$. Solving this inequality for x, we obtain $x > 5$. Thus, the domain of h is $(5, \infty)$.

8. Substitute the boy's age, 10, for x and evaluate the function at 10.
$$f(10) = 29 + 48.8\ \log(10+1)$$
$$= 29 + 48.8\ \log(11)$$
$$\approx 80$$
Thus, a 10-year-old boy is approximately 80% of his adult height.

9. Because $I = 10{,}000\, I_0$,
$$R = \log\frac{10{,}000 I_0}{I_0}$$
$$= \log 10{,}000$$
$$= 4$$
The earthquake registered 4.0 on the Richter scale.

10. a. The domain of f consists of all x for which $4 - x > 0$. Solving this inequality for x, we obtain $x < 4$. Thus, the domain of f is $(-\infty, 4)$

b. The domain of g consists of all x for which $x^2 > 0$. Solving this inequality for x, we obtain $x < 0$ or $x > 0$. Thus the domain of g is $(-\infty, 0)$ or $(0, \infty)$.

11. a. Because $\ln e^x = x$, we conclude $\ln e^{25x} = 25x$.

b. Because $e^{\ln x} = x$, we conclude $e^{\ln\sqrt{x}} = \sqrt{x}$.

12. Substitute 197 for P, the population in thousands. $W = 0.35\ln 197 + 2.74 \approx 4.6$ The average walking speed in Jackson, Mississippi is approximately 4.6 feet per second.

Exercise Set 4.2

1. $2^4 = 16$

3. $3^2 = x$

5. $b^5 = 32$

7. $6^y = 216$

9. $\log_2 8 = 3$

11. $\log_2 \frac{1}{16} = -4$

13. $\log_8 2 = \frac{1}{3}$

15. $\log_{13} x = 2$

17. $\log_b 1000 = 3$

19. $\log_7 200 = y$

21. $\log_4 16 = 2$ because $4^2 = 16$.

23. $\log_2 64 = 6$ because $2^6 = 64$.

25. $\log_7 \sqrt{7} = \frac{1}{2}$ because $7^{1/2} = \sqrt{7}$.

27. $\log_2 \frac{1}{8} = -3$ because $2^{-3} = \frac{1}{8}$.

29. $\log_{64} 8 = \frac{1}{2}$ because $64^{1/2} = \sqrt{64} = 8$.

31. Because $\log_b b = 1$, we conclude $\log_5 5 = 1$.

33. Because $\log_b 1 = 0$, we conclude $\log_4 1 = 0$.

35. Because $\log_b b^x = x$, we conclude $\log_5 5^7 = 7$.

37. Because $b^{\log_b x} = x$, we conclude $8^{\log_8 19} = 19$.

39. First, set up a table of coordinates for $f(x) = 4^x$.

x	-2	-1	0	1	2	3
$f(x) = 4x$	$\frac{1}{16}$	$\frac{1}{4}$	1	4	16	64

Reversing these coordinates gives the coordinates for the inverse function $g(x) = \log_4 x$.

x	$\frac{1}{16}$	$\frac{1}{4}$	1	4	16	64
$g(x) = \log_{4x}$	-2	-1	0	1	2	3

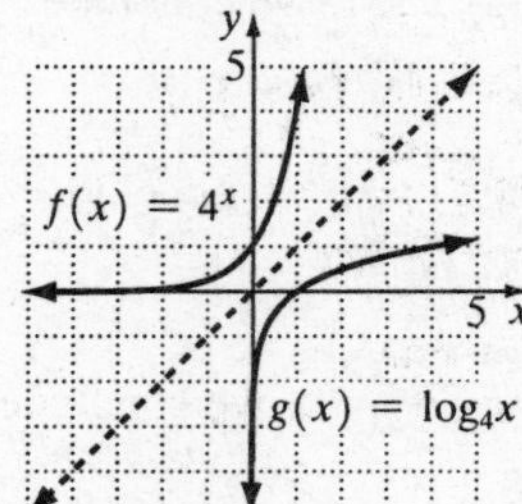

41. First, set up a table of coordinates for $f(x)=\left(\frac{1}{2}\right)^x$.

x	−2	−1	0	1	2	3
$f(x)=\left(\frac{1}{2}\right)^x$	4	2	1	$\frac{1}{2}$	$\frac{1}{4}$	$\frac{1}{8}$

Reversing these coordinates gives the coordinates for the inverse function $g(x)=\log_{1/2} x$.

x	4	2	1	$\frac{1}{2}$	$\frac{1}{4}$	$\frac{1}{8}$
$g(x)=\log_{1/2} x$	−2	−1	0	1	2	3

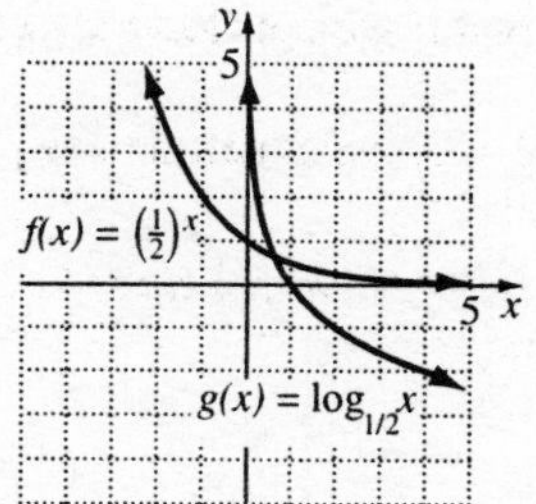

43. This is the graph of $f(x)=\log_3 x$ reflected about the x-axis and shifted up one unit, so the function is $H(x)=1-\log^x$.

45. This is the graph of $f(x)=\log_3 x$ shifted down one unit, so the function is $h(x)=\log_3 x-1$.

47. This is the graph of $f(x)=\log_3 x$ shifted right one unit, so the function is $g(x)=\log_3(x-1)$.

49.

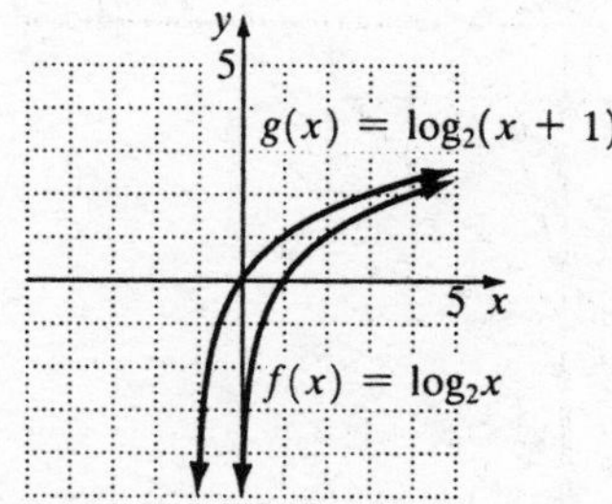

x-intercept: (0,0)
vertical asymptote: $x=-1$

51.

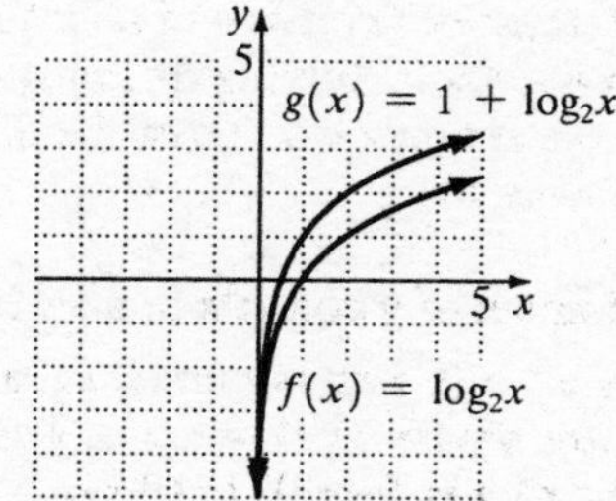

x-intercept: (0.5,0)
vertical asymptote: $x=0$

53.

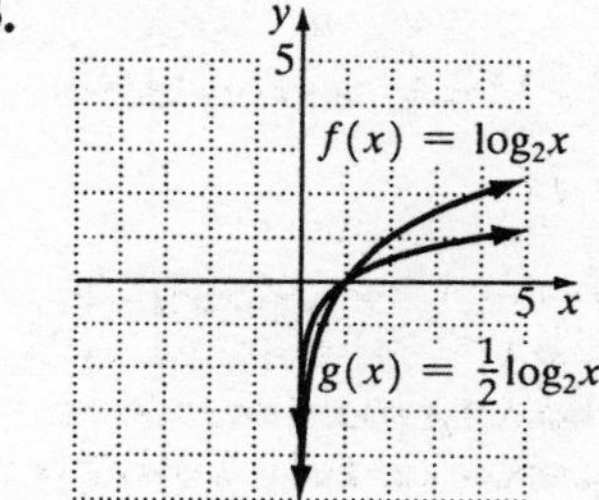

x-intercept: (1,0)
vertical asymptote: $x=0$

55. The domain of f consists of all x for which $x+4>0$. Solving this inequality for x, we obtain $x>-4$. Thus, the domain of f is $(-4, \infty)$.

57. The domain of f consists of all x for which $2-x>0$. Solving this inequality for x, we obtain $x<2$. Thus, the domain of f is $(-\infty, 2)$.

59. The domain of f consists of all x for which $(x-2)^2>0$. Solving this inequality for x, we obtain $x<2$ or $x>2$. Thus, the domain of f is $(-\infty, 2)$ or $(2, -\infty)$.

61. $\log 100=\log_{10} 100=2$ because $10^2=100$.

63. Because $\log 10^x=x$, we conclude $\log 10^7=7$.

65. Because $10^{\log x}=x$, we conclude $10^{\log 33}=33$.

67. $\ln 1 = 0$ because $e^0 = 1$.

69. Because $\ln e^x = x$, we conclude $\ln e^6 = 6$.

71. $\ln \frac{1}{e^6} = \ln e^{-6}$

Because $\ln e^x = x$ we conclude $\ln e^{-6} = -6$, so $\ln \frac{1}{e^6} = -6$.

73. Because $e^{\ln x} = x$, we conclude $e^{\ln 125} = 125$.

75. Because $\ln e^x = x$, we conclude $\ln e^{9x} = 9x$.

77. Because $e^{\ln x} = x$, we conclude $e^{\ln 5x^2} = 5x^2$.

79. Because $10^{\log x} = x$, we conclude $10^{\log \sqrt{x}} = \sqrt{x}$.

81. $f(13) = 62 + 35\log(13–4) \approx 95.4$
She is approximately 95.4% of her adult height.

83. $f(16) = 2.05 + 1.3\ln(16) \approx 5.65$ billion
Approximately \$5.65 billion was spent in 2000.

85. $D = 10\log\left[10^{12}(6.3\times10^6)\right] \approx 188$

Yes, the sound can rupture the human eardrum.

87. **a.** $f(0) = 88–15\ln(0 + 1) = 88$
The average score on the original exam was 88.

b. $f(2) = 88–15\ln(2 + 1) = 71.5$
$f(4) = 88–15\ln(4 + 1) = 63.9$
$f(6) = 88–15\ln(6 + 1) = 58.8$
$f(8) = 88–15\ln(8 + 1) = 55$
$f(10) = 88–15\ln(10 + 1) = 52$
$f(12) = 88–15\ln(12 + 1) = 49.5$

The average score after 2 months was about 71.5, after 4 months was about 63.9, after 6 months was about 58.8, after 8 months was about 55, after 10 months was about 52, and after one year was about 49.5.

c.

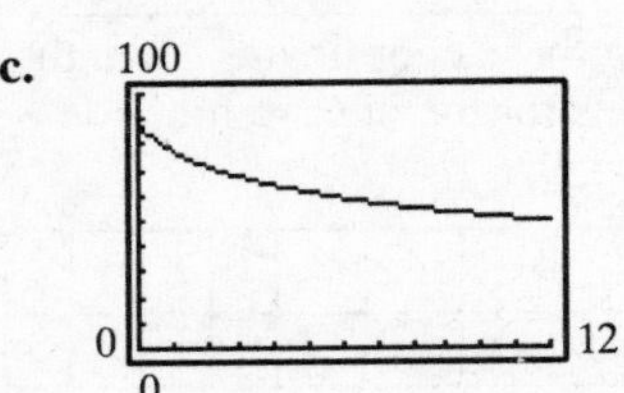

Material retention decreases as time passes.

89.–95. Answers may vary.

97.

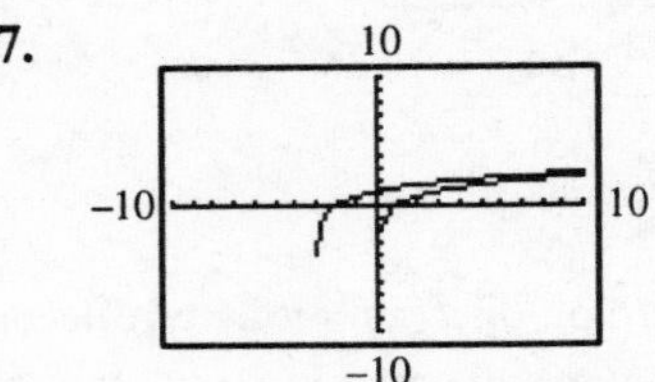

$g(x)$ is $f(x)$ shifted 3 units left.

99.

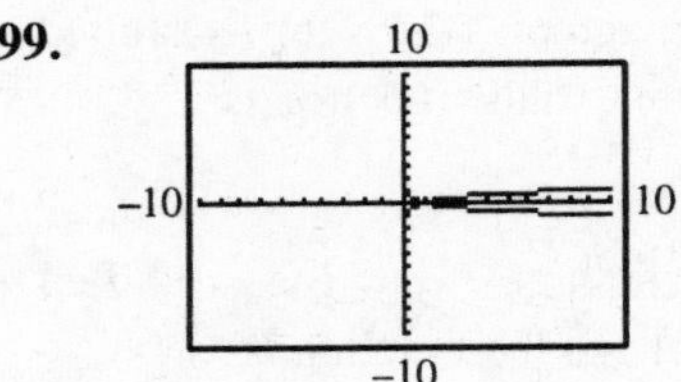

$g(x)$ is $f(x)$ reflected about the x-axis.

101.

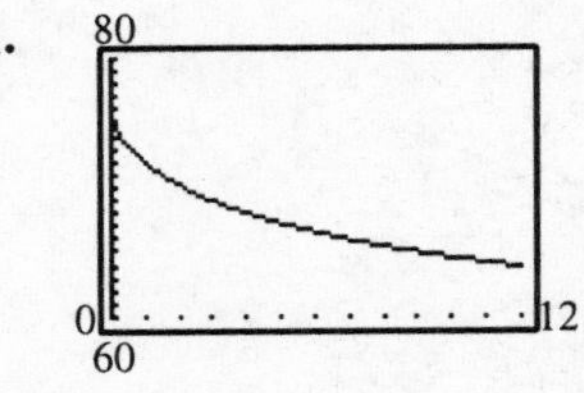

The score falls below 65 after 9 months.

103.

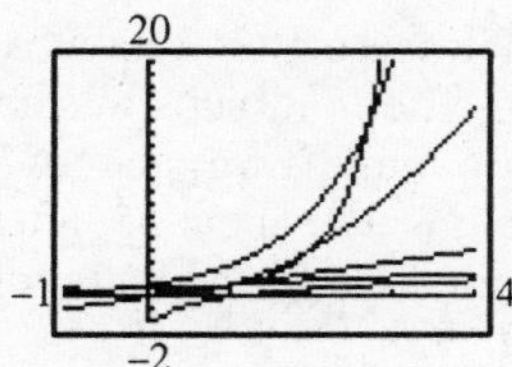

$y = \ln x,\ y = \sqrt{x},\ y = x,$
$y = x^2,\ y = e^x,\ y = x^x$

105. $\dfrac{\log_3 81 - \log_\pi 1}{\log_{2\sqrt{2}} 8 - \log 0.001} = \dfrac{4-0}{2-(-3)} = \dfrac{4}{5}$

107. $\log_4 60 < \log_4 64 = 3$ so $\log_4 60 < 3$.
$\log_3 40 > \log_3 27 = 3$ so $\log_3 40 > 3$.
So $\log_4 60 < 3 < \log_3 40$.
Thus, $\log_3 > \log_4 60$.

Section 4.3

Check Point Exercises

1. a. $\log_6(10 \cdot 9) = \log_6 10 + \log_6 9$

b. $\log(100x) = \log 100 + \log x$
$= 2 + \log x$

2. a. $\log_8\left(\dfrac{23}{x}\right) = \log_8 23 - \log_8 x$

b. $\ln\left(\dfrac{e^5}{11}\right) = \ln e^5 - \ln 11$
$= 5 - \ln 11$

3. a. $\log_6 8^9 = 9 \log_6 8$

b. $\ln \sqrt[3]{x} = \ln x^{1/3}$
$= \dfrac{1}{3} \ln x$

4. a. $\log_b x^4 \sqrt[3]{y}$
$= \log_6 x^4 y^{1/3}$
$= \log_b x^4 + \log_b y^{1/3}$
$= 4 \log_b x + \dfrac{1}{3} \log_b y$

b. $\log_5 \dfrac{\sqrt{x}}{25y^3}$
$= \log_5 \dfrac{x^{1/2}}{25y^3}$
$= \log_5 x^{1/2} - \log_5 25y^3$
$= \log_5 x^{1/2} - \left(\log_5 25 + \log_5 y^3\right)$
$= \dfrac{1}{2} \log_5 x - (\log_5 25 + 3 \log_5 y)$
$= \dfrac{1}{2} \log_5 x - \log_5 25 - 3 \log_5 y$
$= \dfrac{1}{2} \log_5 x - 2 - 3 \log_5 y$

5. a. $\log 25 + \log 4 = \log(25 \cdot 4)$
$= \log 100$
$= 2$

b. $\log(7x + 6) - \log x = \log \dfrac{7x+6}{x}$

6. a. $\ln x^2 + \dfrac{1}{3} \ln(x+5)$
$= \ln x^2 + \ln(x+5)^{1/3}$
$= \ln x^2 (x+5)^{1/3}$
$= \ln x^2 \sqrt[3]{x+5}$

b. $2 \log(x-3) - \log x$
$= \log(x-3)^2 - \log x$
$= \log \dfrac{(x-3)^2}{x}$

7. $\log_7 2506 = \dfrac{\log 2506}{\log 7}$
≈ 4.02

8. $\log_7 2506 = \dfrac{\ln 2506}{\ln 7}$
≈ 4.02

9. $y = \log_3 x = \dfrac{\ln x}{\ln 3}$

$y = \log_{15} x = \dfrac{\ln x}{\ln 15}$

Using a [0, 10, 1] by [–3, 3, 1] viewing rectangle, the graphs are:

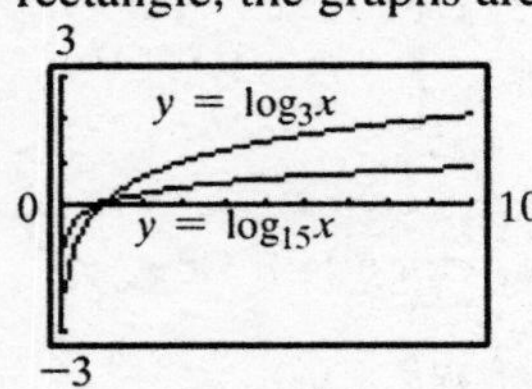

Exercise Set 4.3

1. $\log_5(12 \cdot 3) = \log_5 12 + \log_5 3$

3. $\log_7(7x) = \log_7 7 + \log_7 x$
$= 1 + \log_7 x$

5. $\log(1000x) = \log 1000 + \log x$
$= 3 + \log x$

7. $\log_7\left(\dfrac{7}{x}\right) = \log_7 7 - \log_7 x$
$= 1 - \log_7 x$

9. $\log\left(\dfrac{x}{100}\right) = \log x - \log 100$
$= \log_x - 2$

11. $\log_4\left(\dfrac{64}{y}\right) = \log_4 64 - \log_4 y$
$= 3 - \log_4 y$

13. $\ln\left(\dfrac{e^2}{5}\right) = \ln e^2 - \ln 5$
$= 2\ln e - \ln 5$
$= 2 - \ln 5$

15. $\log_b x^3 = 3\log_b x$

17. $\log N^{-b} = -b \log N$

19. $\ln \sqrt[5]{x} = \ln x^{(1/5)}$
$= \dfrac{1}{5}\ln x$

21. $\log_b x^2 y = \log_b x^2 + \log_b y$
$= 2\log_b x + \log_b y$

23. $\log_4\left(\dfrac{\sqrt{x}}{64}\right) = \log_4 x^{1/2} - \log_4 64$
$= \dfrac{1}{2}\log_4 x - 3$

25. $\log_6\left(\dfrac{36}{\sqrt{x+1}}\right) = \log_6 36 - \log_6 (x+1)^{1/2}$
$= 2 - \dfrac{1}{2}\log_6(x+1)$

27. $\log_b\left(\dfrac{x^2 y}{z^2}\right) = \log_b\left(x^2 y\right) - \log_b z^2$
$= \log_b x^2 + \log_b y - \log_b z^2$
$= 2\log_b x + \log_b y - 2\log_b z$

29. $\log\sqrt{100x} = \log(100x)^{1/2}$
$= \dfrac{1}{2}\log(100x)$
$= \dfrac{1}{2}(\log 100 + \log x)$
$= \dfrac{1}{2}(2 + \log x)$
$= 1 + \dfrac{1}{2}\log x$

31. $\log \sqrt[3]{\dfrac{x}{y}} = \log\left(\dfrac{x}{y}\right)^{1/3}$
$= \dfrac{1}{3}\left[\log\left(\dfrac{x}{y}\right)\right]$
$= \dfrac{1}{3}(\log x - \log y)$
$= \dfrac{1}{3}\log x - \dfrac{1}{3}\log y$

33. $\log 5 + \log 2 = \log(5 \cdot 2)$
$= \log 10$
$= 1$

35. $\ln x + \ln 7 = \ln(7x)$

37. $\log_2 96 - \log_2 3 = \log_2\left(\frac{96}{3}\right)$
$= \log_2 32$
$= 5$

39. $\log(2x+5) - \log x = \log\left(\frac{2x+5}{x}\right)$

41. $\log x + 3\log y = \log x + \log y^3$
$= \log(xy^3)$

43. $\frac{1}{2}\ln x + \ln y = \ln x^{1/2} + \ln y$
$= \ln\left(x^{\frac{1}{2}}y\right)$ or $\ln\left(\sqrt{x}y\right)$

45. $2\log_b x + 3\log_b y = \log_b x^2 + \log_b y^3$
$= \log_b(x^2y^3)$

47. $5\ln x - 2\ln y = \ln x^5 - \ln y^2$
$= \ln\left(\frac{x^5}{y^2}\right)$

49. $3\ln x - \frac{1}{3}\ln y = \ln x^3 - \ln y^{1/3}$
$= \ln\left(\frac{x^3}{y^{1/3}}\right)$ or $\ln\left(\frac{x^3}{\sqrt[3]{y}}\right)$

51. $4\ln(x+6) - 3\ln x = \ln(x+6)^4 - \ln x^3$
$= \ln\frac{(x+6)^4}{x^3}$

53. $\log_5 13 = \frac{\log 13}{\log 5} \approx 1.5937$

55. $\log_{14} 87.5 = \frac{\ln 87.5}{\ln 14} \approx 1.6944$

57. $\log_{0.1} 17 = \frac{\log 17}{\log 0.1} \approx -1.2304$

59. $\log_\pi 63 = \frac{\ln 63}{\ln \pi} \approx 3.6193$

61. a. $D = 10\log\left(\frac{I}{I_0}\right)$

b. $D_1 = 10\log\left(\frac{100I}{I_0}\right)$
$= 10\log(100I - I_0)$
$= 10\log 100 + 10\log I - 10\log I_0$
$= 10(2) + 10\log I - 10\log I_0$
$= 20 + 10\log\left(\frac{I}{I_0}\right)$

This is 20 more than the loudness level of the softer sound. This means that the 100 times louder sound will be 20 decibels louder.

63.–69. Answers may vary.

71. a. $y = \log_3 x = \frac{\ln x}{\ln 3}$

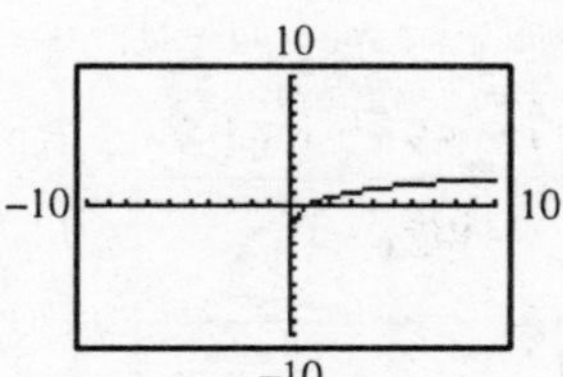

b.

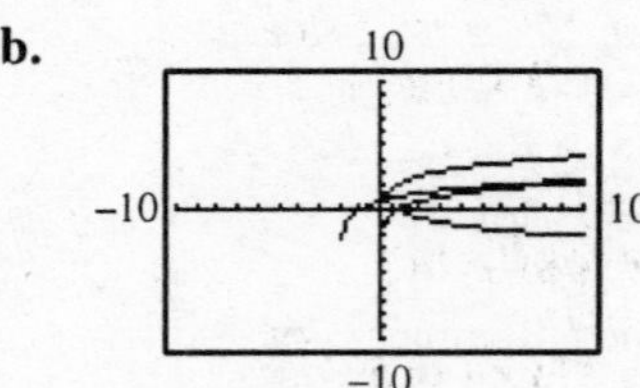

To obtain the graph of $y = 2 + \log_3 x$, shift the graph of $y = \log_3 x$ two units upward. To obtain the graph of $y = \log_3(x + 2)$, shift the graph of $y = \log_3 x$ two units left. To obtain the graph of $y = -\log_3 x$, reflect the graph of $y = \log_3 x$ about the x-axis.

73. $\log_3 x = \dfrac{\log x}{\log 3}$;

$\log_{25} x = \dfrac{\log x}{\log 25}$;

$\log_{100} x = \dfrac{\log x}{\log 100}$

5
$\log_{25} x$
$\log_3 x$
−5 5
$\log_{100} x$
−5

a. top graph: $y = \log_{100} x$
bottom graph: $y = \log_3 x$

b. top graph: $y = \log_3 x$
bottom graph: $y = \log_{100} x$

c. Comparing graphs of $\log_b x$ for $b > 1$, the graph of the equation with the largest b will be on the top in the interval (0, 1) and on the bottom in the interval $(1, \infty)$.

75. a. Values of y may vary.
b. For $y = 3$, the graphs are:

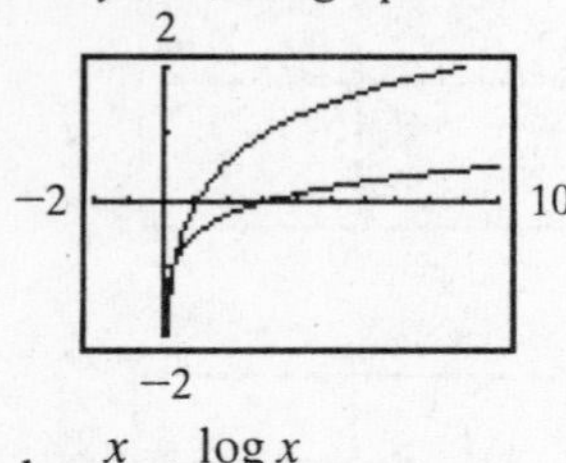

$\log \dfrac{x}{3} \neq \dfrac{\log x}{\log 3}$

77. a. Values of y may vary.
b. For $y = 6$, the graphs are:

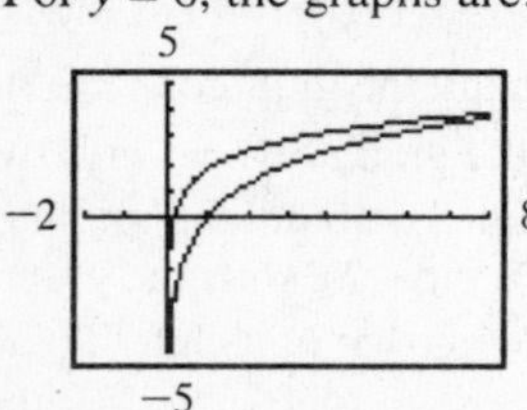

$\ln(6x) \neq (\ln x)(\ln 6)$

79. a. False;

$\log_7 49 - \log_7 7 = \log_7 \dfrac{49}{7} = \log_7 7 = 1$;

$\dfrac{\log_7 49}{\log_7 7} = \dfrac{2}{1} = 2$

b. False;

$3\log_b x + 3\log_b y = \log_b (xy)^3$
$\neq \log_b\left(x^3 + y^3\right)$

c. False;

$\log_b (xy)^5 = 5\log_b (xy)$
$= 5(\log_b x + \log_b y)$
$\neq (\log_b x + \log_b y)^5$

d. True;

$\ln\sqrt{2} = \ln 2^{1/2}$
$= \dfrac{1}{2}\ln 2 = \dfrac{\ln 2}{2}$

(d) is true.

81. $\log_7 9 = \dfrac{\log 9}{\log 7} = \dfrac{\log 3^2}{\log 7} = \dfrac{2\log 3}{\log 7}$
$= \dfrac{2A}{B}$

Section 4.4

Check Point Exercises

1. $5^x = 134$

$\ln 5^x = \ln 134$

$x \ln 5 = \ln 134$

$x = \dfrac{\ln 134}{\ln 5} \approx 3.04$

The solution set is $\left\{\dfrac{\ln 134}{\ln 5}\right\}$, approximately 3.04.

2. $7e^{2x} = 63$

$$\begin{aligned} e^{2x} &= 9 \\ \ln e^{2x} &= \ln 9 \\ 2x &= \ln 9 \\ x &= \frac{\ln 9}{2} \approx 1.10 \end{aligned}$$

The solution set is $\left\{\frac{\ln 9}{2}\right\}$, approximately 1.10.

3.

$$\begin{aligned} 6^{3x-4} - 7 &= 2081 \\ 6^{3x-4} &= 2088 \\ \ln 6^{3x-4} &= \ln 2088 \\ (3x-4)\ln 6 &= \ln 2088 \\ 3x\ln 6 - 4\ln 6 &= \ln 2088 \\ 3x\ln 6 &= \ln 2088 + 4\ln 6 \\ x &= \frac{\ln 2088 + 4\ln 6}{3\ln 6} \approx 2.76 \end{aligned}$$

The solution set is $\left\{\frac{\ln 2088 + 4\ln 6}{3\ln 6}\right\}$, approximately 2.76.

4. $e^{2x} - 8e^x + 7 = 0$

$$\left(e^x - 7\right)\left(e^x - 1\right) = 0$$

$$\begin{aligned} e^x - 7 &= 0 \quad \text{or} \quad & e^x - 1 &= 0 \\ e^x &= 7 & e^x &= 1 \\ \ln e^x &= \ln 7 & \ln e^x &= \ln 1 \\ x &= \ln 7 & x &= 0 \end{aligned}$$

The solution set is {0, ln7}. The solutions are 0 and (approximately) 1.95.

5. $\log_2(x-4) = 3$

$$\begin{aligned} 2^3 &= x - 4 \\ 8 &= x - 4 \\ 12 &= x \end{aligned}$$

Check:

$$\begin{aligned} \log_2(x-4) &= 3 \\ \log_2(12-4) &\stackrel{?}{=} 3 \\ \log_2 8 &\stackrel{?}{=} 3 \\ 3 &= 3 \end{aligned}$$

The solution set is {12}.

6. $\log x + \log(x-3) = 1$

$$\begin{aligned} \log x(x-3) &= 1 \\ 10^1 &= x(x-3) \\ 10 &= x^2 - 3x \\ 0 &= x^2 - 3x - 10 \\ 0 &= (x-5)(x+2) \end{aligned}$$

$$\begin{aligned} x - 5 &= 0 \quad \text{or} \quad & x + 2 &= 0 \\ x &= 5 \quad \text{or} & x &= -2 \end{aligned}$$

Check

Checking 5:

$$\begin{aligned} \log x + \log(x-3) &= 1 \\ \log 5 + \log(5-3) &\stackrel{?}{=} 1 \\ \log 5 + \log 2 &\stackrel{?}{=} 1 \\ \log(5 \cdot 2) &\stackrel{?}{=} 1 \\ \log 10 &\stackrel{?}{=} 1 \\ 1 &= 1 \end{aligned}$$

Checking –2:

$$\begin{aligned} \log x + \log(x-3) &= 1 \\ \log(-2) + \log(-2-3) &\stackrel{?}{=} 1 \end{aligned}$$

Negative numbers do not have logarithms so –2 does not check.

The solution set is {5}.

7. $4\ln 3x = 8$

$$\begin{aligned} \ln 3x &= 2 \\ e^{\ln 3x} &= e^2 \\ 3x &= e^2 \\ x &= \frac{e^2}{3} \approx 2.46 \end{aligned}$$

Check

$$\begin{aligned} 4\ln 3x &= 8 \\ 4\ln 3\left(\frac{e^2}{3}\right) &\stackrel{?}{=} 8 \\ 4\ln e^2 &\stackrel{?}{=} 8 \\ 8 &= 8 \end{aligned}$$

The solution set is $\left\{\frac{e^2}{3}\right\}$, approximately 2.46.

8. For a risk of 7%, let $R = 7$ in

$$R = 6e^{12.77x}$$
$$6e^{12.77x} = 7$$
$$e^{12.77x} = \frac{7}{6}$$
$$\ln e^{12.77x} = \ln\left(\frac{7}{6}\right)$$
$$12.77x = \ln\left(\frac{7}{6}\right)$$
$$x = \frac{\ln\left(\frac{7}{6}\right)}{12.77} \approx 0.01$$

For a blood alcohol concentration of 0.01, the risk of a car accident is 7%.

9. $A = P\left(1 + \frac{r}{n}\right)^{nt}$

$$3600 = 1000\left(1 + \frac{0.08}{4}\right)^{4t}$$
$$1000\left(1 \_ \frac{0.08}{4}\right)^{4t} = 3600$$
$$1000(1 + 0.02)^{4t} = 3600$$
$$1000(1.02)^{4t} = 3600$$
$$(1.02)^{4t} = \ln 3.6$$
$$4t \ln(1.02) = \ln 3.6$$
$$t = \frac{\ln 3.6}{4 \ln 1.02}$$
$$\approx 16.2$$

After approximately 16.2 years, the $1000 will grow to an accumulated value of $3600.

10.
$$N = 461.87 + 299.4 \ln x$$
$$2000 = 461.87 + 299.4 \ln x$$
$$461.87 + 299.4 \ln x = 2000$$
$$299.4 \ln x = 1538.13$$
$$\ln x = \frac{1538.13}{299.4}$$
$$e^{\ln x} = e^{1538.13/299.4}$$
$$x = e^{1538.13/299.4}$$
$$\approx 170$$

Approximately 170 years after 1979, in 2149, there will be 2 million U.S. workers in the environmental industry.

Exercise Set 4.4

1.
$$10^x = 3.91$$
$$\ln 10^x = \ln 3.91$$
$$x \ln 10 = \ln 3.91$$
$$x = \frac{\ln 3.91}{\ln 10} \approx 0.59$$

The solution set is $\left\{\frac{\ln 3.91}{\ln 10}\right\}$, approximately 0.59.

3.
$$e^x = 5.7$$
$$\ln e^x = 5.7$$
$$x = \ln 5.7 \approx 1.74$$

The solution set is {ln 5.7}, approximately 1.74.

5.
$$5^x = 17$$
$$\ln 5^x = \ln 17$$
$$x \ln 5 = \ln 17$$
$$x = \frac{\ln 17}{\ln 5} \approx 1.76$$

The solution set is $\left\{\frac{\ln 17}{\ln 5}\right\}$, approximately 1.76.

7.
$$5e^x = 23$$
$$e^x = \frac{23}{5}$$
$$\ln e^x = \ln \frac{23}{5}$$
$$x = \ln \frac{23}{5} \approx 1.53$$

The solution set is $\left\{\ln \frac{23}{5}\right\}$, approximately 1.53.

9. $3e^{5x} = 1977$

$e^{5x} = 659$

$\ln e^{5x} = \ln 659$

$x = \dfrac{\ln 659}{5} \approx 1.30$

The solution set is $\left\{\dfrac{\ln 659}{5}\right\}$, approximately 1.30.

11. $e^{1-5x} = 793$

$\ln e^{1-5x} = \ln 793$

$(1-5x)(\ln e) = \ln 793$

$1-5x = \ln 793$

$5x = 1 - \ln 793$

$x = \dfrac{1-\ln 793}{5} \approx -1.14$

The solution set is $\left\{\dfrac{1-\ln 793}{5}\right\}$, approximately −1.14.

13. $e^{5x-3} - 2 = 10{,}476$

$e^{5x-3} = 10{,}478$

$\ln e^{5x-3} = \ln 10{,}478$

$(5x-3)\ln e = \ln 10{,}478$

$5x - 3 = \ln 10{,}478$

$5x = \ln 10{,}478 + 3$

$x = \dfrac{\ln 10{,}478 + 3}{5} \approx 2.45$

The solution set is $\left\{\dfrac{\ln 10{,}478+3}{5}\right\}$, approximately 2.45.

15. $7^{x+2} = 410$

$\ln 7^{x+2} = \ln 410$

$(x+2)\ln 7 = \ln 410$

$x + 2 = \dfrac{\ln 410}{\ln 7}$

$x = \dfrac{\ln 410}{\ln 7} - 2 \approx 1.09$

The solution set is $\left\{\dfrac{\ln 410}{\ln 7} - 2\right\}$, approximately 1.09.

17. $7^{0.3x} = 813$

$\ln 7^{0.3x} = \ln 813$

$0.3x \ln 7 = \ln 813$

$x = \dfrac{\ln 813}{0.3 \ln 7} \approx 11.48$

The solution set is $\left\{\dfrac{\ln 813}{0.3\ln 7}\right\}$, approximately 11.48.

19. $e^{2x} - 3e^x + 2 = 0$

$(e^x - 2)(e^x - 1) = 0$

$e^x - 2 = 0$ or $e^x - 1 = 0$

$e^x = 2$ $\quad e^x = 1$

$\ln e^x = \ln 2$ $\quad \ln e^x = \ln 1$

$x = \ln 2$ $\quad x = 0$

The solution set is {0, ln 2). The solutions are 0 and (approximately) 0.69.

21. $e^{4x} + 5e^{2x} - 24 = 0$

$(e^{2x} + 8)(e^{2x} - 3) = 0$

$e^{2x} + 8 = 0$ or $e^{2x} - 3 = 0$

$e^{2x} = -8$ $\quad e^{2x} = 3$

$\ln e^{2x} = \ln(-8)$ $\quad \ln e^{2x} = \ln 3$

$2x = \ln(-8)$ $\quad 2x = \ln 3$

$\ln(-8)$ does not exist $\quad x = \dfrac{\ln 3}{2}$

$x = \dfrac{\ln 3}{2} \approx 0.55$

The solution set is $\left\{\dfrac{\ln 3}{2}\right\}$, approximately 0.55.

23. $\log_3 x = 4$

$x = 3^4$

$x = 81$

The solution set is {81}.

25. $\log_4(x+5) = 3$

$x + 5 = 4^3$

$x + 5 = 64$

$x = 59$

The solution set is {59}.

27. $\log_3(x-4)=-3$

$$x-4=3^{-3}$$
$$x-4=\frac{1}{27}$$
$$x=\frac{109}{27}$$

The solution set is $\left\{\frac{109}{27}\right\}$.

29. $\log_4(3x+2)=3$

$$3x+2=4^3$$
$$3x+2=64$$
$$3x=62$$
$$x=\frac{62}{3}$$

The solution set is $\left\{\frac{62}{3}\right\}$.

31. $\log_5 x+\log_5(4x-1)=1$

$$\log_5\left(4x^2-x\right)=1$$
$$4x^2-x=5$$
$$4x^2-x-5=0$$
$$(4x-5)(x+1)=0$$
$$x=\frac{5}{4} \text{ or } x=-1$$

$x=-1$ does not check because $\log_5(-1)$ does not exist.

The solution set is $\left\{\frac{5}{4}\right\}$.

33. $\log_3(x-5)+\log_3(x+3)=2$

$$\log_3[(x-5)(x+3)]=2$$
$$(x-5)(x+3)=3^2$$
$$x^2-2x-15=9$$
$$x^2-2x-24=0$$
$$(x-6)(x+4)=0$$
$$x=6 \text{ or } x=-4$$

$x=-4$ does not check because $\log_3(-4-5)$ does not exist.
The solution set is $\{6\}$.

35. $\log_2(x+2)-\log_2(x-5)=3$

$$\log_2\left(\frac{x+2}{x-5}\right)=3$$
$$\frac{x+2}{x-5}=2^3$$
$$\frac{x+2}{x-5}=8$$
$$x+2=8(x-5)$$
$$x+2=8x-40$$
$$7x=42$$
$$x=6$$

The solution set is $\{6\}$.

37. $\ln x=2$

$$e^{\ln x}=e^2$$
$$x=e^2\approx 7.39$$

The solution set is $\left\{e^2\right\}$, approximately 7.39.

39. $5\ln 2x=20$

$$\ln 2x=4$$
$$e^{\ln 2x}=e^4$$
$$2x=e^4$$
$$x=\frac{e^4}{2}\approx 27.30$$

The solution set is $\left\{\frac{e^4}{2}\right\}$, approximately 27.30.

41. $6+2\ln x=5$

$$2\ln x=-1$$
$$\ln x=-\frac{1}{2}$$
$$e^{\ln x}=e^{-1/2}$$
$$x=e^{-1/2}\approx 0.61$$

The solution set is $\left\{e^{-1/2}\right\}$, approximately 0.61.

43. $\ln\sqrt{x+3} = 1$

$$e^{\ln\sqrt{x+3}} = e^1$$
$$\sqrt{x+3} = e$$
$$x+3 = e^2$$
$$x = e^2 - 3 \approx 4.39$$

The solution set is $\{e^2 - 3\}$, approximately 4.39.

45.

$$100 = 6e^{12.77x}$$
$$e^{12.77x} = \frac{50}{3}$$
$$\ln e^{12.77x} = \ln\left(\frac{50}{3}\right)$$
$$12.77x = \ln\left(\frac{50}{3}\right)$$
$$x = \frac{\ln(50/3)}{12.77} \approx 0.22$$

A blood alcohol level of about 0.22 corresponds to a 100% risk of a car accident.

47. a. In 1994, $t = 0$.
$A = 18.2e^{0.001(0)}$
$A = 18.2$ million
In 1994, the population was 18.2 million.

b.

$$18.5 = 18.2e^{0.001t}$$
$$e^{0.001t} = \frac{18.5}{18.2}$$
$$\ln e^{0.001t} = \ln\left(\frac{18.5}{18.2}\right)$$
$$0.001t = \ln\left(\frac{18.5}{18.2}\right)$$
$$t = \frac{\ln\left(\frac{18.5}{18.2}\right)}{0.001} \approx 16$$

The population will reach 18.5 million about 16 years after 1994, in 2010.

49.

$$20,000 = 12,500\left(1+\frac{0.0575}{4}\right)^{4t}$$
$$12,500(1.014375)^{4t} = 20,000$$
$$(1.014375)^{4t} = 1.6$$
$$\ln(1.014375)^{4t} = \ln 1.6$$
$$4t\ln(1.014375) = \ln 1.6$$
$$t = \frac{\ln 1.6}{4\ln 1.014375} \approx 8$$

8 years

51.

$$1400 = 1000\left(1+\frac{r}{360}\right)^{360\cdot 2}$$
$$\left(1+\frac{r}{360}\right)^{720} = 1.4$$
$$\ln\left(1+\frac{r}{360}\right)^{720} = \ln 1.4$$
$$720\ln\left(1+\frac{r}{360}\right) = \ln 1.4$$
$$\ln\left(1+\frac{r}{360}\right) = \frac{\ln 1.4}{720}$$
$$e^{\ln(1+r/360)} = e^{(\ln 1.4)/720}$$
$$1+\frac{r}{360} = e^{(\ln 1.4)/720} - 1$$
$$r = 360(e^{(\ln 1.4)/720)} - 1$$
$$\approx 0.168$$

16.8%

53. accumulated amount = 2(8000) = 16,000

$$16,000 = 800e^{0.08t}$$
$$e^{0.08t} = 2$$
$$\ln e^{0.08t} = \ln 2$$
$$0.08t = \ln 2$$
$$t = \frac{\ln 2}{0.08} \approx 9$$

15.7%

55. accumulated amount = 3(2350) = 7050

$$7050 = 2350e^{r\cdot 7}$$
$$e^{7r} = 3$$
$$\ln e^{7r} = \ln 3$$
$$7r = \ln 3$$
$$r = \frac{\ln 3}{7} \approx 0.157$$

15.7%

57. $25,000 = 15,557 + 5259 \ln x$

$$5259 \ln x = 9443$$
$$\ln x = \frac{9443}{5259}$$
$$e^{\ln x} = e^{9443/5259}$$
$$x = e^{9443/5259} \approx 6$$

The average cost was $25,000 6 years after 1989, in 1995.

59. $30 \log_2 x = 45$

$$\log_2 x = 1.5$$
$$x = 2^{1.5} \approx 2.8$$

Only half the students recall the important features of the lecture after 2.8 days.

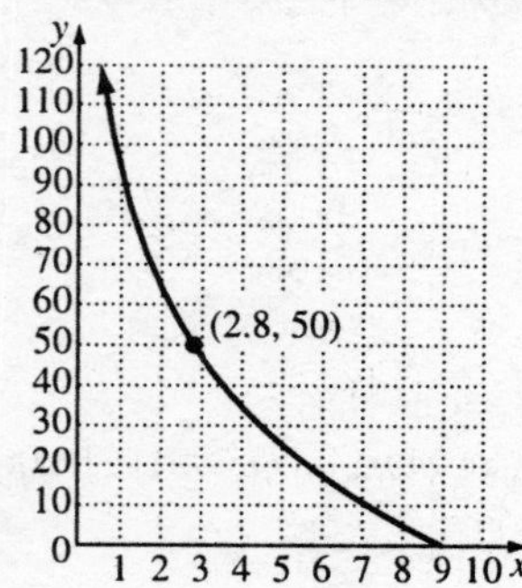

61. $2.4 = -\log x$

$$\log x = -2.4$$
$$x = 10^{-2.4} \approx 0.004$$

The hydrogen ion concentration was $10^{-2.4}$, approximately 0.004 moles per liter.

63.–65. Answers may vary.

67.

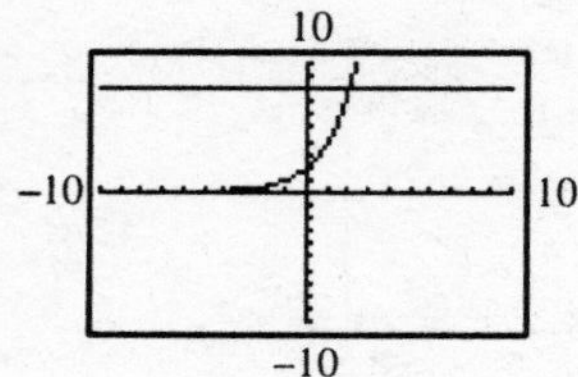

The intersection point is (2, 8).
Verify $x = 2$:

$$2^{x+1} = 8$$
$$2^2 + 1 \stackrel{?}{=} 8$$
$$2^3 \stackrel{?}{=} 8$$
$$8 = 8$$

The solution set is {2}.

69.

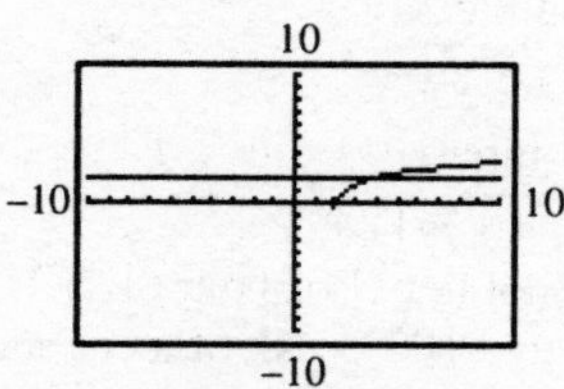

The intersection point is (4, 2).
Verify $x = 4$:

$$\log_3(4x - 7) = 2$$
$$\log_3(4 \cdot 4 - 7) = 2$$
$$\log_3 9 \stackrel{?}{=} 2$$
$$9 \stackrel{?}{=} 3^2$$
$$9 = 9$$

The solution set is {4}.

71.

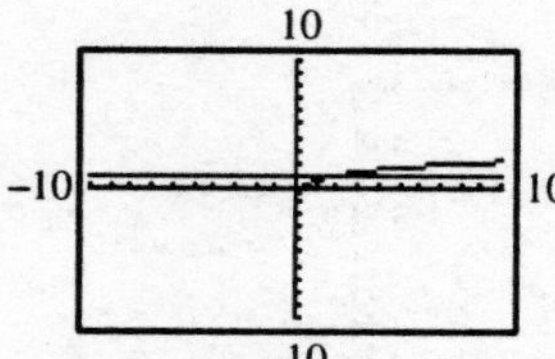

The intersection point is (2, 1).
Verify $x = 2$:

$$\log(x + 3) + \log x = 1$$
$$\log(2 + 3) + \log 2 \stackrel{?}{=} 1$$
$$\log 5 + \log 2 \stackrel{?}{=} 1$$
$$\log 10 \stackrel{?}{=} 1$$
$$10 \stackrel{?}{=} 10^1$$
$$10 = 10$$

The solution set is {2}.

73. 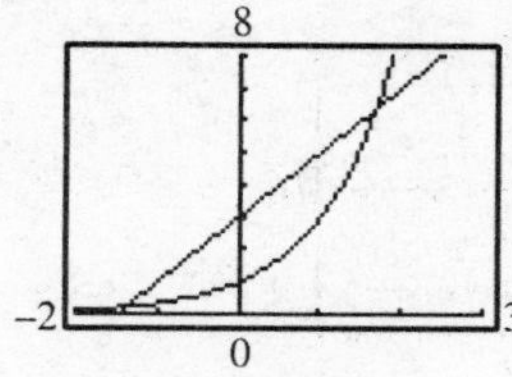

There are 2 points of intersection, approximately
(–1.391606, 0.21678798) and
(1.6855579, 6.3711158).
Verify $x \approx -1.391606$:

$$3x = 2x+3$$
$$3^{-1.391606} \stackrel{?}{=} 2(-1.391606)+3$$
$$0.2167879803 \approx 0.216788$$

Verify $x \approx 1.6855579$:

$$3^x = 2x+3$$
$$3^{1.6855579} \stackrel{?}{=} 2(1.6855579)+3$$
$$6.37111582 \approx 6.371158$$

The solution set is $\{-1.391606, 1.6855579\}$.

75. 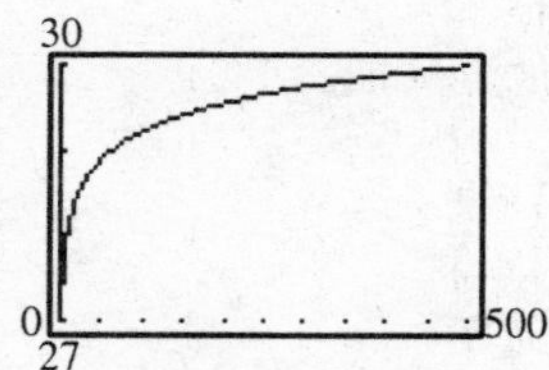

As the distance from the eye increases, barometric air pressure increases, leveling off at about 30 inches of mercury.

77. 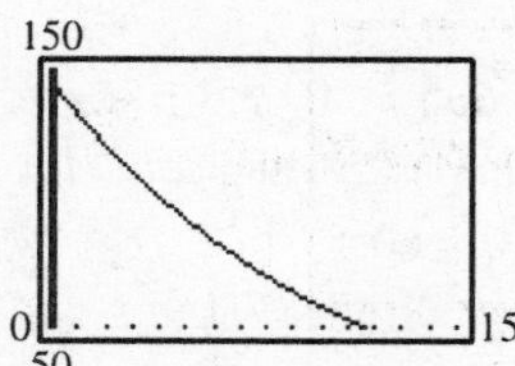

When $P = 70$, $t \approx 7.9$, so it will take about 7.9 minutes.
Verify:

$$70 \stackrel{?}{=} 145e^{-0.092(7.9)}$$
$$70 \approx 70.10076749$$

The runner's pulse will be 70 beats per minute after about 7.9 minutes.

79. **a.** False; $\log(x+3) = 2$ means $x+3 = 10^2$

b. False; $\log(7x+3) - \log(2x+5) = 4$ means $\log\dfrac{7x+3}{2x+5} = 4$ which means $\dfrac{7x+3}{2x+5} = 10^4$

c. True; $x = \dfrac{1}{k}\ln y$

$$kx = \ln y$$
$$e^{kx} = e^{\ln y}$$
$$e^{kx} = y$$

d. False; The equation $x^{10} = 5.71$ has no variable in an exponent so is not an exponential equation.

(c) is true

81.
$$(\ln x)^2 = \ln x^2$$
$$(\ln x)^2 = 2\ln x$$
$$(\ln x)^2 - 2\ln x = 0$$
$$\ln x(\ln x - 2) = 0$$
$$\ln x = 0 \quad \text{or} \quad \ln x - 2 = 0$$
$$x = 1 \qquad \ln x = 2$$
$$e^{\ln x} = e^2$$
$$x = e$$

The solution set is $\{1, e^2\}$.
Check with graphing utility:

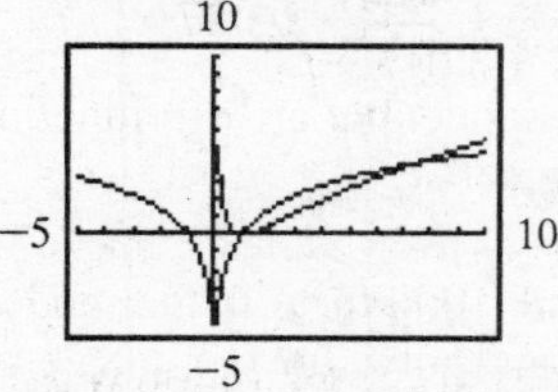

There are two points of intersection: (1, 0) and approximately (7.3890561, 4). Since $e^2 \approx 7.3890566099$, the graph verifies $x = 1$ and $x = e^2$, so the solution set is $\{1, e^2\}$ as determined algebraically.

83. $\ln(\ln x) = 0$
$e^{\ln(\ln x)} = e^0$
$\ln x = 1$
$e^{\ln x} = e^1$
$x = e$
The solution set is $\{e\}$.
Check by direct substitution:
$\ln(\ln x) = 0$
$\ln(\ln e) \stackrel{?}{=} 0$
$\ln(1) \stackrel{?}{=} 0$
$0 = 0$

Section 4.5

Check Point Exercises

1. a. Use the exponential growth model $A = A_0 e^{kt}$ with 1980 corresponding to $t = 0$ when the population was 491 million:
$A = 491e^{kt}$
Substitute $t = 1990 - 1980 = 10$ when the population was 643 million, so $A = 643$, to find k.

$$643 = 491e^{k \cdot 10}$$
$$e^{10k} = \frac{643}{491}$$
$$\ln e^{10k} = \ln\left(\frac{643}{491}\right)$$
$$10k = \ln\left(\frac{643}{491}\right)$$
$$k = \frac{\ln\left(\frac{643}{491}\right)}{10} \approx 0.027$$

So the exponential growth function is $A = 491e^{0.027t}$.

b. Substitute 1000 for A in the model from part (a) and solve for t.

$$1000 = 491e^{0.027t}$$
$$e^{0.027t} = \frac{1000}{491}$$
$$\ln e^{0.027t} = \ln\left(\frac{1000}{491}\right)$$
$$0.027t = \ln\left(\frac{1000}{491}\right)$$
$$t = \frac{\ln\left(\frac{1000}{491}\right)}{0.027} \approx 26$$

The population will reach 1000 million, or one billion, about 26 years after 1980, in 2006.

2. a. In the exponential decay model $A = A_0 e^{kt}$, substitute $\frac{A_0}{2}$ for A since the amount present after 28 years is half the original amount.

$$\frac{A_0}{2} = A_0 e^{k \cdot 28}$$
$$e^{28k} = \frac{1}{2}$$
$$\ln e^{28k} = \ln\frac{1}{2}$$
$$28k = \ln\frac{1}{2}$$
$$k = \frac{\ln^{1/2}}{28} \approx -0.0248$$

So the exponential decay model is $A = A_0 e^{-0.0248t}$

b. Substitute 60 for A_0 and 10 for A in the model from part (a) and solve for t.

$$10 = 60e^{-0.0248t}$$
$$e = ^{-0.0248t} = \frac{1}{6}$$
$$\ln e^{-0.0248t} = \ln\frac{1}{6}$$
$$-0.0248t = \ln\frac{1}{6}$$
$$t = \frac{\ln\frac{1}{6}}{-0.0248} \approx 72$$

The strontium-90 will decay to a level of 10 grams about 72 years after the accident.

3. a. The time prior to learning trials corresponds to $t = 0$.

$$f(0) = \frac{0.8}{1+e^{-0.2(0)}} = 0.4$$

The proportion of correct responses prior to learning trials was 0.4.

b. Substitute 10 for t in the model:

$$f(10) = \frac{0.8}{1+e^{-0.2(10)}} \approx 0.7$$

The proportion of correct responses after 10 learning trials was 0.7.

c. In the logistic growth model,

$f(t) = \dfrac{c}{1+ae^{-bt}}$, the constant c represents the limiting size that $f(t)$ can attain. The limiting size of the proportion of correct responses as continued learning trials take place is 0.8.

4. $y = ab^x$ is equivalent to $y = ae^{(\ln b)x}$.

For $y = 4(7.8)^x$, $a = 4$, $b = 7.8$.

Thus, $y = 4(7.8)^x$ is equivalent to $y = 4e^{(\ln 7.8)x}$ in terms of a natural logarithm. Rounded to three decimal places, the model is approximately equivalent to $y = 4e^{2.054x}$.

Exercise Set 4.5

1. 1970 corresponds to $t = 0$.

$A = 208e^{0.008(0)} = 208$ million

In 1970, the population was 208 million.

3.

$$300 = 208e^{0.008t}$$
$$\frac{75}{52} = e^{0.008t}$$
$$\ln\frac{75}{52} = \ln e^{0.008t}$$
$$\ln\frac{75}{52} = 0.008t$$
$$t = \frac{\ln\frac{75}{52}}{0.008} \approx 46$$

The population will be 300 million about 46 years after 1970, in 2016.

5. In the exponential growth model, $A = A_0e^{kt}$, k represents the growth rate. The population was increasing by about 2.6% each year.

7.

$$1624 = 574e^{0.026t}$$
$$\frac{116}{41} = e^{0.026t}$$
$$\ln\frac{116}{41} = \ln e^{0.026t}$$
$$\ln\frac{116}{41} = 0.026t$$
$$t = \frac{\ln\frac{116}{41}}{0.026} \approx 40$$

The population will be 1624 million about 40 years after 1974, in 2014.

9. The time of purchase corresponds to $t = 0$.

$V = 140e^{0.068(0)} = 140$

The purchase price was $140,000.

11.

$$200 = 140e^{0.068t}$$
$$\frac{10}{7} = e^{0.068t}$$
$$\ln\frac{10}{7} = \ln e^{0.068t}$$
$$\ln\frac{10}{7} = 0.068t$$
$$t = \frac{\ln\frac{10}{7}}{0.068} \approx 5$$

The house will be worth $200,000 about 5 years after 2000, in 2005.

13. $t = 7$ corresponds to $A = 680$.

Substitute these values to find k.

$$680 = 200e^{k(7)}$$
$$\frac{17}{5} = e^{7k}$$
$$\ln\frac{17}{5} = \ln e^{7k}$$
$$\ln\frac{17}{5} = 7k$$
$$k = \frac{\ln\frac{17}{5}}{7} \approx 0.175$$

The exponential growth function is
$A = 200e^{0.175t}$
$k = 0.175$ corresponds to a 17.5% increase each year.

15. $A = 16e^{-0.000121(5715)} \approx 8.01$
In 5715 years, 8.01 grams of carbon-14 will be present.

17. After 10 seconds, $\frac{16}{2}$ or 8 grams;

After 20 seconds, $\frac{8}{2}$ or 4 grams;

After 30 seconds, $\frac{4}{2}$ or 2 grams;

After 40 seconds, $\frac{2}{2}$ or 1 gram;

After 50 seconds, $\frac{1}{2}$ or 0.5 gram.

19. For an original amount of A_0, for the amount remaining is $A = 0.15A_0$.

$$0.15A_0 = A_0e^{-0.000121t}$$
$$0.15 = e^{-0.000121t}$$
$$\ln 0.15 = \ln e^{-0.000121t}$$
$$\ln 0.15 = -0.000121t$$
$$t = \ln\frac{0.15}{-0.000121} \approx 15{,}679$$

The paintings were about 15,679 years old.

21. a. Half the original anount corresponds to an amount remaining of $A = \frac{1}{2}A_0$. This amount corresponds to $t = 1.31$.

$$\frac{1}{2}A_0 = A_0e^{1.31k}$$
$$\frac{1}{2} = e^{1.31k}$$
$$\ln\frac{1}{2} = \ln e^{1.31k}$$
$$k = \frac{\ln\frac{1}{2}}{1.31} \approx -0.52912$$

The dacay model is given by
$A = A_0e^{-0.52912t}$

b.
$$0.945A_0 = A_0e^{-0.52912t}$$
$$0.945 = e^{-0.52912t}$$
$$\ln 0.945 = -0.52912t$$
$$t = \frac{\ln 0.945}{-0.52912} \approx 0.107$$

The bones of the dinosaur were about 0.107 billion, or 107 million years old.

23. The doubling of the original population corresponds to $A = 2A$.

$$2A_0 = A_0e^{kt}$$
$$2 = e^{kt}$$
$$\ln 2 = \ln e^{kt}$$
$$\ln 2 = kt$$
$$t = \frac{\ln 2}{k}$$

25. $t = \frac{\ln 2}{0.011} \approx 63$
It will take China about 63 years to double its population.

27. a. When the epidemic began, $t = 0$.

$$f(0) = \frac{100{,}000}{1 + 5000e^0} \approx 20$$

Twenty people became ill when the epidemic began.

b. $f(4) = \frac{100{,}000}{1 + 5{,}000e^{-4}} \approx 1080$

About 1080 people were ill at the end of the fourth week.

c. In the logistic growth model,

$$f(t) = \frac{c}{1 + ae^{-bt}},$$

the constant c represents the limiting size that $f(t)$ can attain. The limiting size of the population that becomes ill is 100,000 people.

29. $P(20) = \frac{0.9}{1 + 271e^{-0.122(20)}} \approx 0.037$
The probability that a 20-year-old has some coronary heart disease is about 3.7%.

31.
$$0.5 = \frac{1.9}{1+271e^{-0.122t}}$$
$$0.5\left(1+271e^{-0.122t}\right) = 0.9$$
$$1+271e^{-0.122t} = 1.8$$
$$271e^{-0.122t} = 0.8$$
$$e^{-0.122t} = \frac{0.8}{271}$$
$$\ln e^{-0.122t} = \ln\frac{0.8}{271}$$
$$-0.122t = \ln\frac{0.8}{271}$$
$$t = \frac{\ln\frac{0.8}{271}}{-0.122} \approx 48$$

The probability of some coronary heart disease is 0.5 at about age 48.

33. $y = 100(4.6)^x$ is equivalent to
$y = 100e^{(\ln 4.6)x}$;
Using $\ln 4.6 \approx 1.526$,
$y = 100e^{1.526x}$.

35. $y = 2.5(0.7)^x$ is equivalent to
$y = 2.5e^{(\ln 0.7)x}$;
Using $\ln 0.7 \approx -0.357$,
$y = 2.5e^{-0.357x}$.

37.–45. Answers may vary.

47. $y = 51.75985638 + 109.7788574 \ln x$
The correlation coefficient,
$r = 0.8974781617$, is somewhat close to 1, indicating that the model is a good fit.

49. $y = 98.06189365x^{0.4398361087}$
The correlation coefficient, $r =$ 0.9546621296, is close to 1, indicating that the model is a good fit.

51.

The probability of coronary heart disease starts increasing at a more rapid rate at about age 20. At about age 60, the rate of increase starts to slow down.

53. linear model:
$y = 74.52833333x + 214.7694444$
$r = 0.973863504$

quadratic model:
$y = -4.438852814x^2 + 118.9168615x + 133.390$
$R^2 = 0.9656802033$

exponential model:
$y = 271.7360257(1.151326831)^x$
$r = 0.9601071451$

logarithmic model:
$y = 192.4568631 + 277.6625633\ln x$
$r = 0.9529069638$

The linear model best fits the data; Answers for prediction may vary.

55.
$$140 = 70 + (210-70)e^{-k(30)}$$
$$70 = (140)e^{-30k}$$
$$0.5 = e^{-30k}$$
$$\ln 0.5 = \ln e^{-30k}$$
$$\ln 0.5 = -30k$$
$$k = \frac{\ln 0.5}{-30} \approx 0.023$$
$$T = 70 + (210-70)e^{-0.023(40)} \approx 126°$$

Substitute $t = 40$ in the model
$T = C + \left(T_0 - C\right)e^{-0.023t}$

Review Exercises

1. This is the graph of $f(x) = 4^x$ reflected about the y-axis, so the function is $g(x) = 4^{-x}$.

2. This is the graph of $f(x) = 4^x$ reflected about the x-axis and about the y-axis, so the function is $h(x) = -4^{-x}$.

3. This is the graph of $f(x) = 4^x$ reflected about the x-axis and about the y-axis then shifted upward 3 units, so the function is $r(x) = -4^{-x} + 3$.

4. This is the graph of $f(x) = 4^x$.

5.

x	$f(x) = 2x$	$g(x) = 2^{x-1}$
-2	$2^{-2} = \frac{1}{4}$	$2^{-2-1} = 2^{-3} = \frac{1}{8}$
-1	$2^{-1} = \frac{1}{2}$	$2^{-1-1} = 2^{-2} = \frac{1}{2}$
0	$2^0 = 1$	$2^{0-1} = 2^{-1} = \frac{1}{2}$
1	$2^1 = 2$	$2^{1-1} = 2^0 = 1$
2	$2^2 = 4$	$2^{2-1} = 2^1 = 2$

The graph of $g(x)$ shifts the graph of $f(x)$ one unit to the right.

6.

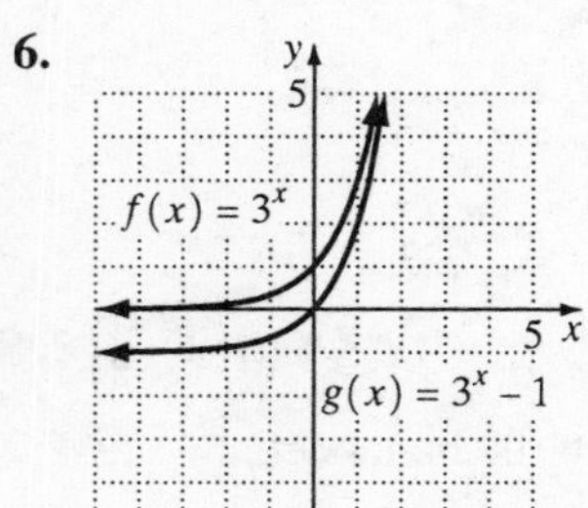

x	$f(x) = 3^x$	$g(x) = 3^x - 1$
-2	$3^{-2} = \frac{1}{9}$	$3^{-2} - 1 = \frac{1}{9} - 1 = -\frac{8}{9}$
-1	$3^{-1} = \frac{1}{3}$	$3^{-1} - 1 = \frac{1}{3} - 1 = -\frac{2}{3}$
0	$3^0 = 1$	$3^0 - 1 = 1 - 1 = 0$
1	$3^1 = 3$	$3^1 - 1 = 3 - 1 = 2$
2	$3^2 = 9$	$3^2 - 1 = 9 - 1 = 8$

The graph of $g(x)$ shifts the graph of $f(x)$ one unit downward.

7.

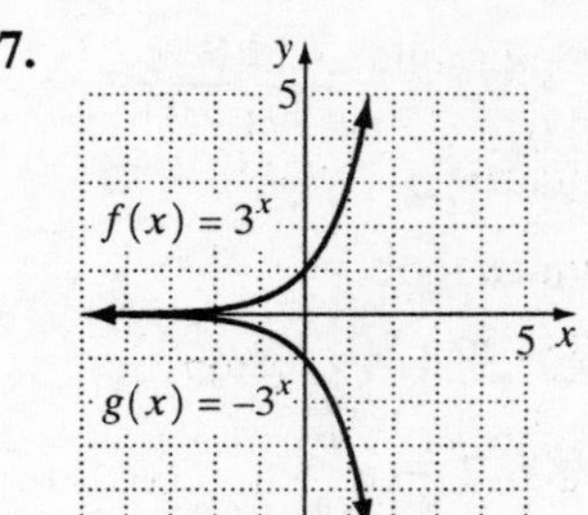

x	$f(x) = 3^x$	$g(x) = -3x$
-2	$3^{-2} = \frac{1}{9}$	$-3^{-2} = -\frac{1}{9}$
-1	$3^{-1} = \frac{1}{3}$	$-3^{-1} = -\frac{1}{3}$
0	$3^0 = 1$	$-3^0 = -1$
1	$3^1 = 3$	$-3^1 = -3$
2	$3^2 = 9$	$-3^2 = -9$

The graph of $g(x)$ reflects the graph of $f(x)$ about the x-axis.

8.

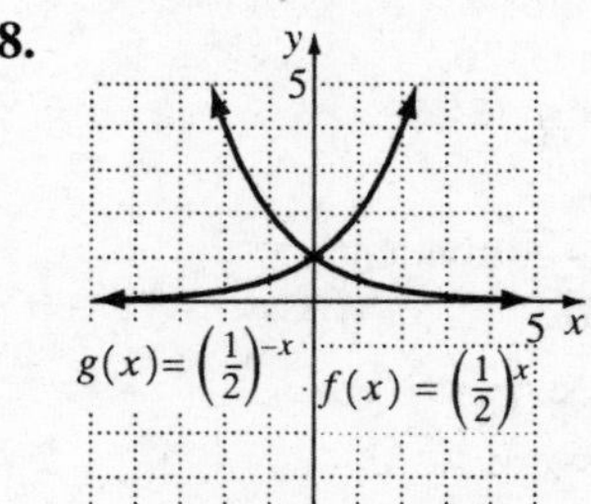

x	$f(x) = \left(\frac{1}{2}\right)^x$	$g(x) = \left(\frac{1}{2}\right)^{-x}$
-2	$\left(\frac{1}{2}\right)^{-2} = 4$	$\left(\frac{1}{2}\right)^{-(-2)} = \left(\frac{1}{2}\right)^2 = \frac{1}{4}$
-1	$\left(\frac{1}{2}\right)^{-1} = 2$	$\left(\frac{1}{2}\right)^{-1(-1)} = \left(\frac{1}{2}\right)^1 = \frac{1}{2}$
0	$\left(\frac{1}{2}\right)^0 = 1$	$\left(\frac{1}{2}\right)^{-(0)} = \left(\frac{1}{2}\right)^0 = 1$
1	$\left(\frac{1}{2}\right)^1 = \frac{1}{2}$	$\left(\frac{1}{2}\right)^{-1(1)} = \left(\frac{1}{2}\right)^{-1} = 2$
2	$\left(\frac{1}{2}\right)^2 = \frac{1}{4}$	$\left(\frac{1}{2}\right)^{-2(2)} = \left(\frac{1}{2}\right)^{-2} = 4$

The graph of $g(x)$ reflects the graph of $f(x)$ about the y-axis.

9. 5.5% compounded semiannually:
$$A = 5000\left(1+\frac{0.055}{2}\right)^{2\cdot 5} \approx 6558.26$$
5.25% compounded monthly:
$$A = 5000\left(1+\frac{0.0525}{12}\right)^{12\cdot 5} \approx 6497.16$$
5.5% compounded semiannually yields the greater return.

10. 7% compounded monthly:
$$A = 14,000\left(1+\frac{0.07}{12}\right)^{12\cdot 10} \approx 28,135.26$$
6.85% compounded continuously:
$$A = 14,000e^{0.0685(10)} \approx 27,772.81$$
7% compounded monthly yields the greater return.

11. a. When first taken out of the microwave, the temperature of the coffee was 200°.

b. After 20 minutes, the temperature of the coffee was about 120°.
$$T = 70 + 130e^{-0.04855(20)} \approx 119.23$$
Using a calculator, the temperature is about 119°.

c. The coffee will cool to about 70°; The temperature of the room is 70°.

12. $49^{1/2} = 7$

13. $4^3 = x$

14. $3^y = 81$

15. $\log_6 216 = 3$

16. $\log_b 625 = 4$

17. $\log_{13} 874 = y$

18. $\log_4 64 = 3$ because $4^3 = 64$.

19. $\log_5 \frac{1}{25} = -2$ because $5^{-2} = \frac{1}{25}$.

20. $\log_3(-9)$ cannot be evaluated since $\log_b x$ is defined only for $x > 0$.

21. $\log_{16} 4 = \frac{1}{2}$ because $16^{1/2} = \sqrt{16} = 4$.

22. Because $\log_b b = 1$, we conclude $\log_{17} 17 = 1$.

23. Because $\log_b b^x = x$, we conclude $\log_3 3^8 = 8$.

24. Because $\ln e^x = x$, we conclude $e^5 = 5$.

25. Because $\log_b = 1$,
we conclude $\log_8 8 = 1$.
So, $\log_3(\log_8 8) = \log_3 1$.
Because $\log_b 1 = 0$
we conclude $\log_3 1 = 0$.
Therefore, $\log_3(\log_8 8) = 0$.

26.

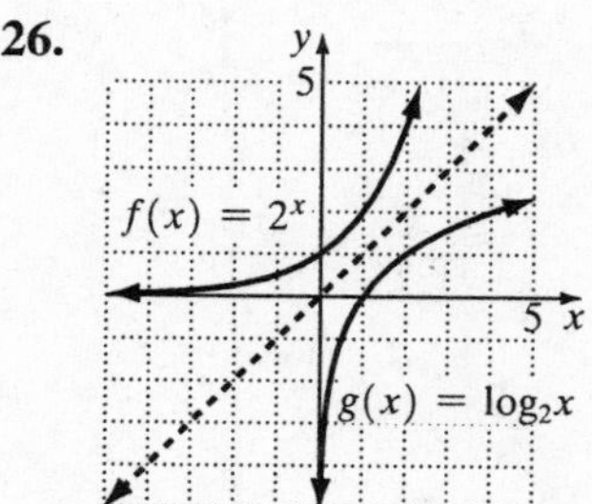

27.

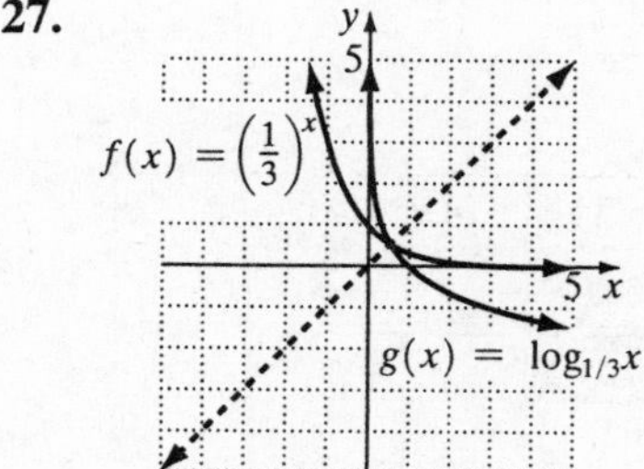

28. This is the graph of $f(x) = \log x$ reflected about the *y*-axis, so the function is $g(x) = \log(-x)$.

29. This is the graph of $f(x) = \log x$ shifted left 2 units, reflected about the y-axis, then shifted upward one unit, so the function is $r(x) = 1 + \log(2 - x)$.

30. This is the graph of $f(x) = \log x$ shifted left 2 units then reflected about the y-axis, so the function is $h(x) = \log(2 - x)$.

31. This is the graph of $f(x) = \log x$.

32.

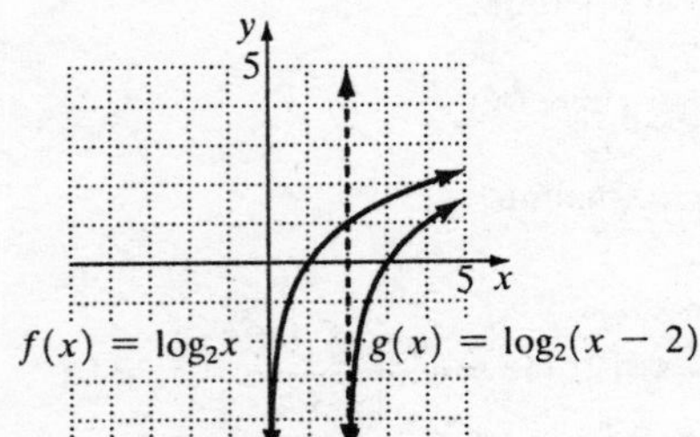

x-intercept: (3, 0)
vertical asymptote: $x = 2$

33.

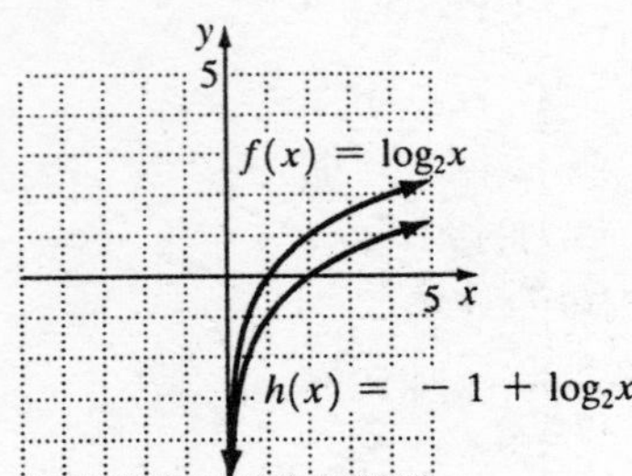

x-intercept: (2, 0)
vertical asymptote: $x = 0$

34.

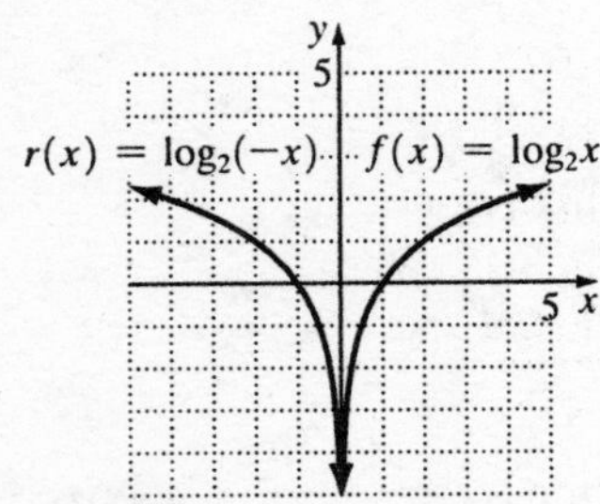

x-intercept: (–1, 0)
vertical asymptote: $x = 0$

35. The domain of f consists of all x for which $x + 5 > 0$.
Solving this inequality for x, we obtain $x > -5$.
Thus the domain of f is $(-5, \infty)$

36. The domain of f consists of all x for which $3 - x > 0$.
Solving this inequality for x, we obtain $x < 3$.
Thus, the domain of f is $(-\infty, 3)$.

37. The domain of f consists of all x for which $(x - 1)^2 > 0$.
Solving this inequality for x, we obtain $x < 1$ or $x > 1$. Thus, the domain of f is $(-\infty, 1)$ or $(1, \infty)$.

38. Because $\ln e^x = x$, we conclude $\ln e^{6x} = 6x$.

39. Because $e^{\ln x} = x$, we conclude $e^{\ln \sqrt{x}} = \sqrt{x}$.

40. Because $10^{\log x} = x$, we conclude $10^{\log 4x^2} = 4x^2$.

41. $R = \log \dfrac{1000 I_0}{I_0} = \log 1000 = 3$
The Richter scale magnitude is 3.0.

42. **a.** $f(0) = 76 - 18\log(0 + 1) = 76$
When first given, the average score was 76.

b. $f(2) = 76 - 18\log(2 + 1) \approx 67$
$f(4) = 76 - 18\log(4 + 1) \approx 63$
$f(6) = 76 - 18\log(6 + 1) \approx 61$
$f(8) = 76 - 18\log(8 + 1) \approx 59$
$f(12) = 76 - 18\log(12 + 1) \approx 56$
After 2, 4, 6, 8, and 12 months, the average scores are about 67, 63, 61, 59, and 56, respectively.

c. 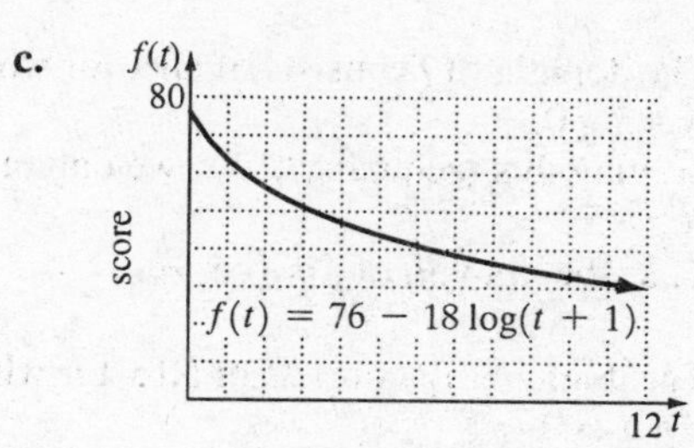

Retention decreases as time passes.

43. $t = \frac{1}{0.06} \ln\left(\frac{12}{12-5}\right) \approx 8.98$

It will take about 9 weeks.

44. $\log_6(36x^3)$

$= \log_6 36 + \log_6 x^3$

$= \log_6 36 + 3\log_6 x$

$= 2 + 3\log_6 x$

45. $\log_4 \frac{\sqrt{x}}{64} = \log_4 x^{1/2} - \log_4 64$

$= \frac{1}{2}\log_4 x - 3$

46. $\log_2 \frac{xy^2}{64} = \log_2 xy^2 - \log_2 64$

$= \log_2 x + \log_2 y^2 - \log_2 64$

$= \log_2 x + 2\log_2 y - 6$

47. $\ln \sqrt[3]{\frac{x}{e}}$

$= \ln\left(\frac{x}{e}\right)^{1/3}$

$= \frac{1}{3}[\ln x - \ln e]$

$= \frac{1}{3}\ln x - \frac{1}{3}\ln e$

$= \frac{1}{3}\ln x - \frac{1}{3}$

48. $\log_b 7 + \log_b 3$

$= \log_b(7 \cdot 3)$

$= \log_b 21$

49. $\log 3 - 3\log x$

$= \log 3 - \log x^3$

$= \log \frac{3}{x^3}$

50. $3\ln x + 4\ln y$

$= \ln x^3 + \ln y^4$

$= \ln\left(x^3 y^4\right)$

51. $\frac{1}{2}\ln x - \ln y$

$= \ln x^{1/2} - \ln y$

$= \ln \frac{\sqrt{x}}{y}$

52. $\log_6 72{,}348 = \frac{\log 72{,}348}{\log 6} \approx 6.2448$

53. $\log_4 0.863 = \frac{\ln 0.863}{\ln 4} \approx -0.1063$

54. $8^x = 12{,}143$

$\ln 8^x = \ln 12{,}143$

$x \ln 8 = \ln 12{,}143$

$x = \frac{\ln 12{,}143}{\ln 8} \approx 4.523$

The solution set is $\left\{\frac{\ln 12{,}143}{\ln 8}\right\}$, approximately 4.523.

55. $9e^{5x} = 1269$

$e^{5x} = 141$

$\ln e^{5x} = \ln 141$

$5x = \ln 141$

$x = \frac{\ln 141}{5}$

The solution set is $\left\{\frac{\ln 141}{5}\right\}$, approximately 0.990.

56. $e^{12-5x} - 7 = 123$
$e^{12-5x} = 130$
$\ln e^{12-5x} = \ln 130$
$12 - 5x = \ln 130$
$5x = 12 - \ln 130$
$x = \frac{12 - \ln 130}{5} \approx 1.426$
The solution set is
$x = \frac{12 - \ln 130}{5}$, approximately 1.426

57. $5^{4x+2} = 37,500$
$\ln 5^{4x+2} = \ln 37,500$
$(4x+2)\ln 5 = \ln 37,500$
$4x \ln 5 + 2\ln 5 = \ln 37,500$
$4x \ln 5 = \ln 37,500 - 2\ln 5$
$x = \frac{\ln 37,500 - 2\ln 5}{4\ln 5}$
The solution set is $\left\{\frac{\ln 37,500 - 2\ln 5}{4\ln 5}\right\}$,
approximately 1.136.

58. $e^{2x} - e^x - 6 = 0$
$\left(e^x - 3\right)\left(e^x + 2\right) = 0$
$e^x - 3 = 0$ or $e^x + 2 = 0$
$e^x = 3$ $\quad$ $e^x = -2$
$\ln e^x = \ln 3$ $\quad$ $\ln e^x - \ln(-2)$
$x = \ln 3$ $\quad$ $x = \ln(-2)$
$x = \ln 3 \approx 1.099$ $\quad$ $\ln(-2)$ does not exist.
The solution set is $\{\ln 3\}$,
approximately 1.099.

59. $\log_4(3x - 5) = 3$
$3x - 5 = 4^3$
$3x - 5 = 64$
$3x = 69$
$x = 23$
The solutions set is $\{23\}$.

60. $\log_2(x+3) + \log_2(x-3) = 4$
$\log_2(x+3)(x-3) = 4$
$\log_2(x^2 - 9) = 4$
$x^2 - 9 = 2^4$
$x^2 - 9 = 16$
$x^2 = 25$
$x = \pm 5$
$x = -5$ does not check because $\log_2(-5+3)$ does not exist.
The solution set is $\{5\}$.

61. $\log_3(x-1) - \log_3(x+2) = 2$
$\log_3 \frac{x-1}{x+2} = 2$
$\frac{x-1}{x-2} = 3^2$
$\frac{x-1}{x+2} = 9$
$x - 1 = 9(x + 2)$
$x - 1 = 9x + 18$
$8x = -19$
$x = -\frac{19}{8}$
$x = -\frac{19}{8}$ does not check because
$\log_3\left(-\frac{19}{8} - 1\right)$ does not exist.
The solution set is $\varnothing$.

62. $\ln x = -1$
$x = e^{-1} = \frac{1}{e} \approx 0.368$
The solution set is $\left\{\frac{1}{e}\right\}$,
approximately 0.368.

63. $3 + 4\ln 2x = 15$
$4\ln 2x = 12$
$\ln 2x = 3$
$2^x = e^3$
$x = \frac{e^3}{2} \approx 10.043$
The solution set is $\left\{\frac{e^3}{2}\right\}$,
approximately 10.043

64. $13 = 10.1e^{0.005t}$

$$e^{0.005t} = \frac{13}{10.1}$$
$$\ln e^{0.005t} = \ln\frac{13}{10.1}$$
$$0.005t = \ln\frac{13}{10.1}$$
$$t = \frac{\ln\frac{13}{10.1}}{0.005} \approx 50$$

The population will reach 13 million about 50 years after 1992, in 2042.

65. $280 \cdot 2 = 364(1.005)^t$

$$364(1.005)^t = 560$$
$$1.005^t = \frac{20}{13}$$
$$\ln 1.005^t = \ln\frac{20}{13}$$
$$t \ln 1.005 = \ln\frac{20}{13}$$
$$t = \frac{\ln\frac{20}{13}}{\ln 1.005} \approx 86$$

The carbon dioxide concentration will be double the preindustrial level about 86 years after 2000, in 2086.

66. $30,000 = 15,557 + 5259 \ln x$

$$5259 \ln x = 14,443$$
$$\ln x = \frac{14,443}{5259}$$
$$x = e^{14,443/5259} \approx 16$$

The average cost of a new car will be $30,000 about 16 years after 1989, in 2005.

67. $20,000 = 12,500\left(1+\frac{0.065}{4}\right)^{4t}$

$$12,500(1.01625)^{4t} = 20,000$$
$$(1.01625)^{4t} = 1.6$$
$$\ln(1.01625)^{4t} = \ln 1.6$$
$$4t \ln 1.01625 = \ln 1.6$$
$$t = \frac{\ln 1.6}{4 \ln 1.01625} \approx 7.3$$

It will take about 7.3 years.

68. $3 \cdot 50,000 = 50,000e^{0.075t}$

$$50,000e^{0.075t} = 150,000$$
$$e^{0.075} = 3$$
$$\ln e^{0.075t} = \ln 3$$
$$0.075t = \ln 3$$
$$t = \frac{\ln 3}{0.075} \approx 14.6$$

It will take about 14.6 years.

69. When an investment value triples, $A = 3P$.

$$3P = Pe^{5r}$$
$$e^{5r} = 3$$
$$\ln e^{5r} = \ln 3$$
$$5r = \ln 3$$
$$r = \frac{\ln 3}{5} \approx 0.2197$$

The interest rate would need to be about 21.97%

70. a. $t = 1997 - 1980 = 17$

$$e^{17k} = \frac{29.3}{14.6}$$
$$\ln e^{17k} = \ln\frac{29.3}{14.6}$$
$$17k = \ln\frac{29.3}{14.6}$$
$$k = \frac{\ln\left(\frac{29.3}{14.6}\right)}{14.6} \approx 0.041$$

b. $t = 2005 - 1980 = 25$

$$A = 14.6e^{0.041(25)} \approx 40.7$$

In 2005, the population will be about 40.7 million.

c. $50 = 14.6e^{0.041t}$

$$e^{0.041t} = \frac{50}{14.6}$$
$$\ln e^{0.041t} = \ln\frac{50}{14.6}$$
$$0.041t = \ln\frac{50}{14.6}$$
$$t = \frac{\ln\left(\frac{50}{14.6}\right)}{0.041} \approx 30$$

The population will reach 50 million about 30 years after 1980, in 2010.

71. If the remaining amount is 15% of the original amount, them $A = 0.15A_0$.

$$0.15A_0 = A_0e^{-0.000121t}$$
$$e^{-0.000121t} = 0.15$$
$$\ln e^{-0.000121t} = \ln 0.15$$
$$-0.000121t = \ln 0.15$$
$$t = \frac{\ln 0.15}{-0.000121} \approx 15,67$$

At the time of discovery, the paintings were about 15,679 years old.

72. a. When the outbreak began, $t = 0$.

$$f(0) = \frac{171}{1+18.6e^{-0.0747(0)}} \approx 9$$

When the outbreak began, about 9 people were infected.

b. $f(45) = \dfrac{171}{1+18.6e^{-0.0747(45)}} \approx 104$

After 45 days, about 104 people were infected.

c. In the logistics growth model,

$f(t) = \dfrac{c}{1+ae^{-bt}}$, the constant c

represents the limiting size that $f(t)$ can attain. The limiting size of the population that became infected was 171; Yes, the limiting size according to the model is 171, but 261 − 83 = 178 people actually died.

73. $y = 73(2.6)^x$ is equivalent to

$y = 73e^{(\ln 2.6)x}$; Using $\ln 2.6 \approx 0.956$;

$y = 73e^{0.956x}$.

74. $y = 6.5(0.43)^x$ is equivalent to

$y = 6.5e^{(\ln 0.43)x}$; Using $\ln 0.43 \approx -0.844$;

$y = 6.5e^{-0.844x}$.

75. The high projection might be best modeled by an exponential function, the medium projection by a linear function, and the low projection by a quadratic function; If the low projection is modeled by a quadratic function, the leading coefficient would be negative since the parabola opens downward.

76. linear model:

$y = 0.5055x - 8.5905$

$r = 0.9451995388$

quadratic model:

$$y = 0.0042934712x^2 - 0.1041729153x + 5.038408856$$

$R^2 = 0.9883582557$

exponential model:

$y = 3.38051786(1.0235357)^x$

$r = 0.9945619484$

logarithmic model:

$y = -20.94062012 + 12.53110237\ln x$

$r = 0.6748503469$

The exponential model best fits the given data. 2050 is 151 years after 1899.

$y = 3.38051786(1.0235357)^{151} \approx 113.4$

In 2050, the U.S. population age 65 and over will be about 113.4 million.

Chapter 4 Test

1.

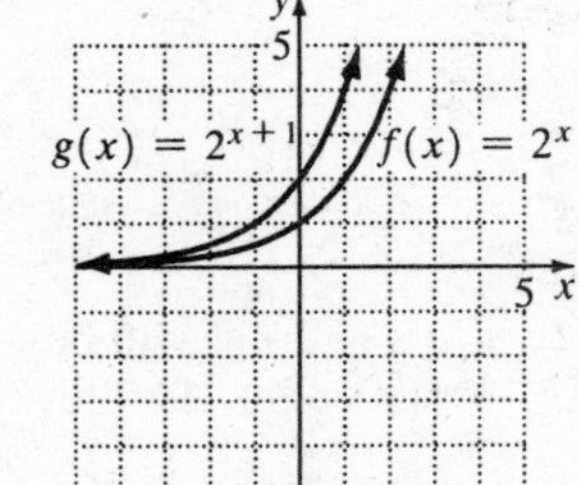

2.

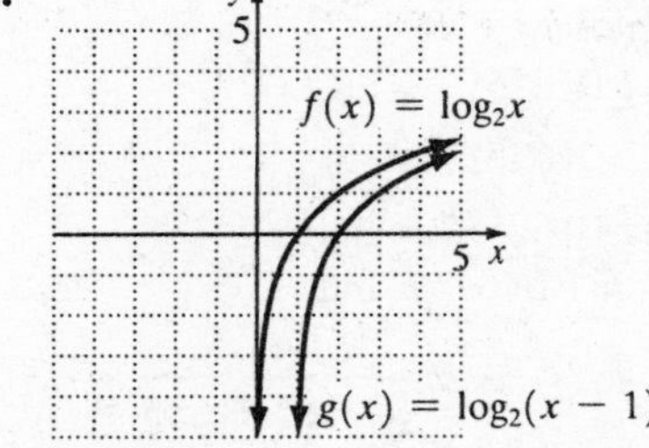

3. $125 = 5^3$

4. $\log_{36} 6 = \frac{1}{2}$

5. The domain of f consists of all x for which $3 - x > 0$. Solving this inequality for x, we obtain $x < 3$.
Thus, the domain of f is $(-\infty, 3)$.

6. $\log_4(64x^5) = \log_4 64 + \log_4 x^5$
$= 3 + 5\log_4 x$

7. $\log_3 \frac{\sqrt[3]{x}}{81} = \log_3 x^{\frac{1}{3}} - \log_3 81$
$= \frac{1}{3}\log_3 x - 4$

8. $6\log x + 2\log y = \log x^6 + \log y^2$
$= \log(x^6 y^2)$

9. $\ln 7 - 3\ln x = \ln 7 - \ln x^3$
$= \ln \frac{7}{x^3}$

10. $\log_{15} 71 = \frac{\log 71}{\log 15} \approx 1.5741$

11. $5^x = 1.4$
$\ln 5^x = \ln 1.4$
$x \ln 5 = \ln 1.4$
$x = \frac{\ln 1.4}{\ln 5} \approx 0.2091$
The solution set is $\left\{\frac{\ln 1.4}{\ln 5}\right\}$, approximately 0.2091.

12. $400e^{0.005x} = 1600$
$e^{0.005x} = 4$
$\ln e^{0.005x} = \ln 4$
$0.005x = \ln 4$
$x = \frac{\ln 4}{0.005} \approx 277.2589$
The solution set is $\left\{\frac{\ln 4}{0.005}\right\}$, approximately 277.2589.

13. $e^{2x} - 6e^x + 5 = 0$
$(e^x - 5)(e^x - 1) = 0$
$e^x - 5 = 0$ or $e^x - 1 = 0$
$e^x = 5$ $\quad e^x = 1$
$\ln e^x = \ln 5$ $\quad \ln e^x = \ln 1$
$x = \ln 5$ $\quad x = \ln 1$
$x \approx 1.6094$ $\quad x = 0$
The solution set is $\{0, \ln 5\}$; $\ln \approx 1.6094$.

14. $\log_6(4x - 1) = 3$
$4x - 1 = 6^3$
$4x - 1 = 216$
$4x = 217$
$x = \frac{217}{4}$
The solution set is $\left\{\frac{217}{4}\right\}$.

15. $\log x + \log(x + 15) = 2$
$\log(x^2 + 15x) = 2$
$x^2 + 15x = 10^2$
$x^2 + 15x - 100 = 0$
$(x + 20)(x - 5) = 0$
$x + 20 = 0$ or $x - 5 = 0$
$x = -20$ $\quad x = 5$
$x = -20$ does not check because $\log(-20)$ does not exist.
The solution set is $\{5\}$.

16. $2\ln 3x = 8$

$\ln 3x = 4$

$3x = e^4$

$x = \frac{e^4}{3} \approx 18.1994$

The solution set is $\left\{\frac{e^4}{3}\right\}$, approximately 18.1994.

17. 6.5% compounded semiannualy:

$A = 3{,}000\left(1 + \frac{0.065}{2}\right)^{2(10)} \approx \$5{,}687.51$

6% compounded continuously:

$A = 3{,}000e^{0.06(10)} \approx \$5{,}466.36$

6.5% compounded semiannually yields about $221 more than 6% compounded continuously.

18. $D = 10\log\frac{10^{12}I_0}{I_0}$

$= 10\log 10^{12}$

$= 10 \cdot 12$

$= 120$

The loudness of the sound is 120 decibels.

19. a. In 1959, $t = 0$.

$89.18e^{-0.004(0)} = 89.18$

In 1959, about 89% of married men were employed.

b. The percentage is decreasing since $k = -0.004 < 1$.

c. $77 = 89.18e^{-0.004t}$

$e^{-0.004t} = \frac{77}{89.18}$

$\ln e^{-0.004t} = \ln\frac{77}{89.18}$

$-0.004t = \ln\frac{77}{89.18}$

$t = \frac{\ln\frac{77}{89.18}}{-0.004} \approx 37$

77% of U.S. married men were employed about 37 years after 1959, in 1996.

20. In 1980, $t = 0$ and $A_0 = 484$.

In 1990, $t = 1990 - 1980 = 10$ and $A = 509$.

$509 = 484e^{k(10)}$

$e^{k(10)} = \frac{509}{484}$

$\ln e^{k(10)} = \ln\frac{509}{484}$

$k = \frac{\ln\frac{509}{484}}{10} \approx 0.005$

The exponential growth function is $A = 484e^{0.005t}$

21. When the amount remaining is 5%, $A = 0.05A_0$.

$0.05A_0 = A_0e^{-0.000121t}$

$e^{-0.000121t} = 0.05$

$\ln e^{-0.000121t} = \ln 0.05$

$-0.000121t = \ln 0.05$

$t = \frac{\ln 0.05}{-0.000121} \approx 24{,}758$

The man died about 24,758 years ago.

22. a. $f(0) = \frac{140}{1 + 9e^{-0.165(0)}} = 14$

Fourteen elk were initially introduced to the habitat.

b. $f(10) = \frac{140}{1 + 9e^{-0.165(10)}} \approx 51$

After 10 years, about 51 elk are expected.

c. In the logistic growth model,

$f(t) = \frac{c}{1 + ae^{-bt}}$,

the constant c represents the limiting size that $f(t)$ can attain. The limiting size of the elk population is 140 elk.

Cumulative Review Exercises (Chapters 1–4)

1. $|3x-4|=2$

$3x-4=2$ or $3x-4=-2$

$3x=6$ $\quad 3x=2$

$x=2$ $\quad x=\frac{2}{3}$

The solution set is $\left\{\frac{2}{3}, 2\right\}$.

2. $\sqrt{2x-5}-\sqrt{x-3}=1$

$$\sqrt{2x-5}=1+\sqrt{x-3}$$
$$\left(\sqrt{2x-5}\right)^2=\left(1+\sqrt{x-3}\right)^2$$
$$2x-5=1+2\sqrt{x-3}+x-3$$
$$2x-5=x-2+2\sqrt{x-3}$$
$$x-3=2\sqrt{x-3}$$
$$(x-3)^2=\left(2\sqrt{x-3}\right)^2$$
$$(x-3)^2=4(x-3)$$
$$x^2-6x+9=4x-12$$
$$x^2-10x+21=0$$
$$(x-3)(x-7)=0$$

$x=3$ or $x=7$

Both solutions satisfy the original equation when checked.

The solution set is $\{3, 7\}$.

3. $x^4+x^3-3x^2-x+2=0$

p: ±1, ±2

q: ±1

$\frac{p}{q}$: ±1, ±2

−2	1	1	−3	−1	2
		−2	2	2	−2
	1	−1	−1	1	0

$$(x+2)(x^3-x^2-x+1)=0$$
$$(x+2)[x^2(x-1)-(x-1)]=0$$
$$(x+2)(x^2-1)(x-1)=0$$
$$(x+2)(x+1)(x-1)(x-1)=0$$
$$(x+2)(x+1)(x-1)^2=0$$

$x+2=0$ or $x+1=0$ or $x-1=0$

$x=-2$ $\quad x=-1$ $\quad x=1$

The solution set is $\{-2, -1, 1\}$.

4. $e^{5x}-32=96$

$$e^{5x}=128$$
$$\ln e^{5x}=\ln 128$$
$$5x=\ln 128$$
$$x=\frac{\ln 128}{5}\approx 0.9704$$

The solution set is $\left\{\frac{\ln 128}{5}\right\}$, approximately 0.9704.

5. $\log_2(x+5)+\log_2(x-1)=4$

$$\log_2[(x+5)(x-1)]=4$$
$$(x+5)(x-1)=2^4$$
$$x^2+4x-5=16$$
$$x^2+4x-21=0$$
$$(x+7)(x-3)=0$$

$x+7=0$ or $x-3=0$

$x=-7$ $\quad x=3$

$x=-7$ does not check because $\log_2(-7+5)$ does not exist.

The solution set is $\{3\}$.

6. $14-5x\ge -6$

$-5x\ge -20$

$x\le 4$

The solution set is $(-\infty, 4]$.

7. $|2x-4|\le 2$

$2x-4\le 2$ and $2x-4\ge -2$

$2x\le 6$ $\quad 2x\ge 2$

$x\le 3$ and $x\ge 1$

The solution set is $[1,3]$.

8. $m = \frac{3-(-3)}{1-3} = \frac{6}{-2} = -3$

Using (1, 3) point-slope form:

$y - 3 = -3(x-1)$

slope-intercept form:

$y - 3 = -3(x-1)$

$y - 3 = -3x + 3$

$y = -3x + 6$

9. $(f \circ g)(x) = f(x+2)$

$= (x+2)^2$

$= x^2 + 4x + 4$

$(g \circ f)(x) = g(x^2)$

$= x^2 + 2$

10. $f(x) = 2x - 7$

$y = 2x - 7$

$x = 2y - 7$

$x + 7 = 2y$

$\frac{x+7}{2} = y$

$f^{-1}(x) = \frac{x+7}{2}$

11.

$$
\begin{array}{r}
x^2 + 3x - 3 \\
x+2\overline{)\,x^3 + 5x^2 + 3x - 10} \\
\underline{x^3 + 2x^2} \quad\quad\quad\quad \\
3x^2 + 3x \quad\quad\; \\
\underline{3x^2 + 6x} \quad\quad\; \\
-3x - 10 \\
\underline{-3x - \;\;6} \\
-4
\end{array}
$$

Quotient: $x^2 + 3x - 3 - \frac{4}{x+2}$

12. $f(x) = 4x^3 - 7x - 3$

$p = \pm 1, \pm 3$

$q = \pm 1, \pm 2, \pm 4$

$\frac{p}{q} = \pm 1, \pm\frac{1}{2}, \pm\frac{1}{4}, \pm 3, \pm\frac{3}{2}, \pm\frac{3}{4}$

13. $y = kx^2$

$12 = k \cdot 3^2$

$k = \frac{12}{9} = \frac{4}{3}$

$y = \frac{4}{3}x^2$

$y = \frac{4}{3}(15)^2$

$y = 300$

14. If $1 + i$ is a root, $1 - i$ is a root.

$(x - 1 + i)(x - 1 - i)$

$= x^2 - x - xi - x + 1 + i + xi - i - i^2$

$= x^2 - 2x + 2$

$$
\begin{array}{r}
x - 2 \\
x^2 - 2x + 2\overline{)\,x^3 - 4x^2 + 6x - 4} \\
\underline{x^3 - 2x^2 + 2x} \quad\;\; \\
-2x^2 + 4x - 4 \\
\underline{-2x^2 + 4x - 4} \\
0
\end{array}
$$

$x - 2 = 0$

$x = 2$

The solution set is $\{1+i, 1-i, 2\}$.

15. Circle with center: (3, –2) and radius of 2

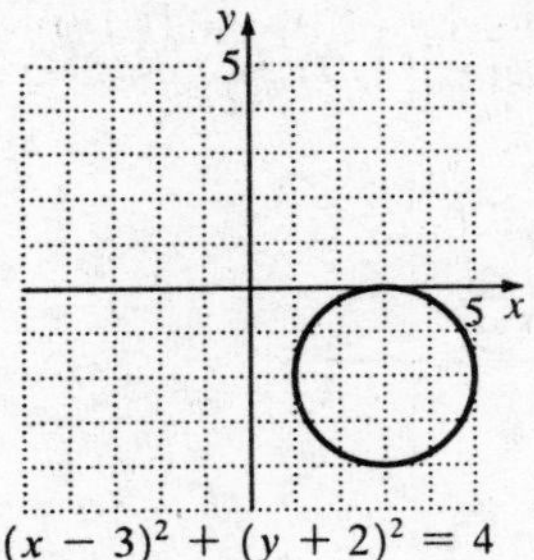

16. Parabola with vertex: (2, –1)

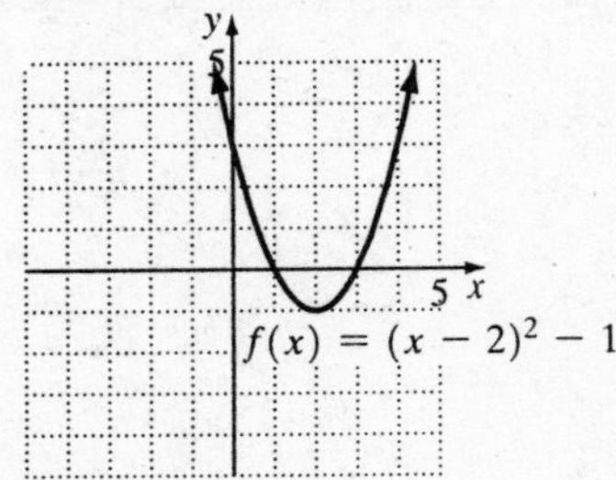

17. x-intercepts:

$$x^2 - 1 = 0$$
$$x^2 = 1$$
$$x = \pm 1$$

The x-intercepts are $(1, 0)$ and $(-1, 0)$.

vertical asymptotes:

$$x^2 - 4 = 0$$
$$x^2 = 4$$
$$x = \pm 2$$

The vertical asymptotes are $x = 2$ and $x = -2$.

Horizontal asymptote: $y = 1$

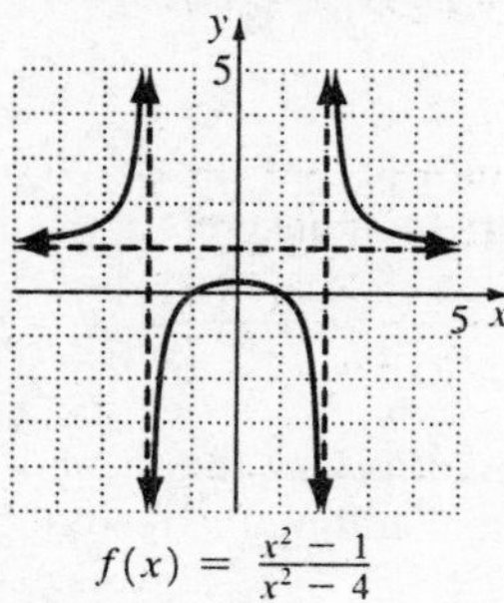

18. x-intercepts:

$x - 2 = 0$ or $x + 1 = 0$

$x = 2$ or $x = -1$

The x-intercepts are $(2, 0)$ and $(-1, 0)$.

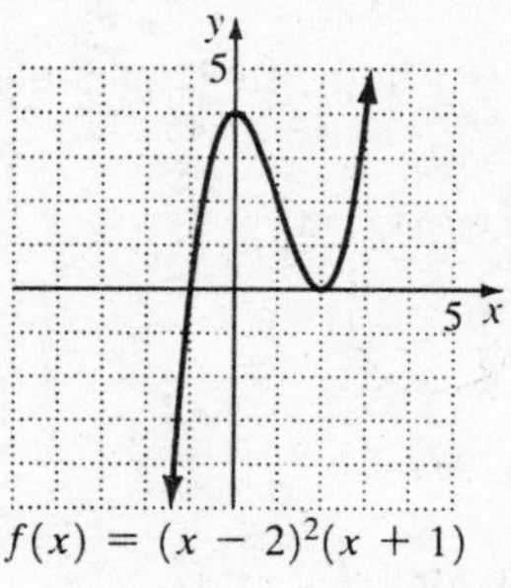

19.
$$40x + 10(1.5x) = 660$$
$$40x + 15x = 660$$
$$55x = 660$$
$$x = 12$$

Your normal hourly salary is \$12 per hour.

20.
$$\frac{1}{2} = 1 - K\ln(3+1)$$
$$K\ln 4 = \frac{1}{2}$$
$$K = \frac{\frac{1}{2}}{\ln 4} \approx 0.361$$
$$F = 1 - 0.361\ln(t+1)$$
$$= 1 - 0.361\ln(6+1)$$
$$= 1 - 0.361\ln 7$$
$$\approx 0.3$$

About $\frac{3}{10}$ of the people in the group remember all the words in a list 6 hours after memorizing them.

Chapter 5

Section 5.1

Check Point Exercises

1. $2x - 3y = -4$
$2(1) - 3(2) \stackrel{?}{=} -4$
$2 - 6 \stackrel{?}{=} -4$
$-4 = -4$ true
$2x + y = 4$
$2(1) + 2 \stackrel{?}{=} 4$
$2 + 2 \stackrel{?}{=} 4$
$4 = 4$ true
(1, 2) is a solution of the system.

2. $y = 5x - 13$
$2x + 3y = 12$
Substitute the expression $5x - 13$ for y in the second equation and solve for x.
$2x + 3(5x - 13) = 12$
$2x + 15x - 39 = 12$
$17x = 51$
$x = 3$
Substitute 3 for x in the first equation.
$y = 5(3) - 13 = 15 - 13 = 2$
The solution set is $\{(3, 2)\}$.

3. $3x + 2y = -1$
$x - y = 3$
Solve the second equation for x.
$x = y + 3$
Substitute the expression $y + 3$ for x in the first equation and solve for x.
$3(y + 3) + 2y = -1$
$3y + 9 + 2y = -1$
$5y = -10$
$y = -2$
Substitute -2 for y in the equation $x = y + 3$.
$x = -2 + 3 = 1$
The solution set is $\{(1, -2)\}$.

4. $4x + 5y = 3$
$2x - 3y = 7$
Eliminate x by multiplying the second equation by -2 and adding the resulting equations.
$4x + 5y = 3$
$-4x + 6y = -14$
$11y = -11$
$y = -1$
Substitute -1 for y in the first equation.
$4x + 5(-1) = 3$
$4x - 5 = 3$
$4x = 8$
$x = 2$
The solution set is $\{(2, -1)\}$.

5. $4x = 5 + 2y$
$3y = 4 - 2x$
Arrange the system so that variable terms appear on the left and constants appear on the right.
$4x - 2y = 5$
$2x + 3y = 4$
Eliminate x by multiplying the second equation by -2 and adding the resulting equations.
$4x - 2y = 5$
$-4x - 6y = -8$
$-8y = -3$
$y = \frac{3}{8}$
Substitute $\frac{3}{8}$ for y in the first equation.
$4x = 5 + 2\left(\frac{3}{8}\right)$
$4x = 5 + \frac{6}{8} = \frac{46}{8} = \frac{23}{4}$
$x = \frac{23}{16}$
The solution set is $\left\{\left(\frac{23}{16}, \frac{3}{8}\right)\right\}$.

6. The elimination method is used here to solve the system.

$x+2y=4$
$3x+6y=13$

Eliminate x by multiplying the first equation by -3 and adding the resulting equations.

$$\begin{array}{r} -3x-6y=-12 \\ 3x+6y=13 \\ \hline 0=1 \end{array}$$

The false statement $0 = 1$ indicates that the system has no solution. The solution set is the empty set, $\varnothing$.

7. The substitution method is used here to solve the system.

$y=4x-4$
$8x-2y=8.$

Substitute the expression $4x-4$ for y in the second equation and solve for y.

$8x-2(4x-4)=8$
$8x-8x+8=8$
$8=8$

This true statement indicates that the system has infinitely many solutions. The solution set is

$\{(x, y)\,|\,y=4x-4\}$ or $\{(x, y)\,|\,8x-2y=8\}$.

8. $N=-20p+1000$
$N=5p+250$

Substitute $-20p + 1000$ for N in the second equation. $-20p+1000=5p+250$

$750=25p$
$p=30$

Supply and demand are equal at \$30. To find the number of units supplied and sold each week at this price, substitute 30 for p in either the demand or the supply model.

$N=-20(30)+1000$
$=-600+1000$
$=400$

At a price of \$30, 400 units of the product can be supplied and sold.

Exercise Set 5.1

1. $x+3y=11$
$2+3(3) \stackrel{?}{=} 11$
$2+9 \stackrel{?}{=} 11$
$11=11$ true

$x-5y=-13$
$2-5(3) \stackrel{?}{=} -13$
$2-15 \stackrel{?}{=} -13$
$-13=-13$ true

(2, 3) is a solution.

3. $2x+3y=17$
$2(2)+3(5) \stackrel{?}{=} 17$
$4+15 \stackrel{?}{=} 17$
$19=17$ false

(2, 5) is not a solution.

5. $x+y=4$
$y=3x$

Substitute the expression $3x$ for y in the first equation and solve for x.

$x+3x=4$
$4x=4$
$x=1$

Substitute 1 for x in the second equation.

$y=3(1)=3$

The solution set is $\{(1, 3)\}$.

7. $x+3y=8$
$y=2x-9$

Substitute the expression $2x-9$ for y in the first equation and solve for x.

$x+3(2x-9)=8$
$x+6x-27=8$
$7x=35$
$x=5$

Substitute 5 for x in the second equation.

$y=2(5)-9=10-9=1$

The solution set is $\{(5, 1)\}$.

9. $x+3y=5$
$4x+5y=13$

Solve the first equation for x.

$x=5-3y$

Substitute the expression $5-3y$ for x in the second equation and solve for y.

$4(5-3y)+5y=13$
$20-12y+5y=13$
$-7y=-7$
$y=1$

Substitute 1 for y in the equation $x=5-3y$.

$x=5-3(1)=2$

The solution set is $\{(2, 1)\}$.

11. $2x - y = -5$
$x + 5y = 14$
Solve the first equation for y.
$2x + 5 = y$
Substitute the expression $2x + 5$ for y in the second equation and solve for x.
$x + 5(2x + 5) = 14$
$x + 10x + 25 = 14$
$11x = -11$
$x = -1$
Substitute -1 for x in the equation $y = 2x + 5$
$y = 2(-1) + 5 = -2 + 5 = 3$
The solution set is $\{(-1, 3)\}$.

13. $2x - y = 3$
$5x - 2y = 10$
Solve the first equation for y.
$2x - 3 = y$
Substitute the expression $2x - 3$ for y in the second equation and solve for x.
$5x - 2(2x - 3) = 10$
$5x - 4x + 6 = 10$
$x = 4$
Substitute 4 for x in the equation $y = 2x - 3$.
$y = 2(4) - 3 = 8 - 3 = 5$
The solution set is $\{(4, 5)\}$.

15. $x + 8y = 6$
$2x + 4y = -3$
Solve the first equation for x.
$x = 6 - 8y$
Substitute the expression $6 - 8y$ for x in the second equation and solve for y.
$2(6 - 8y) + 4y = -3$
$12 - 16y + 4y = -3$
$-12y = -15$
$y = \frac{15}{12} = \frac{5}{4}$
Substitute $\frac{5}{4}$ for y in the equation $x = 6 - 8y$.
$x = 6 - 8\left(\frac{5}{4}\right) = 6 - 10 = -4$
The solution set is $\left\{\left(-4, \frac{5}{4}\right)\right\}$.

17. Eliminate y by adding the equations.
$x + y = 1$
$x - y = 3$
$2x = 4$
$x = 2$
Substitute 2 for x in the first equation.
$2 + y = 1$
$y = -1$
The solution set is $\{(2, -1)\}$.

19. Eliminate y by adding the equations.
$2x + 3y = 6$
$2x - 3y = 6$
$4x = 12$
$x = 3$
Substitute 3 for x in the first equation.
$2(3) + 3y = 6$
$6 + 3y = 6$
$3y = 0$
$y = 0$
The solution set is $\{(3, 0)\}$.

21. $x + 2y = 2$
$-4x + 3y = 25$
Eliminate x by multiplying the first equation by 4 and adding the resulting equations.
$4x + 8y = 8$
$-4x + 3y = 25$
$11y = 33$
$y = 3$
Substitute 3 for y in the first equation.
$x + 2(3) = 2$
$x + 6 = 2$
$x = -4$
The solution set is $\{(-4, 3)\}$.

23. $4x + 3y = 15$
$2x - 5y = 1$
Eliminate x by multiplying the second equation by -2 and adding the resulting equations.
$4x + 3y = 15$
$-4x + 10y = -2$
$13y = 13$
$y = 1$
Substitute 1 for y in the second equation.
$2x - 5(1) = 1$
$2x = 6$
$x = 3$
The solution set is $\{(3, 1)\}$.

25. $3x - 4y = 11$
$2x + 3y = -4$
Eliminate x by multiplying the first equation by 2 and the second equation by –3. Add the resulting equations.

$$\begin{array}{r} 6x - 8y = 22 \\ \underline{-6x - 9y = 12} \\ -17y = 34 \\ y = -2 \end{array}$$

Substitute –2 for y in the second equation.

$$\begin{aligned} 2x + 3(-2) &= -4 \\ 2x - 6 &= -4 \\ 2x &= 2 \\ x &= 1 \end{aligned}$$

The solution set is $\{(1, -2)\}$.

27. $3x = 4y + 1$
$3y = 1 - 4x$
Arrange the system so that variable terms appear on the left and constants appear on the right.
$3x - 4y = 1$
$4x + 3y = 1$
Eliminate y by multiplying the first equation by 3 and the second equation by 4. Add the resulting equations.

$$\begin{array}{r} 9x - 12y = 3 \\ \underline{16x + 12y = 4} \\ 25x = 7 \\ x = \frac{7}{25} \end{array}$$

Substitute $\frac{7}{25}$ for x in the second equation.

$$3y = 1 - 4\left(\frac{7}{25}\right)$$

$$3y = \frac{-3}{25}$$

$$y = \frac{-1}{25}$$

The solution set is $\left\{\left(\frac{7}{25}, -\frac{1}{25}\right)\right\}$.

29. The substitution method is used here to solve the system.
$x = 9 - 2y$
$x + 2y = 13$
Substitute the expression $9 - 2y$ for x in the second equation and solve for y.
$9 - 2y + 2y = 13$
$9 = 13$
The false statement $9 = 13$ indicates that the sytem has no solution.
The solution set is the empty set, $\varnothing$.

31. The substitution method is used here to solve the system.
$y = 3x - 5$
$21x - 35 = 7y$
Substitute the expression $3x - 5$ for y in the second equation and solve for x.
$21x - 35 = 7(3x - 5)$
$21x - 35 = 21x - 35$
$-35 = -35$
This true statement indicates that the system has infinitely many solutions.
The solution set is $\{(x, y) \mid y = 3x - 5\}$ or $\{(x, y) \mid 21x - 35 = 7y\}$.

33. The elimination method is used here to solve the system.
$3x - 2y = -5$
$4x + y = 8$
Eliminate y by multiplying the second equation by 2 and adding the resulting equations.

$$\begin{array}{r} 3x - 2y = -5 \\ \underline{8x + 2y = 16} \\ 11x = 11 \\ x = 1 \end{array}$$

Substitute 1 for x in the second equation.
$4(1) + y = 8$
$y = 4$
The solution set is $\{(1, 4)\}$.

35. The elimination method is used here to solve the system.
$x+3y=2$
$3x+9y=6$
Eliminate x by multiplying the first equation by –3 and adding the resulting equations.
$-3x-9y=-6$
$3x+9y=6$
$0=0$
This true statement indicates that the system has infinitely many solutions.
The solution set is $\{(x, y) \mid x+3y=2\}$ or $\{(x, y) \mid 3x+9y=6\}$.

37. Add the equations to eliminate y.
$x+y=7$
$x-y=-1$
$2x=6$
$x=3$
Substitute 3 for x in the first equation.
$3+y=7$
$y=4$
The numbers are 3 and 4.

39. $3x-y=1$
$x+2y=12$
Eliminate y by multiplying the first equation by 2 and adding the resulting equations.
$6x-2y=2$
$x+2y=12$
$7x=14$
$x=2$
Substitute 2 for x in the first equation.
$3(2)-y=1$
$6-y=1$
$-y=-5$
$y=5$
The numbers are 2 and 5.

41. $N=-25p+7500$
$N=5p+6000$

a. Substitute 40 for p in the demand model.
$N=-25(40)+7500$
$=-1000+7500$
$=6500$
At \$40 a ticket, 6500 tickets can be sold.

Substitute 40 for p in the supply model.
$N=5(40)+6000$
$=200+6000$
$=6200$
At \$40 a ticket, 6200 tickets can be supplied.

b. Substitute $-25p+7500$ for N in the second equation.
$-25p+7500=5p+6000$
$1500=30p$
$50=p$
Supply and demand are equal at \$50 a ticket.
To find the number of tickets supplied and sold at this price, substitute 50 for p into either the demand or supply model.
$N=-25(50)+7500$
$=-1250+7500$
$=6250$
At a price of \$50, 6250 tickets can be supplied and sold.

43. $C(x)=1.2x+1080$
$R(x)=1.6x$
Substitute $1.6x$ for $C(x)$ in the first equation.
$1.6x=1.2x+1080$
$0.4x=1080$
$x=2700$
2700 gallons must be sold weekly for the station to break even.

45. x = mg of cholesterol in a Quarter Pounder
y = mg of cholesterol in a Whopper with cheese
$2x+3y=520$
$3x+y=353$
Eliminate y by multiplying the first equation by –3 and adding the resulting equations.
$2x+3y=520$
$-9x-3y=-1059$
$-7x=-539$
$x=77$
Substitute 77 for x in the second equation.
$3(77)+y=353$
$231+y=353$
$y=122$
A Quarter Pounder contains 77 mg of cholesterol. A Whopper contains 122 mg of cholesterol.

47. $10(x-y)=12.0$
$x+y=10.4$
Expand the first equation and multiply the second equation by 10. Add the resulting two equations to eliminate y.
$$\begin{aligned}10x-10y&=12.0\\10x+10y&=104\\\hline 20x&=116\\x&=5.8\end{aligned}$$
Substitute 5.8 for x in the second equation.
$$\begin{aligned}5.8+y&=10.4\\y&=4.6\end{aligned}$$
On Super Bowl Sunday, 5.8 million pounds of potato chips are consumed.
On Super Bowl Sunday, 4.6 million pounds of tortilla chips are consumed.

49. $M=-0.41x+22$
$M=-0.18x+10$
Substitute $-0.41x+22$ for M in the second equation.
$$\begin{aligned}-0.41x+22&=-0.18x+10\\12&=0.23x\\x&\approx 52\end{aligned}$$
Infant mortality for blacks and whites will be the same about 52 years after 1980 or in the year 2032.
To find the infant mortality of both groups, substitute 52 for x in either mortality model.
$$\begin{aligned}M&=-0.18(52)+10\\&=9.36+10\\&=0.64\end{aligned}$$
The rate will be less than 1 death in 1000 live births.

51.–59. Answers may vary.

63. $a_1x+b_1y=c_1$
$a_2x+b_2y=c_2$
Solve the first equation for x.
$$x=\frac{c_1-b_1y}{a_1}$$
Substitute the expression $\frac{c_1-b_1y}{a_1}$ for x in the second equation and solve for y.
$$a_2\left(\frac{c_1-b_1y}{a_1}\right)+b_2y=c_2$$
$$a_2\left(\frac{c_1-b_1y}{a_1}\right)+\frac{a_1b_2y}{a_1}=c_2$$
$$\frac{a_2c_1-a_2b_1y+a_1b_2y}{a_1}=c_2$$
$$a_2c_1-a_2b_1y+a_1b_2y=a_1c_2$$
$$y(a_1b_2-a_2b_1)=a_1c_2-a_2c_1$$
$$y=\frac{a_1c_2-a_2c_1}{a_1b_2-a_2b_1}$$
Substitute the expression $\frac{a_1c_2-a_2c_1}{a_1b_2-a_2b_1}$ for y in the first equation and solve for x.
$$a_1x+b_1\left(\frac{a_1c_2-a_2c_1}{a_1b_2-a_2b_1}\right)=c_1$$
$$a_1x+\frac{a_1b_1c_2-a_2b_1c_1}{a_1b_2-a_2b_1}=c_1$$
$$\begin{aligned}a_1x&=c_1-\frac{a_1b_1c_2-a_2b_1c_1}{a_1b_2-a_2b_1}\\&=\frac{c_1(a_1b_2-a_2b_1)}{a_1b_2-a_2b_1}-\frac{a_1b_1c_2-a_2b_1c_1}{a_1b_2-a_2b_1}\\&=\frac{a_1b_2c_1-a_1b_1c_2}{a_1b_2-a_2b_1}\end{aligned}$$
$$\begin{aligned}x&=\frac{a_1b_2c_1-a_1b_1c_2}{a_1b_2-a_2b_1}\div a_1\\&=\frac{a_1b_2c_1-a_1b_1c_2}{a_1(a_1b_2-a_2b_1)}=\frac{a_1(b_2c_1-b_1c_2)}{a_1(a_1b_2-a_2b_1)}\end{aligned}$$
$$x=\frac{b_2c_1-b_1c_2}{a_1b_2-a_2b_1}$$

65. x = number of hexagons formed
y = number of squares formed
$6x + y = 52$
$x + 4y = 24$
Eliminate x by multiplying the second equation by –6 and adding the resulting equations.

$$\begin{aligned} 6x + y &= 52 \\ -6x - 24y &= -144 \\ \hline -23y &= -92 \\ y &= 4 \end{aligned}$$

Substitute 4 for y in the second equation.

$$\begin{aligned} x + 4(4) &= 24 \\ x + 16 &= 24 \\ x &= 8 \end{aligned}$$

Yes, they should make 8 hexagons and 4 squares.

Section 5.2

Check Point Exercises

1.
$$\begin{aligned} x - 2y + 3z &= 22 \\ -1 - 2(-4) + 3(5) &\stackrel{?}{=} 22 \\ -1 + 8 + 15 &\stackrel{?}{=} 22 \\ 22 &= 22 \text{ true} \end{aligned}$$

$$\begin{aligned} 2x - 3y - z &= 5 \\ 2(-1) - 3(-4) - 5 &\stackrel{?}{=} 5 \\ -2 + 12 - 5 &\stackrel{?}{=} 5 \\ 5 &= 5 \text{ true} \end{aligned}$$

$$\begin{aligned} 3x + y - 5z &= -32 \\ 3(-1) - 4 - 5(5) &\stackrel{?}{=} -32 \\ -3 - 4 - 25 &\stackrel{?}{=} -32 \\ -32 &= -32 \text{ true} \end{aligned}$$

(–1, –4, 5) is a solution of the system.

2.
$$\begin{aligned} x + 4y - z &= 20 \\ 3x + 2y + z &= 8 \\ 2x - 3y + 2z &= -16 \end{aligned}$$

Eliminate z from Equations 1 and 2 by adding Equation 1 and Equation 2.

$$\begin{aligned} x + 4y - z &= 20 \\ 3x + 2y + z &= 8 \\ \hline 4x + 6y &= 28 \quad \text{Equation 4} \end{aligned}$$

Eliminate z from Equations 2 and 3 by multiplying Equation 2 by –2 and adding the resulting equation to Equation 3.

$$\begin{aligned} -6x - 4y - 2z &= -16 \\ 2x - 3y + 2z &= -16 \\ \hline -4x - 7y &= -32 \quad \text{Equation 5} \end{aligned}$$

Solve Equations 4 and 5 for x and y by adding Equation 4 and Equation 5.

$$\begin{aligned} 4x + 6y &= 28 \\ -4x - 7y &= -32 \\ \hline -y &= -4 \\ y &= 4 \end{aligned}$$

Substitute 4 for y in Equation 4 and solve for x.

$$\begin{aligned} 4x + 6(4) &= 28 \\ 4x + 24 &= 28 \\ 4x &= 4 \\ x &= 1 \end{aligned}$$

Substitute 1 for x and 4 for y in Equation 2 and solve for z.

$$\begin{aligned} 3(1) + 2(4) + z &= 8 \\ 3 + 8 + z &= 8 \\ 11 + z &= 8 \\ z &= -3 \end{aligned}$$

The solution set is {(1, 4, –3)}.

3.
$$\begin{aligned} 2y - z &= 7 \\ x + 2y + z &= 17 \\ 2x - 3y + 2z &= -1 \end{aligned}$$

Eliminate x and z from Equations 2 and 3 by multiplying Equation 2 by –2 and adding the resulting equation to Equation 3.

$$\begin{aligned} -2x - 4y - 2z &= -34 \\ 2x - 3y + 2z &= -1 \\ \hline -7y &= -35 \\ y &= 5 \end{aligned}$$

Substitute 5 for y in Equation 1 and solve for z.

$$\begin{aligned} 2(5) - z &= 7 \\ 10 - z &= 7 \\ -z &= -3 \\ z &= 3 \end{aligned}$$

Substitute 5 for y and 3 for z in Equation 2 and solve for x.

$$\begin{aligned} x + 2(5) + 3 &= 17 \\ x + 10 + 3 &= 17 \\ x + 13 &= 17 \\ x &= 4 \end{aligned}$$

The solution set is {(4, 5, 3)}.

4. (1, 4), (2, 1), (3, 4)

$y = ax^2 + bx + c$

Substitute 1 for x and 4 for y in $y = ax^2 + bx + c$.

$4 = a(1)^2 + b(1) + c$

$4 = a + b + c$ Equation 1

Substitute 2 for x and 1 for y in $y = ax^2 + bx + c$.

$1 = a(2)^2 + b(2) + c$

$1 = 4a + 2b + c$ Equation 2

Substitute 3 for x and 4 for y in $y = ax^2 + bx + c$.

$4 = a(3)^2 + b(3) + c$

$4 = 9a + 3b + c$ Equation 3

Eliminate c from Equations 1 and 2 by multiplying Equation 2 by –1 and adding the resulting equation to Equation 1.

$4 = a + b + c$

$\underline{-1 = -4a - 2b - c}$

$3 = -3a - b$ Equation 4

Eliminate c from Equation 2 and 3 by multiplying Equation 3 by –1 and adding the resulting equation to Equation 2.

$1 = 4a + 2b + c$

$\underline{-4 = -9a - 3b - c}$

$-3 = -5a - b$ Equation 5

Solve Equations 4 and 5 for a and b by multiplying Equation 5 by –1 and adding the resulting equation to Equation 4.

$3 = -3a - b$

$\underline{3 = 5a + b}$

$6 = 2a$

$a = 3$

Substitute 3 for a in Equation 4 and solve for b.

$3 = -3(3) - b$

$3 = -9 - b$

$12 = -b$

$b = -12$

Substitute 3 for a and –12 for b in Equation 1 and solve for c.

$4 = 3 - 12 + c$

$4 = -9 + c$

$c = 13$

Substituting 3 for a, –12 for b, and 13 for c in the quadratic equation $y = ax^2 + bx + c$ gives $y = 3x^2 - 12x + 13$.

Exercise Set 5.2

1. $x + y + z = 4$

$2 - 1 + 3 \stackrel{?}{=} 4$

$4 = 4$ true

$x - 2y - z = 1$

$2 - 2(-1) - 3 \stackrel{?}{=} 1$

$2 + 2 - 3 \stackrel{?}{=} 1$

$1 = 1$ true

$2x - y - 2 = -1$

$2(2) - (-1) - 2 \stackrel{?}{=} -1$

$4 + 1 - 2 \stackrel{?}{=} -1$

$3 = -1$ false

(2, –1, 3) is not a solution.

3. $x - 2y = 2$

$4 - 2(1) \stackrel{?}{=} 2$

$4 - 2 \stackrel{?}{=} 2$

$2 = 2$ true

$2x + 3y = 11$

$2(4) + 3(1) \stackrel{?}{=} 11$

$8 + 3 \stackrel{?}{=} 11$

$11 = 11$ true

$y - 4z = -7$

$1 - 4(2) \stackrel{?}{=} -7$

$1 - 8 \stackrel{?}{=} -7$

$-7 = -7$ true

(4, 1, 2) is a solution.

5. $x+y+2z=11$
$x+y+3z=14$
$x+2y-z=5$
Eliminate x and y from Equations 1 and 2 by multiplying Equation 2 by –1 and adding the resulting equation to Equation 1.

$$\begin{array}{r} -x-y-3z=-14 \\ x+y+2z=11 \\ \hline -z=-3 \\ z=3 \end{array}$$

Substitute 3 for z in Equations 1 and 3.
$x+y+2(3)=11$
$x+2y-(3)=5$
Simplify:
$x+y=5$ Equation 4
$x+2y=8$ Equation 5
Solve Equations 4 and 5 for x and y by multiplying Equation 5 by –1 and adding the resulting equation to Equation 4.

$$\begin{array}{r} x+y=5 \\ -x-2y=-8 \\ \hline -y=-3 \\ y=3 \end{array}$$

Substitute 3 for z and 3 for y in Equation 2 and solve for x.
$x+3+3(3)=14$
$x+12=14$
$x=2$
The solution set is $\{(2, 3, 3)\}$.

7. $4x-y+2z=11$
$x+2y-z=-1$
$2x+2y-3z=-1$
Eliminate y from Equation 1 and 2 by multiplying Equation 1 by 2 and adding the resulting equation to Equation 2 and 3.

$$\begin{array}{r} 8x-2y+4z=22 \\ x+2y-z=-1 \\ \hline 9x+3z=21 \end{array} \quad \text{Equation 4}$$

Eliminate y from Equations 1 and 3 by multiplying Equation 1 by 2 and adding the resulting equation to Equation 3.

$$\begin{array}{r} 8x-2y+4z=22 \\ 2x+2y-3z=-1 \\ \hline 10x+z=21 \end{array} \quad \text{Equation 5}$$

Solve Equations 4 and 5 for x and z by multiplying Equation 5 by –3 and adding the resulting equation to Equation 4.

$$\begin{array}{r} 9x+3z=21 \\ -30x-3z=-63 \\ \hline -21x=-42 \\ x=2 \end{array}$$

Substitute 2 for x in Equation 5 and solve for z. $10(2)+z=21$
$20+z=21$
$z=1$
Substitute 2 for x and 1 for z in Equation 2 and solve for y.
$2+2y-1=-1$
$2y+1=-1$
$2y=-2$
$y=-1$
The solution set is $\{(2,-1,1)\}$.

9. $3x+5y+2z=0$
$12x-15y+4z=12$
$6x-25y-8z=8$
Eliminate z from Equations 1 and 3 by multiplying Equation 1 by –2 and adding the resulting equation to Equation 2.

$$\begin{array}{r} -6x-10y-4z=0 \\ 12x-15y+4z=12 \\ \hline 6x-25y=12 \end{array} \quad \text{Equation 4}$$

Eliminate z from Equations 1 and 3 by multiplying Equation 1 by 4 and adding the resulting equation to Equation 3.

$$\begin{array}{r} 12x+20y+8z=0 \\ 6x-25y-8z=8 \\ \hline 18x-5y=8 \end{array} \quad \text{Equation 5}$$

Solve Equations 4 and 5 for x and y by multiplying Equation 4 by –3 and adding the resulting equation to Equation 5.

$$\begin{array}{r} -18x+75y=-36 \\ 18x-5y=8 \\ \hline 70y=-28 \\ y=-\frac{2}{5} \end{array}$$

Substitute $-\frac{2}{5}$ for y in Equation 4 and solve for x.

$$6x - 25\left(-\frac{2}{5}\right) = 12$$
$$6x + 10 = 12$$
$$6x = 2$$
$$x = \frac{2}{6} = \frac{1}{3}$$

Substitute $\frac{1}{3}$ for x and $-\frac{2}{5}$ for y in Equation 1 and solve for z.

$$3\left(\frac{1}{3}\right) + 5\left(-\frac{2}{5}\right) + 2z = 0$$
$$1 - 2 + 2z = 0$$
$$2z - 1 = 0$$
$$2z = 1$$
$$z = \frac{1}{2}$$

The solution set is $\left\{\left(\frac{1}{3}, -\frac{2}{5}, \frac{1}{2}\right)\right\}$.

11. $2x - 4y + 3z = 17$
$x + 2y - z = 0$
$4x - y - z = 6$

Eliminate z from Equations 1 and 2 by multiplying Equation 2 by 3 and adding the resulting equation to Equation 1.

$$2x - 4y + 3z = 17$$
$$3x + 6y - 3z = 0$$
$$5x + 2y = 17 \quad \text{Equation 4}$$

Eliminate z from Equations 2 and 3 by multiplying Equation 2 by –1 and adding the resulting equation to Equation 3.

$$-x - 2y + z = 0$$
$$3x - y - z = 6$$
$$3x - 3y = 6 \quad \text{Equation 5}$$

Solve Equations 4 and 5 for x and y by multiplying Equation 5 by $\frac{2}{3}$ and adding the resulting equation to Equation 4.

$$5x + 2y = 17$$
$$2x - 2y = 4$$
$$7x = 21$$
$$x = 3$$

Substitute 3 for x in Equation 4 and solve for y.

$$5(3) + 2y = 17$$
$$15 + 2y = 17$$
$$2y = 2$$
$$y = 1$$

Substitute 3 for x and 1 for y in Equation 2 and solve for z.

$$3 + 2(1) - z = 0$$
$$3 + 2 - z = 0$$
$$5 - z = 0$$
$$5 = z$$

The solution set is $\{(3, 1, 5)\}$.

13. $2x + y = 2$
$x + y - z = 4$
$3x + 2y + z = 0$

Eliminate z from Equations 2 and 3 by adding Equation 2 and Equation 3.

$$x + y - z = 4$$
$$3x + 2y + z = 0$$
$$4x + 3y = 4 \quad \text{Equation 4}$$

Solve Equations 1 and 4 for x and y by multiplying Equation 1 by –3 and adding the resulting equation to Equation 4.

$$-6x - 3y = -6$$
$$4x + 3y = 4$$
$$-2x = -2$$
$$x = 1$$

Substitute 1 for x in Equation 1 and solve for y.

$$2(1) + y = 2$$
$$2 + y = 2$$
$$y = 0$$

Substitute 1 for x and 0 for y in Equation 2 and solve for z.

$$1 + 0 - z = 4$$
$$1 - z = 4$$
$$-z = 3$$
$$z = -3$$

The solution set is $\{(1, 0, -3)\}$.

15. $x + y = -4$

$y - z = 1$

$2x + y + 3z = -21$

Eliminate y from Equations 1 and 2 by multiplying Equation 1 by –1 and adding the resulting equation to Equation 2.

$$\begin{array}{r} -x - y = 4 \\ y - z = 1 \\ \hline -x - z = 5 \end{array} \quad \text{Equation 4}$$

Eliminate y from Equations 2 and 3 by multiplying Equation 2 by –1 and adding the resulting equation to Equation 3.

$$\begin{array}{r} -y + z = -1 \\ 2x + y + 3z = -21 \\ \hline 2x + 4z = -22 \end{array} \quad \text{Equation 5}$$

Solve Equations 4 and 5 for x and z by multiplying Equation 4 by 2 and adding the resulting equation to Equation 5.

$$\begin{array}{r} -2x - 2z = 10 \\ 2x + 4z = -22 \\ \hline 2z = -12 \end{array}$$

$$z = -6$$

Substitute –6 fo z in Equation 2 and solve for y.

$y - (-6) = 1$

$y + 6 = 1$

$y = -5$

Substitute –5 for y in Equation 1 and solve for x

$x + (-5) = -4$

$x = 1$

The solution set is $\{(1, -5, -6)\}$.

17. $3(2x + y) + 5z = -1$

$2(x - 3y + 4z) = -9$

$4(1 + x) = -3(z - 3y)$

Simplify each equation.

$6x + 3y + 5z = -1$ Equation 4

$2x - 6y + 8z = -9$ Equation 5

$4 + 4x = -3z + 9y$

$4x - 9y + 3z = -4$ Equation 6

Eliminate x from Equations 4 and 5 by multiplying Equation 5 by –3 and adding the resulting equation to Equation 4.

$$\begin{array}{r} -6x + 3y + 5z = -1 \\ -6x + 18y - 24z = 27 \\ \hline 21y - 19z = 26 \end{array} \quad \text{Equation 7}$$

Eliminate x from Equations 5 and 6 by multiplying Equation 5 by –2 and adding the resulting equation to Equation 6.

$$\begin{array}{r} -4x + 12y - 16z = 18 \\ 4x - 9y + 3z = -4 \\ \hline 3y - 13z = 14 \end{array} \quad \text{Equation 8}$$

Solve Equations 7 and 8 for y and z by multiplying Equation 8 by –7 and adding the resulting equation to Equation 7.

$$\begin{array}{r} 21y - 19z = 26 \\ -21y + 91z = -98 \\ \hline 72z = -72 \end{array}$$

$$z = -1$$

Substitute –1 for z in Equation 8 and solve for y.

$3y - 13(-1) = 14$

$3y + 13 = 14$

$3y = 1$

$y = \frac{1}{3}$

Substitute $\frac{1}{3}$ for y and –1 for z in Equation 5 and solve for x.

$2x - 6\left(\frac{1}{3}\right) + 8(-1) = -9$

$2x - 2 - 8 = -9$

$2x - 10 = -9$

$2x = 1$

$x = \frac{1}{2}$

The solution set is $\left\{\left(\frac{1}{2}, \frac{1}{3}, -1\right)\right\}$.

19. $x + y + z = 16$
$2x + 3y + 4z = 46$
$5x - y = 31$
Eliminate z from Equations 1 and 2 by multiplying Equation 1 by –4 and adding the resulting equation to Equation 2.
$-4x - 4y - 4z = -64$
$2x + 3y + 4z = 46$
$-2x - y = -18$ Equation 4
Solve Equations 3 and 4 for x and y by multiplying Equation 4 by –1 and adding the resulting equation to Equation 3.
$5x - y = 31$
$2x + y = 18$
$7x = 49$
$x = 7$
Substitute 7 for x in Equation 3 and solve for y.
$5(7) - y = 31$
$35 - y = 31$
$-y = -4$
$y = 4$
Substitute 7 for x and 4 for y in Equation 1 and solve for z.
$7 + 4 + z = 16$
$z + 11 = 16$
$z = 5$
The numbers are 7, 4 and 5.

21. (–1, 6), (1, 4), (2, 9)
$y = ax^2 + bx + c$
Substitute –1 for x and 6 for y in $y = ax^2 + bx + c$.
$6 = a(-1)^2 + b(-1) + c$
$6 = a - b + c$ Equation 1
Substitute 1 for x and 4 for y in $y = ax^2 + bx + c$.
$4 = a(1)^2 + b(1) + c$
$4 = a + b + c$ Equation 2
Substitute 2 for x and 9 for y in $y = ax^2 + bx + c$.
$9 = a(2)^2 + b(2) + c$
$9 = 4a + 2b + c$ Equation 3
Eliminate b from Equations 1 and 2 by adding Equation 1 and Equation 2.
$6 = a - b + c$
$4 = a + b + c$
$10 = 2a + 2c$ Equation 4
Eliminate b from Equations 1 and 3 by multiplying Equation 1 by 2 and adding the resulting equation to Equation 3.
$12 = 2a - 2b + 2c$
$9 = 4a + 2b + c$
$21 = 6a + 3c$ Equation 5
Solve Equations 4 and 5 for a and c by multiplying Equation 4 by –3 and adding the resulting equation to Equation 5.
$-30 = -6a - 6c$
$21 = 6a + 3c$
$-9 = -3c$
$c = 3$
Substitute 3 for c in Equation 4 and solve for a.
$10 = 2a + 2(3)$
$10 = 2a + 6$
$4 = 2a$
$a = 2$
Substitute 2 for a and 3 for c in Equation 2 and solve for b.
$4 = 2 + b + 3$
$4 = b + 5$
$b = -1$

Substituting 2 for a, –1 for b, and 3 for c in the quadratic equation $y = ax^2 + bx + c$ gives $y = 2x^2 - x + 3$.

23. $(-1, -4), (1, -2), (2, 5)$
Substitute -1 for x and -4 for y in $y = ax^2 + bx + c$.
$-4 = a(-1)^2 + b(-1) + c$
$-4 = a - b + c$ Equation 1
Substitute 1 for x and -2 for y in $y = ax^2 + bx + c$.
$-2 = a(1)^2 + b(1) + c$
$-2 = a + b + c$ Equation 2
Substitute 2 for x and 5 for y in $y = ax^2 + bx + c$.
$5 = a(2)^2 + b(2) + c$
$5 = 4a + 2b + c$ Equation 3
Eliminate a and b from Equations 1 and 2 by multiplying Equation 1 by -1 and adding the resulting equation to Equation 2.
$4 = -a + b - c$
$\underline{-2 = a + b + c}$
$2 = 2b$
$b = 1$
Eliminate c from Equations 1 and 3 by multiplying Equation 1 by -1 and adding the resulting equation to Equation 3.
$4 = -a + b - c$
$\underline{5 = 4a + 2b + c}$
$9 = 3a + 3b$ Equation 4
Substitute 1 for b in Equation 4 and solve for a.
$9 = 3a + 3(1)$
$9 = 3a + 3$
$6 = 3a$
$a = 2$
Substitute 2 for a and 1 for b in Equation 2 and solve for c.
$-2 = 2 + 1 + c$
$-2 = c + 3$
$c = -5$
Substituting 2 for a, 1 for b, and -5 for c in quadratic equation $y = ax^2 + bx + c$ gives $y = 2x^2 + x - 5$.

25. $x + y + z = 121,421$
$x - y = 2906$
$y - z = 1041$
Eliminate z from Equations 1 and 3 by adding Equation 1 and Equation 3.
$x + y + z = 121,421$
$\underline{y - z = 1041}$
$x + 2y = 122,462$ Equation 4
Solve Equations 2 and 4 for x and y by multiplying Equation 2 by 2 and adding the resulting equation to Equation 4.
$2x - 2y = 5812$
$\underline{x + 2y = 122,462}$
$3x = 128,274$
$x = 42,758$
Substitute 42,758 for x in Equation 2 and solve for y.
$42,758 - y = 2906$
$y = 39,852$
Substitute 39,852 for y in Equation 3 and solve for z.
$39,852 - z = 1041$
$z = 38,811$
The average starting salary for a chemical engineer is \$42,758.
The average starting salary for a mechanical engineer is \$39,852.
The average starting salary for a electrical engineer is \$38,811.

27. Substitute 1 for x and 46 for y in

$y = \frac{1}{2}Ax^2 + Bx + C$.

$46 = \frac{1}{2}A(1)^2 + B(1) + C$

$46 = \frac{1}{2}A + B + C$ Equation 1

Substitute 2 for x and 84 for y in

$y = \frac{1}{2}Ax^2 + Bx + C$.

$84 = \frac{1}{2}A(2)^2 + B(2) + C$

$84 = 2A + 2B + C$ Equation 2

Substitute 3 for x and 114 for y in

$y = \frac{1}{2}Ax^2 + Bx + C$.

$114 = \frac{1}{2}A(3)^2 + B(3) + C$

$114 = \frac{9}{2}A + 3B + C = 114$ Equation 3

Eliminate C from Equation 1 and 2 by multiplying Equation 1 by –1 and adding the resulting equation to Equation 2.

$-46 = -\frac{1}{2}A - B - C$

$\underline{84 = 2A + 2B + C}$

$38 = \frac{3}{2}A + B$

$76 = 3A + 2B$ Equation 4

Eliminate C from Equation 2 and 3 by multiplying Equation 2 by –1 and adding the resulting equation to Equation 3.

$-84 = -2A - 2B - C$

$\underline{114 = \frac{9}{2}A + 3B + C}$

$30 = \frac{5}{2}A + B$

$60 = 5A + 2B$ Equation 5

Solve Equations 4 and 5 for A and B by multiplying Equation 5 by –1 and adding the resulting equation to Equation 4.

$76 = 3A + 2B$

$\underline{-60 = -5A - 2B}$

$16 = -2A$

$-8 = A$

Substitute –8 for A in Equation 4 and solve for B.

$76 = 3(-8) + 2B$

$76 = -24 + 2B$

$100 = 2B$

$B = 50$

Substitute –8 for A and 50 for B in Equation 2 and solve for C.

$2(-8) + 2(50) + C = 84$

$-16 + 100 + C = 84$

$84 + C = 84$

$C = 0$

$A = -8$; $B = 50$; $C = 0$

Substitute –8 for A, 50 for B, 0 for C and 6 for x in $y = \frac{1}{2}Ax^2 + Bx + C$.

$y = \frac{1}{2}(-8)(6)^2 + (6)(50) + 0$

$y = 156$ when $x = 6$

When a car is in motion for 6 seconds after the brakes are applied it travels 156 feet.

29. x = number of \$8 tickets sold
y = number of \$10 tickets sold
z = number of \$12 tickets sold
From the given conditions we have the following system of equations.

$$x + y + z = 400$$
$$8x + 10y + 12z = 3700$$
$$x + y = 7z \text{ or } x + y - 7z = 0$$

Eliminate z from Equations 1 and 2 multiplying Equation 1 by –12 and adding the resulting equation to Equation 2.

$$-12x - 12y - 12z = -4800$$
$$8x + 10y + 12z = 3700$$
$$-4x - 2y = -1100 \quad \text{Equation 4}$$

Eliminate z from Equations 1 and 3 by multiplying Equation 1 by 7 and adding the resulting equation to Equation 3.

$$7x + 7y + 7z = 2800$$
$$x + y - 7z = 0$$
$$8x + 8y = 2800 \quad \text{Equation 5}$$

Solve Equations 4 and 5 for x and y by multiplying Equation 4 by 2 and adding the resulting equation to Equation 5.

$$-8x - 4y = -2200$$
$$8x + 8y = 2800$$
$$4y = 600$$
$$y = 150$$

Substitute 150 for y in Equation 5 and solve for x.

$$8x + 8(150) = 2800$$
$$8x = 2800 - 1200$$
$$8x = 1600$$
$$x = 200$$

Substitute 200 for x and 150 for y in Equation 1 and solve for z.

$$200 + 150 + z = 400$$
$$350 + z = 400$$
$$z = 50$$

The number of \$8 tickets sold was 200.
The number of \$10 tickets sold was 150.
The number of \$12 tickets sold was 50.

31. x = amount of money invested at 10%
y = amount of money invested at 12%
z = amount of money invested at 15%

$$x + y + z = 6700$$
$$0.08x + 0.10y + 0.12z = 716$$
$$z = x + y + 300$$

Arrange Equation 3 so that variable terms appear on the left and constants appear on the right.

$$-x - y + z = 300 \quad \text{Equation 4}$$

Eliminate x and y from Equations 1 and 4 by adding Equations 1 and 4.

$$x + y + z = 6700$$
$$-x - y + z = 300$$
$$2z = 7000$$
$$z = 3500$$

Substitute 3500 for z in Equation 1 and Equation 2 and simplify.

$$x + y + 3500 = 6700$$
$$x + y = 3200 \quad \text{Equation 5}$$
$$0.08x + 0.10y + 0.12(3500) = 716$$
$$0.08x + 0.10y + 420 = 716$$
$$0.08x + 10y = 296 \quad \text{Equation 6}$$

Solve Equations 5 and 6 for x and y by multiplying Equation 5 by –0.10 and adding the resulting equation to Equation 6.

$$-0.10x - 0.10y = -320$$
$$0.08x + 0.10y = 296$$
$$-0.02x = 24$$
$$x = 1200$$

Substitute 1200 for x and 3,500 for z in Equation 1 and solve for y.

$$1200 + y + 3500 = 6700$$
$$y + 4700 = 6700$$
$$y = 2000$$

The person invested \$1200 at 8%, \$2000 at 10%, and \$3500 at 12%.

33.–35. Answers may vary.

41. x = number of triangles
y = number of rectangles
z = number of pentagons

$$x+y+z=40$$
$$3x+4y+5z=153$$
$$2y+5z=72$$

Eliminate x from Equations 1 and 2 by multiplying Equation 1 by –3 and adding the resulting equation to Equation 2.

$$-3x-3y-3z=-120$$
$$3x+4y+5z=153$$
$$y+2z=33 \quad \text{Equation 4}$$

Solve for z by multiplying Equation 4 by –2 and adding the resulting equation to Equation 3.

$$2y+5z=72$$
$$-2y-4z=-66$$
$$z=6$$

Substitute 6 for z in Equation 4 and solve for y.

$$y+2(6)=33$$
$$y+12=33$$
$$y=21$$

Substitute 21 for y and 6 for z in Equation 1 and solve for x.

$$x+21+6=40$$
$$x+27=40$$
$$x=13$$

The painting has 13 triangles, 21 rectangles, and 6 pentagons.

Section 5.3

Check Point Exercises

1. $$\frac{5x-1}{(x-3)(x+4)}=\frac{A}{x-3}+\frac{B}{x+4}$$

Multiply both sides of the equation by the least common denominator $(x-3)(x+4)$ and divide out common factors.

$$5x-1=A(x+4)+B(x-3)$$
$$5x-1=Ax+4A+Bx-3B$$
$$5x-1=(A+B)x+4A-3B$$

Equate coefficients of like powers of x and equate constant terms.

$$A+B=5$$
$$4A-3B=-1$$

Solving the above system for A and B we find $A = 2$ and $B = 3$.

$$\frac{5x-1}{(x-3)(x+4)}=\frac{2}{x-3}+\frac{3}{x+4}$$

2. $$\frac{x+2}{x(x-1)^2}=\frac{A}{x}+\frac{B}{x-1}+\frac{C}{(x-1)^2}$$

Multiply both sides of the equation by the least common denominator $x(x-1)^2$ and divide out common factors.

$$x+2=A(x-1)^2+Bx(x-1)+Cx$$
$$x+2=A\left(x^2-2x+1\right)+Bx^2-Bx+Cx$$
$$x+2=Ax^2-2Ax+A+Bx^2-Bx+Cx$$
$$x+2=Ax^2+Bx^2-2Ax-Bx+Cx+A$$
$$x+2=(A+B)x^2+(-2A-B+C)x+A$$

Equate coefficients of like powers of x and equate constant terms.

$$A+B=0$$
$$-2A-B+C=1$$
$$A=2$$

Since $A = 2$, we find that $B = -2$ and $C = 3$ by substitution.

$$\frac{x+2}{x(x-1)^2}=\frac{2}{x}-\frac{2}{x-1}+\frac{3}{(x-1)^2}$$

3. $\dfrac{8x^2+12x-20}{(x+3)(x^2+x+2)}=\dfrac{A}{x+3}+\dfrac{Bx+C}{x^2+x+2}$

Multiply both sides of the equation by the least common denominator $(x+3)(x^2+x+2)$ and divide out common factors.

$8x^2+12x-20=A(x^2+x+2)+(Bx+C)(x+3)$
$8x^2+12x-20=Ax^2+Ax+2A+Bx^2+3Bx+Cx+3C$
$8x^2+12x-20=Ax^2+Bx^2+Ax+3Bx+Cx+2A+3C$
$8x^2+12x-20=(A+B)x^2+(A+3B+C)x+2A+3C$

Equate coefficients of like powers of x and equate constant terms.

$A+B=8$
$A+3B+C=12$
$2A+3C=-20$

Solving the above system for A, B, and C we find $A = 2$, $B = 6$, and $C = -8$.

$\dfrac{8x^2+12x-20}{(x+3)(x^2+x+2)}=\dfrac{2}{x+3}+\dfrac{6x-8}{x^2+x+2}$

4. $\dfrac{2x^3+x+3}{(x^2+1)^2}=\dfrac{Ax+B}{x^2+1}+\dfrac{Cx+D}{(x^2+1)^2}$

Multiply both sides of the equation by the common denominator $(x^2+1)^2$ and divide out common factors.

$2x^3+x+3=(Ax+B)(x^2+1)+Cx+D$
$2x^3+x+3=Ax^3+Bx^2+Ax+B+Cx+D$
$2x^3+x+3=Ax^3+Bx^2+Ax+Cx+B+D$
$2x^3+x+3=Ax^3+Bx^2+(A+C)x+B+D$

Equate coefficients of like powers of x and equate constant terms.

$A=2$
$B=0$
$A+C=1$
$B+D=3$

Since $A = 2$ and $B = 0$ we find that $C = -1$ and $D = 3$ by substitution.

$\dfrac{2x^3+x+3}{(x^2+1)^2}=\dfrac{2x}{x^2+1}-\dfrac{x-3}{(x^2+1)^2}$

Exercise Set 5.3

1. $\frac{11x-10}{(x-2)(x+1)}=\frac{A}{x-2}+\frac{B}{x+1}$

3. $\frac{6x^2-14x-27}{(x+2)(x-3)^2}=\frac{A}{x+2}+\frac{B}{x-3}+\frac{C}{(x-3)^2}$

5. $\frac{5x^2-6x+7}{(x-1)(x^2+1)}=\frac{A}{x-1}+\frac{Bx+C}{x^2+1}$

7. $\frac{x^3+x^2}{(x^2+4)^2}=\frac{Ax+B}{x^2+4}+\frac{Cx+D}{(x^2+4)^2}$

9. $\frac{x}{(x-3)(x-2)}=\frac{A}{x-3}+\frac{B}{x-2}$

Multiply both sides of the equation by the least common denominator $(x-3)(x-2)$ and divide out common factors.

$x=A(x-2)+B(x-3)$
$x=Ax-2A+Bx-3B$
$x=Ax+Bx-2A-3B$
$x=(A+B)x-(2A+3B)$

Equate coefficients of like powers of x, and equate constant terms.

$A+B=1$
$2A+3B=0$

Solving the above system for A and B, we find $A = 3$ and $B = -2$.

$\frac{x}{(x-3)(x-2)}=\frac{3}{x-3}-\frac{2}{x-2}$

11. $\frac{3x+50}{(x-9)(x+2)}=\frac{A}{x-9}+\frac{B}{x+2}$

Multiply both sides of the equation by the least common denominator $(x-9)(x+2)$ and divide out common factors.

$3x+50=A(x+2)+B(x-9)$
$3x+50=Ax+2A+Bx-9B$
$3x+50=Ax+Bx+2A-9B$
$3x+50=(A+B)x+(2A-9B)$

Equate coefficients of like powers of x, and equate constant terms.

$A+B=3$
$2A-9B=50$

Solving the above system for A and B, we find $A = 7$ and $B = -4$.

$\frac{3x+50}{(x-9)(x+2)}=\frac{7}{x-9}-\frac{4}{x+2}$

13. $\frac{7x-4}{x^2-x-12}=\frac{7x-4}{(x-4)(x+3)}=\frac{A}{x-4}+\frac{B}{x+3}$

Multiply both sides of the last equation by the least common denominator $(x-4)(x-3)$ and divide out common factors.

$7x-4=A(x+3)+B(x-4)$
$7x-4=Ax+3A+Bx-4B$
$7x-4=Ax+Bx+3A-4B$
$7x-4=(A+B)x+(3A-4B)$

Equate coefficients of like powers of x, and equate constant terms.

$A+B=7$
$3A-4B=-4$

Solving the above system for A and B, we find $A=\frac{24}{7}$ and $B=\frac{25}{7}$.

$\frac{7x-4}{x^2-x-12}=\frac{24}{7(x-4)}+\frac{25}{7(x+3)}$

15. $\frac{4x^2+13x-9}{x(x-1)(x+3)}=\frac{A}{x}+\frac{B}{x-3}+\frac{C}{x+3}$

Multiply both sides of the equation by the least common denominator $x(x-1)(x+3)$ and divide out common factors.

$4x^2+13x-9=A(x-1)(x+3)+Bx(x+3)+Cx(x-1)$

$4x^2+13x-9=A\left(x^2+2x-3\right)+Bx^2+3Bx+Cx^2-Cx$

$4x^2+13x-9=Ax^2+2Ax-3A+Bx^2+3Bx+Cx^2-Cx$

$4x^2+13x-9=Ax^2+Bx^2+Cx^2+2Ax+3Bx-Cx-3A$

$4x^2+13x-9=(A+B+C)x^2+(2A+3B-C)x-3A$

Equate coefficients of like powers of *x*, and equate constant terms.

$A+B+C=4$

$2A+3B-C=13$

$-3A=-9$

Solving the above system for *A*, *B*, and *C*, we find $A = 3$ and $B = 2$, and $C = -1$.

$\frac{4x^2+13x-9}{x(x-1)(x+3)}=\frac{3}{x}+\frac{2}{x-1}-\frac{1}{x+3}$

17. $\frac{4x^2-7x-3}{x^3-x}=\frac{4x^2-7x-3}{x(x+1)(x-1)}=\frac{A}{x}+\frac{B}{x+1}+\frac{C}{x-1}$

Multiply both sides of the last equation by the least common denominator $x(x+1)(x-1)$ and divide out common factors.

$4x^2-7x-3=A(x+1)(x-1)+Bx(x-1)+Cx(x+1)$

$4x^2-7x-3=A(x^2-1)+Bx^2-Bx+Cx^2+Cx$

$4x^2-7x-3=Ax^2-A+Bx^2-Bx+Cx^2+Cx$

$4x^2-7x-3=Ax^2+Bx^2+Cx^2-Bx+Cx-A$

$4x^2-7x-3=(A+B+C)x^2+(-B+C)x-A$

Equate coefficients of like powers of *x*, and equate constant terms.

$A+B+C=4$

$-B+C=-7$

$-A=-3$

Solving the above system for *A*, *B*, and *C*, we find $A = 3$ and $B = 4$, and $C = -3$.

$\frac{4x^2-7x-3}{x^3-x}=\frac{3}{x}+\frac{4}{x+1}-\frac{3}{x-1}$

19. $\dfrac{6x-11}{(x-1)^2}=\dfrac{A}{x-1}+\dfrac{B}{(x-1)^2}$

Multiply both sides of the equation by the least common denominator $(x-1)^2$ and divide out common factors.

$6x-11=A(x-1)+B$
$6x-11=Ax-A+B$

Equate coefficients of like powers of x, and equate constant terms.

$A=6$
$-A+B=-11$

Since $A=6$, we find that $B=-5$ by substitution. $\dfrac{6x-11}{(x-1)^2}=\dfrac{6}{x-1}-\dfrac{5}{(x-1)^2}$

21. $\dfrac{x^2-6x+3}{(x-2)^3}=\dfrac{A}{x-2}+\dfrac{B}{(x-2)^2}+\dfrac{C}{(x-2)^3}$

Multiply both sides of the equation by the least common denominator $(x-2)^3$ and divide out common factors.

$x^2-6x+3=A(x-2)^2+B(x-2)+C$
$x^2-6x+3=A(x^2-4x+4)+Bx-2B+C$
$x^2-6x+3=Ax^2-4Ax+4A+Bx-2B+C$
$x^2-6x+3=Ax^2-4Ax+Bx+4A-2B+C$
$x^2-6x+3=Ax^2+(-4A+B)x+4A-2B+C$

Equate coefficients of like powers of x, and equate constant terms.

$A=1$
$-4A+B=-6$
$4A-2B+C=3$

Since $A=1$, we find that $B=-2$ and $C=-5$ by substitution. $\dfrac{x^2-6x+3}{(x-2)^3}=\dfrac{1}{x-2}-\dfrac{2}{(x-2)^2}-\dfrac{5}{(x-2)^3}$

23. $\dfrac{x^2+2x+7}{x(x-1)^2}=\dfrac{A}{x}+\dfrac{B}{x-1}+\dfrac{C}{(x-1)^2}$

Multiply both sides of the equation by the least common denominator $x(x-1)^2$ and divide out common factors.

$x^2+2x+7=A(x-1)^2+Bx(x-1)+Cx$
$x^2+2x+7=A(x^2-2x+1)+Bx^2-Bx+Cx$
$x^2+2x+7=Ax^2-2Ax+A+Bx^2-Bx+Cx$
$x^2+2x+7=Ax^2+Bx^2-2Ax-Bx+Cx+A$
$x^2+2x+7=(A+B)x^2+(-2A-B+C)x+A$

$A+B=1$
$-2A-B+C=2$
$A=7$

Since $A=7$, we find that $B=-6$ and $C=10$ by substitution. $\dfrac{x^2+2x+7}{x(x-1)^2}=\dfrac{7}{x}-\dfrac{6}{x-1}+\dfrac{10}{(x-1)^2}$

25. $\frac{5x^2+21x+4}{(x+1)^2(x-3)}=\frac{A}{x+1}+\frac{B}{(x+1)^2}+\frac{C}{x-3}$

Multiply both sides of the equation by the least common denominator $(x+1)^2(x-3)$ and divide out common factors.

$5x^2+21x+4=A(x+1)(x-3)+B(x-3)+C(x+1)^2$

$5x^2+21x+4=A(x^2-2x-3)+Bx-3B+C(x^2+2x+1)$

$5x^2+21x+4=Ax^2-2Ax-3A+Bx-3B+Cx^2+2Cx+C$

$5x^2+21x+4=Ax^2+Cx^2-2Ax+Bx+2Cx-3A-3B+C$

$5x^2+21x+4=(A+C)x^2+(-2A+B+2C)x-3A-3B+C$

Equate coefficients of like powers of x, and equate constant terms.

$A+C=5$

$-2A+B+2C=21$

$-3A-3B+C=4$

Solving the above system for A, B, and C, we find $A=-2$, $B=3$, and $C=7$.

$\frac{5x^2+21x+4}{(x+1)^2(x-3)}=-\frac{2}{x+1}+\frac{3}{(x+1)^2}+\frac{7}{x-3}$

27. $\frac{5x^2-6x+7}{(x-1)(x^2+1)}=\frac{A}{x-1}+\frac{Bx+C}{x^2+1}$

Multiply both sides of the equation by the least common denominator $(x-1)(x^2+1)$ and divide out common factors.

$5x^2-6x+7=A(x^2+1)+(Bx+C)(x-1)$

$5x^2-6x+7=Ax^2+A+Bx^2-Bx+Cx-C$

$5x^2-6x+7=Ax^2+Bx^2-Bx+Cx+A-C$

$5x^2-6x+7=(A+B)x^2+(-B+C)x+A-C$

Equate coefficients of like powers of x, and equate constant terms.

$A+B=5$

$-B+C=-6$

$A-C=7$

Solving the above system for A, B, and C, we find $A=3$, $B=2$, and $C=-4$.

$\frac{5x^2-6x+7}{(x-1)(x^2+1)}=\frac{3}{x-1}+\frac{2x-4}{x^2+1}$

29. $\dfrac{5x^2+6x+3}{(x+1)(x^2+2x+2)}=\dfrac{A}{x+1}+\dfrac{Bx+C}{x^2+2x+2}$

Multiply both sides of the equation by the least common denominator $(x+1)(x^2+2x+2)$ and divide out common factors.

$5x^2+6x+3=A(x^2+2x+2)+(Bx+C)(x+1)$

$5x^2+6x+3=Ax^2+2Ax+2A+Bx^2+Bx+Cx+C$

$5x^2+6x+3=Ax^2+Bx^2+2Ax+Bx+Cx+2A+C$

$5x^2+6x+3=(A+B)x^2+(2A+B+C)x+2A+C$

Equate coefficients of like powers of x, and equate constant terms.

$A+B=5$

$2A+B+C=6$

$2A+C=3$

Solving the above system for A, B, and C, we find $A=2$, $B=3$, and $C=-1$.

$\dfrac{5x^2+6x+3}{(x+1)(x^2+2x+2)}=\dfrac{2}{x+1}+\dfrac{3x-1}{x^2+2x+2}$

31. $\dfrac{6x^2-x+1}{x^3+x^2+x+1}=\dfrac{6x^2-x+1}{(x+1)(x^2+1)}=\dfrac{A}{x+1}+\dfrac{Bx+C}{x^2+1}$

Multiply both sides of the last equation by the least common denominator $(x+1)(x^2+1)$ and divide out common factors.

$6x^2-x+1=A(x^2+1)+(Bx+C)(x+1)$

$6x^2-x+1=Ax^2+A+Bx^2+Bx+Cx+C$

$6x^2-x+1=Ax^2+Bx^2+Bx+Cx+A+C$

$6x^2-x+1=(A+B)x^2+(B+C)x+A+C$

Equate coefficients of like powers of x, and equate constant terms.

$A+B=6$

$B+C=-1$

$A+C=1$

Solving the above system for A, B, and C, we find $A=4$, $B=2$, and $C=-3$.

$\dfrac{6x^2-x+1}{x^3+x^2+x+1}=\dfrac{4}{x+1}+\dfrac{2x-3}{x^2+1}$

33. $\dfrac{x^3+x^2+2}{\left(x^2+2\right)^2}=\dfrac{Ax+B}{x^2+2}+\dfrac{Cx+D}{\left(x^2+2\right)^2}$

Multiply both sides of the last equation by the least common denominator $(x^2+2)^2$ and divide out common factors.

$x^3+x^2+2=(Ax+B)\left(x^2+2\right)+Cx+D$

$x^3+x^2+2=Ax^3+Bx^2+2Ax+2B+Cx+D$

$x^3+x^2+2=Ax^3+Bx^2+2Ax+Cx+2B+D$

$x^3+x^2+2=Ax^3+Bx^2+(2A+C)x+(2B+D)$

Equate coefficients of like powers of x, and equate constant terms.

$A=1$

$B=1$

$2A+C=0$

$2B+D=2$

Since $A = 1$ and $B = 1$, we find that $C = -2$ and $D = 0$ by substitution.

$\dfrac{x^3+x^2+2}{\left(x^2+2\right)^2}=\dfrac{x+1}{x^2+2}-\dfrac{2x}{\left(x^2+2\right)^2}$

35. $\dfrac{x^3-4x^2+9x-5}{(x^2-2x+3)^2}=\dfrac{Ax+B}{x^2-2x+3}+\dfrac{Cx+D}{(x^2-2x+3)^2}$

Multiply both sides of the equation by the least common denominator $(x^2-2x+3)^2$ and divide out common factors.

$x^3-4x^2+9x-5=(Ax+B)(x^2-2x+3)+Cx+D$

$x^3-4x^2+9x-5=Ax^3-2Ax^2+3Ax+Bx^2-2Bx+3B+Cx+D$

$x^3-4x^2+9x-5=Ax^3-2Ax^2+Bx^2+3Ax-2Bx+Cx+3B+D$

$x^3-4x^2+9x-5=Ax^3+(-2A+B)x^2+(3A-2B+C)x+3B+D$

Equate coefficients of like powers of x, and equate constant terms.

$A=1$

$-2A+B=-4$

$3A-2B+C=9$

$3B+D=-5$

Since $A = 1$, we find that $B = -2$, $C = 2$, and $D = 1$ by substitution.

$\dfrac{x^3-4x^2+9x-5}{(x^2-2x+3)^2}=\dfrac{x-2}{x^2-2x+3}+\dfrac{2x+1}{(x^2-2x+3)^2}$

37. $\dfrac{4x^2+3x+14}{x^3-8}=\dfrac{4x^2+3x+14}{(x-2)\left(x^2+2x+4\right)}=\dfrac{A}{x-2}+\dfrac{Bx+C}{x^2+2x+4}$

Multiply both sides of the last equation by the least common denominator $(x-2)(x^2+2x+4)$ and divide out common factors.

$4x^2+3x+14=A\left(x^2+2x+4\right)+(Bx+C)(x-2)$

$4x^2+3x+14=A^2+2Ax+4A+Bx^2-2Bx+Cx-2C$

$4x^2+3x+14=Ax^2+Bx^2+2Ax-2Bx+Cx+4A-2C$

$4x^2+3x+14=(A+B)x^2+(2A-2B+C)x+(4A-2C)$

Equate coefficients of like powers of x, and equate constant terms.

$A+B=4$

$2A-2B+C=3$

$4A-2C=14$

Solving the above system for A, B, and C, we find $A = 3$, $B = 1$, and $C = -1$.

$\dfrac{4x^2+3x+4}{x^3-8}=\dfrac{3}{x-2}+\dfrac{x-1}{x^2+2x+4}$

39. $\dfrac{1}{x(x+1)}=\dfrac{A}{x}+\dfrac{B}{x+1}$

Multiply both sides of the equation by the least common denominator $x(x+1)$ and divide out common factors.

$1=A(x+1)+Bx$

$1=Ax+A+Bx$

$1=Ax+Bx+A$

$1=(A+B)x+A$

Equate coefficients of like powers of x, and equate constant terms.

$A+B=0$

$A=1$

Since $A = 1$ we find that $B = -1$ by substitution.

$\dfrac{1}{x(x+1)}=\dfrac{1}{x}-\dfrac{1}{x+1}$

$\dfrac{1}{1\cdot 2}+\dfrac{1}{2\cdot 3}+\dfrac{1}{3\cdot 4}+\cdots+\dfrac{1}{99\cdot 100}=\left(\dfrac{1}{1}-\dfrac{1}{2}\right)+\left(\dfrac{1}{2}-\dfrac{1}{3}\right)+\left(\dfrac{1}{3}-\dfrac{1}{4}\right)+\cdots+\left(\dfrac{1}{99}-\dfrac{1}{100}\right)=\dfrac{1}{1}-\dfrac{1}{100}=\dfrac{99}{100}$

41.–45. Answers may vary.

47. Exercise 9

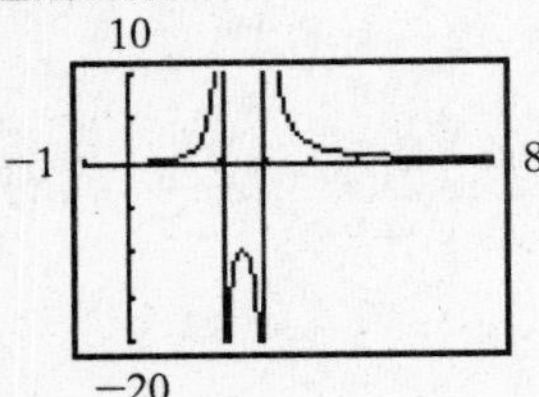

Exercise 11

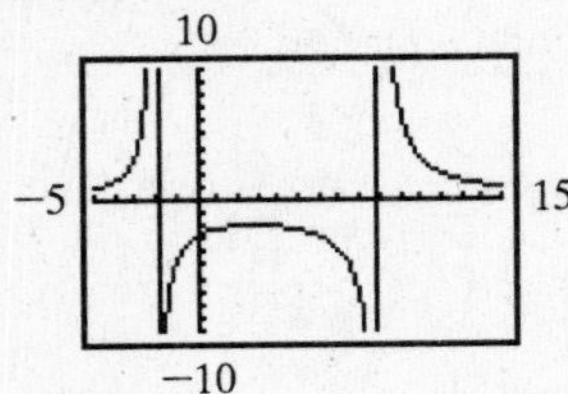

Exercise 13

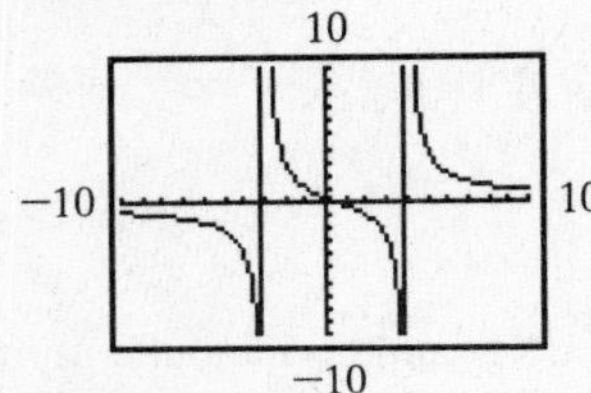

Exercise 15

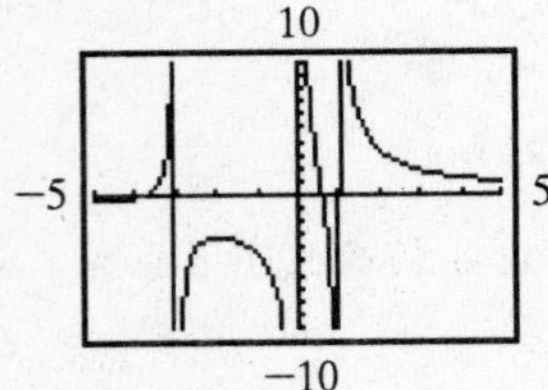

Exercise 17

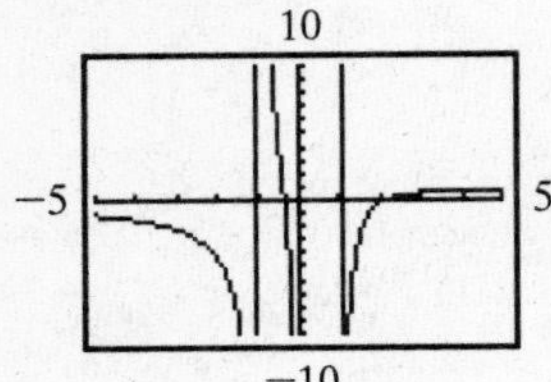

49. $\frac{ax+b}{(x-c)^2}=\frac{A}{x-c}+\frac{B}{(x-c)^2}$

Multiply both sides of the equation by the least common denominator $(x-c)^2$ and divide out common factors.

$ax+b=A(x-c)+B$

$ax+b=Ax-Ac+B$

Equate coefficients of like powers of x, and equate constants terms.

$A=a$

$-Ac+B=b$

Since $A=a$, we find that $B=b+Ac=b+ac$ by substitution.

$$\frac{ax+b}{(x-c)^2}=\frac{a}{x-c}+\frac{b+ac}{(x-c)^2}$$

Section 5.4

Check Point Exercises

1. $x^2=y-1$

$4x-y=-1$

Solve the first Equation for y. $y=x^2+1$.

Substitute the expression x^2+1 for y in the second equation and solve for x.

$4x-(x^2+1)=-1$

$4x-x^2-1=-1$

$x^2-4x=0$

$x(x-4)=0$

$x=0$ or $x-4=0$

$x=4$

If $x=0$, $y=(0)^2+1=1$.

If $x=4$, $y=(4)^2+1=17$.

The solution set is $\{(0, 1), (4, 17)\}$.

2. $x+2y=0$

$(x-1)^2+(y-1)^2=5$

Solve the first equation for x. $x=-2y$

Substitute the expression $-2y$ for x in the second equation and solve for y.

$(-2y-1)^2+(y-1)^2=5$

$4y^2+4y+1+y^2-2y+1=5$

$5y^2+2y-3=0$

$(5y-3)(y+1)=0$

$5y-3=0$ or $y+1=0$

$y=\frac{3}{5}$ or $y=-1$

If $y=\frac{3}{5}$, $x=-2\left(\frac{3}{5}\right)=\frac{-6}{5}$.

If $y=-1$, $x=-2(-1)=2$.

The solution set is $\left\{\left(\frac{-6}{5}, \frac{3}{5}\right), (2, -1)\right\}$.

3. $3x^2 + 2y^2 = 35$
$4x^2 + 3y^2 = 48$
Eliminate the y^2-term by multiplying the first equation by –3 and the second equation by 2. Add the resulting equations.

$$\begin{aligned} -9x^2 - 6y &= -105 \\ \underline{8x^2 + 6y^2} &\underline{= 96} \\ -x^2 &= -9 \\ x^2 &= 9 \\ x &= \pm 3 \end{aligned}$$

If $x = 3$,

$$\begin{aligned} 3(3)^2 + 2y^2 &= 35 \\ y^2 &= 4 \\ y &= \pm 2 \end{aligned}$$

If $x = -3$,

$$\begin{aligned} 3(-3)^2 + 2y^2 &= 35 \\ y^2 &= 4 \\ y &= \pm 2 \end{aligned}$$

The solution set is $\{(3, 2), (3, -2), (-3, 2), (-3, -2)\}$.

4. $y = x^2 + 5$
$x^2 + y^2 = 25$
Arrange the first equation so that variable terms appear on the left, and constants appear on the right. Add the resulting equations to eliminate the x^2-terms and solve for y.

$$\begin{aligned} -x^2 + y &= 5 \\ \underline{x^2 + y^2} &\underline{= 25} \\ y^2 + y &= 30 \\ y^2 + y - 30 &= 0 \\ (y+6)(y-5) &= 0 \end{aligned}$$

$y + 6 = 0$ or $y - 5 = 0$
$y = -6$ or $y = 5$

If $y = -6$,

$$\begin{aligned} x^2 + (-6)^2 &= 25 \\ x^2 &= -11 \end{aligned}$$

no real solution

If $y = 5$,

$$\begin{aligned} x^2 + (5)^2 &= 25 \\ x^2 &= 0 \\ x &= 0 \end{aligned}$$

The solution set is $\{(0, 5)\}$.

5. $2x + 2y = 20$
$xy = 21$

Solve the second equation for x. $x = \dfrac{21}{y}$

Substitute the expression $\dfrac{21}{y}$ for x in the first equation and solve for y.

$$\begin{aligned} 2\left(\frac{21}{y}\right) + 2y &= 20 \\ \frac{42}{y} + 2y &= 20 \\ y^2 - 10y + 21 &= 0 \\ (y-7)(y-3) &= 0 \end{aligned}$$

$y - 7 = 0$ or $y - 3 = 0$
$y = 7$ or $y = 3$

If $y = 7$, $x = \dfrac{21}{3} = 3.$

If $y = 3$, $x = \dfrac{21}{3} = 7.$

The dimensions are 7 feet by 3 feet.

Exercise Set 5.4

1. $x + y = 2$
$y = x^2 - 4$
Solve the first equation for y. $y = 2 - x$.
Substitute the expression $2 - x$ for y in the second equation and solve for x.

$$\begin{aligned} 2 - x &= x^2 - 4 \\ x^2 + x - 6 &= 0 \\ (x+3)(x-2) &= 0 \end{aligned}$$

$x + 3 = 0$ or $x - 2 = 0$
$x = -3$ or $x = 2$

If $x = -3$, $y = 2 - (-3) = 5$.
If $x = 2$, $y = 2 - 2 = 0$.
The solution set is $\{(-3, 5), (2, 0)\}$.

3. $x - y = -1$
$y = x^2 + 2x - 3$

Substitute the expression $x^2 + 2x - 3$ for y in the first equation and solve for x.

$$x - \left(x^2 + 2x - 3\right) = -1$$
$$x - x^2 - 2x + 3 = -1$$
$$x^2 + x - 4 = 0$$
$$x = \frac{-1 \pm \sqrt{1+16}}{2} = \frac{-1 \pm \sqrt{17}}{2}$$

Solve the first equation for y.

$x - y = -1$
$y = x + 1$

Substitute $\frac{-1 \pm \sqrt{17}}{2}$ for x in the equation $y = x + 1$.

$$y = \frac{-1 \pm \sqrt{17}}{2} + 1 = \frac{-1 \pm \sqrt{17} + 2}{2} = \frac{1 \pm \sqrt{17}}{2}$$

The solution set is

$$\left\{\left(\frac{-1+\sqrt{17}}{2}, \frac{1+\sqrt{17}}{2}\right), \left(\frac{-1-\sqrt{17}}{2}, \frac{1-\sqrt{17}}{2}\right)\right\}.$$

5. $y = x^2 - 4x - 10$
$y = -x^2 - 2x + 14$

Substitute the expression $x^2 - 4x - 10$ for y in the second equation and solve for x.

$$x^2 - 4x - 10 = -x^2 - 2x + 14$$
$$2x^2 - 2x - 24 = 0$$
$$x^2 - x - 12 = 0$$
$$(x-4)(x+3) = 0$$
$$x - 4 = 0 \text{ or } x + 3 = 0$$
$$x = 4 \text{ or } x = -3$$

If $x = 4$, $y = (4)^2 - 4(4) - 10 = -10$.

If $x = -3$, $y = (-3)^2 - 4(-3) - 10 = 11$.

The solution set is $\{(4, -10), (-3, 11)\}$.

7. $x^2 + y^2 = 25$
$x - y = 1$

Solve the second equation for y. $y = x - 1$
Substitute the expression $x - 1$ for y in the first equation and solve for x.

$$x^2 + (x-1)^2 = 25$$
$$x^2 + x^2 - 2x + 1 = 25$$
$$2x^2 - 2x - 24 = 0$$
$$x^2 - x - 12 = 0$$
$$(x-4)(x+3) = 0$$
$$x - 4 = 0 \text{ or } x + 3 = 0$$
$$x = 4 \text{ or } x = -3$$

If $x = 4, y = 4 - 1 = 3$.
If $x = -3, y = -3 - 1 = -4$.
The solution set is $\{(4, 3), (-3, -4)\}$.

9. $xy = 6$
$2x - y = 1$

Solve the first equation for y.

$y = \frac{6}{x}$

Substitute the expression $\frac{6}{x}$ for y in the second equation and solve for x.

$$2x - \frac{6}{x} = 1$$
$$2x^2 - 6 = x$$
$$2x^2 - x - 6 = 0$$
$$(2x+3)(x-2) = 0$$
$$2x + 3 = 0 \text{ or } x - 2 = 0$$
$$x = -\frac{3}{2} \text{ or } x = 2$$

If $x = -\frac{3}{2}, y = \frac{6}{-\frac{3}{2}} = -4$.

If $x = 2$, $y = \frac{6}{2} = 3$.

The solution set is $\left\{\left(-\frac{3}{2}, -4\right), (2, 3)\right\}$.

11. $y^2 = x^2 - 9$
$2y = x - 3$
Solve the second equation for y.
$$y = \frac{x-3}{2}$$
Substitute the expression $\frac{x-3}{2}$ for y in the first equation and solve for x.
$$\left(\frac{x-3}{2}\right)^2 = x^2 - 9$$
$$\frac{x^2 - 6x + 9}{4} = x^2 - 9$$
$$x^2 - 6x + 9 = 4x^2 - 36$$
$$3x^2 + 6x - 45 = 0$$
$$x^2 + 2x - 15 = 0$$
$$(x+5)(x-3) = 0$$
$x + 5 = 0$ or $x - 3 = 0$
$x = -5$ or $x = 3$
If $x = -5, y = \frac{-5-3}{2} = -4.$
If $x = 3, y = \frac{3-3}{2} = 0.$
The solution set is $\{(-5,-4),(3,0)\}$.

13. $xy = 3$
$x^2 + y^2 = 10$
Solve the second equation for y.
$$y = \frac{3}{x}$$
Substitute the expression $\frac{3}{x}$ for y in the second equation and solve for x.
$$x^2 + \left(\frac{3}{x}\right)^2 = 10$$
$$x^2 + \frac{9}{x^2} - 10 = 0$$
$$x^4 - 10x^2 + 9 = 0$$
$$\left(x^2 - 9\right)\left(x^2 - 1\right) = 0$$
$$(x-3)(x+3)(x-1)(x+1) = 0$$
$x - 3 = 0$ or $x + 3 = 0$ or $x - 1 = 0$ or $x + 1 = 0$
$x = 3$ or $x = -3$ or $x = 1$ or $x = -1$
If $x = 3, y = \frac{3}{3} = 1.$
If $x = -3, y = \frac{3}{-3} = -1.$
If $x = 1, y = \frac{3}{1} = 3.$
If $x = -1, y = \frac{3}{-1} = -3.$
The solution set is $\{(3,1),(-3,-1),(1,3),(-1,-3)\}$.

15. $x + y = 1$
$x^2 + xy - y^2 = -5$
Solve the first equation for y. $y = 1 - x$
Substitute the expression $1 - x$ for y in the second equation and solve for x.
$$x^2 + x(1-x) - (1-x)^2 = -5$$
$$x^2 + x - x^2 - \left(1 - 2x + x^2\right) = -5$$
$$x - 1 + 2x - x^2 = -5$$
$$x^2 - 3x - 4 = 0$$
$$(x-4)(x+1) = 0$$
$x - 4 = 0$ or $x + 1 = 0$
$x = 4$ or $x = -1$
If $x = 4, y = 1 - 4 = -3.$
If $x = -1, y = 1 - (-1) = 2.$
The solution set is $\{(4,-3),(-1,2)\}$.

17. $x+y=1$

$(x-1)^2+(y+2)^2=10$

Solve the first equation for y.

$y=1-x$

Substitute the expression $1-x$ for y in the second equation and solve for x.

$(x-1)^2+(1-x+2)^2=10$

$(x-1)^2+(3-x)^2=10$

$x^2-2x+1+9-6x+x^2-10=0$

$2x^2-8x=0$

$x^2-4x=0$

$x(x-4)=0$

$x=0$ or $x-4=0$

$x=4$

If $x=0, y=1-0=1$.

If $x=4, y=1-4=-3$.

The solution set is $\{(0,1),(4,-3)\}$.

19. Eliminate the y^2 –terms by adding the equations.

$x^2+y^2=13$

$\underline{x^2-y^2=5}$

$2x^2=18$

$x^2=9$

$x=\pm3$

If $x=3$,

$(3)^2+y^2=13$

$y^2=4$

$y=\pm2$

If $x=-3$,

$(-3)^2+y^2=13$

$y^2=4$

$y=\pm2$

The solution set is $\{(3, 2), (3, -2), (-3, 2), (-3, -2)\}$.

21. $x^2-4y^2=-7$

$3x^2+y^2=31$

Eliminate the x^2–terms by multiplying the first equation by –3 and adding the resulting equations.

$-3x^2+12y^2=21$

$\underline{3x^2+y^2=31}$

$13y^2=52$

$y^2=4$

$y=\pm2$

If $y=2$,

$x^2-4(2)^2=-7$

$x^2=9$

$x=\pm3$

If $y=-2$,

$x^2-4(-2)^2=-7$

$x^2=9$

$x=\pm3$

The solution set is

$\{(3,2),(3,-2),(-3,2),(-3,-2)\}$.

23. Arrange the equations so that variable terms appear on the left and constants appear on the right.

$3x^2+4y^2=16$

$2x^2-3y^2=5$

Eliminate the y^2–terms by multiplying the first equation by 3 and the second equation by 4. Add the resulting equations.

$9x^2+12y^2=48$

$\underline{8x^2-12y^2=20}$

$17x^2=68$

$x^2=4$

$x=\pm2$

If $x=2$,

$3(2)^2+4y^2=16$

$y^2=1$

$y=\pm1$

If $x=-2$,

$3(-2)^2+4y^2=16$

$y=\pm1$

The solution set is

$\{(2, 1), (2, -1), (-2, 1), (-2, -1)\}$.

25. $x^2 + y^2 = 25$
$(x-8)^2 + y^2 = 41$
Expand the second equation and eliminate x^2 and y^2–terms by multiplying the first equation by –1 and adding the resulting equations.

$$\begin{aligned} x^2 - 16x + 64 + y^2 &= 41 \\ -x^2 - y^2 &= -25 \\ \hline -16x + 64 &= 16 \\ -16x &= -48 \\ x &= 3 \end{aligned}$$

If $x = 3$,

$$\begin{aligned} (3)^2 + y^2 &= 25 \\ y^2 &= 16 \\ y &= \pm 4 \end{aligned}$$

The solution set is $\{(3, 4), (3, -4)\}$.

27. $y^2 - x = 4$
$x^2 + y^2 = 4$
Eliminate the y^2–terms by multiplying the first equation by –1 and adding the resulting equations.

$$\begin{aligned} x - y^2 &= -4 \\ x^2 + y^2 &= 4 \\ \hline x^2 + x &= 0 \end{aligned}$$

$$x(x+1) = 0$$

$x = 0$ or $x + 1 = 0$
$x = -1$

If $x = 0$,

$$\begin{aligned} y^2 &= 4 \\ y &= \pm 2 \end{aligned}$$

If $x = -1$,

$$\begin{aligned} y^2 - (-1) &= 4 \\ y^2 &= 3 \\ y &= \pm\sqrt{3} \end{aligned}$$

The solution set is
$\{(0, 2), (0, -2), (-1, \sqrt{3}), (-1, -\sqrt{3})\}$.

29. The addition method is used here to solve the system.
$3x^2 + 4y^2 = 16$
$2x^2 - 3y^2 = 5$
Eliminate the y^2–terms by multiplying the first equation by 3 and the second equation by 4. Add the resulting equations.

$$\begin{aligned} 9x^2 + 12y^2 &= 48 \\ 8x^2 - 12y^2 &= 20 \\ \hline 17x^2 &= 68 \\ x^2 &= 4 \\ x &= \pm 2 \end{aligned}$$

If $x = 2$,

$$\begin{aligned} 3(2)^2 + 4y^2 &= 16 \\ y^2 &= 1 \\ y &= \pm 1 \end{aligned}$$

If $x = -2$,

$$\begin{aligned} 3(-2)^2 + 4y^2 &= 16 \\ y &= \pm 1 \end{aligned}$$

The solution set is
$\{(2, 1), (2, -1), (-2, 1), (-2, -1)\}$.

31. The substitution method is used here to solve the system.

$2x^2 + y^2 = 18$

$xy = 4$

Solve the second equation for y.

$y = \frac{4}{x}$

Substitute the expression $\frac{4}{x}$ for y in the first equation and solve for x.

$$2x^2 + \left(\frac{4}{x}\right)^2 = 18$$

$$2x^2 + \frac{16}{x^2} = 18$$

$$2x^4 + 16 = 18x^2$$

$$x^4 - 9x^2 + 8 = 0$$

$$\left(x^2 - 8\right)\left(x^2 - 1\right) = 0$$

$x^2 - 8 = 0$ or $x^2 - 1 = 0$

$x^2 = 8$ or $x^2 = 1$

$x = \pm 2\sqrt{2}$ or $x = \pm 1$

If $x = 2\sqrt{2}$, $y = \frac{4}{2\sqrt{2}} = \sqrt{2}$.

If $x = -2\sqrt{2}$, $y = \frac{4}{-2\sqrt{2}} = -\sqrt{2}$.

If $x = 1$, $y = \frac{4}{1} = 4$.

If $x = -1$, $y = \frac{4}{-1} = -4$.

The solution set is

$\left\{\left(2\sqrt{2}, \sqrt{2}\right), \left(-2\sqrt{2}, -\sqrt{2}\right), (1, 4), (-1, -4)\right\}$.

33. The substitution method is used here to solve the system.

$x^2 + 4y^2 = 20$

$x + 2y = 6$

Solve the second equation for x.

$x = 6 - 2y$

Substitute the expression $6 - 2y$ for x in the first equation and solve for y.

$$(6 - 2y)^2 + 4y^2 = 20$$

$$36 - 24y + 4y^2 + 4y^2 - 20 = 0$$

$$8y^2 - 24y + 16 = 0$$

$$y^2 - 3y + 2 = 0$$

$$(y - 2)(y - 1) = 0$$

$y - 2 = 0$ or $y - 1 = 0$

$y = 2$ or $y = 1$

If $y = 2, x = 6 - 2(2) = 2$.

If $y = 1, x = 6 - 2(1) = 4$.

The solution set is $\{(2, 2), (4, 1)\}$.

35. Eliminate y by adding the equations.

$$\begin{array}{r} x^3 + y = 0 \\ x^2 - y = 0 \\ \hline x^3 + x^2 = 0 \end{array}$$

$x^2(x + 1) = 0$

$x^2 = 0$ or $x + 1 = 0$

$x = 0$ or $x = -1$

If $x = 0$,

$(0)^3 + y = 0$

$y = 0$

If $x = -1$,

$(-1)^3 + y = 0$

$y = 1$

The solution set is $\{(0, 0), (-1, 1)\}$.

37. The substitution method is used here to solve the system.

$x^2+(y-2)^2=4$

$x^2-2y=0$

Solve the second equation for x^2.

$x^2=2y$

Substitute the expression $2y$ for x^2 in the first equation and solve for y.

$$2y+(y-2)^2=4$$
$$2y+y^2-4y+4=4$$
$$y^2-2y=0$$
$$y(y-2)=0$$
$$y=0 \quad \text{or} \quad y-2=0$$
$$y=2$$

If $y=0$,

$x^2=2(0)$

$x^2=0$

$x=0$

If $y=2$,

$x^2=2(2)$

$x^2=4$

$x=\pm 2$

The solution set is $\{(0, 0), (-2, 2), (2, 2)\}$.

39. The substitution method is used here to solve the system.

$y=(x+3)^2$

$x+2y=-2$

Solve the first equation for x.

$x=-2y-2$

Substitute the expression $-2y-2$ for x in the first equation and solve for y.

$$y=(-2y-2+3)^2=(-2y+1)^2$$
$$y=4y^2-4y+1$$
$$4y^2-5y+1=0$$
$$(4y-1)(y-1)=0$$
$$4y-1=0 \quad \text{or} \quad y-1=0$$
$$y=\frac{1}{4} \quad \text{or} \quad y=1$$

If $y=\frac{1}{4}$, $x=-2\left(\frac{1}{4}\right)-2=-\frac{5}{2}$.

If $y=1$, $x=-2(1)-2=-4$.

The solution set is $\left\{(-4, 1), \left(-\frac{5}{2}, \frac{1}{4}\right)\right\}$.

41. The substitution method is used here to solve the system.

$x^2+y^2+3y=22$

$2x+y=-1$

Solve the second equation for y.

$y=-2x-1$

Substitute the expression $-2x-1$ for y in the first equation and solve for x.

$$x^2+(-2x-1)^2+3(-2x-1)-22=0$$
$$x^2+4x^2+4x+1-6x-3-22=0$$
$$5x^2-2x-24=0$$
$$(5x-12)(x+2)=0$$
$$5x-12=0 \quad \text{or} \quad x+2=0$$
$$x=\frac{12}{5} \quad \text{or} \quad x=-2$$

If $x=\frac{12}{5}$, $y=-2\left(\frac{12}{5}\right)-1=-\frac{29}{5}$.

If $x=-2$, $y=-2(-2)-1=3$.

The solution set is $\left\{\left(\frac{12}{5}, -\frac{29}{5}\right), (-2, 3)\right\}$.

43. The substitution method is used here to solve the system.

$x+y=10$

$xy=24$

Solve the first equation for y.

$y=10-x$

Substitute the expression $10-x$ for y in the second equation and solve for x.

$$x(10-x)=24$$
$$10x-x^2=24$$
$$x^2-10x+24=0$$
$$(x-4)(x-6)=0$$
$$x-4=0 \quad \text{or} \quad x-6=0$$
$$x=4 \quad \text{or} \quad x=6$$

If $x=4$, $y=10-4=6$.

If $x=6$, $y=10-6=4$.

The numbers are 4 and 6.

45. Eliminate the y^2–terms by adding the equations.

$$x^2 - y^2 = 3$$
$$\underline{2x^2 + y^2 = 9}$$
$$3x^2 = 12$$
$$x^2 = 4$$
$$x = \pm 2$$

If $x = 2$,

$$2(2)^2 + y^2 = 9$$
$$y^2 = 1$$
$$y = \pm 1$$

If $x = -2$,

$$2(-2)^2 + y^2 = 9$$
$$y^2 = 1$$
$$y = \pm 1$$

The numbers are 2 and 1, 2 and –1, –2 and 1, or –2 and –1.

47. $16x^2 + 4y^2 = 64$
$y = x^2 - 4$

Substitute the expression $x^2 - 4$ for y in the first equation and solve for x.

$$16x^2 + 4\left(x^2 - 4\right)^2 = 64$$
$$16x^2 + 4\left(x^4 - 8x^2 + 16\right) = 64$$
$$16x^2 + 4x^4 - 32x^2 + 64 = 64$$
$$4x^4 - 16x^2 = 0$$
$$x^4 - 4x^2 = 0$$
$$x^2\left(x^2 - 4\right) = 0$$

$x^2 = 0$ or $x^2 - 4 = 0$
$x = 0$ or $x^2 = 4$
$x = \pm 2$

If $x = 0$, $y = (0)^2 - 4 = -4$.
If $x = 2$, $y = (2)^2 - 4 = 0$.
If $x = -2$, $y = (-2)^2 - 4 = 0$.

It is possible for the comet to intersect the orbiting body at (0, –4), (–2, 0), (2, 0).

49. $2L + 2W = 36$
$LW = 77$

Divide each term in the first equation by 2 and solve L.

$$L + W = 18$$
$$L = 18 - W$$

Substitute the expression $18 - W$ for L in the second equation and solve for W.

$$(18 - W)W = 77$$
$$18W - W^2 = 77$$
$$W^2 - 18W + 77 = 0$$
$$(W - 11)(W - 7) = 0$$

$W - 11 = 0$ or $W - 7 = 0$
$W = 11$ or $W = 7$

If $W = 11$, $L = 18 - 11 = 7$.
If $W = 7$, $L = 18 - 7 = 11$.

The dimensions are 11 feet by 7 feet.

51. $L^2 + W^2 = 10^2 = 100$
$LW = 48$

Solve the second equation for L. $L = \dfrac{48}{W}$

Substitute the expression $\dfrac{48}{W}$ for L in the first equation and solve for W.

$$\left(\frac{48}{W}\right)^2 + W^2 = 100$$
$$\frac{2304}{W^2} + W^2 - 100 = 0$$
$$2304 + W^4 - 100W^2 = 0$$
$$W^4 - 100W^2 + 2304 = 0$$
$$\left(W^2 - 36\right)\left(W^2 - 64\right) = 0$$

$W^2 - 36 = 0$ or $W^2 - 64 = 0$
$W^2 = 36$ or $W^2 = 64$
$W = \pm 6$ or $W = \pm 8$

The width cannot be –6 or –8 inches.

If $W = 6$,

$$L = \frac{48}{6} = 8$$

If $W = 8$,

$$L = \frac{48}{8} = 6$$

The dimensions are 8 inches by 6 inches.

53. $x^2 - y^2 = 21$
$4x + 2y = 24$
Divide each term in the second equation by 2 and solve for y.
$2x + y = 12$
$y = 12 - 2x$
Substitute the expression $12 - 2x$ for y in the first equation and solve for x.

$$x^2 - (12 - 2x)^2 = 21$$
$$x^2 - \left(144 - 48x + 4x^2\right) = 21$$
$$3x^2 - 48x + 165 = 0$$
$$x^2 - 16x + 55 = 0$$
$$(x - 5)(x - 11) = 0$$
$$x - 5 = 0 \quad \text{or} \quad x - 11 = 0$$
$$x = 5 \quad \text{or} \quad x = 11$$

If $x = 11,\ y = 12 - 2(11) = -10$.
If $x = 5,\ y = 12 - 2(5) = 2$.
The dimensions of the floor are 5 meters by 5 meters and the dimensions of the square that will accomodate the pool are 2 meters by 2 meters.

55.–57. Answers may vary.

59. Exercise 1

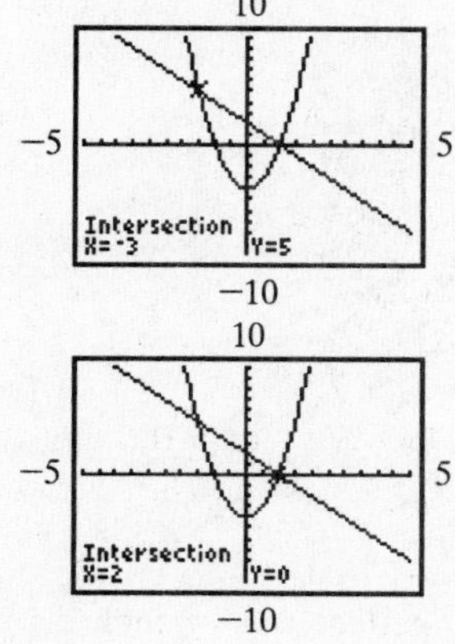

Exercise 3

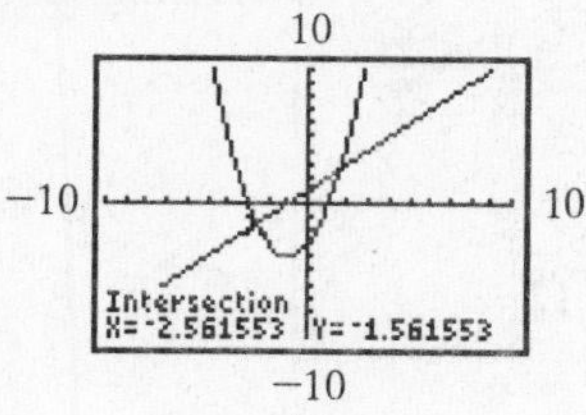

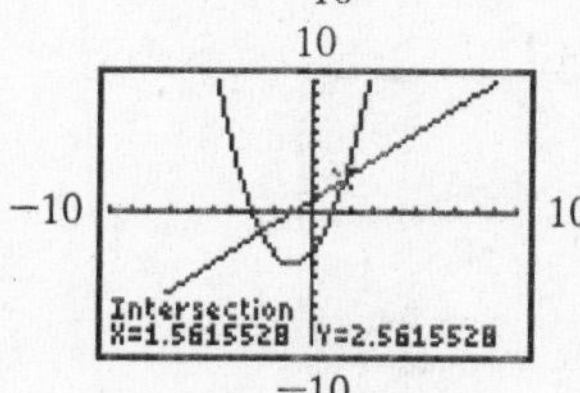

Exercise 5

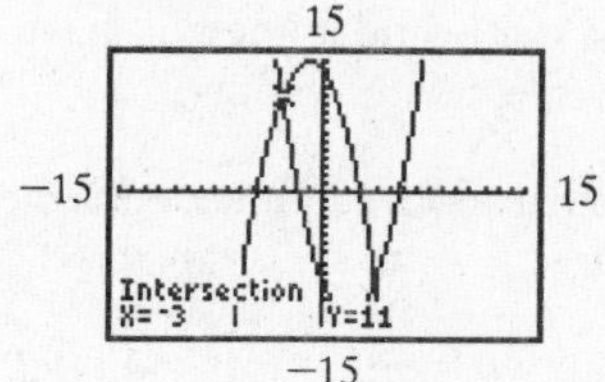

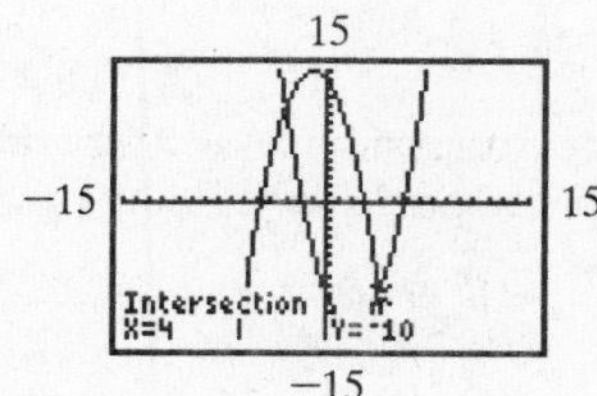

Exercise 7

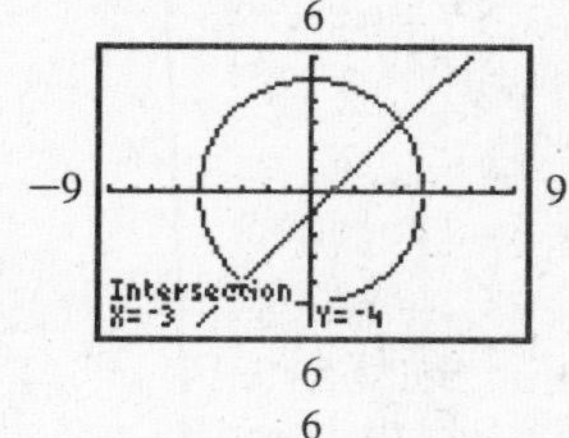

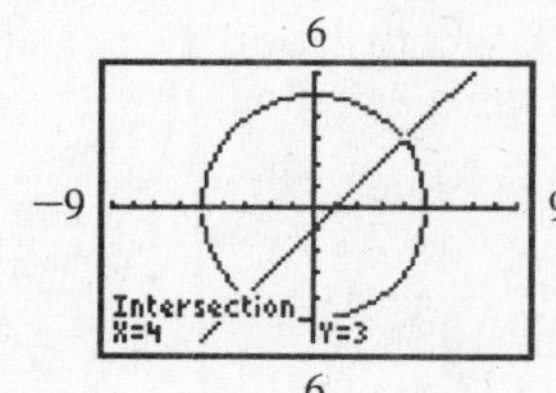

Exercise 9

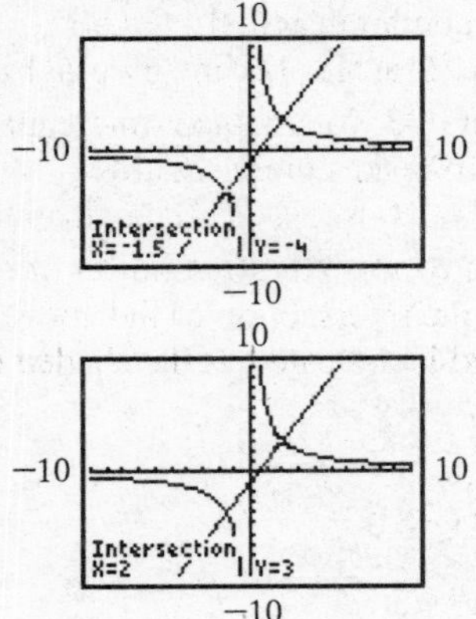

61. a. False; a circle and a line will have at most 2 intersection points.

b. True; a parabola can intersect a circle in 4 points.

c. False; It is possible for two circles to not intersect.

d. False; A circle can intersect a parabola at one point. See Check Point 4 for an example.

(b) is true.

63. By the Pythagorean Theorem:

$a^2 + b^2 = 10^2 = 100$

$a^2 + (b+9)^2 = 17^2$

Expand the second equation.

$a^2 + b^2 + 18b + 81 = 289$

Eliminate the a^2 and b^2–terms by multiplying the first equation by –1 and adding the resulting equations.

$$\begin{aligned} a^2 + b^2 + 18b &= 208 \\ -a^2 - b^2 &= -100 \\ \hline 18b &= 108 \\ b &= 6 \end{aligned}$$

$$\begin{aligned} a^2 + (6)^2 &= 100 \\ a^2 &= 64 \\ a &= 8 \end{aligned}$$

65. $\log x^2 = y + 3$

$\log x = y - 1$

$10^{y+3} = x^2$

$10^{y-1} = x$

Substitute the expression 10^{y-1} for x in the equation $10^{y+3} = x^2$ and solve for y.

$10^{y+3} = \left(10^{y-1}\right)^2$

$10^{y+3} = 10^{2y-2}$

$y + 3 = 2y - 2$

$y = 5$

$x = 10^{5-1} = 10,000$

The solution set is $\{(10,000, 5)\}$.

Section 5.5

Check Point Exercises

1. $2x - 4y < 8$

Graph $2x - 4y = 8$ as a dashed line using its x-intercept (4, 0), and its y-intercept (0, –2).

Test (0, 0):

$2(0) - 4(0) < 8$?

$0 < 8$ true

Shade the half-plane containing (0, 0).

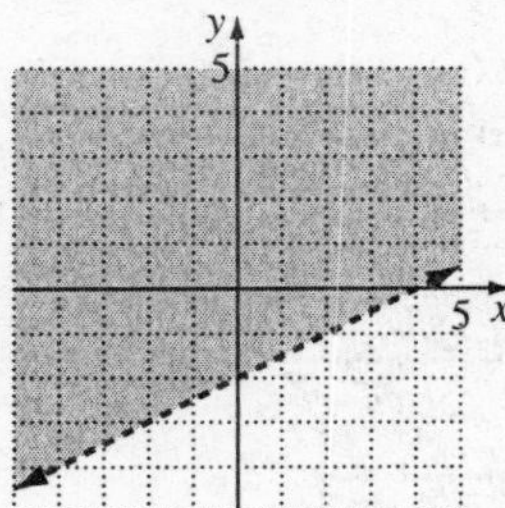

2. $y \ge \frac{1}{2}x$

Graph $y = \frac{1}{2}x$ as a solid line by using its slope, $\frac{1}{2}$, and its y-intercept (0, 0).

Test (1, 1):

$1 \ge \frac{1}{2}(1)?$

$1 \ge \frac{1}{2}$ true

Shade the half plane containing (1, 1).

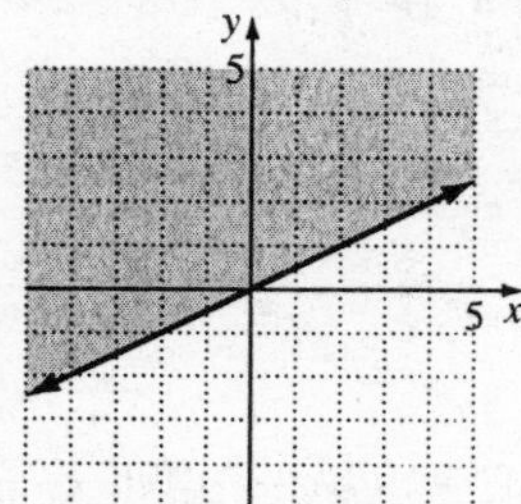

3. $x^2 + y^2 \ge 16$

Graph $x^2 + y^2 = 16$ as a solid circle with radius 4 and center (0, 0).

Test (0, 0):

$(0)^2 + (0)^2 \ge 16?$

$0 \ge 16$ false

Shade the half plane not containing (0, 0).

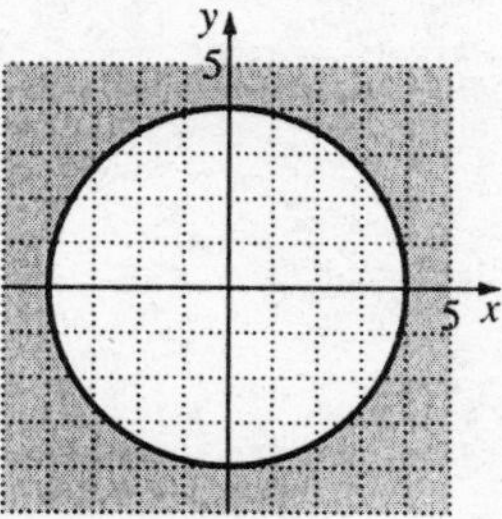

4. $x + 2y > 4$

$2x - 3y \le -6$

Begin by graphing $x + 2y = 4$ as a dashed line by using its x-intercept, (4, 0), and its y-intercept (0, 2). Since (0, 0) makes the inequality $x + 2y > 4$ false, shade the half-plane not containing (0, 0). Graph $2x - 3y = -6$ as a solid line by graphing its x-intercept, (–3, 0), and its y-intercept (0, 2). Since (0, 0) makes the inequality $2x - 3y \le -6$ false, shade the half-plane not containing (0, 0). The solution set of the system is the intersection of the above half-planes, and is indicated as the shaded region in the following graph.

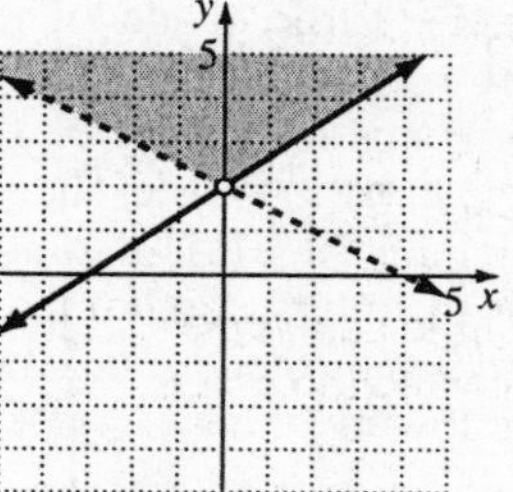

5. $y \ge x^2 - 4$

$x + y \le 2$

Begin by graphing $y = x^2 - 4$ as a solid parabola with vertex (0, –4) and x-intercepts (–2, 0) and (2, 0). Since (0, 0) makes the inequality $y \ge x^2 - 4$ true, shade the half-plane containing (0, 0). Graph $x + y = 2$ as a solid line by using its x-intercept, (2, 0), and its y-intercept (0, 2). Since (0, 0) makes the inequality $x + y \le 2$ true, shade the half-plane containing (0, 0). The solution set of the system is the intersection of the above half-planes, and is indicated as the shaded region in the following graph.

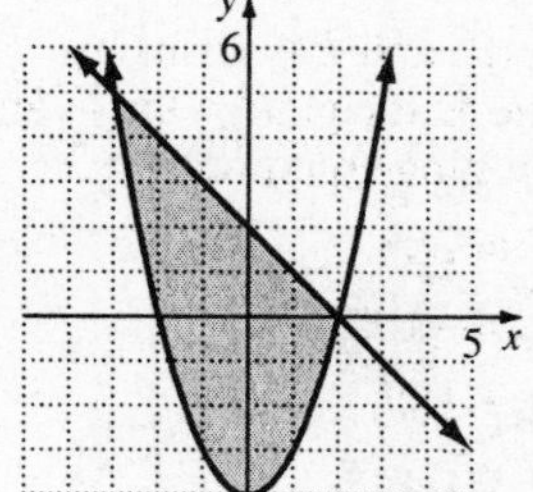

6. $x + y < 2$
$-2 \le x < 1$
$y > -3$
Begin by graphing $x + y = 2$ as a dashed line by using its x-intercept, (2, 0), and its y-intercept (0, 2). Since (0, 0) makes the inequality $x + y < 2$ true, shade the half-plane containing (0, 0). Graph $x = -2$ as a solid vertical line and $x = 1$ as a dashed vertical line. Since (0, 0) makes the inequality $-2 \le x < 1$ true, shade the region between the two vertical lines. Graph $y = -3$ as a dashed horizontal line. Since (0, 0) makes the inequality $y > -3$ true, shade the half-plane containing (0, 0). The solution set of the system is the intersection of the above half-planes, and is indicated as the shaded region in the following graph.

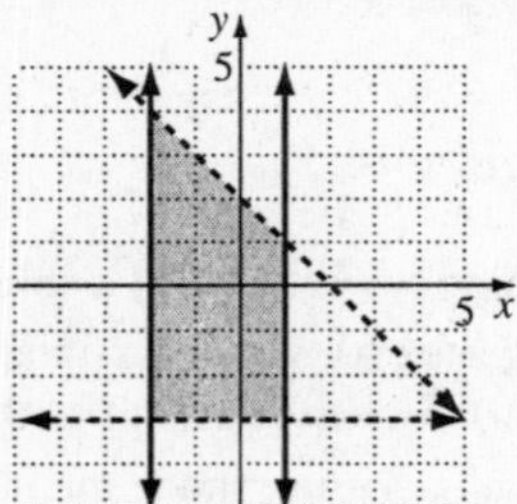

7. Answers may vary.

Exercise Set 5.5

1. $x + 2y \le 8$
Graph $x + 2y = 8$ as a solid line using its x-intercept, (8, 0), and its y-intercept, (0, 4).
Test (0, 0):
$0 + 2(0) \le 8$?
$0 \le 8$ true
Shade the half-plane containing (0, 0).

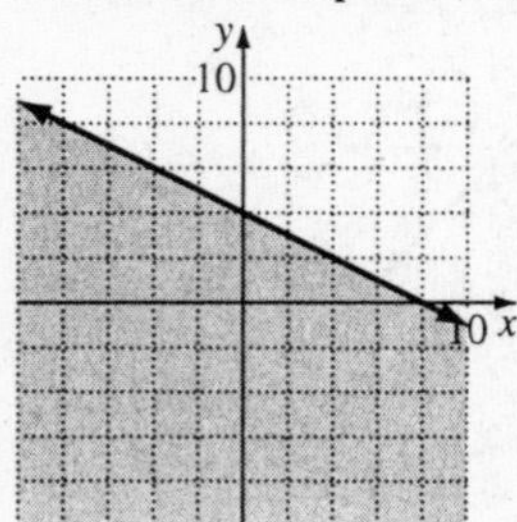

3. $x - 2y > 10$
Graph $x - 2y = 10$ as a dashed line using its x-intercept, (10, 0), and its y-intercept, (0, –5).
Test (0, 0):
$0 - 2(0) > 10$?
$0 > 10$ false
Shade the half-plane not containing (0, 0).

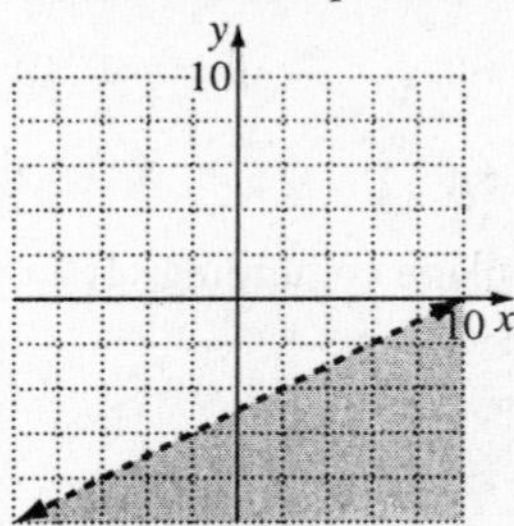

5. $y \le \frac{1}{3}x$

Graph $y = \frac{1}{3}x$ as a solid line using its slope, $\frac{1}{3}$, and its y-intercept (0, 0).
Test (1, 1):
$1 \le \frac{1}{3}(1)$?
$1 \le \frac{1}{3}$ false
Shade the half-plane not containing (1, 1).

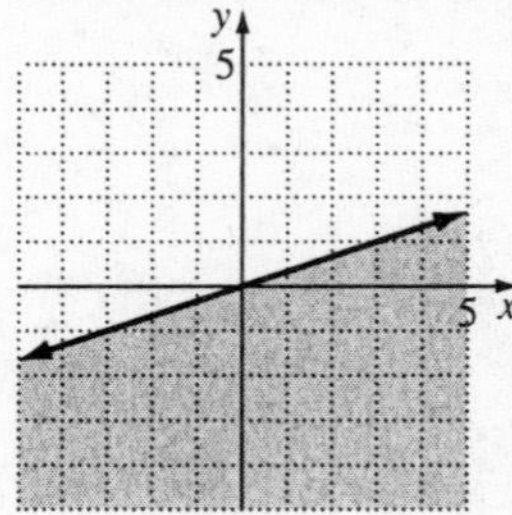

7. $y > 2x - 1$
Graph $y = 2x - 1$ as a dashed line using its x-intercept, $\left(\frac{1}{2}, 0\right)$ and its y-intercept, $(0, -1)$.
Test (0,0):
$0 > 2(0) - 1$?
$0 > -1$ true
Shade the half-plane containing (0, 0).

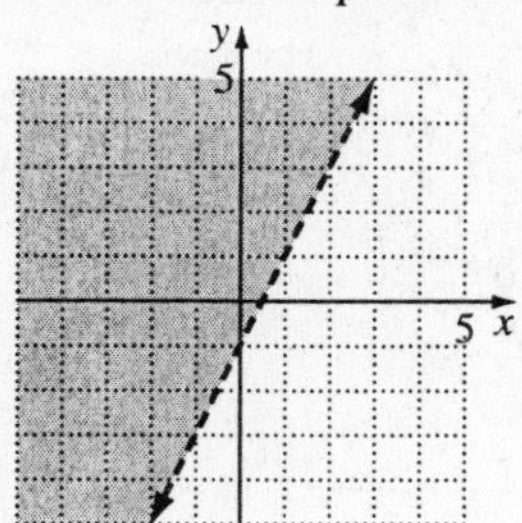

9. $x \le 1$
Graph $x = 1$ as a solid vertical line.
Test (0, 0):
$0 \le 1$ true
Shade the half-plane containing (0, 0).

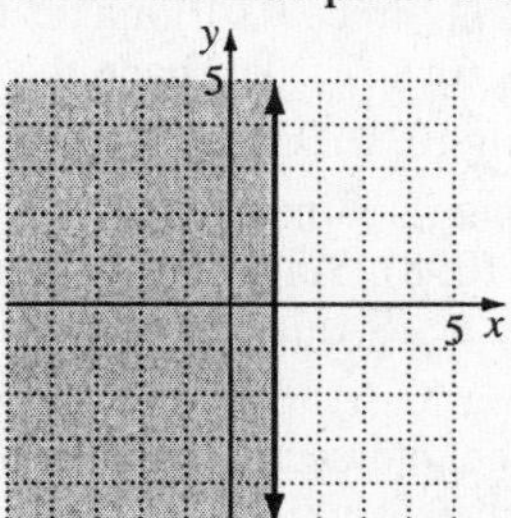

11. $y > 1$
Graph $y = 1$ as a dashed horizontal line.
Test (0, 0):
$0 > 1$ false
Shade the half-plane not containing (0, 0).

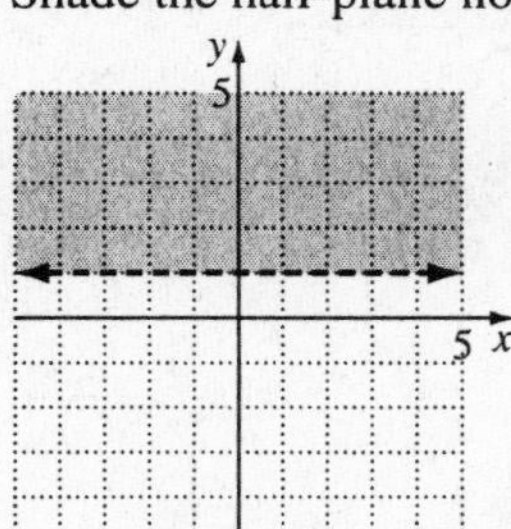

13. $x^2 + y^2 \le 1$
Graph $x^2 + y^2 = 1$ as a solid circle with radius 1 and center (0, 0).
Test (0, 0):
$(0)^2 + (0)^2 \le 1$?
$0 \le 1$ true
Shade the half-plane containing (0, 0).

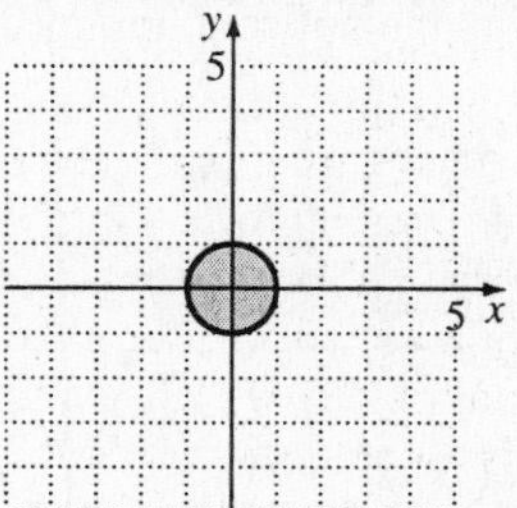

15. $x^2 + y^2 > 25$
Graph $x^2 + y^2 = 25$ as a dashed circle with radius 5 and center (0, 0).
Test (0, 0):
$(0)^2 + (0)^2 > 25$?
$0 > 25$ false
Shade the half-plane not containing (0, 0).

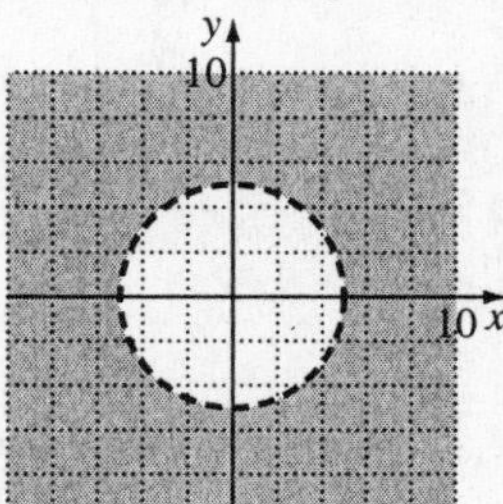

17. $y < x^2 - 1$

Graph $y = x^2 - 1$ as a dashed parabola with vertex (0, –1) and x-intercepts (1, 0) and (–1, 0).
Test (0, 0):
$0 < (0)^2 - 1$?
$0 < -1$ false
Shade the half-plane not containing (0, 0).

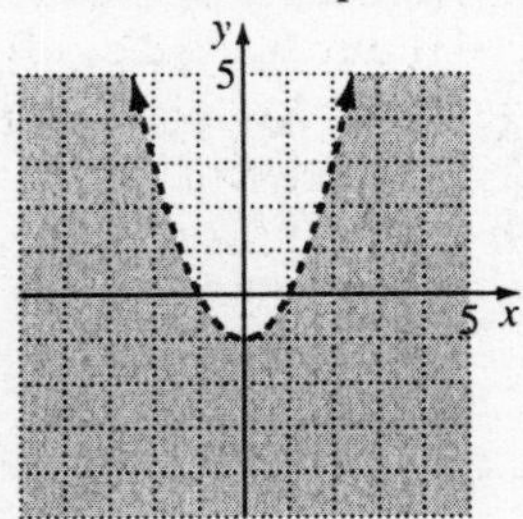

19. $y \geq x^2 - 9$

Graph $y = x^2 - 9$ as a solid parabola with vertex (0, –9) and x-intercepts (3, 0) and (–3, 0).
Test (0, 0):
$0 \geq (0)^2 - 9$?
$0 \geq -9$ true
Shade the half-plane containing (0, 0).

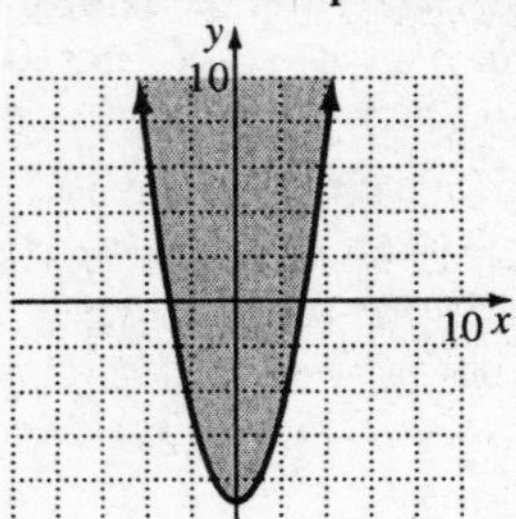

21. $y > 2^x$

Graph $y = 2^x$ as a dashed exponental function with base 2 that passes through the point (0, 1).
Test (0, 0):
$0 > 2^0$?
$0 > 1$ false
Shade the half-plane not containing (0, 0).

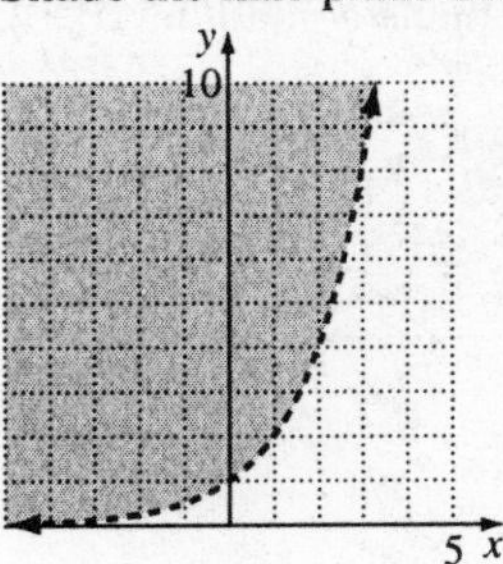

23. $3x + 6y \leq 6$
$2x + y \leq 8$

Begin by graphing $3x + 6y = 6$ as a solid line using its x-intercept, (2, 0), and its y-intercept, (0, 1). Since (0, 0) makes the inequality $3x + 6y \leq 6$ true, shade the half-plane containing (0, 0). Graph $2x + y = 8$ as a solid line using its x-intercept, (4, 0), and its y-intercept, (0, 8). Since (0, 0) makes the inequality $2x + y \leq 8$ true, shade the half-plane containing (0, 0). The solution set of the system is the intersection of the above shaded half-planes, and is shown as the shaded region in the following graph.

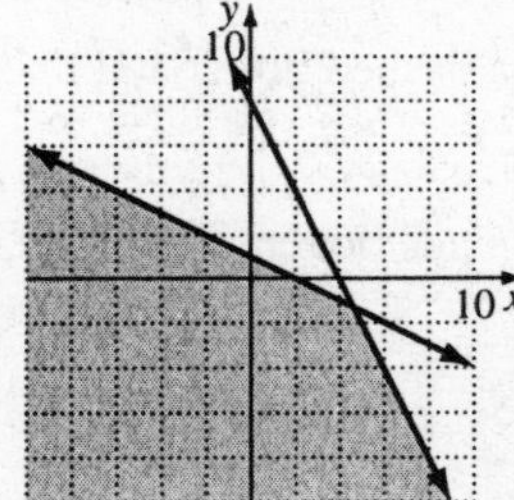

25. $2x - 5y \le 10$
$3x - 2y > 6$
Begin by graphing $2x - 5y = 10$ as a solid line using its x-intercept, (5, 0), and its y-intercept, (0, –2). Since (0, 0) makes the inequality $2x - 5y \le 10$ true, shade the half-plane containing (0, 0). Graph $3x - 2y = 6$ as a dashed line using its x-intercept, (2, 0), and its y-intercept, (0, –3). Since (0, 0) makes the inequality $3x - 2y > 6$ false, shade the half-plane containing (0, 0). The solution set of the system is the intersection of the above shaded half-planes, and is shown as the shaded region in the following graph.

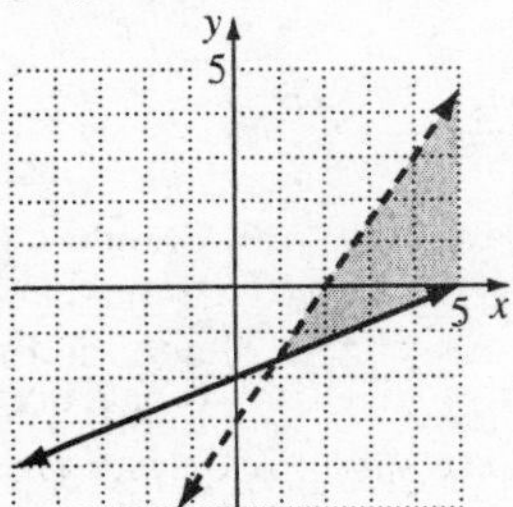

27. $y > 2x - 3$
$y < -x + 6$
Begin by graphing $y = 2x - 3$ as a dashed line using its slope, 2, and its y-intercept, (0, –3). Since (0, 0) makes the inequality $y > 2x - 3$ true, shade the half-plane containing (0, 0). Graph $y = -x + 6$ as a dashed line using its slope, –1, and its y-intercept, (0, 6). Since (0, 0) makes the inequality $y < -x + 6$ true, shade the half-plane containing (0, 0). The solution set of the system is the intersection of the above shaded half-planes, and is shown as the shaded region in the following graph.

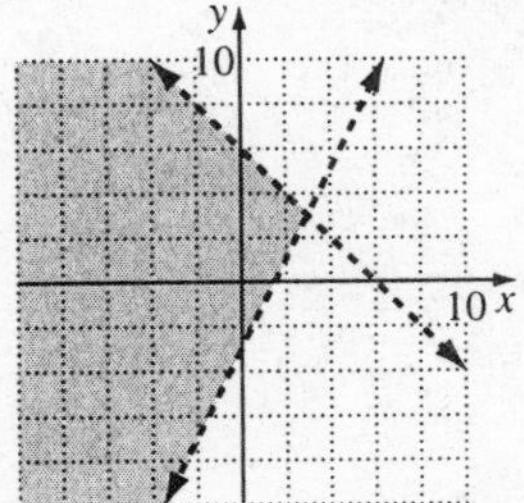

29. $x + 2y \le 4$
$y \ge x - 3$
Begin by graphing $x + 2y = 4$ as a solid line using its x-intercept, (4, 0), and its y-intercept, (0, 2). Since (0, 0) makes the inequality $x + 2y \le 4$ true, shade the half-plane containing (0, 0). Graph $y = x - 3$ as a solid line using its slope, 1, and its y-intercept, (0, –3). Since (0, 0) makes the inequality $y \ge x - 3$ true, shade the half-plane containing (0, 0). The solution set of the system is the intersection of the above shaded half-planes, and is shown as the shaded region in the following graph.

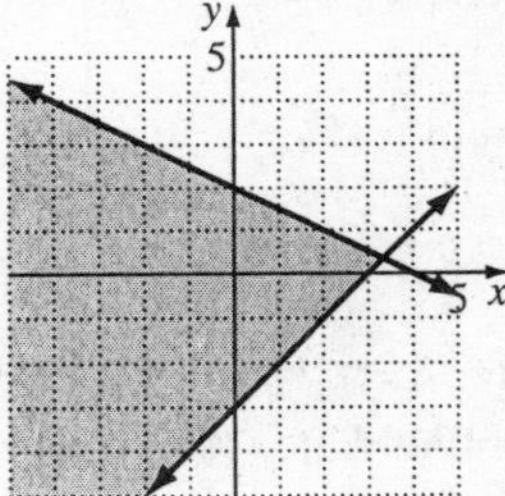

31. $x \le 2$
$y \ge -1$
Begin by graphing $x = 2$ as a solid vertical line . Since (0, 0) makes the inequality $x \le 2$ true, shade the half-plane containing (0, 0). Graph $y = 1$ as a solid horizontal line. Since (0, 0) makes the inequality $y \ge -1$ true, shade the half-plane containing (0, 0). The solution set of the system is the intersection of the above shaded half-planes, and is shown as the shaded region in the following graph.

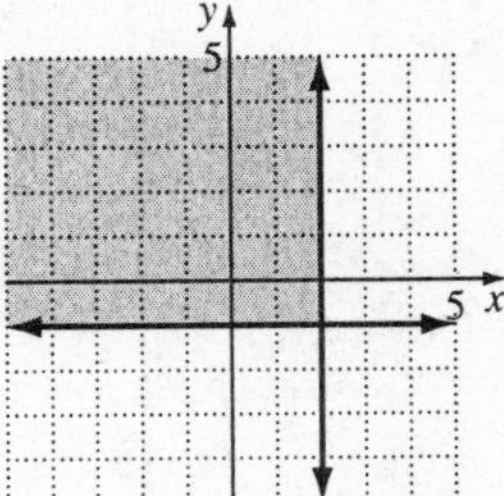

33. $-2 \le x < 5$
Graph $x = -2$ as a solid vertical line and $x = 5$ as a dashed vertical line. Since (0, 0) makes the inequality $-2 \le x < 5$ true, shade the region between the two lines.

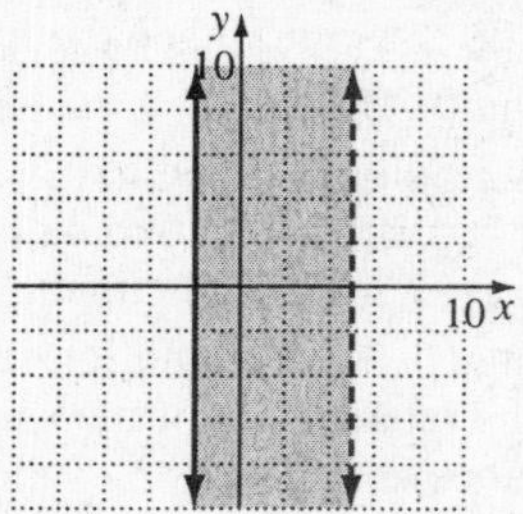

35. $x - y \le 1$
$x \ge 2$
Begin by graphing $x - y = 1$ as a solid line using its x-intercept, (1, 0), and its y-intercept (0, -1). Since (0, 0) makes the inequality $x - y \le 1$ true, shade the half-plane containing (0, 0). Graph $x = 2$ as a solid horizontal line. Since (0, 0) makes the inequality $x \ge 2$ false, shade the half-plane not containing (0, 0). The solution set of the system is the intersection of the above shaded half-planes, and is shown as the shaded region in the following graph.

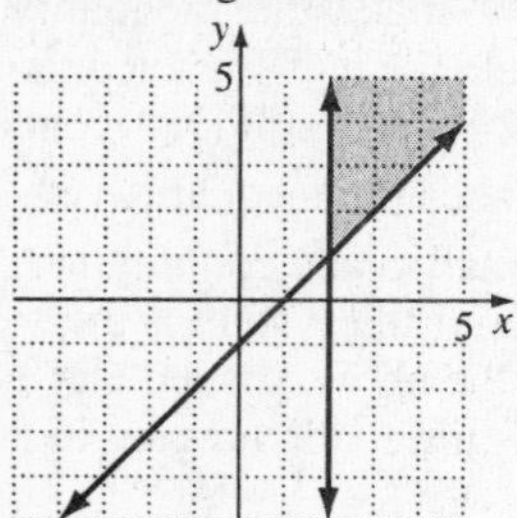

37. $x + y > 4$
$x + y < -1$
Begin by graphing $x + y = 4$ as a dashed line using its x-intercept, (4, 0), and its y-intercept (0, 4). Since (0, 0) makes the inequality $x + y > 4$ false, shade the half-plane not containing (0, 0). Graph $x + y = -1$ as a dashed line using its x-intercept, (–1, 0), and its y-intercept, (0, –1). Since (0, 0) makes the inequality $x + y < -1$ false, shade the half-plane not containing (0, 0). The solution set of the system is the intersection of the above half-planes. Since these half-planes do not intersect the system has no solution.

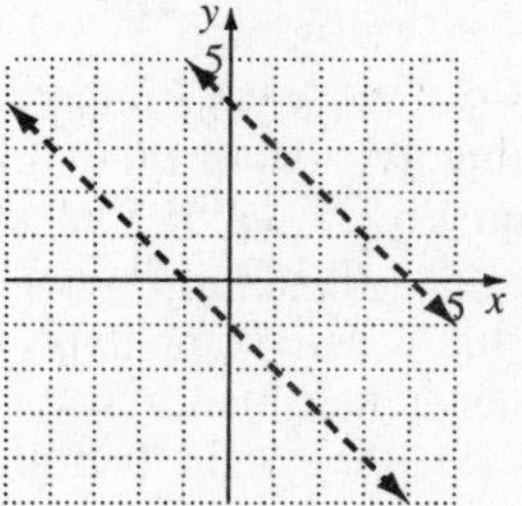

39. $x + y > 4$
$x + y > -1$
Begin by graphing $x + y = 4$ as a dashed line using its x-intercept, (4, 0), and its y-intercept, (0, 4). Since (0, 0) makes the inequality $x + y > 4$ false, shade the half-plane not containing (0, 0). Graph $x + y = -1$ as a dashed line using its x-intercept, (-1, 0), and its y-intercept, (0, –1). Since (0, 0) makes the inequality $x + y > -1$ true, shade the half-plane containing (0, 0). The solution set of the system is the intersection of the above half-planes, and is shown as the shaded region in the following graph.

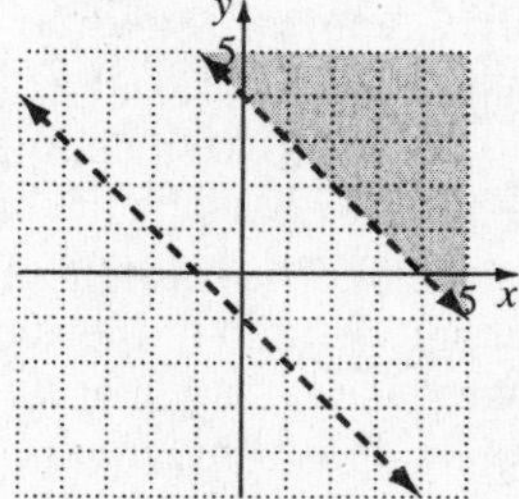

41. $y \ge x^2 - 1$
$x - y \ge -1$

Begin by graphing $y = x^2 - 1$ as a solid parabola with vertex (0, –1) and x-intercepts, (–1, 0), and (1, 0). Since (0, 0) makes the inequality $y \ge x^2 - 1$ true, shade the half-plane containing (0, 0). Graph $x - y = -1$ as a solid line using its x-intercept, (–1, 0), and its y-intercept, (0, 1). Since (0, 0) makes the inequality $x - y \ge -1$ true, shade the half-plane containing (0, 0). The solution set of the system is the intersection of the above half-planes, and is shown as the shaded region in the following graph.

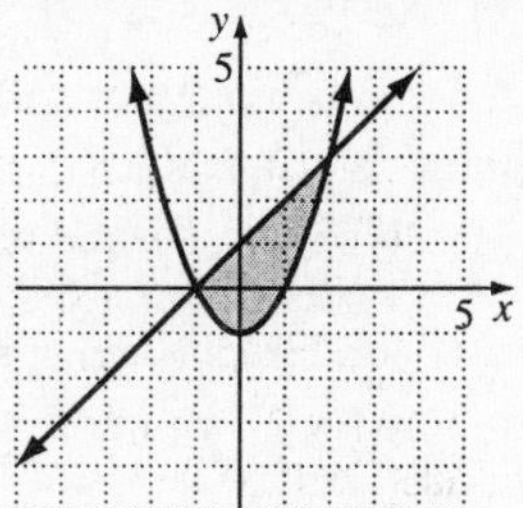

43. $x^2 + y^2 \le 16$
$x + y > 2$

Begin by graphing $x^2 + y^2 = 16$ as a solid circle with radius 4 and center, (0, 0). Since (0, 0) makes the inequality $x^2 + y^2 \le 16$ true, shade the half-plane containing (0, 0). Graph $x + y = 2$ as a dashed line using its x-intercept, (2, 0), and its y-intercept, (0, 2). Since (0, 0) makes the inequality $x + y > 2$ false, shade the half-plane not containing (0, 0). The solution set of the system is the intersection of the above half-planes, and is shown as the shaded region in the following graph.

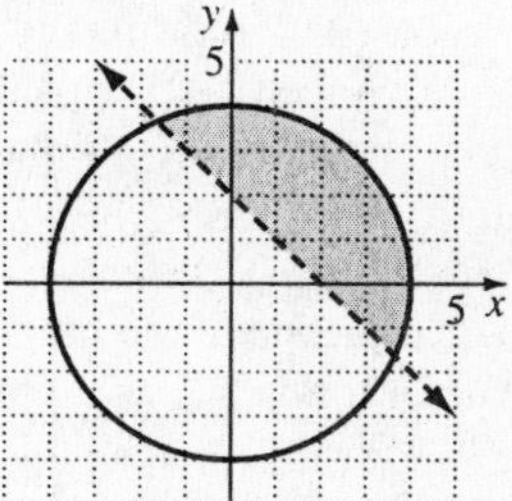

45. $x^2 + y^2 > 1$
$x^2 + y^2 < 4$

Begin by graphing $x^2 + y^2 = 1$ as a dashed circle with radius 1 and center, (0, 0). Since (0, 0) makes the inequality $x^2 + y^2 > 1$ false, shade the half-plane not containing (0, 0). Graph $x^2 + y^2 = 4$ as a dashed circle with radius 2 and center (0, 0). Since (0, 0) makes the inequality $x^2 + y^2 < 4$ true, shade the half-plane containing (0, 0). The solution set of the system is the intersection of the above half-planes, and is shown as the shaded region in the following graph.

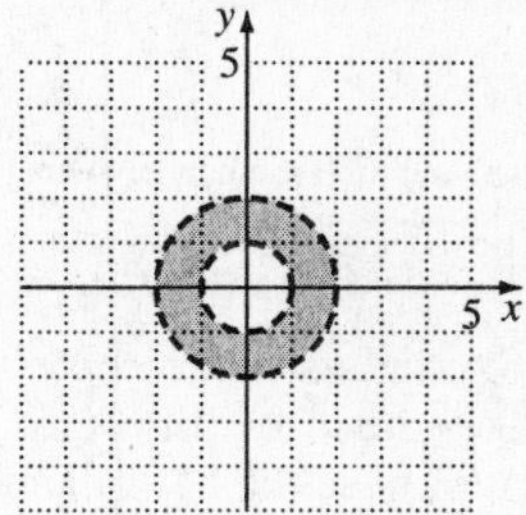

47. $x - y \le 2$
$x \ge -2$
$y \le 3$
Begin by graphing $x - y = 2$ as a solid line using its x-intercept, (2, 0), and its y-intercept, (0, –2). Since (0, 0) makes the inequality $x - y \le 2$ true, shade the half-plane containing (0, 0). Graph $x = -2$ as a solid vertical line. Since (0, 0) makes the inequality $x \ge -2$ true, shade the half-plane containing (0, 0). Graph $y = 3$ as a solid horizontal line. Since (0, 0) makes the inequality $y \le 3$ true, shade the half-plane containing (0, 0).The solution set of the system is the intersection of the above half-planes, and is shown as the shaded region in the following graph.

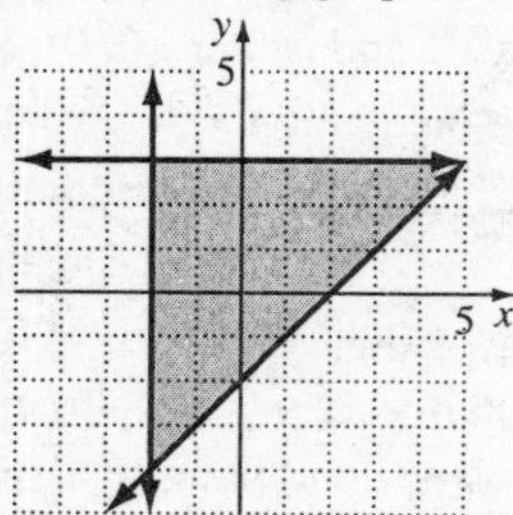

49. $x \ge 0$
$y \ge 0$
$2x + 5y \le 10$
$3x + 4y \le 12$
Since $x \ge 0$ and $y \ge 0$ the solution to the system lies in the first quadrant. Graph $2x + 5y = 10$ as a solid line using its x-intercept, (5, 0), and its y-intercept, (0, 2). Since (0, 0) makes the inequality $2x + 5y \le 10$ true, shade the half-plane containing (0, 0). Graph $3x + 4y = 12$ as a solid line by using its x-intercept, (4, 0), and its y-intercept, (0, 3). Since (0, 0) makes the inequality $3x + 4y \le 12$ true, shade the half-plane containing (0, 0). The solution set of the system is the intersection of the above half-planes which lies in the first quadrant, and is shown as the shaded region in the following graph.

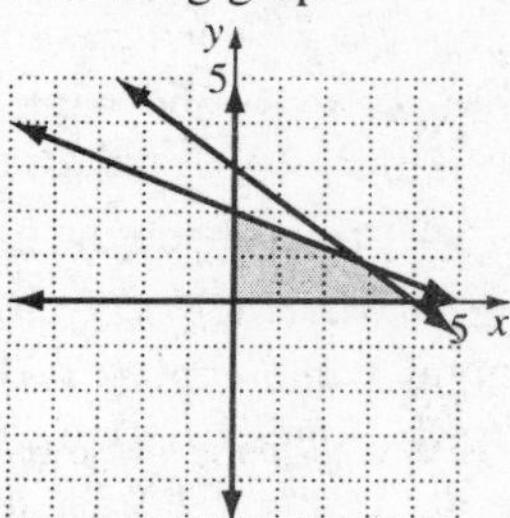

51. $3x + y \le 6$
$2x - y \le -1$
$x \ge -2$
$y \le 4$
Begin by graphing $3x + y = 6$ as a solid line using its x-intercept, (2, 0), and its y-intercept, (0, 6). Since (0, 0) makes the inequality $3x + y \le 6$ true, shade the half-plane containing (0, 0). Graph $2x - y = -1$ as a solid line using its x-intercept, $\left(-\frac{1}{2}, 0\right)$, and its y-intercept, (0, 1). Since (0, 0) makes the inequality $2x - y \le -1$ false, shade the half-plane not containing (0, 0). Graph $x = -2$ as a solid vertical line. Since (0, 0) makes the inequality $x \ge -2$ true, shade the half-plane containing (0, 0). Graph $y = 4$ as a solid horizontal line. Since (0, 0) makes the inequality $y \le 4$ true, shade the half-plane containing (0, 0).The solution set of the system is the intersection of the above half-planes, and is shown as the shaded region in the following graph.

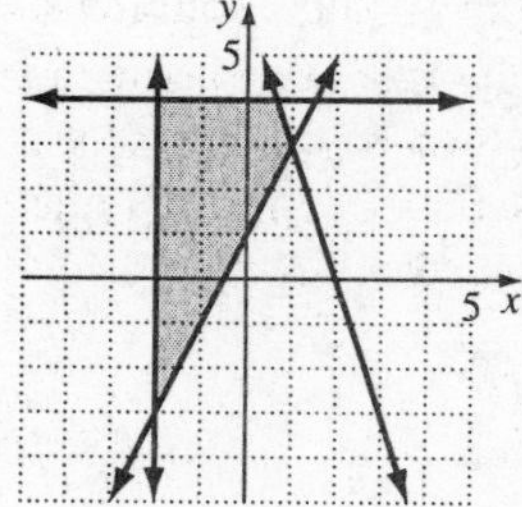

53. Answers may vary.

55. No

57. $7w - 25h \geq -800$
$w - 5h \leq -170$

59. $5T - 7P \leq 70$

61. $50x + 150y > 2000$
Graph $50x + 150y$ as a dashed line using its x-intercept, (40, 0), and its y-intercept, $\left(0, \frac{40}{3}\right)$.
Test (0, 0):
$50(0) + 150(0) > 2000$?
$0 > 2000$ false
Shade the half-plane not containing (0, 0).

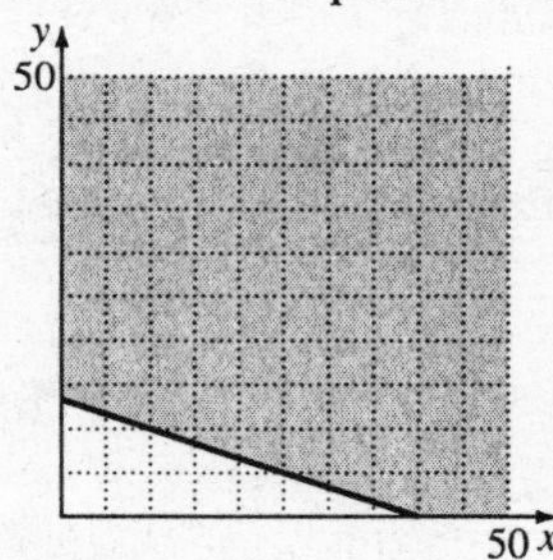

Ordered pairs may vary.

63. x = amount invested at high risk.
y = amount invested at high risk.
$x + y \leq 15,000$
$x \geq 2000$
$y \geq 3x$
$x \geq 0$
$y \geq 0$
Since $x \geq 0$ and $y \geq 0$ the solution set to the system lies in the first quadrant. Graph $x + y = 15,000$ as a solid line using its x-intercept, (15,000, 0), and its y-intercept, (0, 15,000). Since (0, 0) makes the inequality $x + y \leq 15,000$ true, shade the half-plane containing (0, 0). Graph $y = 3x$ as a solid line by using its slope, 3, and its y-intercept, (0, 0). Since (1, 1) makes the inequality $y \geq 3x$ false, shade the half-plane not containing (0, 0). Graph $x = 2000$ as a solid vertical line. Since (0, 0) makes the inequality $x \geq 2000$ false, shade the half-plane not containing (0, 0). The solution set of the system is the intersection of the above half-planes, and is shown as the shaded region in the following graph.

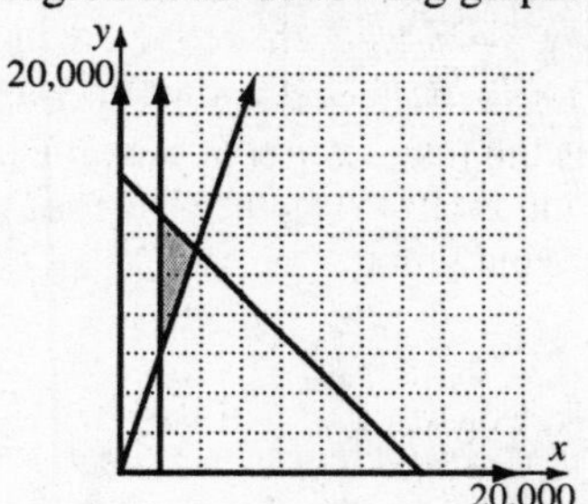

65.–69. Answers may vary.

71.

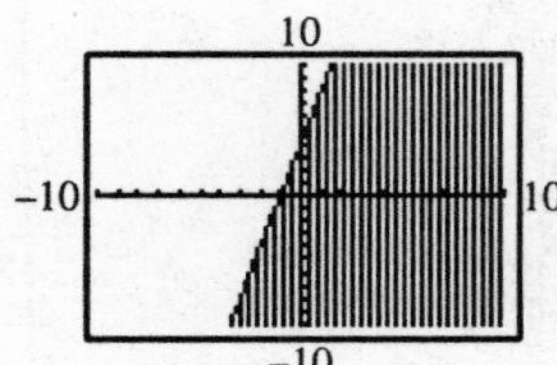

73. $y \geq x^2 - 4$

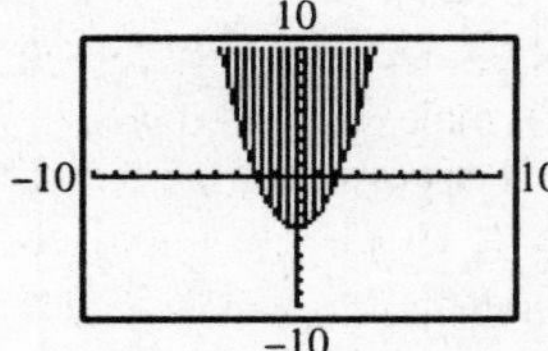

75. Answers may vary.

77. Exercise 23

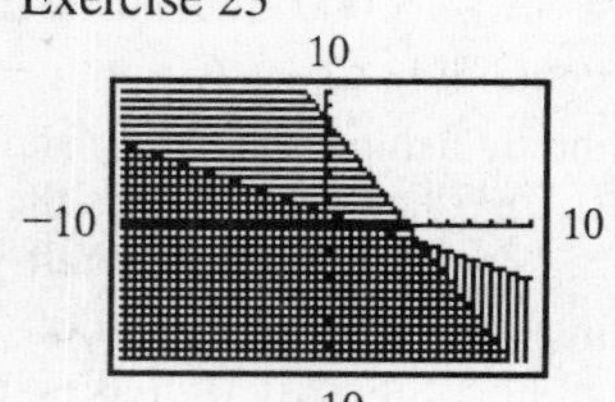

Exercise 25

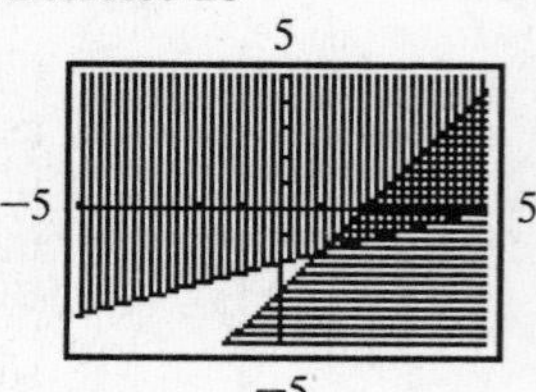

Exercise 27

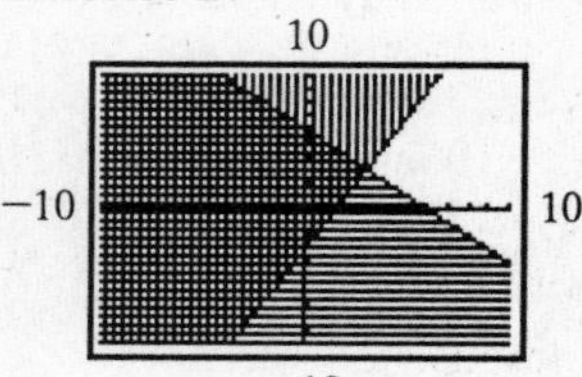

Exercise 29

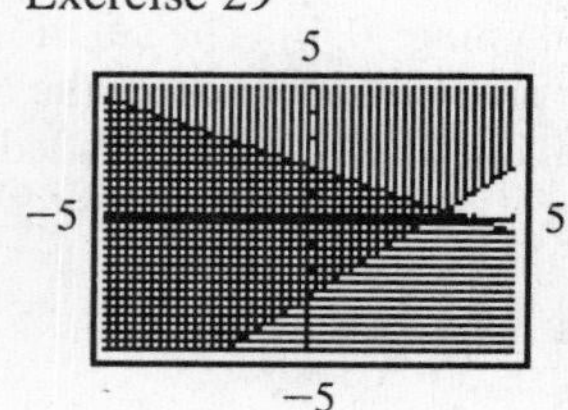

Exercise 31

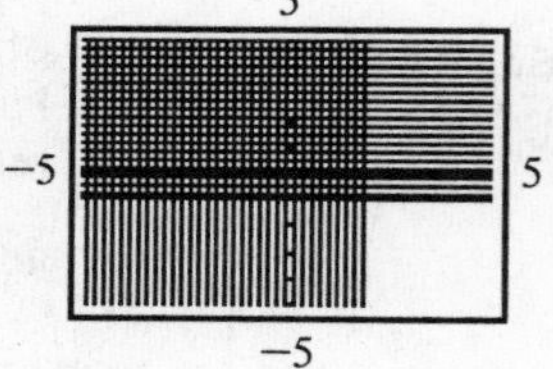

79. $x^2 + y^2 \le 9$
$y < x^2$

81. $|x + y| \le 3$ is equivalent to $-3 \le x + y \le 3$, and $|y| \le z$ is equivalent to $-2 \le y \le 2$, so the system is equivalent to

$x + y \le 3$
$x + y \ge -3$
$y \le 2$
$y \ge -2$

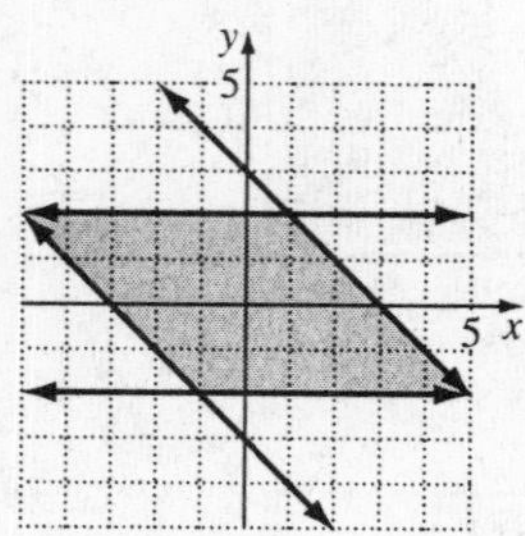

Section 5.6

Check Point Exercises

1.

The total daily profit	is	the number of book shelves times the profit per bookshelf	plus	the number of desks times the profit per desk.
(z)	$=$	$(x) \cdot (25)$	$+$	$(y) \cdot (55)$

$z = 25x + 55y$

2.

The number of bookshelves	plus	the number of desks	is not more than	80.
(x)	$+$	(y)	$\le$	80

$x + y \le 80$

3. Let x represent the number of bookshelves and y represent the number of desks.
between 30 and 80 bookselves: $30 \le x \le 80$
at least 10 and no more than 30 desks:
$10 \le y \le 30$
objective function: $z = 25x + 55y$
constraints: $x + y \le 80$
$30 \le x \le 80$
$10 \le y \le 30$

4. We must maximize $z = 25x + 55y$ subject to the constraints
$x + y \le 80$
$30 \le x \le 80$
$10 \le y \le 30$
Because x(the number of bookshelves) and y(the number of desks) must be nonnegative, graph the system of inequalitites in quadrant I and its boundary only. To graph the inequality $x + y \le 80$, graph the equation $x + y = 80$ as a solid line with x-intercept (80, 0) and y-intercept (0, 80). The test point (0, 0) satisfies the inequality so shade the region containing (0, 0). To graph the inequality $30 \le x \le 80$, graph the equations $x = 30$ and $x = 80$ as solid vertical lines and shade the region between these lines. To graph the inequality $10 \le y \le 30$, graph the equations $y = 10$ and $y = 30$ as solid horizontal lines and shade the region between these lines. The system of inequalities representing the constraints is shown where all shaded regions overlap.

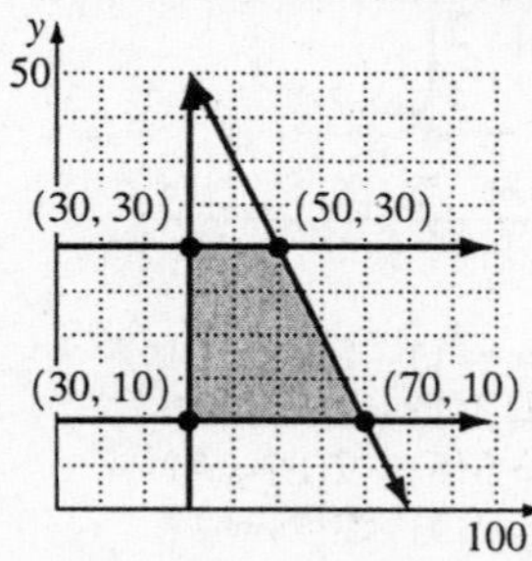

The lines $x = 30$ and $y = 10$ intersect at (30, 10).
The lines $x = 30$ and $y = 10$ intersect at (30, 30).
Use the substitution method to find where $x + y = 80$ and $y = 10$ intersect.

$$x + y = 80$$
$$x + 10 = 80$$
$$x = 70$$

So the intersection point is (70, 10).
Use the substitution method to find where $x + y = 80$ and $y = 30$ intersect.

$$x + y = 80$$
$$x + 30 = 80$$
$$x = 50$$

So the intersection point is (50, 30).
Evaluate the objective function $z = 25x + 55y$ at the four corner points of the region found above.
(30, 10): $25(30) + 55(10) = 1300$
(30, 30): $25(30) + 55(30) = 2400$
(50, 30): $25(50) + 55(30) = 2900$
(70, 10): $25(70) + 55(10) = 2300$
The maximum value of z is 2900 and this occurs when $x = 50$ and $y = 30$. This means 50 bookshelves and 30 desks should be manufactured per day. The maximum profit is $2900.

5. objective function: $z = 3x + 5y$
constraints: $x \ge 0,\ y \ge 0$
$x + y \ge 1$
$x + y \le 6$

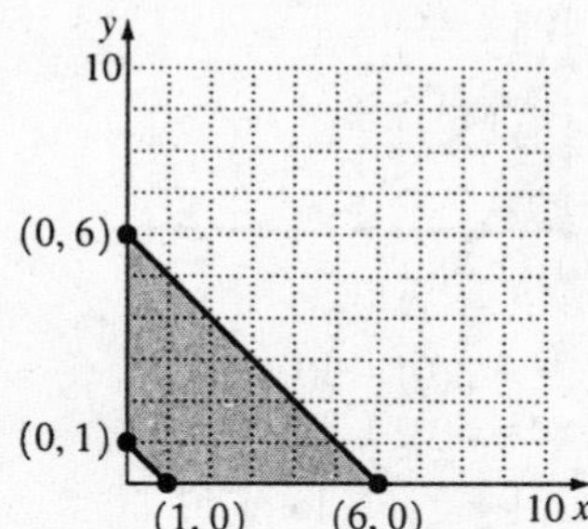

Evaluate the objective function at the four vertices of the region shown:
(1, 0): $3(1) + 5(0) = 3$
(0, 1): $3(0) + 5(1) = 5$
(0, 6): $3(0) + 5(6) = 30$
(6, 0): $3(6) + 5(0) = 18$
The maximum value of z is 30 and this occurs when $x = 0$ and $y = 6$.

Exercise Set 5.6

1. $z = 5x + 6y$
(1, 2): 5(1) + 6(2) = 5 + 12 = 17
(2, 10): 5(2) + 6(10) = 10 + 60 = 70
(7, 5): 5(7) + 6(5) = 35 + 30 = 65
(8, 3): 5(8) + 6(3) = 40 + 18 = 58
The maximum value is $z = 70$; the minimum value is $z = 17$.

3. $z = 40x + 50y$
(0, 0): 40(0) + 50(0) = 0 + 0 = 0
(0, 8): 40(0) + 50(8) = 0 + 400 = 400
(4, 9): 40(4) + 50(9) = 160 + 450 = 610
(8, 0): 40(8) + 50(0) = 320 + 0 = 320
The maximum value is $z = 610$; the minimum value is $z = 0$.

5. $z = 2x + 3y$
$x \ge 0, y \ge 0$
$3x + y \le 6$
$2x + 3y \le 12$

a.

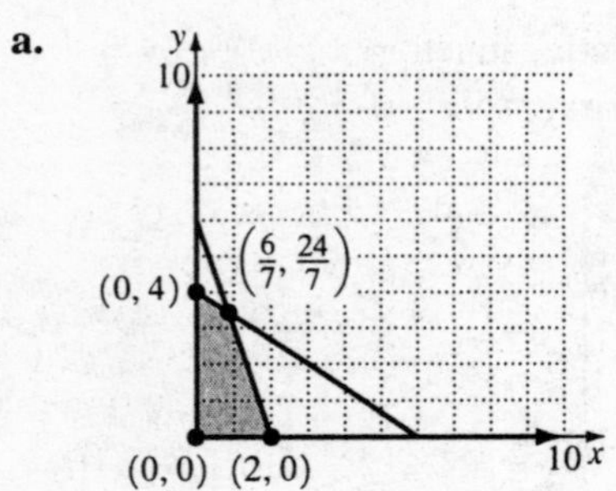

b. (0, 0): $z = 2(0) + 3(0) = 0$
(0, 4): $z = 2(0) + 3(4) = 12$
$\left(\frac{6}{7}, \frac{24}{7}\right): z = 2\left(\frac{6}{7}\right) + 3\left(\frac{24}{7}\right)$
$= \frac{12}{7} + \frac{72}{7} = \frac{84}{7} = 12$
$(2, 0): z = 2(2) + 3(0) = 4$

c. The maximum value is 12 at $x = 0$ and $y = 4$ and at $x = \frac{6}{7}$ and $y = \frac{24}{7}$.

7. $z = 4x + y$
$x \ge 0, y \ge 0$
$2x + 3y \le 12$
$x + y \ge 3$

a.

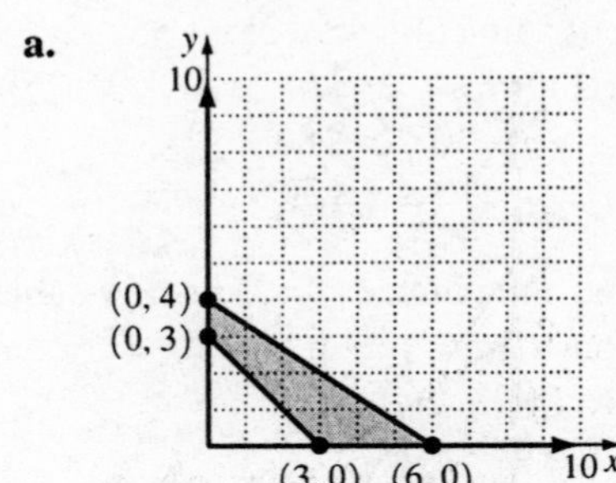

b. (0, 4): $z = 4(0) + 4 = 4$
(0, 3): $z = 4(0) + 3 = 3$
(3, 0): $z = 4(3) + 0 = 12$
(6, 0): $z = 4(6) + 0 = 24$

c. The maximum value is 24 at $x = 6$ and $y = 0$.

9. $z = 3x - 2y$
$1 \le x \le 5$
$y \ge 2$
$x - y \ge -3$

a.

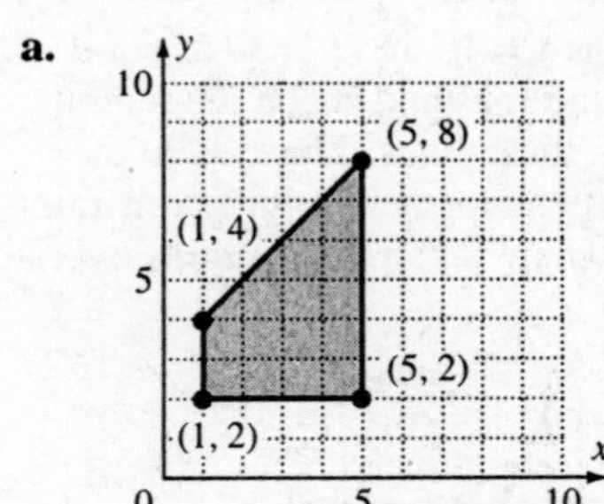

b. (1, 2): $z = 3(1) - 2(2) = -1$
(1, 4): $z = 3(1) - 2(4) = -5$
(5, 8): $z = 3(5) - 2(8) = -1$
(5, 2): $z = 3(5) - 2(2) = 11$

c. Maximum value is 11 at $x = 5$ and $y = 2$.

11. $z = 4x + 2y$
$x \geq 0, y \geq 0$
$2x + 3y \leq 12$
$3x + 2y \leq 12$
$x + y \geq 2$

a.

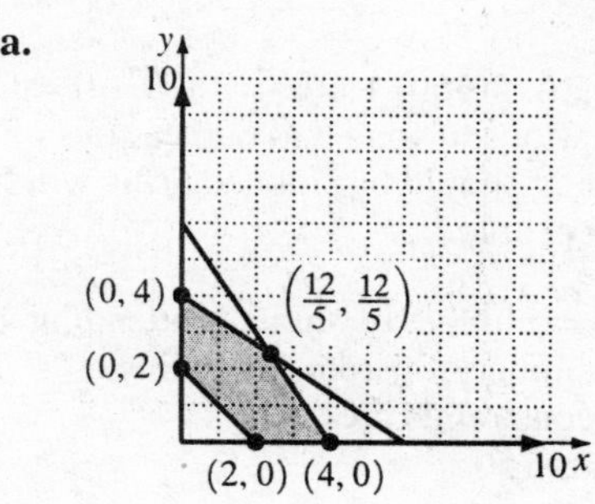

b. (0, 4): $z = 4(0) + 2(4) = 8$
(0, 2): $z = 4(0) + 2(2) = 4$
(2, 0): $z = 4(2) + 2(0) = 8$
(4, 0): $z = 4(4) + 2(0) = 16$
$\left(\frac{12}{5}, \frac{12}{5}\right): z = 4\left(\frac{12}{5}\right) + 2\left(\frac{12}{5}\right)$
$= \frac{48}{5} + \frac{24}{5} = \frac{72}{5}$

c. The maximum value is 16 at $x = 4$ and $y = 0$.

13. $z = 10x + 12y$
$x \geq 0, y \geq 0$
$x + y \leq 7$
$2x + y \leq 10$
$2x + 3y \leq 18$

a.

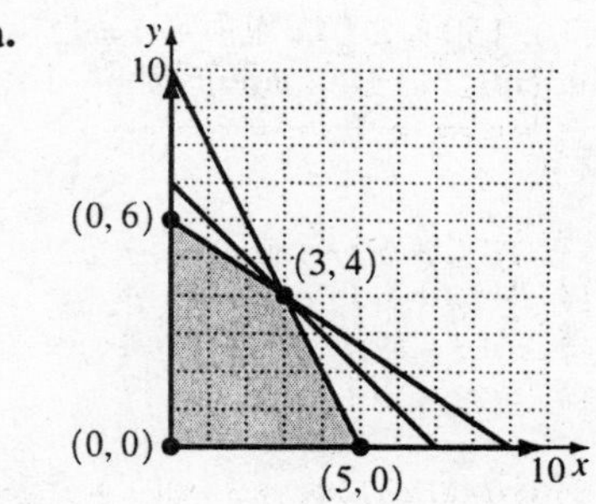

b. (0, 6): $z = 10(0) + 12(6) = 72$
(0, 0): $z = 10(0) + 12(0) = 0$
(5, 0): $z = 10(5) + 12(0) = 50$
(3, 4): $z = 10(3) + 12(4) =$
$= 30 + 48 = 78$

c. The maximum value is 78 at $x = 3$ and $y = 4$.

15. a. $z = 125x + 200y$

b. $x \leq 450$
$y \leq 200$
$600x + 900y \leq 360{,}000$

c. Simplify the third inequality by dividing by 300 to get $2x + 3y \leq 1200$.

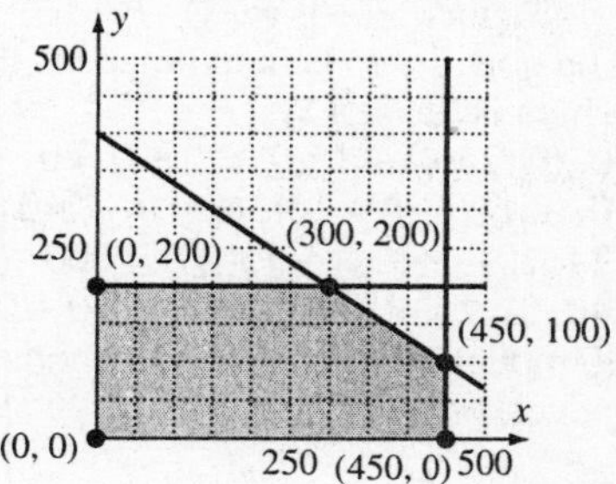

d. (0, 0): $125(0) + 200(0) = 0 + 0 = 0$
(0, 200): $125(0) + 200(200)$
$= 0 + 40{,}000 = 40{,}000$
(300, 200): $125(300) + 200(200)$
$= 37{,}500 + 40{,}000 = 77{,}500$
(450, 100): $125(450) + 200(100)$
$= 56{,}250 + 20{,}000 = 76{,}250$
(450, 0): $125(450) + 200(0)$
$= 56{,}250 + 0 = 56{,}250$

e. The television manufacturer will make the greatest profit by manufacturing <u>300</u> console televisions each month and <u>200</u> wide-screen televisions each month. The maximum monthly profit is <u>$77,500</u>.

17. Let x = number of model A bicycles and y = number of model B bicycles.
The constraints are
$5x + 4y \leq 200$
$2x + 3y \leq 108$
Graph these inequalities in the first quadrant, since x and y cannot be negative.

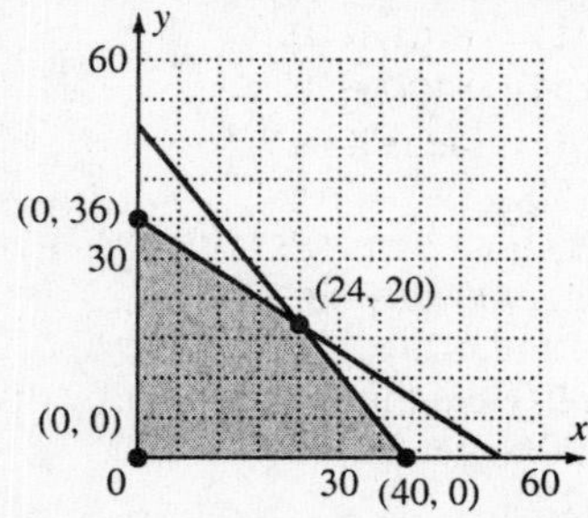

The quantity to be maximized is the profit, which is $25x + 15y$.
$(0, 0)$: $25(0) + 15(0) = 0 + 0 = 0$
$(0, 36)$: $25(0) + 15(36) = 0 + 540 = 540$
$(24, 20)$: $25(24) + 15(20) = 600 + 300 = 900$
$(40, 0)$: $25(40) + 15(0) = 1000 + 0 = 1000$
40 model A bicycles and no model B bicycles should be produced.

19. Let x = the number of cartons of food and y = the number of cartons of clothing.
The constraints are:
$50x + 5y \leq 18{,}000$ or $10x + y \leq 3600$
$30x + 20y \leq 12{,}000$ or $3x + 2y \leq 1200$
Graph these inequalities in the first quadrant, since x and y cannot be negative.

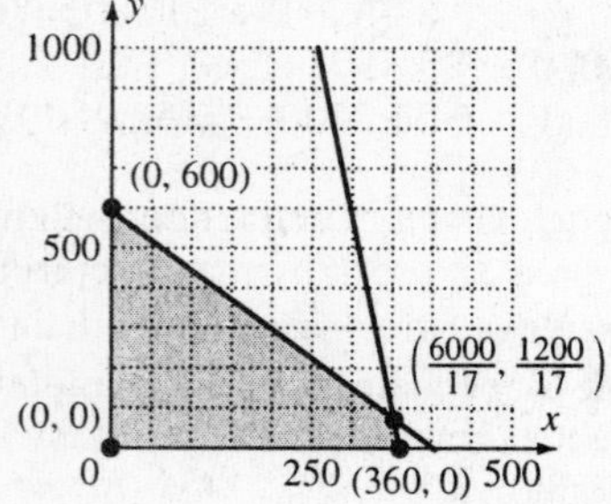

The quantity to be maximized is the number of people helped, which is $5x + 6y$.
$(0, 0)$: $5(0) + 6(0) = 0 + 0 = 0$
$(0, 600)$: $5(0) + 6(600) = 0 + 3600 = 3600$

$$\left(\frac{6000}{17}, \frac{1200}{17}\right): 5\left(\frac{6000}{17}\right) + 6\left(\frac{1200}{17}\right) = \frac{30{,}000}{17} + \frac{7200}{17} = \frac{37{,}200}{17} \approx 2188$$

$(360, 0)$: $5(360) + 6(0) = 1800 + 0 = 1800$
No cartons of food and 600 cartons of clothing should be shipped. This will help 3600 people.

21. Let x = number of students attending and y = number of parents attending.
The constraints are
$x + y \leq 150$
$2x \geq y$
or
$x + y \leq 150$
$2x - y \geq 0$
Graph these inequalities in the first quadrant, since x and y cannot be negative.

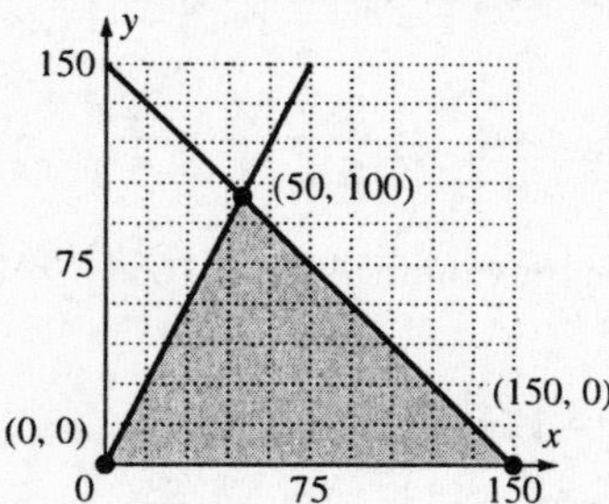

The quantity to be maximized is the amount of money raised, which is $x + 2y$.
$(0, 0)$: $0 + 2(0) = 0 + 0 = 0$
$(50, 100)$: $50 + 2(100) = 50 + 200 = 250$
$(150, 0)$: $150 + 2(0) = 150 + 0 = 150$
50 students and 100 parents should attend.

23. Let x = number of Boeing 727s, y = number of Falcon 20s.
Maximize $z = x + y$ with the following constraints:
$1400x + 500y \le 35{,}000$ or $14x + 5y \le 350$
$42{,}000x + 6000y \ge 672{,}000$ or
$7x + y \ge 112$
$x \le 20$
$x \ge 0, y \ge 0$

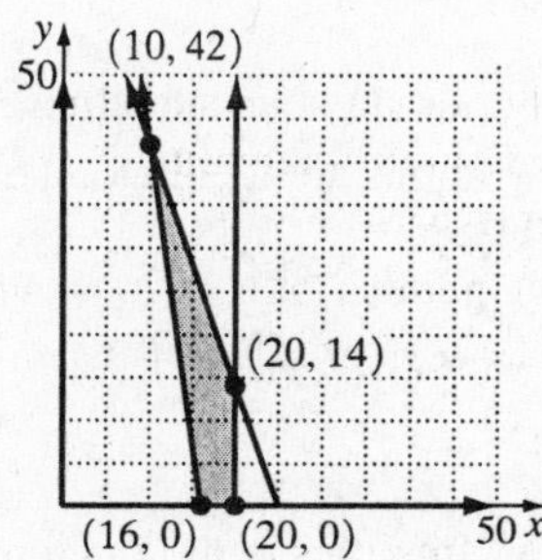

$(16,0): z = 16$
$(20,0): z = 20$
$(20,14): z = 34$
$(10,42): z = 52$
Federal Express should have purchased 10 Boeing 727s and 42 Falcon 20s.

25.–27. Answers may vary.

29. $z = 6x + 8y$
$x \ge 0, y \ge 0$
$x + 2y \le 6$ or $y \le -0.5x + 3$

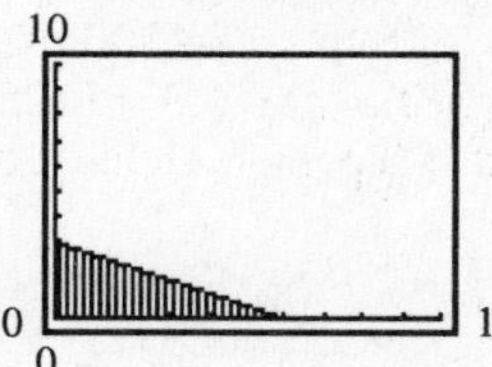

(6, 0): 6(6) + 8(0) = 36
(0, 3): 6(0) + 8(3) = 24
Maximum value is 36.

31. $z = 9x + 14y$
$x \ge 0, y \ge 0$
$2x + y \le 10$ or $y \le -2x + 10$
$2x + 3y \le 18$ or $y \le -\frac{2}{3}x + 6$

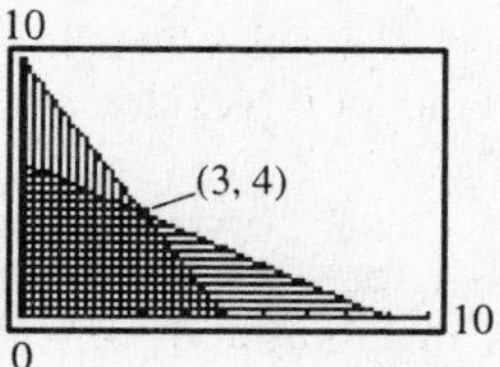

(3, 4): 9(3) + 14(4) = 83
(5, 0): 9(5) + 14(0) = 45
(0, 6): 9(0) + 14(6) = 84
Maximum value is 84.

33. Let x = amount invested in stocks and y = amount invested in bonds.
The constraints are:
$x + y \le 10{,}000$
$y \ge 3000$
$x \ge 2000$
$y \ge x$
Graph these inequalities in the first quadrant, since x and y cannot be negative.

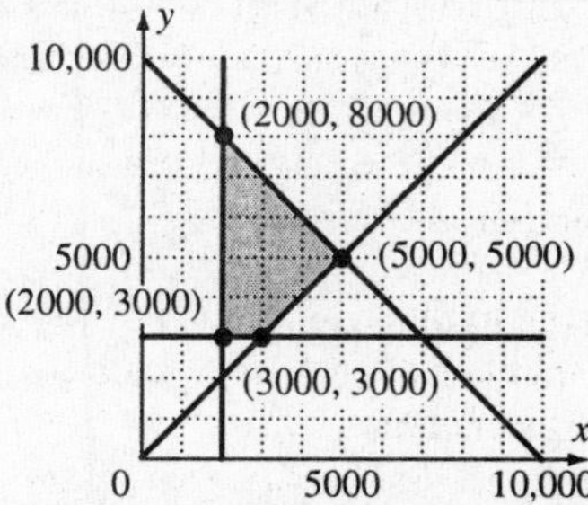

The quantity to be maximized is the return on the investment, which is $0.12x + 0.08y$.
(2000, 3000):
0.12(2000) + 0.08(3000) = 240 + 240 = 480
(2000, 8000):
0.12(2000) + 0.08(8000) = 240 + 640 = 880
(5000, 5000):
0.12(5000) + 0.08(5000) = 600 + 400 = 1000
(3000, 3000):
0.12(3000) + 0.08(3000) = 360 + 240 = 600
The greatest return occurs when $5000 is invested in stocks and $5000 is invested in bonds.

Review Exercises

1. $y = 4x + 1$
$3x + 2y = 13$
Substitute $4x + 1$ for y in the second equation:
$3x + 2(4x + 1) = 13$
$3x + 8x + 2 = 13$
$11x = 11$
$x = 1$
$y = 4(1) + 1 = 5$
The solution set is $\{(1, 5)\}$.

2. $x + 4y = 14$
$2x - y = 1$
Multiply the second equation by 4 and add to the first equation.
$x + 4y = 14$
$8x - 4y = 4$
$9x = 18$
$x = 2$
$2(2) - y = 1$
$-y = -3$
$y = 3$
The solution set is $\{(2, 3)\}$.

3. $5x + 3y = 1$
$3x + 4y = -6$
Multiply the first equation by 4 and the second equation by –3.
Then add.
$20x + 12y = 4$
$-9x - 12y = 18$
$11x = 22$
$x = 2$
$5(2) + 3y = 1$
$3y = -9$
$y = -3$
The solution set is $\{(2, -3)\}$.

4. $2y - 6x = 7$
$3x - y = 9$
The second equation can be written as $y = 3x - 9$.
Substitute:
$2(3x - 9) - 6x = 7$
$6x - 18 - 6x = 7$
$-18 = 7$
Since this is false, the system has no solution. The solution set is the empty set, $\varnothing$.

5. $4x - 8y = 16$
$3x - 6y = 12$
Divide the first equation by 4 and the second equation by 3.
$x - 2y = 4$
$x - 2y = 4$
Since these equations are identical, the system
ihas an infinite number of solutions.
The solution set is $\{(x, y) \mid 4x - 8y = 16\}$ or $\{(x, y) \mid 3x - 6y = 12\}$.

6. No, (–1, 3) is not a solution to $2x + y = -5$.
$2(-1) + 3 = 1 \neq -5$

7. x = mg of cholesterol in one ounce of shrimp
y = mg of cholesterol in one ounce of scallops
$3x + 2y = 156$
$5x + 3y = 255$
Multiply the first equation by –3 and multiply the second equation by 2.
Add the resulting equations together.
$-9x - 6y = -468$
$10x + 6y = 510$
$x = 42$
$3(42) + 2y = 156$
$126 + 2y = 156$
$2y = 30$
$y = 15$
$3(42) + 2y = 156$
$126 + 2y = 156$
$2y = 30$
$y = 15$
Shrimp: 42 mg of cholesterol per ounce
Scallops: 15 mg of cholesterol per ounce

8. x = number of apples
y = number of avocados

$$100x + 350y = 1000$$
$$24x + 14y = 100$$

$$100x + 350y = 1000$$
$$\underline{-600x - 350y = -2500}$$
$$-500x = -1500$$
$$x = 3$$

$$100(3) + 350y = 1000$$
$$350y = 700$$
$$y = 2$$

3 apples and 2 avocados supply 1000 calories and 100 grams of carbohydrates.

9.
$$N = -60p + 100$$
$$N = 4p + 200$$
$$-60p + 1000 = 4p + 200$$
$$800 = 64p$$
$$p = 12.5$$
$$N = 4(12.5) + 200 = 250$$

250 copies can be supplied and sold for \$12.50 each.

10.
$$2x - y + z = 1 \quad (1)$$
$$3x - 3y + 4z = 5 \quad (2)$$
$$4x - 2y + 3z = 4 \quad (3)$$

Eliminate y from (1) and (2) by multiplying (1) by –3 and adding the result to (2).

$$-6x + 3y - 3z = -3$$
$$\underline{3x - 3y + 4z = 5}$$
$$-3x + z = 2 \quad (4)$$

Eliminate y from (1) and (3) by multiplying (1) by –2 and adding the result to (3).

$$-4x + 2y - 2z = -2$$
$$\underline{4x - 2y + 3z = 4}$$
$$z = 2$$

Substituting $z = 2$ into (4), we get:

$$-3x + 2 = 2$$
$$-3x = 0$$
$$x = 0$$

Substituting $x = 0$ and $z = 2$ into (1), we have:

$$2(0) - y + 2 = 1$$
$$-y = -1$$
$$y = 1$$

The solution set is $\{(0, 1, 2)\}$.

11.
$$x + 2y - z = 5 \quad (1)$$
$$2x - y + 3z = 0 \quad (2)$$
$$2y + z = 1 \quad (3)$$

Eliminate x from (1) and (2) by multiplying (1) by –2 and adding the result to (2).

$$-2x - 4y + 2z = -10$$
$$\underline{2x - y + 3z = 0}$$
$$-5y + 5z = -10$$
$$y - z = 2 \quad (4)$$

Adding (3) and (4), we get:

$$2y + z = 1$$
$$\underline{y - z = 2}$$
$$3y = 3$$
$$y = 1$$

Substituting $y = 1$ into (3), we have:

$$2(1) + z = 1$$
$$z = -1$$

Substituting $y = 1$ and $z = -1$ into (1), we obtain:

$$x + 2(1) - (-1) = 5$$
$$x + 3 = 5$$
$$x = 2$$

The solution set is $\{(2, 1, -1)\}$.

12. $y = ax^2 + bx + c$

$$(1, 4): 4 = a + b + c \quad (1)$$
$$(3, 20): 20 = 9a + 3b + c \quad (2)$$
$$(-2, 25): 25 = 4a - 2b + c \quad (3)$$

Multiply (1) by –1 and add to (2).

$$20 = 9a + 3b + c$$
$$\underline{-4 = -a - b - c}$$
$$16 = 8a + 2b$$
$$8 = 4a + b \quad (4)$$

Multiply (1) by –1 and add to (3).

$$25 = 4a - 2b + c$$
$$\underline{-4 = -a - b - c}$$
$$21 = 3a - 3b$$
$$7 = a - b \quad (5)$$

Add (4) and (5).

$$8 = 4a + b$$
$$\underline{7 = a - b}$$
$$15 = 5a$$
$$a = 3$$

$$8 = 4(3) + b$$
$$b = -4$$

$$3 - 4 + c = 4$$
$$c = 5$$

The quadratic function is $y = 3x^2 - 4x + 5$.

13. $x+y+z=0.45$ (1)
$x=y+0.01$ (2)
$x=2z-0.12$ (3)
Rewrite (2) as $y=x-0.01$, then substitute into (1).
$x+x-0.01+z=0.45$
$2x+z=0.46$
Substitute (3) into the above equation.
$$2(2z-0.12)+z=0.46$$
$$4z-0.24+z=0.46$$
$$5z=0.70$$
$$z=0.14$$
$$x=2(0.14)-0.12=0.16$$
$$y=0.16-0.01=0.15$$
Japan: 16%
Germany: 15%
France: 14%

14. Substitute the ordered pairs into $y=ax^2+bx+c$, solve the resulting system for a, b, and c. Then substitute these values into the equation to form a quadratic model.

15. $$\frac{x}{(x-3)(x+2)}=\frac{A}{x-3}+\frac{B}{x+2}$$
$$x=A(x+2)+B(x-3)$$
$$=(A+B)x+(2A-3B)$$
$A+B=1$
$2A-3B=0$
Multiply first equation by 3, then add to second equation.
$3A+3B=3$
$2A-3B=0$
$5A=3$
$A=\frac{3}{5}$, $B=\frac{2}{5}$
$$\frac{x}{(x-3)(x+2)}=\frac{3}{5(x-3)}+\frac{2}{5(x+2)}$$

16. $$\frac{11x-2}{x^2-x-12}=\frac{11x-2}{(x-4)(x+3)}$$
$$=\frac{A}{x-4}+\frac{B}{x+3}$$
$$11x-2=A(x+3)+B(x-4)$$
$$=Ax+3A+Bx-4B$$
$$=(A+B)x+(3A-4B)$$
$A+B=11$
$3A-4B=-2$
Multiply first equation by 4, then add to second equation.
$3A-4B=-2$
$4A+4B=44$
$7A=42$
$A=6$, $B=5$
$$\frac{11x-2}{x^2-x-12}=\frac{6}{x-4}+\frac{5}{x+3}$$

17. $\dfrac{4x^2-3x-4}{x^3+x^2-2x}=\dfrac{4x^2-3x-4}{x(x+2)(x-1)}=\dfrac{A}{x}+\dfrac{B}{x+2}+\dfrac{C}{x-1}$

$$\begin{aligned}4x^2-3x-4&=A(x+2)(x-1)+Bx(x-1)+Cx(x+2)\\&=A(x^2+x-2)+Bx^2-Bx+Cx^2+2Cx\\&=Ax^2+Ax-2A+Bx^2-Bx+Cx^2+2Cx\\&=(A+B+C)x^2+(A-B+2C)x-2A\end{aligned}$$

$$\begin{aligned}A+B+C&=4\\A-B+2C&=-3\\-2A&=-4\\A&=2\end{aligned}$$

$$\begin{aligned}B+C&=2\\-B+2C&=-5\\\hline 3C&=-3\\C&=-1\\B-1&=2\\B&=3\end{aligned}$$

$$\frac{4x^2-3x-4}{x^3+x^2-2x}=\frac{2}{x}+\frac{3}{x+2}-\frac{1}{x-1}$$

18. $\dfrac{2x+1}{(x-2)^2}=\dfrac{A}{x-2}+\dfrac{B}{(x-2)^2}$

$$2x+1=A(x-2)+B=Ax-2A+B$$

$$\begin{aligned}A&=2\\-2A+B&=1\\-2(2)+B&=1\\B&=5\end{aligned}$$

$$\frac{2x+1}{(x-2)^2}=\frac{2}{x-2}+\frac{5}{(x-2)^2}$$

19. $\dfrac{2x-6}{(x-1)(x-2)^2}=\dfrac{A}{x-1}+\dfrac{B}{x-2}+\dfrac{C}{(x-2)^2}$

$$\begin{aligned}2x-6 &= A(x-2)^2+B(x-1)(x-2)+C(x-1)\\ &= A(x^2-4x+4)+B(x^2-3x+2)+C(x-1)\\ &= Ax^2-4Ax+4A+Bx^2-3Bx+2B+Cx-C\\ &= (A+B)x^2+(-4A-3B+C)x+(4A+2B-C)\end{aligned}$$

$$\begin{aligned}A+B&=0\\ -4A-3B+C&=2\\ \underline{4A+2B-C}&\underline{=-6}\\ -B&=-4\\ B&=4\\ A&=-4\\ 4(-4)+2(4)-C&=-6\\ -16+8-C&=-6\\ -C-8&=-6\\ -C&=2\\ C&=-2\end{aligned}$$

$$\frac{2x-6}{(x-1)(x-2)^2}=-\frac{4}{x-1}+\frac{4}{x-2}-\frac{2}{(x-2)^2}$$

20. $\dfrac{3x}{(x-2)(x^2+1)}=\dfrac{A}{x-2}+\dfrac{Bx+C}{x^2+1}$

$$\begin{aligned}3x &= A(x^2+1)+(Bx+C)(x-2)\\ &= Ax^2+A+Bx^2-2Bx+Cx-2C\\ &= (A+B)x^2+(-2B+C)x-(2C-A)\end{aligned}$$

$$\begin{aligned}A+B&=0\\ -2B+C&=3\\ 2C-A&=0\\ A&=2C\\ B+2C&=0\\ \underline{4B-2C}&\underline{=-6}\\ 5B&=-6\\ B&=-\frac{6}{5}\\ A&=\frac{6}{5}\\ C&=\frac{6}{10}=\frac{3}{5}\end{aligned}$$

$$\frac{3x}{(x-2)(x^2+1)}=\frac{6}{5(x-2)}+\frac{-6x+3}{5(x^2+1)}$$

21. $\frac{7x^2-7x+23}{(x-3)(x^2+4)}=\frac{A}{x-3}+\frac{Bx+C}{x^2+4}$

$$7x^2-7x+23=A(x^2+4)+(Bx+C)(x-3)$$
$$=Ax^2+4A+Bx^2-3Bx+Cx-3C$$
$$=(A+B)x^2+(-3B+C)x+(4A-3C)$$

$A+B=7$

$-3B+C=-7$

$4A-3C=23$

$3A+3B=21$

$-3B+C=-7$

$3A+C=14$

$9A+3C=42$

$4A-3C=23$

$13A=65$

$A=5$

$5+B=7$

$B=7-5=2$

$-3(2)+C=-7$

$C=-7+6=-1$

$$\frac{7x^2-7x+23}{(x-3)(x^2+4)}=\frac{5}{(x-3)}+\frac{2x-1}{(x^2+4)}$$

22. $\frac{x^3}{(x^2+4)^2}=\frac{Ax+B}{x^2+4}+\frac{Cx+D}{(x^2+4)^2}$

$$x^3=(Ax+B)(x^2+4)+Cx+D$$
$$=Ax^3+4Ax+Bx^2+4B+Cx+D$$
$$=Ax^3+Bx^2+(4A+C)x+(4B+D)$$

$A=1$

$B=0$

$4A+C=0$

$4B+D=0$

$C=-4$

$0+D=0, D=0$

$$\frac{x^2}{(x^2+4)^2}=\frac{x}{x^2+4}-\frac{4x}{(x^2+4)^2}$$

23. $\dfrac{4x^3+5x^2+7x-1}{(x^2+x+1)^2}=\dfrac{Ax+B}{x^2+x+1}+\dfrac{Cx+D}{(x^2+x+1)^2}$

$$\begin{aligned}4x^3+5x^2+7x-1&=(Ax+B)(x^2+x+1)+Cx+D\\&=Ax^3+Ax^2+Ax+Bx^2+Bx+B+Cx+D\\&=Ax^3+(A+B)x^2(A+B+C)x+(B+D)\end{aligned}$$

$$\begin{aligned}A&=4\\A+B&=5\\A+B+C&=7\\B+D&=-1\\4+B&=5, B=1\\4+1+C&=7, C=2\\1+D&=-1, D=-2\end{aligned}$$

$$\frac{4x^3+5x^2+7x-1}{(x^2+x+1)^2}=\frac{4x+1}{x^2+x+1}+\frac{2x-2}{(x^2+x+1)^2}$$

24.

$$\begin{aligned}5y&=x^2-1\\x-y&=1\\y&=x-1\\5(x-1)&=x^2-1\\5x-5&=x^2-1\\x^2-5x+4&=0\\(x-4)(x-1)&=0\\x&=4,1\end{aligned}$$

If $x=4, y=4-1=3$.
If $x=1, y=1-1=0$.
The solution set is $\{(4,3),(1,0)\}$.

25.

$$\begin{aligned}y&=x^2+2x+1\\x+y&=1\\y&=1-x\\1-x&=x^2+2x+1\\x^2+3x&=0\\x(x+3)&=0\\x&=0,-3\end{aligned}$$

If $x=0, y=1-0=1$.
If $x=-3, y=1-(-3)=4$.
The solution set is $\{(0,1),(-3,4)\}$.

26. $x^2 + y^2 = 2$
$x + y = 0$
$x = -y$
$(-y)^2 + y^2 = 2$
$2y^2 = 2$
$y^2 = 1$
$y = 1, -1$
If $y = 1, x = -1$.
If $y = -1, x = 1$.
The solution set is $\{(1,-1),(-1,1)\}$.

27. $2x^2 + y^2 = 24$
$x^2 + y^2 = 15$
$2x^2 + y^2 = 24$
$\underline{-x^2 - y^2 = -15}$
$x^2 = 9$
$x = 3, -3$
If $x = 3, 3^2 + y^2 = 15, y^2 = 6$ and $y = \pm\sqrt{6}$.
If $x = -3, y = \pm\sqrt{6}$.
The solution set is
$\left\{\left(3,\sqrt{6}\right),\left(3,-\sqrt{6}\right),\left(-3,\sqrt{6}\right),\left(-3,-\sqrt{6}\right)\right\}$.

28. $xy - 4 = 0$
$y - x = 0$
$y = x$
$xy = 4$
$x^2 = 4$
$x = 2, -2$
If $x = 2, y = 2$.
If $x = -2, y = -2$.
The solution set is $\{(2,2),(-2,-2)\}$.

29. $y^2 = 4x$
$x - 2y + 3 = 0$
$x = \frac{y^2}{4}$
$\frac{y^2}{4} - 2y + 3 = 0$
$y^2 - 8y + 12 = 0$
$(y-6)(y-2) = 0$
$y = 6, 2$
If $y = 6, x = \frac{36}{4} = 9$.
If $y = 2, x = \frac{4}{4} = 1$.
The solution set is $\{(9,6),(1,2)\}$.

30. $x^2 + y^2 = 10$
$y = x + 2$
$x^2 + (x+2)^2 = 10$
$x^2 + x^2 + 4x + 4 - 10 = 0$
$2x^2 + 4x - 6 = 0$
$x^2 + 2x - 3 = 0$
$(x+3)(x-1) = 0$
$x = -3, 1$
If $x = -3, y = -3 + 2 = -1$.
If $x = 1, y = 1 + 2 = 3$.
The solution set is $\{(-3,-1),(1,3)\}$.

31. $xy = 1$
$y = 2x + 1$
$x(2x+1) = 1$
$2x^2 + x - 1 = 0$
$(2x-1)(x+1) = 0$
$x = \frac{1}{2}, -1$
If $x = \frac{1}{2}, y = 2\left(\frac{1}{2}\right) + 1 = 2$.
If $x = -1, y = 2(-1) + 1 = -1$.
The solution set is $\left\{\left(\frac{1}{2}, 2\right),(-1,-1)\right\}$.

32.
$$x + y + 1 = 0$$
$$x^2 + y^2 + 6y - x = -5$$
$$x = -y - 1$$
$$(-y-1)^2 + y^2 + 6y - (-y-1) + 5 = 0$$
$$y^2 + 2y + 1 + y^2 + 6y + y + 1 + 5 = 0$$
$$2y^2 + 9y + 7 = 0$$
$$(2y+7)(y+1) = 0$$
$$y = -\frac{7}{2}, -1$$

If $y = -\frac{7}{2}, x = \frac{7}{2} - 1 = \frac{5}{2}$.
If $y = -1, x = 1 - 1 = 0$.
The solution set is $\left\{\left(\frac{5}{2}, -\frac{7}{2}\right), (0, -1)\right\}$.

33. $x^2 + y^2 = 13$
$$x^2 - y = 7$$
$$x^2 + y^2 = 13$$
$$\underline{-x^2 + y = -7}$$
$$y^2 + y = 6$$
$$y^2 + y - 6 = 0$$
$$(y+3)(y-2) = 0$$
$$y = -3, 2$$
If $y = -3, x^2 + 3 = 7$
$x^2 = 4, x = 2, -2$
If $y = 2, x^2 - 2 = 7, x^2 = 9, x = 3, -3$.
The solution set is
$\{(2,-3), (-2,-3), (3,2), (-3,2)\}$.

34. $2x^2 + 3y^2 = 21$
$$3x^2 - 4y^2 = 23$$
$$8x^2 + 12y^2 = 84$$
$$\underline{9x^2 - 12y^2 = 69}$$
$$17x^2 = 153$$
$$x^2 = \frac{153}{17} = 9$$
$$x = 3, -3$$

If $x = 3, 2(3)^2 + 3y^2 = 21$.
$3y^2 = 21 - 18 = 3$
$y^2 = 1, y = 1, -1$
If $x = -3, y = 1, -1$.
The solution set is
$\{(3,1), (3,-1), (-3,1), (-3,-1)\}$.

35. $2L + 2W = 26$
$$LW = 40$$
$$L = \frac{40}{W}$$
$$2\left(\frac{40}{W}\right) + 2W = 26$$
$$\frac{80}{W} + 2W = 26$$
$$80 + 2W^2 = 26W$$
$$2W^2 - 26W + 80 = 0$$
$$W^2 - 13W + 40 = 0$$
$$(W-8)(W-5) = 0$$
$$W = 8, 5$$
If $W = 5, L = \frac{40}{5} = 8$
The dimensions are 8 m by 5 m.

36.
$$xy = 6$$
$$y = \frac{6}{x}$$
$$2x + y = 8$$
$$2x + \frac{6}{x} = 8$$
$$2x^2 + 6 = 8x$$
$$2x^2 - 8x + 6 = 0$$
$$x^2 - 4x + 3 = 0$$
$$(x-1)(x-3) = 0$$
$$x = 1, 3$$
If $x = 1, y = 6$.
If $x = 3, y = 2$.
The solution set is $\{(1, 6), (3, 2)\}$.

37. $x^2 + y^2 = 2900$

$4x + 2y = 240$

$2x + y = 120$

$y = 120 - 2x$

$$x^2 + (120 - 2x)^2 = 2900$$
$$x^2 + 14,400 - 480x + 4x^2 - 2900 = 0$$
$$5x^2 - 480x + 11,500 = 0$$
$$x^2 - 96x + 2300 = 0$$
$$(x - 46)(x - 50) = 0$$
$$x = 46, 50$$

If $x = 46, y = 120 - 2(46) = 28$.
If $x = 50, y = 120 - 2(50) = 20$.
$x = 46$ ft and $y = 28$ ft or $x = 50$ ft and $y = 20$ ft

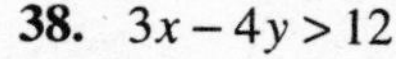

38. $3x - 4y > 12$

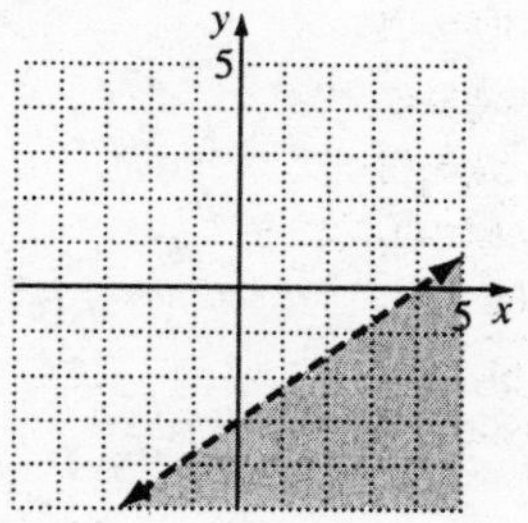

39. $y \le -\frac{1}{2}x + 2$

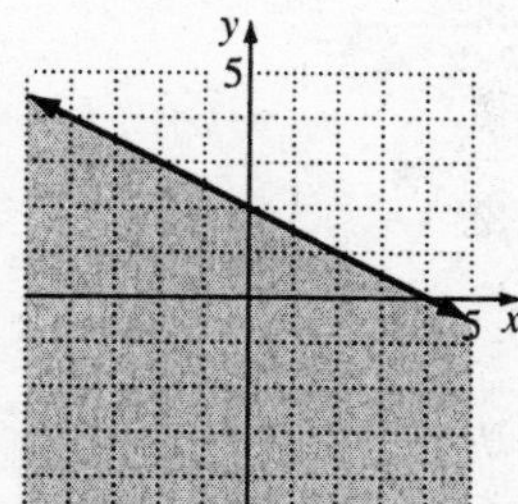

40. $x < -2$

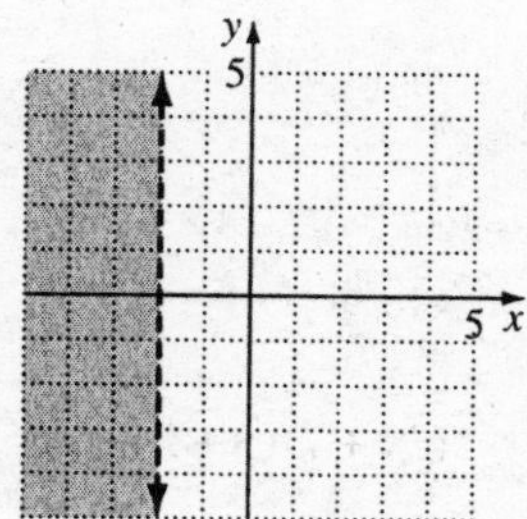

41. $y \ge 3$

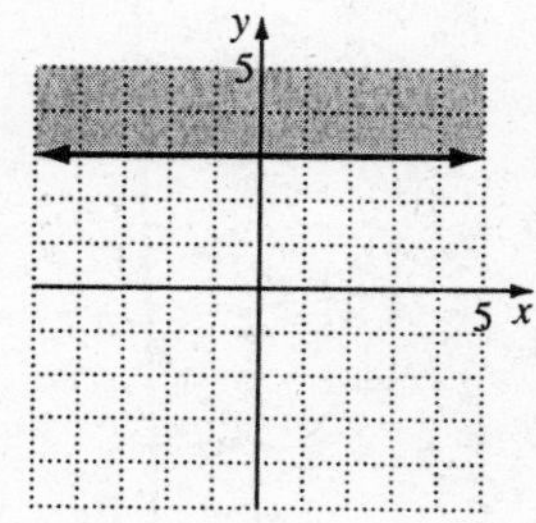

42. $x^2 + y^2 > 4$

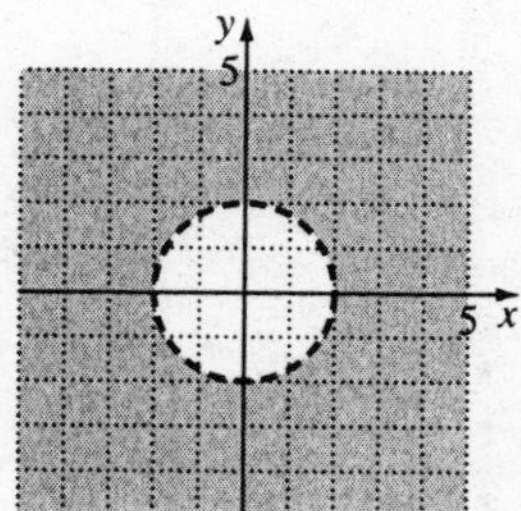

43. $y \le x^2 - 1$

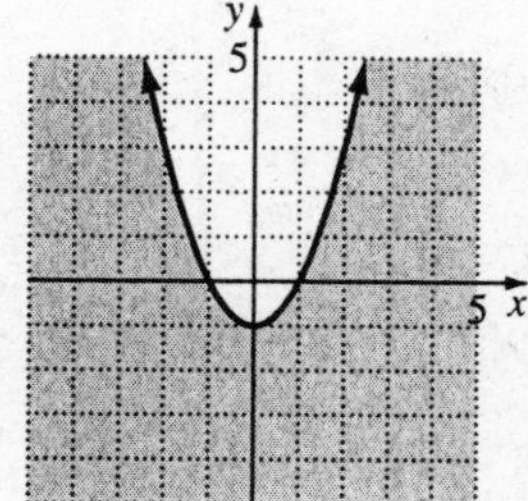

44. $y \le 2^x$

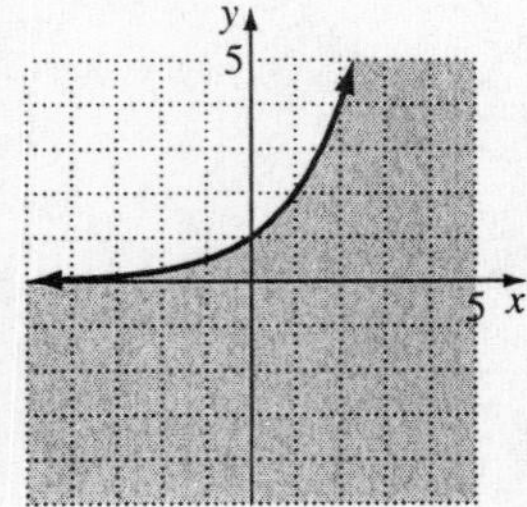

45. $3x + 2y \ge 6$
$2x + y \ge 6$

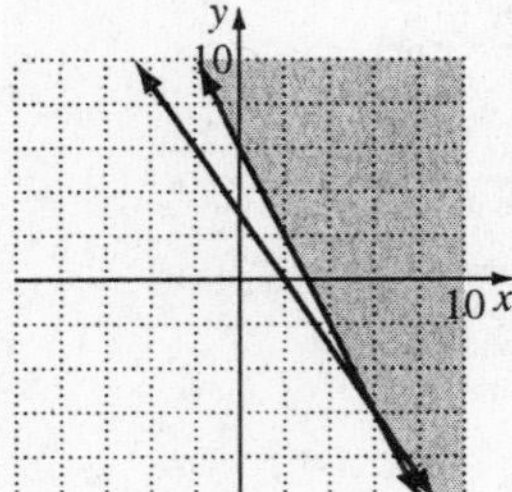

46. $2x - y \ge 4$
$x + 2y < 2$

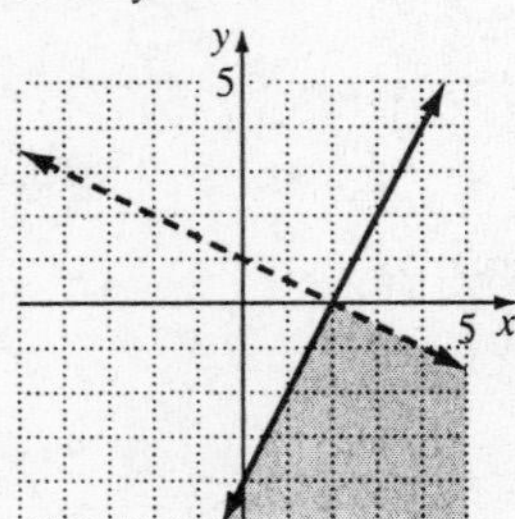

47. $y < x$
$y \le 2$

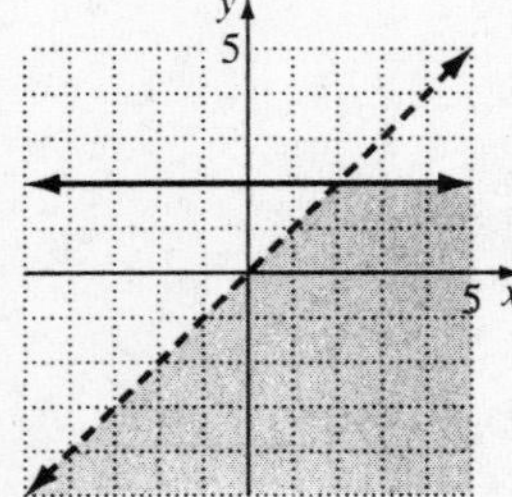

48. $y \le x$
$2x + 5y \le 10$

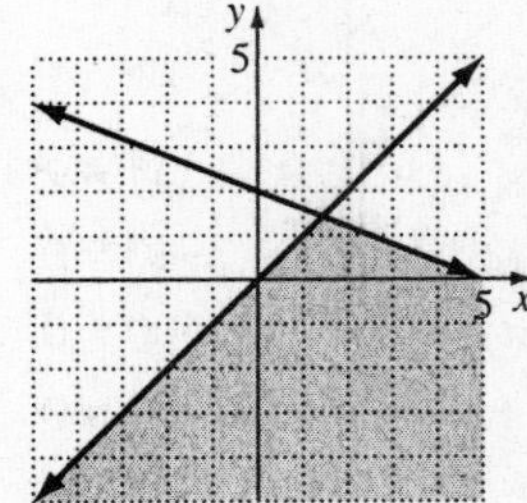

49. $0 \le x \le 3$
$y > 2$

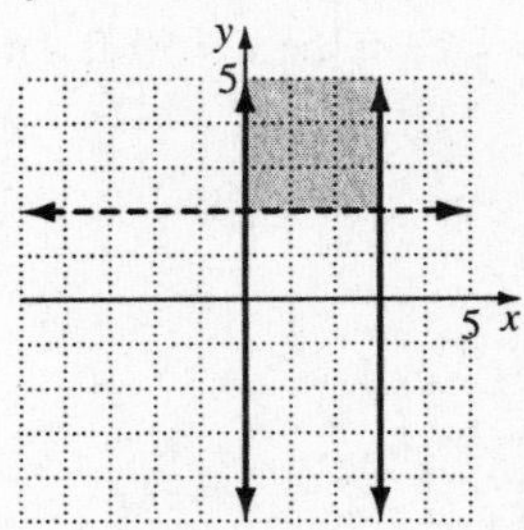

50. $2x + y < 4$
$2x + y > 6$

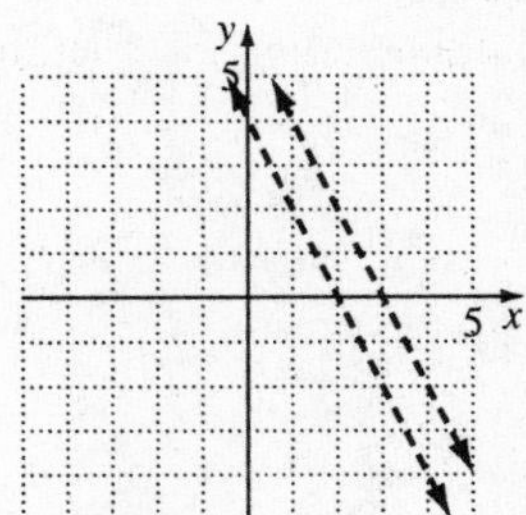

No solution

51. $x^2 + y^2 \le 16$
$x + y < 2$

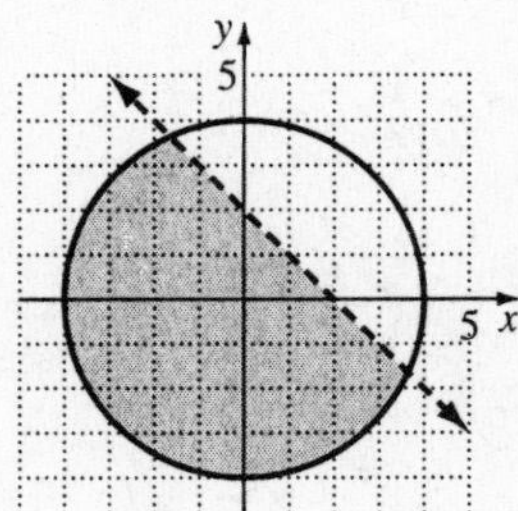

52. $x^2 + y^2 \le 9$
$y < -3x + 1$

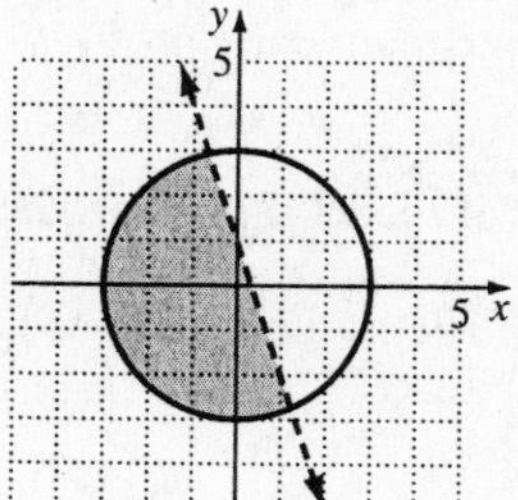

53. $y > x^2$
$x + y < 6$
$y < x + 6$

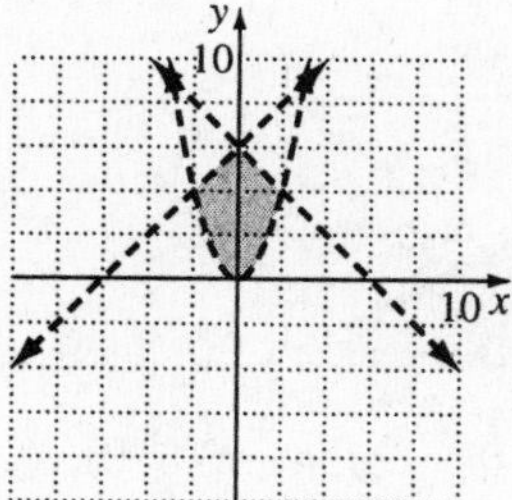

54. $x \ge 0, y \ge 0$
$2x + 3y \le 12$
$3x + y \le 6$

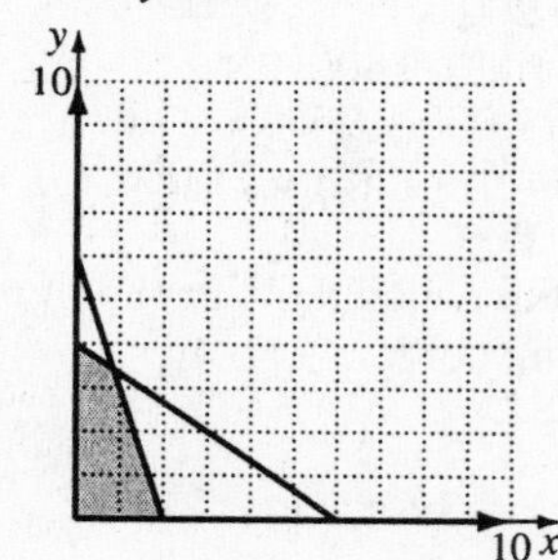

55. $z = 2x + 3y$
$(2,2): z = 2(2) + 3(2) = 10$
$(4,0): z = 2(4) + 3(0) = 8$
$\left(\frac{1}{2}, \frac{1}{2}\right): z = 2\left(\frac{1}{2}\right) + 3\left(\frac{1}{2}\right) = \frac{5}{2}$
$(1,0): z = 2(1) + 3(0) = 2$
The maximum value is 10 and the minimum value is 2.

56. $z = 2x + 3y$
$x \ge 0, y \ge 0$
$x + y \le 8$
$3x + 2y \ge 6$

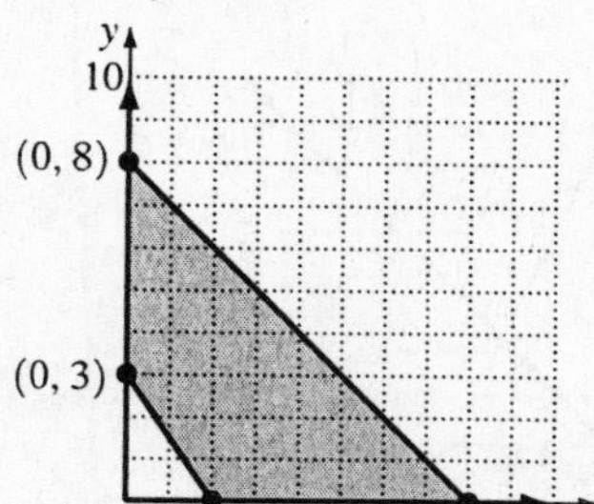

$(0,8): z = 2(0) + 3(8) = 24$
$(8,0): z = 2(8) + 3(0) = 16$
$(0,3): z = 2(0) + 3(3) = 9$
$(2,0): z = 2(2) + 3(0) = 6$
Maximum value is 24.

57. $z = x + 4y$
$0 \le x \le 5$
$0 \le y \le 7$
$x + y \ge 3$

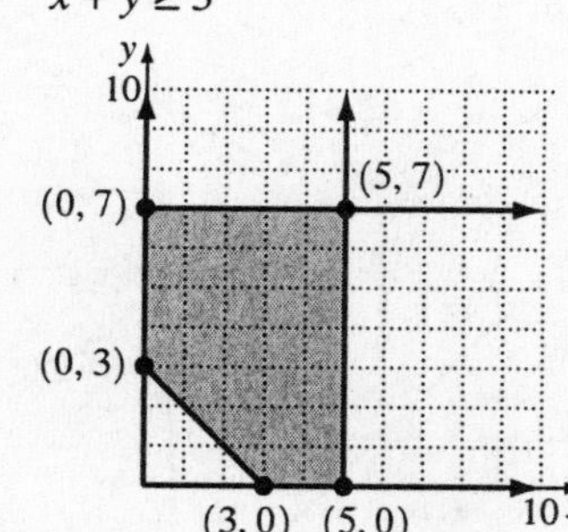

$(0,3): z = 0 + 4(3) = 12$
$(3,0): z = 3 + 4(0) = 3$
$(0,7): z = 0 + 4(7) = 28$
$(5,0): z = 5 + 4(0) = 5$
$(5,7): z = 5 + 4(7) = 33$
Maximum value is 33.

58. $z = 5x + 6y$
$x \ge 0,\ y \ge 0,\ y \le x$
$2x + y \le 12$
$2x + 3y > 6$

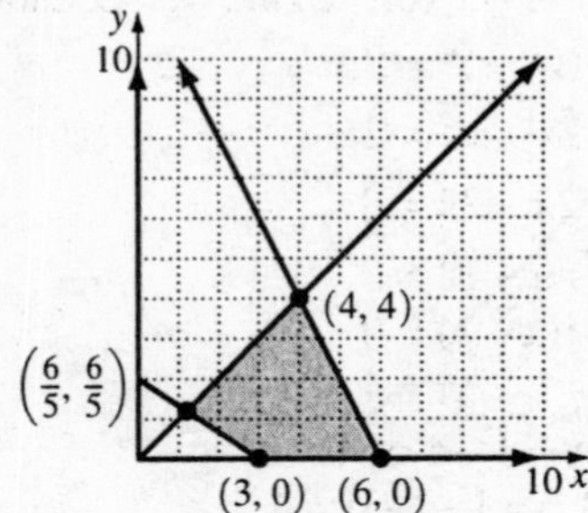

$(3, 0)$: $z = 5(3) + 6(0) = 15$
$(6, 0)$: $z = 5(6) + 6(0) = 30$
$\left(\frac{6}{5}, \frac{6}{5}\right)$: $z = 5\left(\frac{6}{5}\right) + 6\left(\frac{6}{5}\right) = \frac{66}{5} = 13.2$
$(4, 4)$: $5(4) + 6(4) = 44$
The maximum value is 44.

59. a. $z = 500x + 350y$

b. $x + y \le 200$
$x \ge 10$
$y \ge 80$

c.

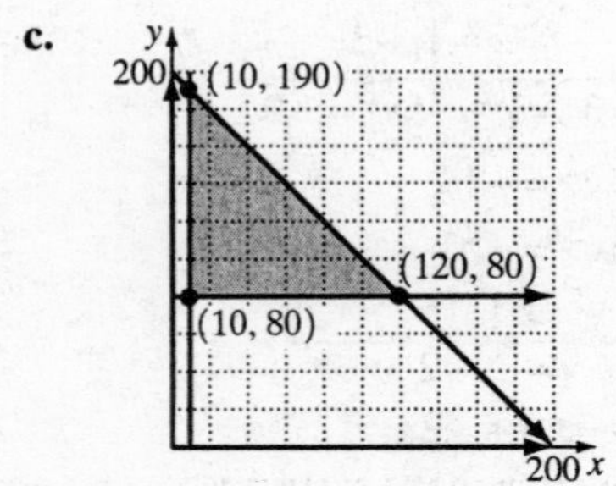

d.

Vertex	Objective Function $z = 500x + 350y$
(10, 80)	$z = 500(10) + 350(80) = 33,000$
(10, 190)	$z = 500(10) + 350(190) = 71,500$
(120, 80)	$z = 500(120) + 350(80) = 88,000$

e. The company will make the greatest profit by producing 120 units of writing paper and 80 units of newsprint each day. The maximum daily profit is \$88,000.

60. Let x = number of model A tents produced and
y = number of model B tents produced.
The constraints are:
$0.9x + 1.8y \le 864$
$0.8x + 1.2y \le 672$
$x \ge 0$
$y \ge 0$

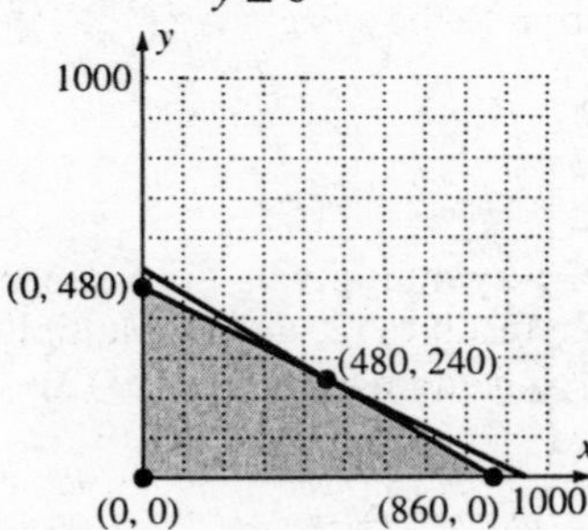

The vertices of the region are (0, 0), (0, 480), (480, 240), and (840, 0).
The objective is to maximize $25x + 40y$.
(0, 0): $25(0) + 40(0) = 0 + 0 = 0$
(0, 480): $25(0) + 40(480) = 0 + 19,200 = 19,200$
(480,240): $25(480) + 40(240) = 12,000 + 9600 = 21,600$
(840, 0): $25(840) + 40(0) = 21,000 + 0 = 21,000$
The manufacturer should make 480 of model *A* and 240 of model *B*.

Chapter 5 Test

1. $x = y + 4$
$3x + 7y = -18$
Substitute $y + 4$ for x into second equation.
$3(y + 4) + 7y = -18$
$3y + 12 + 7y = -18$
$10y = -30$
$y = -3$
$x = -3 + 4 = 1$
The solution set to the system is $\{(1, -3)\}$.

2. $2x + 5y = -2$
$3x - 4y = 20$
Multiply the first equation by 3 and the second equation by –2 and add the result.
$$\begin{array}{r} 6 + 15y = -6 \\ -6x + 8y = -40 \\ \hline 23y = -46 \\ y = -2 \end{array}$$
Substitute $y = -2$ into the first equation:
$2x + 5(-2) = -2$
$2x - 10 = -2$
$2x = 8$
$x = 4$
The solution to the system is $\{(4, -2)\}$.

3. $x + y + z = 6 \quad (1)$
$3x + 4y - 7z = 1 \quad (2)$
$2x - y + 3z = 5 \quad (3)$
Eliminate x by multiplying (1) by –3 and adding the result to (2) and by multiplying (1) by –2 and adding the result to (3).
$$\begin{array}{r} -3x - 3y - 3z = -18 \\ 3x + 4y - 7z = 1 \\ \hline y - 10z = -17 \ (4) \end{array}$$
$$\begin{array}{r} -2x - 2y - 2z = -12 \\ 2x - y + 3z = 5 \\ \hline -3y + z = -7 \ (5) \end{array}$$
Multiply (4) by 3 and add the result to (5) to eliminate y.
$$\begin{array}{r} 3y - 30z = -51 \\ -3y + z = -7 \\ \hline -29z = -58 \\ z = 2 \end{array}$$
Substitute $z = 2$ into (5).
$-3y + 2 = -7$
$-3y = -9$
$y = 3$
Substitute $z = 2$ and $y = 3$ into (1).
$x + 3 + 2 = 6$
$x = 1$
The solution to the system is $\{(1, 3, 2)\}$.

4. $x^2 + y^2 = 25$
$x + y = 1$
$y = 1 - x$
Substitute $1 - x$ for y in the first equation.
$x^2 + (1 - x)^2 = 25$
$x^2 + 1 - 2x + x^2 = 25$
$2x^2 - 2x - 24 = 0$
$x^2 - x - 12 = 0$
$(x - 4)(x + 3) = 0$
$x = 4, -3$
If $x = 4, y = 1 - 4 = -3$.
If $x = -3, y = 1 - (-3) = 4$.
The solution set is $\{(4, -3), (-3, 4)\}$.

5. $2x^2 - 5y^2 = -2$
$3x^2 + 2y^2 = 35$
Multiply first equation by 2 and the second equation by 5. Then add.
$$\begin{array}{r} 4x^2 - 10y^2 = -4 \\ 15x^2 + 10y^2 = 175 \\ \hline 19x^2 = 171 \end{array}$$
$x^2 = 9$
$x = 3, -3$
If $x = 3, 2(3)^2 - 5y^2 = -2$.
$18 - 5y^2 = -2$
$-5y^2 = -20$
$y^2 = 4$
$y = 2, -2$
If $x = -3, y = -2$.
The solution to the system is $\{(3, 2), (3, -2), (-3, 2), (-3, -2)\}$.

6. $\dfrac{x}{(x+1)(x^2+9)} = \dfrac{A}{x+1} + \dfrac{Bx+C}{x^2+9}$

$x = A(x^2+9)+(Bx+C)(x+1)$

$\quad = Ax^2+9A+Bx^2+Bx+Cx+C$

$\quad = (A+B)x^2+(B+C)x+(9A+C)$

$A+B=0 \to A=-B$

$B+C=1$

$9A+C=0$

$-9B+C=0$

$9B-C=0$

$\underline{B+C=1}$

$10B=1$

$B=\dfrac{1}{10}$

$A=-\dfrac{1}{10}$

$\dfrac{1}{10}+C=1,\ C=\dfrac{9}{10}$

$\dfrac{x}{(x+1)(x^2+9)} = \dfrac{-1}{10(x+1)} + \dfrac{x+9}{10(x^2+9)}$

7. $x-2y<8$

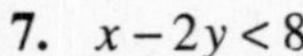

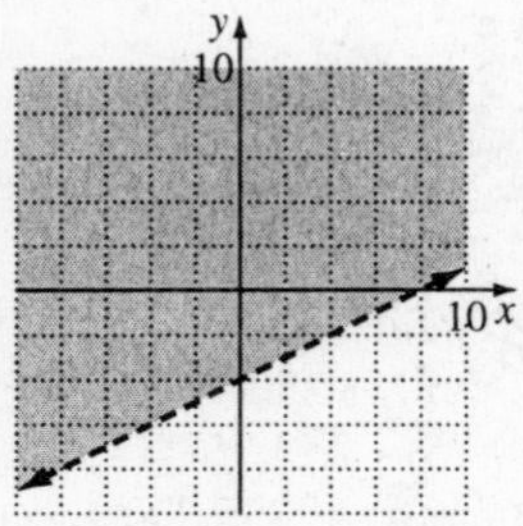

8. $x \geq 0, y \geq 0$

$3x+y \leq 9$

$2x+3y \geq 6$

9. $x^2+y^2>1$

$x^2+y^2<4$

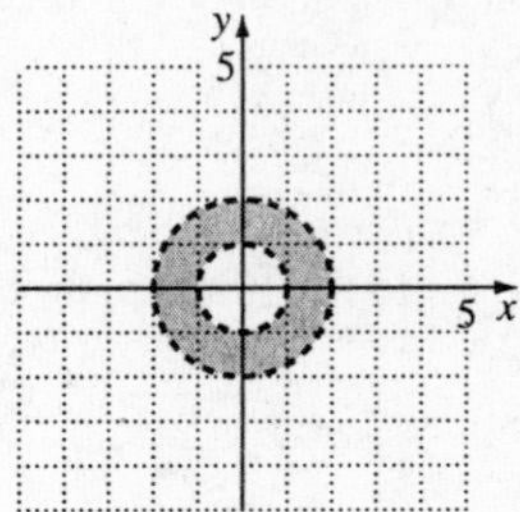

10. $y \leq 1-x^2$

$x^2+y^2 \leq 9$

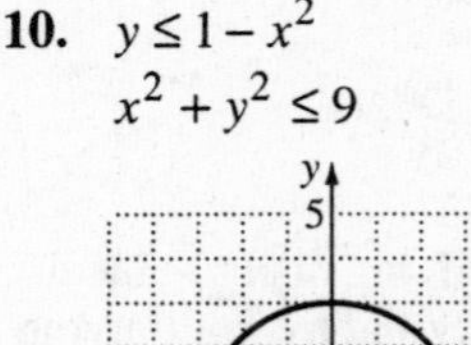

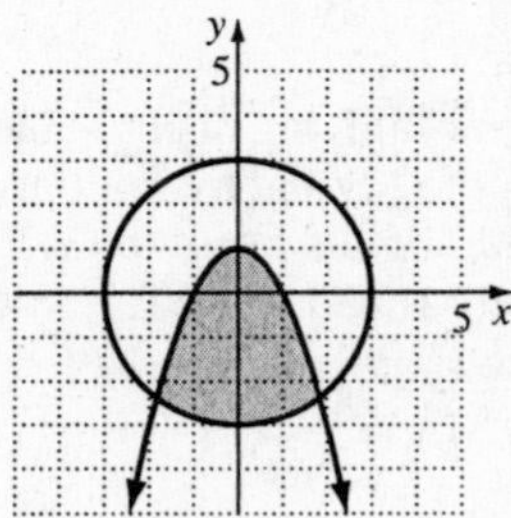

11. $z=3x+5y$

$x \geq 0, y \geq 0$

$x+y \leq 6$

$x \geq 2$

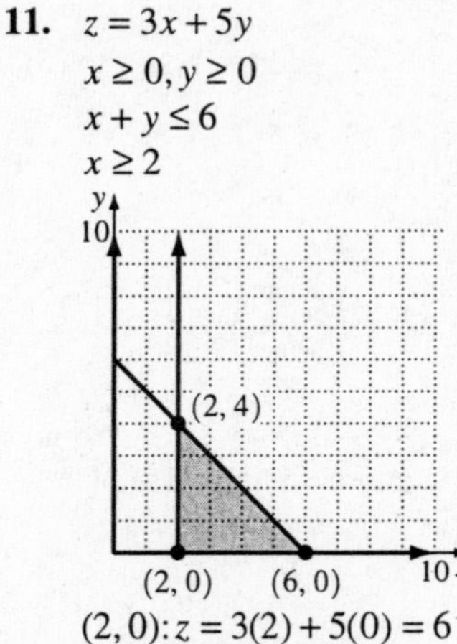

$(2,0): z=3(2)+5(0)=6$

$(6,0): z=3(6)+5(0)=18$

$(2,4): z=3(2)+5(4)=26$

Maximum value is 26.

12. Let x = price of orchestra ticket, y = price of mezzanine ticket.

$$4x+3y=134$$
$$5x+2y=143$$
$$8x+6y=268$$
$$-15x-6y=-429$$
$$-7x=-161$$
$$x=23$$
$$4(23)+3y=134$$
$$3y=134-92=42$$
$$y=14$$

An orchestra ticket costs \$23 and a mezzanine ticket costs \$14.

13.
$$N=1000-20P$$
$$N=250+5p$$
$$1000-20p=250+5p$$
$$750=25p$$
$$p=30$$
$$N=250+5(30)=400$$

400 units will be supplied and sold for \$30 each.

14. $y=ax^2+bx+c$

$(-1,-2): -2=a-b+c$

$(2,1): 1=4a+2b+c$

$(-2,1): 1=4a-2b+c$

$$4a+2b+c=1$$
$$-4a+2b-c=-1$$
$$4b=0$$
$$b=0$$
$$a+c=-2$$
$$4a+c=1$$
$$-a-c=2$$
$$3a=3$$
$$a=1$$
$$a+c=-2$$
$$c=-3$$

The quadratic function is $y=x^2-3$.

15. $2x+y=39$

$xy=180$

$y=39-2x$

$$x(39-2x)=180$$
$$39x-2x^2=180$$
$$2x^2-39x+180=0$$
$$(2x-15)(x-12)=0$$
$$x=\frac{15}{2},12$$

If $x=\frac{15}{2}, \frac{15}{2}y=180$ and $y=24$.

If $x=12, 12y=180$ and $y=15$.

The dimensions are 7.5 ft by 24 ft or 12 ft by 15 ft

16. Let x = regular, y = deluxe.

objective function: $z=200x+250y$

constraints: $x\ge 50, y\ge 75$

$x+y\le 150$

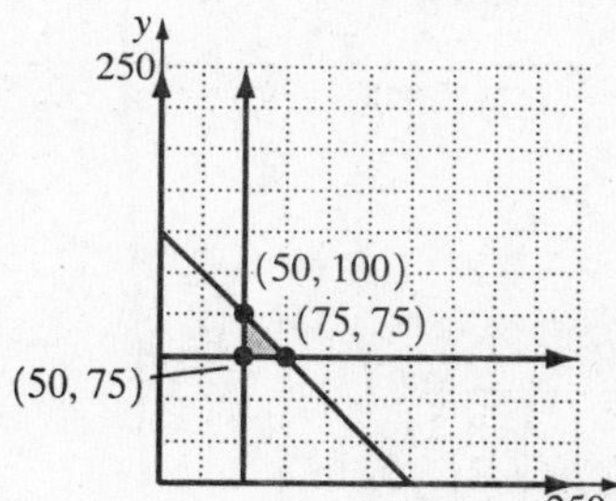

$(50,75): z=200(50)+250(75)=28,750$

$(50,100): z=200(50)+250(100)=35,000$

$(75,75): z=200(75)+250(75)=33,750$

For a maximum profit of \$35,000 a week, the company should manufacture 50 regular and 100 deluxe jet skis.

Cumulative Review Exercises (Chapters 1–5)

1.
$$\sqrt{x^2-3x}=2x-6$$
$$x^2-3x=4x^2-24x+36$$
$$3x^2-21x+36=0$$
$$x^2-7x+12=0$$
$$(x-3)(x-4)=0$$
$$x=3,4$$

The solution set is $\{3,4\}$.

2. $4x^2 = 8x - 7$

$4x^2 - 8x + 7 = 0$

$x = \frac{8 \pm \sqrt{64-112}}{8} = \frac{8 \pm \sqrt{-48}}{8}$

$= \frac{8 \pm 4\sqrt{3}i}{8} = \frac{2 \pm \sqrt{3}i}{2}$

The solutiion set is $\left\{\frac{2+i\sqrt{3}}{2}, \frac{2-i\sqrt{3}}{2}\right\}$.

3. $\left|\frac{x}{3}+2\right| < 4$

$-4 < \frac{x}{3} + 2 < 4$

$-6 < \frac{x}{3} < 2$

$-18 < x < 6$

The soluton set is $\{x \mid -18 < x < 6\}$.

4. $\frac{x+5}{x-1} > 2$

$\frac{x+5}{x-1} - 2 > 0$

$\frac{x+5-2(x-1)}{x-1} > 0$

$\frac{x+5-2x+2}{x-1} > 0$

$\frac{-x+7}{x-1} > 0$

$\frac{-x+7}{x-1} = 0$ when $x = 7$ and is undefined when $x = 1$.

Test $x = 0$:

$\frac{0+5}{0-1} > 2?$

$\frac{5}{-1} > 2?$

$-5 \ngtr 2$

Test $x = 2$:

$\frac{2+5}{2-1} > 2?$

$\frac{7}{1} > 2?$

$7 > 2$

Test $x = 8$:

$\frac{8+5}{8-1} > 2?$

$\frac{13}{7} > 2?$

$\frac{13}{7} \ngtr \frac{14}{7}$

The solution set is $\{x \mid 1 < x < 7\}$.

5. $2x^3 + x^2 - 13x + 6 = 0$

$f(x) = 2x^3 + x^2 - 13x + 6$ has 2 sign changes: 2 or 0 positive real roots.

$f(-x) = -2x^3 + x^2 + 13x + 6$ has 1 sign change: 1 negative real root.

p: ±1, ±2, ±3, ±6

q: ±1, ±2

$\frac{p}{q}$: $\pm 1, \pm\frac{1}{2}, \pm 2, \pm 3, \pm\frac{3}{2}, \pm 6$

−3	2	1	−13	6
		−6	15	−6
	2	−5	2	0

$2x^3 + x^2 - 13x + 6 = (x+3)(2x^2 - 5x + 2)$
$= (x+3)(2x-1)(x-2)$

$x = -3,\ x = \frac{1}{2},\ x = 2$

The solution set is $\left\{-3, \frac{1}{2}, 2\right\}$.

6. $6x - 3(5x+2) = 4(1-x)$

$6x - 15x - 6 = 4 - 4x$

$-9x - 6 = 4 - 4x$

$-5x = 10$

$x = -2$

The solution set is $\{-2\}$.

7. $\log(x+3)+\log x=1$
$\log x(x+3)=1$
$x(x+3)=10$
$x^2+3x-10=0$
$(x+5)(x-2)=0$
$x=-5 \text{ or } x=2$
$x=-5 \text{ is extraneous.}$
$x=2$
The solution set is $\{2\}$.

8. $3^{x+2}=11$
$\log_3 3^{x+2}=\log_3 11$
$x+2=\log_3 11$
$x=-2+\log_3 11$
$x=-2+\frac{\log 11}{\log 3}\approx 0.18$
The solution set is $\{-2+\log_3 11\}$.

9. $f(x)=(x+2)^2-4$
vertex: (–2, –4)
y-intercept:
$f(0)=(0+2)^2-4=0$
x-intercepts:
$(x+2)^2-4=0$
$x^2+4x+4-4=0$
$x^2+4x=0$
$x(x+4)=0$
$x=0, x-4$

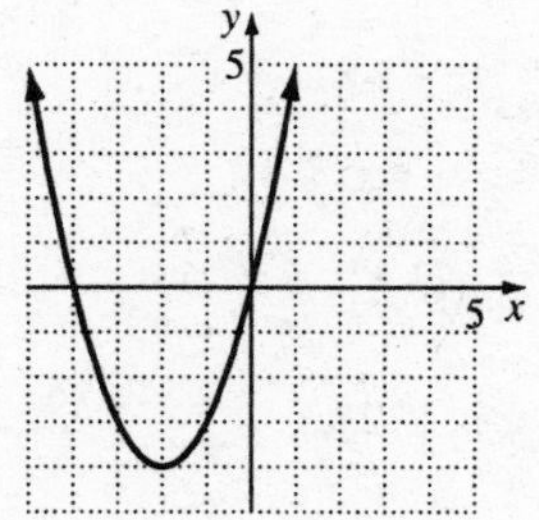

10. $2x-3y\le 6$

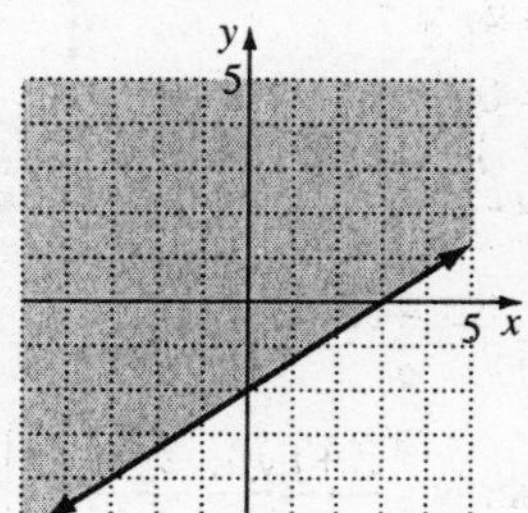

11. $y=3^{x-2}$

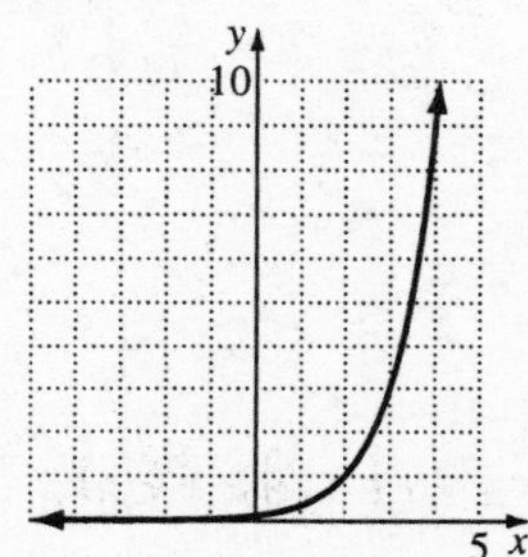

12. $f(x)=\frac{x^2-x-6}{x+1}$
vertical asymptote: $x=-1$
horizontal asymptote: $m>n$, none
x-intercepts:
$x^2-x-6=0$
$(x-3)(x+2)=0$
$x=3, x=-2$
y-intercept:
$f(0)=\frac{0^2-0-6}{0+1}=-6$

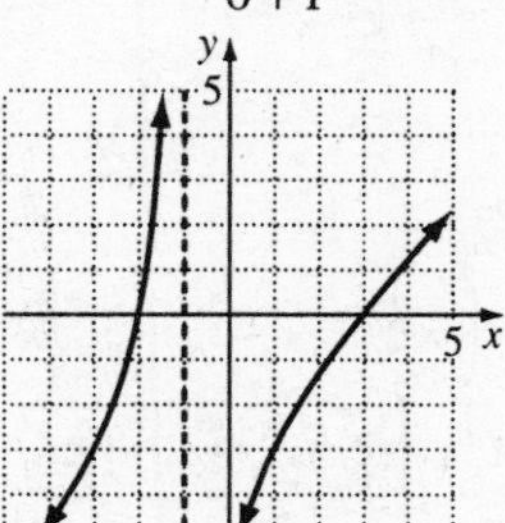

13. $\log_2(8x^5)=\log_2 8+\log_2 x^5$
$=3+5\log_2 x$

14. $A = Pe^{rt}$

$$18,000 = 6000e^{10r}$$
$$3 = e^{10r}$$
$$\ln 3 = \ln e^{10r}$$
$$\ln 3 = 10r$$
$$r = \frac{\ln 3}{10} \approx 0.1099$$

10.99%

15.
$$f(x) = 7x - 3$$
$$x = 7y - 3$$
$$x + 3 = 7y$$
$$y = \frac{1}{7}x + \frac{3}{7}$$
$$f^{-1}(x) = \frac{1}{7}x + \frac{3}{7}$$

16. $f(x) = 7x - 3, g(x) = 3x - 7$

$$g(f(x)) = 3(7x - 3) - 7 = 21x - 9 - 7 = 21x - 16$$

17. Answers may vary.

18. $3x - y = -2$

$2x^2 - y = 0$

Solve the first equation for y.

$y = 3x + 2$

Substitute the expression $3x + 2$ for y in the second equation and solve for x.

$$2x^2 - (3x + 2) = 0$$
$$2x^2 - 3x - 2 = 0$$
$$x = \frac{3 \pm \sqrt{9 + 16}}{4} = \frac{3 \pm 5}{4}$$
$$x = \frac{3+5}{4} = 2 \text{ or } x = \frac{3-5}{4} = -\frac{1}{2}$$

If $x = 2, y = 3(2) + 2 = 8$.

If $x = -\frac{1}{2}, y = 3\left(-\frac{1}{2}\right) + 2 = \frac{1}{2}$.

The solution set is $\left\{(2, 8), \left(-\frac{1}{2}, \frac{1}{2}\right)\right\}$.

19.
$$L = 2W + 1$$
$$LW = 36$$
$$W(2W + 1) = 36$$
$$2W^2 + W - 36 = 0$$
$$(2W + 9)(W - 4) = 0$$
$$W = -\frac{9}{2} \text{ or } 4$$

Length cannot be negative. If $W = 4$, $4L = 36$, $L = 9$. The dimensions are 4 m by 9 m.

20.
$$f(x) = 0.1x^2 - 3x + 22$$
$$f(90) = 0.1(90)^2 - 3(90) + 22$$
$$= 810 - 270 + 22$$
$$= 562$$

A plane with an initial landing speed of 90 feet per second needs 562 feet to land. There is a problem since 550 ft is not enough.

Chapter 6

Section 6.1

Check Point Exercises

1. $\left[\begin{array}{ccc|c} 1 & -1 & 1 & 8 \\ 0 & 1 & -12 & -15 \\ 0 & 0 & 1 & 1 \end{array}\right] \rightarrow \begin{array}{c} 1x - 1y + 1z = 8 \\ 0x + 1y - 12z = -15 \\ 0x + 0y + 1z = 1 \end{array}$

$$\begin{aligned} x - y + z &= 8 \\ y - 12z &= -15 \\ z &= 1 \end{aligned}$$

Solve for y by back-substitution.

$$\begin{aligned} y - 12(1) &= -15 \\ y - 12 &= -15 \\ y &= -3 \end{aligned}$$

Use back substitution for x.

$$\begin{aligned} x - (-3) + 1 &= 8 \\ x + 4 &= 8 \\ x &= 4 \end{aligned}$$

The solution set for the system is $\{(4, -3, 1)\}$.

2. a. The notation $R_1 \leftrightarrow R_2$ means to interchange the elements in row 1 and row 2. This results in the row-equivalent matrix

$$\left[\begin{array}{ccc|c} 1 & 6 & -3 & 7 \\ 4 & 12 & -20 & 8 \\ -3 & -2 & 1 & -9 \end{array}\right].$$

b. The notation $\frac{1}{4}R_1$ means to multiply each element in row 1 by $\frac{1}{4}$. This results in the row-equivalent matrix

$$\left[\begin{array}{ccc|c} \frac{1}{4}(4) & \frac{1}{4}(12) & \frac{1}{4}(-20) & \frac{1}{4}(8) \\ 1 & 6 & -3 & 7 \\ -3 & -2 & 1 & -9 \end{array}\right] = \left[\begin{array}{ccc|c} 1 & 3 & -5 & 2 \\ 1 & 6 & -3 & 7 \\ -3 & -2 & 1 & -9 \end{array}\right]$$

c. The notation $3R_2 + R_3$ means to add 3 times the elements in row 2 to the corresponding elements in row 3. Replace the elements in row 3 by these sums. First, we find 3 times the elements in row 2: $3(1) = 3$, $3(6) = 18$, $3(-3) = -9$, $3(7) = 21$. Now we add these products to the corresponding elements in row 3. This results in the row equivalent matrix

$$\left[\begin{array}{ccc|c} 4 & 12 & -20 & 8 \\ 1 & 6 & -3 & 7 \\ -3+3=0 & -2+18=16 & 1-9=-8 & -9+21=12 \end{array}\right] = \left[\begin{array}{ccc|c} 4 & 12 & -20 & 8 \\ 1 & 6 & -3 & 7 \\ 0 & 16 & -8 & 12 \end{array}\right].$$

3. $\begin{aligned} 2x+y+2z&=18 \\ x-y+2z&=9 \\ x+2y-z&=6 \end{aligned} \rightarrow \left[\begin{array}{ccc|c} 2 & 1 & 2 & 18 \\ 1 & -1 & 2 & 9 \\ 1 & 2 & -1 & 6 \end{array}\right]$

Interchange row 1 with row 2 to get 1 in the top position of the first column.

$$\left[\begin{array}{ccc|c} 1 & -1 & 2 & 9 \\ 2 & 1 & 2 & 18 \\ 1 & 2 & -1 & 6 \end{array}\right]$$

Multiply the first row by –2 and add these products to row 2.

$$\left[\begin{array}{ccc|c} 1 & -1 & 2 & 9 \\ 2+-2=0 & 1+2=3 & 2+-4=-2 & -18+18=0 \\ 1 & 2 & -1 & 6 \end{array}\right] = \left[\begin{array}{ccc|c} 1 & -1 & 2 & 9 \\ 0 & 3 & -2 & 0 \\ 1 & 2 & -1 & 6 \end{array}\right]$$

Next, multiply the top row by –1 and add these products to row 3.

$$\left[\begin{array}{ccc|c} 1 & -1 & 2 & 9 \\ 0 & 3 & -2 & 0 \\ 1+-1=0 & 2+1=3 & -1-2=-3 & 6-9=-3 \end{array}\right] = \left[\begin{array}{ccc|c} 1 & -1 & 2 & 9 \\ 0 & 3 & -2 & 0 \\ 0 & 3 & -3 & -3 \end{array}\right]$$

Next, to obtain a 1 in the second row, second column, multiply 3 by its reciprocal, $\frac{1}{3}$. Therefore, we multiply all the numbers in the second row by $\frac{1}{3}$ to get

$$\left[\begin{array}{ccc|c} 1 & -1 & 2 & 9 \\ 0 & 1 & -\frac{2}{3} & 0 \\ 0 & 3 & -3 & -3 \end{array}\right].$$

Next, to obtain a 0 in the third row, second column, multiply the second row by –3 and add the products to row three. The resulting matrix is

$$\left[\begin{array}{ccc|c} 1 & -1 & 2 & 9 \\ 0 & 1 & -\frac{2}{3} & 0 \\ 0 & 0 & -1 & -3 \end{array}\right].$$

To get 1 in the third row, third column, multiply –1 by its reciprocal, –1. Multiply all numbers in the third row by –1 to obtain the resulting matrix

$$\left[\begin{array}{ccc|c} 1 & -1 & 2 & 9 \\ 0 & 1 & -\frac{2}{3} & 0 \\ 0 & 0 & 1 & 3 \end{array}\right].$$

The system represented by this matrix is:

$$\begin{aligned} x-y+2z&=9 \\ y-\frac{2}{3}z&=0 \\ z&=3 \end{aligned}$$

Use back substitution to find y and x.

$$\begin{aligned} y-\tfrac{2}{3}(3)&=0 \\ y-2&=0 \\ y&=2 \end{aligned} \qquad \begin{aligned} x-2+6&=9 \\ x+4&=9 \\ x&=5 \end{aligned}$$

The solution set for the original system is $\{(5, 2, 3)\}$.

4. $x - 3y - 2z + w = -3$
$2x - 7y - z + 2w = 1$
$3x - 7y - 3z + 3w = -5$
$5x + y + 4z - 2w = 18$

The augmented matrix is

$$\left[\begin{array}{cccc|c} 1 & -3 & -2 & 1 & -3 \\ 2 & -7 & -1 & 2 & 1 \\ 3 & -7 & -3 & 3 & -5 \\ 5 & 1 & 4 & -2 & 18 \end{array}\right].$$

Multiply the top row by –2 and add the products to the second row. Multiply the top row by –3 and add the products to the third row. Multiply the top row by –5 and add the products to the fourth row. The resulting matrix is

$$\left[\begin{array}{cccc|c} 1 & -3 & -2 & 1 & -3 \\ 0 & -1 & 3 & 0 & 7 \\ 0 & 2 & 3 & 0 & 4 \\ 0 & 16 & 14 & -7 & 33 \end{array}\right].$$

Next, multiply the second row by –1 to obtain a 1 in the second row, second column.

$$\left[\begin{array}{cccc|c} 1 & -3 & -2 & 1 & -3 \\ 0 & 1 & -3 & 0 & -7 \\ 0 & 2 & 3 & 0 & 4 \\ 0 & 16 & 14 & -7 & 33 \end{array}\right]$$

Next, multiply the second row by –2 and add the products to the third row. Multiply the second row by –16 and add the products to the fourth row. The resulting matrix is

$$\left[\begin{array}{cccc|c} 1 & -3 & -2 & 1 & -3 \\ 0 & 1 & -3 & 0 & -7 \\ 0 & 0 & 9 & 0 & 18 \\ 0 & 0 & 62 & -7 & 145 \end{array}\right].$$

Next, multiply the third row by $\frac{1}{9}$ to obtain a 1 in the third row, third column. The resulting matrix is

$$\left[\begin{array}{cccc|c} 1 & -3 & -2 & 1 & -3 \\ 0 & 1 & -3 & 0 & -7 \\ 0 & 0 & 1 & 0 & 2 \\ 0 & 0 & 62 & -7 & 145 \end{array}\right].$$

Multiply the third row by –62 and add the products to the fourth row to obtain the resulting matrix

$$\left[\begin{array}{cccc|c} 1 & -3 & -2 & 1 & -3 \\ 0 & 1 & -3 & 0 & -7 \\ 0 & 0 & 1 & 0 & 2 \\ 0 & 0 & 0 & -7 & 21 \end{array}\right].$$

Multiply the fourth row by $-\frac{1}{7}$, the reciprocal of –7. The resulting matrix is

$$\left[\begin{array}{cccc|c} 1 & -3 & -2 & 1 & -3 \\ 0 & 1 & -3 & 0 & -7 \\ 0 & 0 & 1 & 0 & 2 \\ 0 & 0 & 0 & 1 & -3 \end{array}\right]$$

The system of linear equations corresponding to the resulting matrix is

$$\begin{aligned} x - 3y - 2z + w &= -3 \\ y - 3z &= -7 \\ z &= 2 \\ w &= -3 \end{aligned}$$

Using back-substitution solve for x and y.

$$\begin{aligned} y - 6 &= -7 \\ y &= -1 \\ x + 3 - 4 - 3 &= -3 \\ x + 4 &= -3 \\ x - 4 &= -3 \\ x &= 1 \end{aligned}$$

The solution set is $\{(1, -1, 2, -3)\}$.

5. The matrix obtained in $2a$ will be the starting point.

$$\left[\begin{array}{ccc|c} 1 & 6 & -3 & 7 \\ 4 & 12 & -20 & 8 \\ -3 & -2 & 1 & -9 \end{array}\right]$$

First, multiply the first row by –4 and add the products to the second row. Multiply the first row by 3 and add the products to the third row. The resulting matrix is

$$\left[\begin{array}{ccc|c} 1 & 6 & -3 & 7 \\ 0 & -12 & -8 & -20 \\ 0 & 16 & -8 & 12 \end{array}\right].$$

Next, multiply the second row by $-\frac{1}{12}$ to obtain a 1 in the second row, second column.

$$\left[\begin{array}{ccc|c} 1 & 6 & -3 & 7 \\ 0 & 1 & \frac{2}{3} & \frac{5}{3} \\ 0 & 16 & -8 & 12 \end{array}\right].$$

Next, multiply the second row by –16 and add products to the third row.

$$\left[\begin{array}{ccc|c} 1 & 6 & -3 & 7 \\ 0 & 1 & \frac{2}{3} & \frac{5}{3} \\ 0 & 0 & -\frac{56}{3} & -\frac{44}{3} \end{array}\right]$$

Next, multiply the third row by $-\frac{3}{56}$ to obtain 1 in the third row, third column.

$$\left[\begin{array}{ccc|c} 1 & 6 & -3 & 7 \\ 0 & 1 & \frac{2}{3} & \frac{5}{3} \\ 0 & 0 & 1 & \frac{11}{14} \end{array}\right]$$

Next, multiply the second row by –6 and add products to the first row to obtain a 0 in the first row, second column.

$$\left[\begin{array}{ccc|c} 1 & 0 & -7 & -3 \\ 0 & 1 & \frac{2}{3} & \frac{5}{3} \\ 0 & 0 & 1 & \frac{11}{14} \end{array}\right]$$

Next, multiply the third row by $-\frac{2}{3}$ and add the products to the second row. Multiply the third row by 7 and add the products to the first row. The resulting matrix is

$$\left[\begin{array}{ccc|c} 1 & 0 & 0 & \frac{5}{2} \\ 0 & 1 & 0 & \frac{8}{7} \\ 0 & 0 & 1 & \frac{11}{14} \end{array}\right].$$

This matrix corresponds to $x = \frac{5}{2}$, $y = \frac{8}{7}$ and $z = \frac{11}{14}$. The solution set is $\left\{\left(\frac{5}{2}, \frac{8}{7}, \frac{11}{14}\right)\right\}$.

Exercise Set 6.1

1. $\left[\begin{array}{ccc|c} 2 & 1 & 2 & 2 \\ 3 & -5 & -1 & 4 \\ 1 & -2 & -3 & -6 \end{array}\right]$

3. $\left[\begin{array}{ccc|c} 1 & -1 & 1 & 8 \\ 0 & 1 & -12 & -15 \\ 0 & 0 & 1 & 1 \end{array}\right]$

5. $\left[\begin{array}{ccc|c} 5 & -2 & -3 & 0 \\ 1 & 1 & 0 & 5 \\ 2 & 0 & -3 & 4 \end{array}\right]$

7. $\left[\begin{array}{cccc|c} 2 & 5 & -3 & 1 & 2 \\ 0 & 3 & 1 & 0 & 4 \\ 1 & -1 & 5 & 0 & 9 \\ 5 & -5 & -2 & 0 & 1 \end{array}\right]$

9. $5x + 3z = -11$
$y - 4z = 12$
$7x + 2y = 3$

11. $x+y+4z+w=3$
$-x+y-z=7$
$2x+5w=11$
$12z+4w=5$

13. $x-4z=5$
$y-12z=13$
$z=-\frac{1}{2}$
$y-12\left(-\frac{1}{2}\right)=13$
$y+6=13$
$y=7$
$x-4\left(-\frac{1}{2}\right)=5$
$x+2=5$
$x=3$

The solution set is $\{(3, 7, \frac{1}{2})\}$.

15. $\left[\begin{array}{ccc|c} 1 & \frac{1}{2} & 1 & \frac{11}{2} \\ 0 & 1 & \frac{3}{2} & 7 \\ 0 & 0 & 1 & 4 \end{array}\right]$

$x+\frac{1}{2}y+z=\frac{11}{2}$
$y+\frac{3}{2}z=7$
$z=4$
$y+\frac{3}{2}(4)=7$
$y+6=7$
$y=1$
$x+\frac{1}{2}(1)+4=\frac{11}{2}$
$x+\frac{9}{2}=\frac{11}{2}$
$x=\frac{11}{2}-\frac{9}{2}$
$x=1$

The solution set is $\{(1, 1, 4)\}$.

17. $\left[\begin{array}{cccc|c} 1 & -1 & 1 & 1 & 3 \\ 0 & 1 & -2 & -1 & 0 \\ 0 & 0 & 1 & 6 & 17 \\ 0 & 0 & 0 & 1 & 3 \end{array}\right]$

$x-y+z+w=3$
$y-2z-w=0$
$z+6w=17$
$w=3$
$z+6(3)=17$
$z+18=17$
$z=-1$
$y-2(-1)-(3)=0$
$y+2-3=0$
$y=1$
$x-(1)+(-1)+(3)=3$
$x-2+3=3$
$x+1=3$
$x=2$

The solution set is $\{(2, 1, -1, 3)\}$.

19. $\left[\begin{array}{ccc|c} 2(\frac{1}{2}) & -6(\frac{1}{2}) & 4(\frac{1}{2}) & 10 \\ 1 & 5 & -5 & 0 \\ 3 & 0 & 4 & 7 \end{array}\right]\frac{1}{2}R_1$

$\left[\begin{array}{ccc|c} 1 & -3 & 2 & 5 \\ 1 & 5 & -5 & 0 \\ 3 & 0 & 4 & 7 \end{array}\right]$

21. $\left[\begin{array}{ccc|c} 1 & -3 & 2 & 0 \\ -3(1)+3 & -3(-3)+1 & -3(2)+-1 & -3(0)+7 \\ 2 & -2 & 1 & 3 \end{array}\right] -3R_1+R_2$

$\left[\begin{array}{ccc|c} 1 & -3 & 2 & 0 \\ 0 & 10 & -7 & 7 \\ 2 & -2 & 1 & 3 \end{array}\right]$

23. $\left[\begin{array}{cccc|c} 1 & -1 & 1 & 1 & 3 \\ 0 & 1 & -2 & -1 & 0 \\ 2 & 0 & 3 & 4 & 11 \\ 5 & 1 & 2 & 4 & 6 \end{array}\right] \begin{array}{l} \\ -2R_1+R_3 \\ -5R_1+R_4 \\ \end{array}$

$\left[\begin{array}{cccc|c} 1 & -1 & 1 & 1 & 3 \\ 0 & 1 & -2 & -1 & 0 \\ -2(1)+2 & -2(-1)+0 & -2(1)+3 & -2(1)+4 & -2(3)+11 \\ -5(1)+5 & -5(-1)+1 & -5(1)+2 & -5(1)+4 & -5(3)+6 \end{array}\right] = \left[\begin{array}{cccc|c} 1 & -1 & 1 & 1 & 3 \\ 0 & 1 & -2 & -1 & 0 \\ 0 & 2 & 1 & 2 & 5 \\ 0 & 6 & -3 & -1 & -9 \end{array}\right]$

25. $\left[\begin{array}{ccc|c} 1 & -1 & 1 & 8 \\ 2 & 3 & -1 & -2 \\ 3 & -2 & -9 & 9 \end{array}\right]$

$\left[\begin{array}{ccc|c} 1 & -1 & 1 & 8 \\ -2(1)+2 & -2(-1)+3 & -2(1)-1 & -2(8)-2 \\ -3(1)+3 & -3(-1)-2 & -3(1)-9 & -3(8)+9 \end{array}\right]$

$\left[\begin{array}{ccc|c} 1 & -1 & 1 & 8 \\ 0 & 5 & -3 & -18 \\ 0 & 1 & -12 & -15 \end{array}\right]$

$\left[\begin{array}{ccc|c} 1 & -1 & 1 & 8 \\ 0\left(\frac{1}{5}\right) & 1\left(\frac{1}{5}\right) & -3\left(\frac{1}{5}\right) & -18\left(\frac{1}{5}\right) \\ 0 & 1 & -12 & -15 \end{array}\right]$

$\left[\begin{array}{ccc|c} 1 & -1 & 1 & 8 \\ 0 & 1 & -\frac{3}{5} & -\frac{18}{5} \\ 0 & 1 & -12 & -15 \end{array}\right]$

27. $x+y-z=-2$
$2x-y+z=5$
$-x+2y+2z=1$

$$\left[\begin{array}{ccc|c} 1 & 1 & -1 & -2 \\ 2 & -1 & 1 & 5 \\ -1 & 2 & 2 & 1 \end{array}\right] -2R_1+R_2$$

$$\left[\begin{array}{ccc|c} 1 & 1 & -1 & -2 \\ 0 & -3 & 3 & 9 \\ -1 & 2 & 2 & 1 \end{array}\right] 1R_1+R_3$$

$$\left[\begin{array}{ccc|c} 1 & 1 & -1 & -2 \\ 0 & -3 & 3 & 9 \\ 0 & 3 & 1 & -1 \end{array}\right] -\tfrac{1}{3}R_2$$

$$\left[\begin{array}{ccc|c} 1 & 1 & -1 & -2 \\ 0 & 1 & -1 & -3 \\ 0 & 3 & 1 & -1 \end{array}\right] -3R_2+R_3$$

$$=\left[\begin{array}{ccc|c} 1 & 1 & -1 & -2 \\ 0 & 1 & -1 & -3 \\ 0 & 0 & 4 & 8 \end{array}\right]$$

$4z=8$
$z=2$
$y-z=-3$
$y-2=-3$
$y=-1$
$x+y-z=-2$
$x-1-2=-2$
$x-3=-2$
$x=1$

The solution set is $\{(1,-1,2)\}$.

29. $x+3y=0$
$x+y+z=1$
$3x-y-z=11$

$$\left[\begin{array}{ccc|c} 1 & 3 & 0 & 0 \\ 1 & 1 & 1 & 1 \\ 3 & -1 & -1 & 11 \end{array}\right] -1R_1+R_2$$

$$\left[\begin{array}{ccc|c} 1 & 3 & 0 & 0 \\ 0 & -2 & 1 & 1 \\ 3 & -1 & -1 & 11 \end{array}\right] -3R_1+R_3$$

$$\left[\begin{array}{ccc|c} 1 & 3 & 0 & 0 \\ 0 & -2 & 1 & 1 \\ 0 & -10 & -1 & 11 \end{array}\right] -\tfrac{1}{2}R_2$$

$$\left[\begin{array}{ccc|c} 1 & 3 & 0 & 0 \\ 0 & 1 & -\tfrac{1}{2} & -\tfrac{1}{2} \\ 0 & -10 & -1 & 11 \end{array}\right] 10R_2+R_3$$

$$\left[\begin{array}{ccc|c} 1 & 3 & 0 & 0 \\ 0 & 1 & -\tfrac{1}{2} & -\tfrac{1}{2} \\ 0 & 0 & -6 & 6 \end{array}\right] -\tfrac{1}{6}R_3$$

$$\left[\begin{array}{ccc|c} 1 & 3 & 0 & 0 \\ 0 & 1 & -\tfrac{1}{2} & -\tfrac{1}{2} \\ 0 & 0 & 1 & -1 \end{array}\right]$$

$z=-1$
$y-\frac{1}{2}z=-\frac{1}{2}$
$y-\frac{1}{2}(-1)=-\frac{1}{2}$
$y+\frac{1}{2}=-\frac{1}{2}$
$y=-1$
$x+3y=0$
$x+3(-1)=0$
$x=3$

The solution set is $\{(3,-1,-1)\}$.

31. $2x+2y+7z=-1$
$2x+y+2z=2$
$4x+6y+z=15$

$$\left[\begin{array}{ccc|c} 2 & 2 & 7 & -1 \\ 2 & 1 & 2 & 2 \\ 4 & 6 & 1 & 15 \end{array}\right] \tfrac{1}{2}R_1$$

$$\left[\begin{array}{ccc|c} 1 & 1 & \frac{7}{2} & -\frac{1}{2} \\ 2 & 1 & 2 & 2 \\ 4 & 6 & 1 & 15 \end{array}\right] -2R_1+R_2$$

$$\left[\begin{array}{ccc|c} 1 & 1 & \frac{7}{2} & -\frac{1}{2} \\ 0 & -1 & -5 & 3 \\ 4 & 6 & 1 & 15 \end{array}\right] -4R_1+R_3$$

$$\left[\begin{array}{ccc|c} 1 & 1 & \frac{7}{2} & -\frac{1}{2} \\ 0 & -1 & -5 & 3 \\ 0 & 2 & -13 & 17 \end{array}\right] -1R_2$$

$$\left[\begin{array}{ccc|c} 1 & 1 & \frac{7}{2} & -\frac{1}{2} \\ 0 & 1 & 5 & -3 \\ 0 & 2 & -13 & 17 \end{array}\right] -2R_2+R_3$$

$$\left[\begin{array}{ccc|c} 1 & 1 & \frac{7}{2} & -\frac{1}{2} \\ 0 & 1 & 5 & -3 \\ 0 & 0 & -23 & 23 \end{array}\right] -\tfrac{1}{23}R_3$$

$$\left[\begin{array}{ccc|c} 1 & 1 & \frac{7}{2} & -\frac{1}{2} \\ 0 & 1 & 5 & -3 \\ 0 & 0 & 1 & -1 \end{array}\right]$$

$z=-1$
$y+5z=-3$
$y+5(-1)=-3$
$y-5=-3$
$y=2$
$x+y+\frac{7}{2}z=-\frac{1}{2}$
$x+2+\frac{7}{2}(-1)=-\frac{1}{2}$
$x-\frac{3}{2}=-\frac{1}{2}$
$x=1$

The solution set is $\{(1, 2, -1)\}$.

33. $x+y+z+w=4$
$2x+y-2z-w=0$
$x-2y-z-2w=-2$
$3x+2y+z+3w=4$

$$\left[\begin{array}{cccc|c} 1 & 1 & 1 & 1 & 4 \\ 2 & 1 & -2 & -1 & 0 \\ 1 & -2 & -1 & -2 & -2 \\ 3 & 2 & 1 & 3 & 4 \end{array}\right] -2R_1+R_2$$

$$\left[\begin{array}{cccc|c} 1 & 1 & 1 & 1 & 4 \\ 0 & -1 & -4 & -3 & -8 \\ 1 & -2 & -1 & -2 & -2 \\ 3 & 2 & 1 & 3 & 4 \end{array}\right] -1R_1+R_3$$

$$\left[\begin{array}{cccc|c} 1 & 1 & 1 & 1 & 4 \\ 0 & -1 & -4 & -3 & -8 \\ 0 & -3 & -2 & -3 & -6 \\ 3 & 2 & 1 & 3 & 4 \end{array}\right] -3R_1+R_4$$

$$\left[\begin{array}{cccc|c} 1 & 1 & 1 & 1 & 4 \\ 0 & -1 & -4 & -3 & -8 \\ 0 & -3 & -2 & -3 & -6 \\ 0 & -1 & -2 & 0 & -8 \end{array}\right] -1R_2$$

$$\left[\begin{array}{cccc|c} 1 & 1 & 1 & 1 & 4 \\ 0 & 1 & 4 & 3 & 8 \\ 0 & -3 & -2 & -3 & -6 \\ 0 & -1 & -2 & 0 & -8 \end{array}\right] 3R_2+R_3$$

$$\left[\begin{array}{cccc|c} 1 & 1 & 1 & 1 & 4 \\ 0 & 1 & 4 & 3 & 8 \\ 0 & 0 & 10 & 6 & 18 \\ 0 & -1 & -2 & 0 & -8 \end{array}\right] 1R_2+R_4$$

$$\left[\begin{array}{cccc|c} 1 & 1 & 1 & 1 & 4 \\ 0 & 1 & 4 & 3 & 8 \\ 0 & 0 & 10 & 6 & 18 \\ 0 & 0 & 2 & 3 & 0 \end{array}\right] \tfrac{1}{10}R_3$$

$$\left[\begin{array}{cccc|c} 1 & 1 & 1 & 1 & 4 \\ 0 & 1 & 4 & 3 & 8 \\ 0 & 0 & 1 & \frac{3}{5} & \frac{9}{5} \\ 0 & 0 & 2 & 3 & 0 \end{array}\right] -2R_3+R_4$$

$$\left[\begin{array}{cccc|c} 1 & 1 & 1 & 1 & 4 \\ 0 & 1 & 4 & 3 & 8 \\ 0 & 0 & 1 & \frac{3}{5} & \frac{9}{5} \\ 0 & 0 & 0 & \frac{9}{5} & -\frac{18}{5} \end{array}\right] \frac{5}{9}R_4$$

$$\left[\begin{array}{cccc|c} 1 & 1 & 1 & 1 & 4 \\ 0 & 1 & 4 & 3 & 8 \\ 0 & 0 & 1 & \frac{3}{5} & \frac{9}{5} \\ 0 & 0 & 0 & 1 & -2 \end{array}\right]$$

$w = -2$

$$z + \frac{3}{5}w = \frac{9}{5}$$
$$z + \frac{3}{5}(-2) = \frac{9}{5}$$
$$z - \frac{6}{5} = \frac{9}{5}$$
$$z = 3$$
$$y + 4z + 3w = 8$$
$$y + 4(3) + 3(-2) = 8$$
$$y + 6 = 8$$
$$y = 2$$
$$x + y + z + w = 4$$
$$x + 2 + 3 + (-2) = 4$$
$$x + 3 = 4$$
$$x = 1$$

The solution set is $\{(1, 2, 3, -2)\}$.

35. $3x - 4y + z + w = 9$

$x + y - z - w = 0$

$2x + y + 4z - 2w = 3$

$-x + 2y + z - 3w = 3$

$$\left[\begin{array}{cccc|c} 3 & -4 & 1 & 1 & 9 \\ 1 & 1 & -1 & -1 & 0 \\ 2 & 1 & 4 & -2 & 3 \\ -1 & 2 & 1 & -3 & 3 \end{array}\right] R_1 \leftrightarrow R_2$$

$$\left[\begin{array}{cccc|c} 1 & 1 & -1 & -1 & 0 \\ 3 & -4 & 1 & 1 & 9 \\ 2 & 1 & 4 & -2 & 3 \\ -1 & 2 & 1 & -3 & 3 \end{array}\right] -3R_1 + R_2$$

$$\left[\begin{array}{cccc|c} 1 & 1 & -1 & -1 & 0 \\ 0 & -7 & 4 & 4 & 9 \\ 2 & 1 & 4 & -2 & 3 \\ -1 & 2 & 1 & -3 & 3 \end{array}\right] -2R_1 + R_3$$

$$\left[\begin{array}{cccc|c} 1 & 1 & -1 & -1 & 0 \\ 0 & -7 & 4 & 4 & 9 \\ 0 & -1 & 6 & 0 & 3 \\ -1 & 2 & 1 & -3 & 3 \end{array}\right] 1R_1 + R_4$$

$$\left[\begin{array}{cccc|c} 1 & 1 & -1 & -1 & 0 \\ 0 & -7 & 4 & 4 & 9 \\ 0 & -1 & 6 & 0 & 3 \\ 0 & 3 & 0 & -4 & 3 \end{array}\right] R_2 \leftrightarrow R_3$$

$$\left[\begin{array}{cccc|c} 1 & 1 & -1 & -1 & 0 \\ 0 & -1 & 6 & 0 & 3 \\ 0 & -7 & 4 & 4 & 9 \\ 0 & 3 & 0 & -4 & 3 \end{array}\right] -R_2$$

$$\left[\begin{array}{cccc|c} 1 & 1 & -1 & -1 & 0 \\ 0 & 1 & -6 & 0 & -3 \\ 0 & -7 & 4 & 4 & 9 \\ 0 & 3 & 0 & -4 & 3 \end{array}\right] 7R_2 + R_3$$

$$\left[\begin{array}{cccc|c} 1 & 1 & -1 & -1 & 0 \\ 0 & 1 & -6 & 0 & -3 \\ 0 & 0 & -38 & 4 & -12 \\ 0 & 3 & 0 & -4 & 3 \end{array}\right] -3R_2 + R_4$$

$$\left[\begin{array}{cccc|c} 1 & 1 & -1 & -1 & 0 \\ 0 & 1 & -6 & 0 & -3 \\ 0 & 0 & -38 & 4 & -12 \\ 0 & 0 & 18 & -4 & 12 \end{array}\right] -\frac{1}{38}R_3$$

$$\left[\begin{array}{cccc|c} 1 & 1 & -1 & -1 & 0 \\ 0 & 1 & -6 & 0 & -3 \\ 0 & 0 & 1 & -\frac{2}{19} & \frac{6}{19} \\ 0 & 0 & 18 & -4 & 12 \end{array}\right] -18R_3 + R_4$$

$$\left[\begin{array}{cccc|c} 1 & 1 & -1 & -1 & 0 \\ 0 & 1 & -6 & 0 & -3 \\ 0 & 0 & 1 & -\frac{2}{19} & \frac{6}{19} \\ 0 & 0 & 0 & -\frac{40}{19} & \frac{120}{19} \end{array}\right] -\frac{19}{40}R_4$$

$$\begin{bmatrix} 1 & 1 & -1 & -1 & | & 0 \\ 0 & 1 & -6 & 0 & | & -3 \\ 0 & 0 & 1 & -\frac{2}{19} & | & \frac{6}{19} \\ 0 & 0 & 0 & 1 & | & -3 \end{bmatrix}$$

$w = -3$

$z - \frac{2}{19}w = \frac{6}{19}$

$z - \frac{2}{19}(-3) = \frac{6}{19}$

$z + \frac{6}{19} = \frac{6}{19}$

$z = 0$

$y - 6z = -3$

$y - 6(0) = -3$

$y = -3$

$x + y - z - w = 0$

$x - 3 - 0 + 3 = 0$

$x = 0$

The solution set is $\{(0, -3, 0, -3)\}$.

37. $2x + 3y - z - w = -3$

$2x - y - 3z + 2w = -5$

$x - y + z - w = -4$

$3x - 2y + z + w = 0$

$$\begin{bmatrix} 2 & 3 & -1 & -1 & | & -3 \\ 2 & -1 & -3 & 2 & | & -5 \\ 1 & -1 & 1 & -1 & | & -4 \\ 3 & -2 & 1 & 1 & | & 0 \end{bmatrix} R_1 \leftrightarrow R_3$$

$$\begin{bmatrix} 1 & -1 & 1 & -1 & | & -4 \\ 2 & -1 & -3 & 2 & | & -5 \\ 2 & 3 & -1 & -1 & | & -3 \\ 3 & -2 & 1 & 1 & | & 0 \end{bmatrix} -2R_1 + R_2$$

$$\begin{bmatrix} 1 & -1 & 1 & -1 & | & -4 \\ 0 & 1 & -5 & 4 & | & 3 \\ 2 & 3 & -1 & -1 & | & -3 \\ 3 & -2 & 1 & 1 & | & 0 \end{bmatrix} -2R_1 + R_3$$

$$\begin{bmatrix} 1 & -1 & 1 & -1 & | & -4 \\ 0 & 1 & -5 & 4 & | & 3 \\ 0 & 5 & -3 & 1 & | & 5 \\ 3 & -2 & 1 & 1 & | & 0 \end{bmatrix} -3R_1 + R_4$$

$$\begin{bmatrix} 1 & -1 & 1 & -1 & | & -4 \\ 0 & 1 & -5 & 4 & | & 3 \\ 0 & 5 & -3 & 1 & | & 5 \\ 0 & 1 & -2 & 4 & | & 12 \end{bmatrix} -5R_2 + R_3$$

$$\begin{bmatrix} 1 & -1 & 1 & -1 & | & -4 \\ 0 & 1 & -5 & 4 & | & 3 \\ 0 & 0 & 22 & -19 & | & -10 \\ 0 & 1 & -2 & 4 & | & 12 \end{bmatrix} -1R_2 + R_4$$

$$\begin{bmatrix} 1 & -1 & 1 & -1 & | & -4 \\ 0 & 1 & -5 & 4 & | & 3 \\ 0 & 0 & 22 & -19 & | & -10 \\ 0 & 0 & 3 & 0 & | & 9 \end{bmatrix} \frac{1}{22}R_3$$

$$\begin{bmatrix} 1 & -1 & 1 & -1 & | & -4 \\ 0 & 1 & -5 & 4 & | & 3 \\ 0 & 0 & 1 & -\frac{19}{22} & | & -\frac{5}{11} \\ 0 & 0 & 3 & 0 & | & 9 \end{bmatrix} -3R_3 + R_4$$

$$\begin{bmatrix} 1 & -1 & 1 & -1 & | & -4 \\ 0 & 1 & -5 & 4 & | & 3 \\ 0 & 0 & 1 & -\frac{19}{22} & | & -\frac{5}{11} \\ 0 & 0 & 0 & \frac{57}{22} & | & \frac{114}{11} \end{bmatrix} \frac{22}{57}R_4$$

$$\begin{bmatrix} 1 & -1 & 1 & -1 & | & -4 \\ 0 & 1 & -5 & 4 & | & 3 \\ 0 & 0 & 1 & -\frac{19}{22} & | & -\frac{5}{11} \\ 0 & 0 & 0 & 1 & | & 4 \end{bmatrix}$$

$w = 4$

$z - \frac{19}{22}w = -\frac{5}{11}$

$z - \frac{19}{22}(4) = -\frac{5}{11}$

$z - \frac{76}{22} = -\frac{5}{11}$

$22z - 76 = -10$

$22z = 66$

$z = 3$

$$y - 5z + 4w = 3$$
$$y - 5(3) + 4(4) = 3$$
$$y - 15 + 16 = 3$$
$$y + 1 = 3$$
$$y = 2$$
$$x - y + z - w = -4$$
$$x - 2 + 3 - 4 = -4$$
$$x - 3 = -4$$
$$x = -1$$

The solution set is $\{(-1, 2, 3, 4)\}$.

39.
$$2x_1 - 2x_2 + 3x_3 - x_4 = 12$$
$$x_1 + 2x_2 - x_3 + 2x_4 - x_5 = -7$$
$$x_1 + x_3 - x_4 - 5x_5 = 5$$
$$-x_1 + x_2 - x_3 - 2x_4 - 3x_5 = 0$$
$$x_1 - x_2 - x_4 + x_5 = 4$$

$$\left[\begin{array}{ccccc|c} 2 & -2 & 3 & -1 & 0 & 12 \\ 1 & 2 & -1 & 2 & -1 & -7 \\ 1 & 0 & 1 & -1 & -5 & 5 \\ -1 & 1 & -1 & -2 & -3 & 0 \\ 1 & -1 & 0 & -1 & 1 & 4 \end{array}\right] R_1 \leftrightarrow R_5$$

$$\left[\begin{array}{ccccc|c} 1 & -1 & 0 & -1 & 1 & 4 \\ 1 & 2 & -1 & 2 & -1 & -7 \\ 1 & 0 & 1 & -1 & -5 & 5 \\ -1 & 1 & -1 & -2 & -3 & 0 \\ 2 & -2 & 3 & -1 & 0 & 12 \end{array}\right] \begin{array}{l} \\ -1R_1 + R_2 \\ -1R_1 + R_3 \\ 1R_1 + R_4 \\ -2R_1 + R_5 \end{array}$$

$$\left[\begin{array}{ccccc|c} 1 & -1 & 0 & -1 & 1 & 4 \\ 0 & 3 & -1 & 3 & -2 & -11 \\ 0 & 1 & 1 & 0 & -6 & 1 \\ 0 & 0 & -1 & -3 & -2 & 4 \\ 0 & 0 & 3 & 1 & -2 & 4 \end{array}\right] R_2 \leftrightarrow R_3$$

$$\left[\begin{array}{ccccc|c} 1 & -1 & 0 & -1 & 1 & 4 \\ 0 & 1 & 1 & 0 & -6 & 1 \\ 0 & 3 & -1 & 3 & -2 & -11 \\ 0 & 0 & -1 & -3 & -2 & 4 \\ 0 & 0 & 3 & 1 & -2 & 4 \end{array}\right] \begin{array}{l} 1R_2 + R_1 \\ -3R_2 + R_3 \\ \\ \\ \\ \end{array}$$

$$\left[\begin{array}{ccccc|c} 1 & 0 & 1 & -1 & -5 & 5 \\ 0 & 1 & 1 & 0 & -6 & 1 \\ 0 & 0 & -4 & 3 & 16 & -14 \\ 0 & 0 & -1 & -3 & -2 & 4 \\ 0 & 0 & 3 & 1 & -2 & 4 \end{array}\right] R_3 \leftrightarrow R_4$$

$$\left[\begin{array}{ccccc|c} 1 & 0 & 1 & -1 & -5 & 5 \\ 0 & 1 & 1 & 0 & -6 & 1 \\ 0 & 0 & -1 & -3 & -2 & 4 \\ 0 & 0 & -4 & 3 & 16 & -14 \\ 0 & 0 & 3 & 1 & -2 & 4 \end{array}\right] -R_3$$

$$\left[\begin{array}{ccccc|c} 1 & 0 & 1 & -1 & -5 & 5 \\ 0 & 1 & 1 & 0 & -6 & 1 \\ 0 & 0 & 1 & 3 & 2 & -4 \\ 0 & 0 & -4 & 3 & 16 & -14 \\ 0 & 0 & 3 & 1 & -2 & 4 \end{array}\right] \begin{array}{l} -1R_3 + R_1 \\ -1R_3 + R_2 \\ 4R_3 + R_4 \\ -3R_3 + R_5 \\ \\ \end{array}$$

$$\left[\begin{array}{ccccc|c} 1 & 0 & 0 & -4 & -7 & 9 \\ 0 & 1 & 0 & -3 & -8 & 5 \\ 0 & 0 & 1 & 3 & 2 & -4 \\ 0 & 0 & 0 & 15 & 24 & -30 \\ 0 & 0 & 0 & -8 & -8 & 16 \end{array}\right] R_4 \leftrightarrow R_5$$

$$\left[\begin{array}{ccccc|c} 1 & 0 & 0 & -4 & -7 & 9 \\ 0 & 1 & 0 & -3 & -8 & 5 \\ 0 & 0 & 1 & 3 & 2 & -4 \\ 0 & 0 & 0 & -8 & -8 & 16 \\ 0 & 0 & 0 & 15 & 24 & -30 \end{array}\right] -\tfrac{1}{8}R_4$$

$$\left[\begin{array}{ccccc|c} 1 & 0 & 0 & -4 & -7 & 9 \\ 0 & 1 & 0 & -3 & -8 & 5 \\ 0 & 0 & 1 & 3 & 2 & -4 \\ 0 & 0 & 0 & 1 & 1 & -2 \\ 0 & 0 & 0 & 15 & 24 & -30 \end{array}\right] \begin{array}{l} 4R_4 + R_1 \\ 3R_4 + R_2 \\ -3R_4 + R_3 \\ \\ -15R_4 + R_5 \end{array}$$

$$\left[\begin{array}{ccccc|c} 1 & 0 & 0 & 0 & -3 & 1 \\ 0 & 1 & 0 & 0 & -5 & -1 \\ 0 & 0 & 1 & 0 & -1 & 2 \\ 0 & 0 & 0 & 1 & 1 & -2 \\ 0 & 0 & 0 & 0 & 9 & 0 \end{array}\right] \begin{array}{l} \\ \\ \frac{1}{9}R_5 \\ \\ \\ \end{array}$$

$$\left[\begin{array}{ccccc|c} 1 & 0 & 0 & 0 & -3 & 1 \\ 0 & 1 & 0 & 0 & -5 & -1 \\ 0 & 0 & 1 & 0 & -1 & 2 \\ 0 & 0 & 0 & 1 & 1 & -2 \\ 0 & 0 & 0 & 0 & 1 & 0 \end{array}\right] \begin{array}{l} -3R_5 + R_1 \\ 5R_5 + R_2 \\ 1R_5 + R_3 \\ -1R_5 + R_4 \\ \\ \end{array}$$

$$\left[\begin{array}{ccccc|c} 1 & 0 & 0 & 0 & 0 & 1 \\ 0 & 1 & 0 & 0 & 0 & -1 \\ 0 & 0 & 1 & 0 & 0 & 2 \\ 0 & 0 & 0 & 1 & 0 & -2 \\ 0 & 0 & 0 & 0 & 1 & 0 \end{array}\right]$$

$x_1 = 1,\ x_2 = -1,\ x_3 = 2,\ x_4 = -2,\ x_5 = 0$

The solution set is $\{(1, -1, 2, -2, 0)\}$.

41. a. $344 = a(1)^2 = b(1) + c$
$344 = a + b + c$
$480 = a(5)^2 = b(5) + c$
$480 = 25a + 5b + c$
$740 = a(10)^2 = b(10) + c$
$740 = 100a + 10b + c$

$$a + b + c = 344$$
$$25a + 5b + c = 480$$
$$100a + 10b + c = 740$$

$$\left[\begin{array}{ccc|c} 1 & 1 & 1 & 344 \\ 25 & 5 & 1 & 480 \\ 100 & 10 & 1 & 740 \end{array}\right] \begin{array}{l} \\ -25R_1 + R_2 \\ -100R_1 + R_3 \end{array}$$

$$\left[\begin{array}{ccc|c} 1 & 1 & 1 & 344 \\ 0 & -20 & -24 & -8120 \\ 0 & -90 & -99 & -33660 \end{array}\right] \begin{array}{l} \\ -\frac{1}{20}R_2 \\ -\frac{1}{90}R_3 \end{array}$$

$$\left[\begin{array}{ccc|c} 1 & 1 & 1 & 344 \\ 0 & 1 & \frac{6}{5} & 406 \\ 0 & 1 & \frac{11}{10} & 374 \end{array}\right] \begin{array}{l} \\ 1R_2 + R_3 \\ \\ \end{array}$$

$$\left[\begin{array}{ccc|c} 1 & 1 & 1 & 344 \\ 0 & 1 & \frac{6}{5} & 406 \\ 0 & 0 & -\frac{1}{10} & -32 \end{array}\right] \begin{array}{l} \\ \\ -10R_3 \end{array}$$

$$\left[\begin{array}{ccc|c} 1 & 1 & 1 & 344 \\ 0 & 1 & \frac{6}{5} & 406 \\ 0 & 0 & 1 & 320 \end{array}\right]$$

$$a + b + c = 344$$
$$b + \frac{6}{5}c = 406$$
$$c = 320$$
$$b + \frac{6}{5}(320) = 406$$
$$b + 384 = 406$$
$$b = 22$$

$$a + 22 + 320 = 344$$
$$a = 2$$
$$y = 2x^2 + 22x + 320$$

The solution set is $\{(2, 22, 320)\}$.

b. $x = 2010 - 1980 = 30$
$y = 2(30)^2 + 22(30) + 320$
$y = 1800 + 660 + 320$
$y = 2780$

c. Answers may vary.

43. Let x = under 30 age group
Let y = 30–49 age group
Let z = 50 and over age group

$$x + z = y + 2$$
$$2z = x - 3$$
$$x + y + z = 100$$

$$x + y + z = 100$$
$$x - y + z = 2$$
$$-x + 2z = -3$$

$$\left[\begin{array}{ccc|c} 1 & 1 & 1 & 100 \\ 1 & -1 & 1 & 2 \\ -1 & 0 & 2 & -3 \end{array}\right] \begin{array}{l} \\ -1R_1 + R_2 \\ 1R_1 + R_3 \end{array}$$

$$\left[\begin{array}{ccc|c} 1 & 1 & 1 & 100 \\ 0 & -2 & 0 & -98 \\ 0 & 1 & 3 & 97 \end{array}\right] \begin{array}{l} \\ -\frac{1}{2}R_2 \\ \\ \end{array}$$

$$\left[\begin{array}{ccc|c} 1 & 1 & 1 & 100 \\ 0 & 1 & 0 & 49 \\ 0 & 1 & 3 & 97 \end{array}\right] -1R_2 + R_3$$

$$\left[\begin{array}{ccc|c} 1 & 1 & 1 & 100 \\ 0 & 1 & 0 & 49 \\ 0 & 0 & 3 & 48 \end{array}\right] \begin{array}{l} \\ -1R_2 + R_1 \\ \frac{1}{3}R_3 \end{array}$$

$$\left[\begin{array}{ccc|c} 1 & 0 & 1 & 51 \\ 0 & 1 & 0 & 49 \\ 0 & 0 & 1 & 16 \end{array}\right] -1R_3 + R_1$$

$$\left[\begin{array}{ccc|c} 1 & 0 & 0 & 35 \\ 0 & 1 & 0 & 49 \\ 0 & 0 & 1 & 16 \end{array}\right]$$

$x = 35$; $y = 49$; $z = 16$
50 and over—16%
30–49—49%
under 30—35%

45. Let x = Food *A*
Let y = Food *B*
Let z = Food *C*

$$\begin{aligned} 40x + 200y + 400z &= 660 \\ 5x + 2y + 4z &= 25 \\ 30x + 10y + 300z &= 425 \\ 2x + 10y + 20z &= 33 \\ 5x + 2y + 4z &= 25 \\ 6x + 2y + 60z &= 85 \end{aligned}$$

$$\left[\begin{array}{ccc|c} 2 & 10 & 20 & 33 \\ 5 & 2 & 4 & 25 \\ 6 & 2 & 60 & 85 \end{array}\right] \frac{1}{2}R_1$$

$$\left[\begin{array}{ccc|c} 1 & 5 & 10 & \frac{33}{2} \\ 5 & 2 & 4 & 25 \\ 6 & 2 & 60 & 85 \end{array}\right] -5R_1 + R_2$$

$$\left[\begin{array}{ccc|c} 1 & 5 & 10 & \frac{33}{2} \\ 0 & -23 & -46 & -\frac{115}{2} \\ 6 & 2 & 60 & 85 \end{array}\right] -6R_1 + R_3$$

$$\left[\begin{array}{ccc|c} 1 & 5 & 10 & \frac{33}{2} \\ 0 & -23 & -46 & -\frac{115}{2} \\ 0 & -28 & 0 & -14 \end{array}\right] -\frac{1}{23}R_2$$

$$\left[\begin{array}{ccc|c} 1 & 5 & 10 & \frac{33}{2} \\ 0 & 1 & 2 & \frac{5}{2} \\ 0 & -28 & 0 & -14 \end{array}\right] 28R_2 + R_3$$

$$\left[\begin{array}{ccc|c} 1 & 5 & 10 & \frac{33}{2} \\ 0 & 1 & 2 & \frac{5}{2} \\ 0 & 0 & 56 & 56 \end{array}\right] \frac{1}{56}R_3$$

$$\left[\begin{array}{ccc|c} 1 & 5 & 10 & \frac{33}{2} \\ 0 & 1 & 2 & \frac{5}{2} \\ 0 & 0 & 1 & 1 \end{array}\right]$$

$$\begin{aligned} z &= 1 \\ y + 2z &= \frac{5}{2} \\ y + 2 &= \frac{5}{2} \\ 2y + 4 &= 5 \\ 2y &= 1 \\ y &= \frac{1}{2} \end{aligned}$$

$$\begin{aligned} x + 5y + 10z &= \frac{33}{2} \\ x + \frac{5}{2} + 10 &= \frac{33}{2} \\ 2x + 5 + 20 &= 33 \\ 2x + 25 &= 33 \\ 2x &= 8 \\ x &= 4 \end{aligned}$$

4 ounces of Food *A*
$\frac{1}{2}$ ounce of Food *B*
1 ounce of Food *C*

47.–53. Answers may vary.

55. Exercise 27

```
ref([[1,1,-1,-2]
[2,-1,1,5][-1,2,
2,1]])
[[1 -.5 .5 2.5]
 [0 1   -1 -3 ]
 [0 0   1  2  ]]
```

57. $y = ax^3 + bx^2 + cx + d$

$-3 = a(0)^3 + b(0)^2 + c(0) + d$

$-3 = d$

$5 = a + b + c + d$

$-7 = a(-1)^3 + b(-1)^2 + c(-1) + d$

$-7 = -a + b - c + d$

$-13 = a(-2)^3 + b(-2)^2 + c(-2) + d$

$-13 = -8a + 4b - 2c + d$

$$\begin{aligned} a+b+c+d &= 5 \\ -a+b-c+d &= -7 \\ -8a+4b-2c+d &= -13 \\ d &= -3 \end{aligned}$$

$$\left[\begin{array}{cccc|c} 1 & 1 & 1 & 1 & 5 \\ -1 & 1 & -1 & 1 & -7 \\ -8 & 4 & -2 & 1 & -13 \\ 0 & 0 & 0 & 1 & -3 \end{array}\right] \begin{array}{l} \\ R_1 + R_2 \\ 8R_1 + R_3 \\ \\ \end{array}$$

$$\left[\begin{array}{cccc|c} 1 & 1 & 1 & 1 & 5 \\ 0 & 2 & 0 & 2 & -2 \\ 0 & 12 & 6 & 9 & 27 \\ 0 & 0 & 0 & 1 & -3 \end{array}\right] \tfrac{1}{2}R_2$$

$$\left[\begin{array}{cccc|c} 1 & 1 & 1 & 1 & 5 \\ 0 & 1 & 0 & 1 & -1 \\ 0 & 12 & 6 & 9 & 27 \\ 0 & 0 & 0 & 1 & -3 \end{array}\right] \begin{array}{l} \\ -1R_2 + R_1 \\ -12R_2 + R_3 \\ \\ \end{array}$$

$$\left[\begin{array}{cccc|c} 1 & 0 & 1 & 0 & 6 \\ 0 & 1 & 0 & 1 & -1 \\ 0 & 0 & 6 & -3 & 39 \\ 0 & 0 & 0 & 1 & -3 \end{array}\right] \begin{array}{l} \\ \tfrac{1}{6}R_3 \\ -R_4 + R_2 \\ \\ \end{array}$$

$$\left[\begin{array}{cccc|c} 1 & 0 & 1 & 0 & 6 \\ 0 & 1 & 0 & 0 & 2 \\ 0 & 0 & 1 & \frac{-1}{2} & \frac{13}{2} \\ 0 & 0 & 0 & 1 & -3 \end{array}\right] \tfrac{1}{2}R_4 + R_3$$

$$\left[\begin{array}{cccc|c} 1 & 0 & 1 & 0 & 6 \\ 0 & 1 & 0 & 0 & 2 \\ 0 & 0 & 1 & 0 & 5 \\ 0 & 0 & 0 & 1 & -3 \end{array}\right] -R_3 + R_1$$

$$\left[\begin{array}{cccc|c} 1 & 0 & 0 & 0 & 1 \\ 0 & 1 & 0 & 0 & 2 \\ 0 & 0 & 1 & 0 & 5 \\ 0 & 0 & 0 & 1 & -3 \end{array}\right]$$

$a = 1$

$b = 2$

$c = 5$

$d = -3$

$y = x^3 + 2x^2 + 5x - 3$

Section 6.2

Check Point Exercises

1. $$\begin{aligned} x-2y-z &= 5 \\ 2x-3y-z &= 0 \\ 3x-4y-z &= 1 \end{aligned} \rightarrow \left[\begin{array}{ccc|c} 1 & -2 & -1 & -5 \\ 2 & -3 & -1 & 0 \\ 3 & -4 & -1 & 1 \end{array}\right]$$

$$\left[\begin{array}{ccc|c} 1 & -2 & -1 & -5 \\ 2 & -3 & -1 & 0 \\ 3 & -4 & -1 & 1 \end{array}\right] \begin{array}{l} -2R_1 + R_2 \\ -3R_1 + R_3 \end{array}$$

$$\left[\begin{array}{ccc|c} 1 & -2 & -1 & -5 \\ 0 & 1 & 1 & 10 \\ 0 & 2 & 2 & 16 \end{array}\right] -2R_2 + R_3$$

$$\left[\begin{array}{ccc|c} 1 & -2 & -1 & -5 \\ 0 & 1 & -1 & -10 \\ 0 & 0 & 0 & -4 \end{array}\right]$$

$0x + 0y + 0z = -4$ This equation can never be a true statement. Consequently, the system has no solution. The solution set is Ø, the empty set.

2. $$\begin{aligned} x-2y-z &= 5 \\ 2x-5y+3z &= 16 \\ x-3y+4z &= 1 \end{aligned} \rightarrow \left[\begin{array}{ccc|c} 1 & -2 & -1 & 5 \\ 2 & -5 & 3 & 6 \\ 1 & -3 & 4 & 1 \end{array}\right]$$

$$\left[\begin{array}{ccc|c} 1 & -2 & -1 & 5 \\ 2 & -5 & 3 & 6 \\ 1 & -3 & 4 & 1 \end{array}\right] \begin{array}{l} -2R_1 + R_2 \\ -1R_1 + R_3 \end{array}$$

$$\left[\begin{array}{ccc|c} 1 & -2 & -1 & 5 \\ 0 & -1 & 5 & -4 \\ 0 & -1 & 5 & -4 \end{array}\right] -1R_2$$

$$\begin{bmatrix} 1 & -2 & -1 & 5 \\ 0 & 1 & -5 & 4 \\ 0 & -1 & 5 & -4 \end{bmatrix} 1R_2 + R_3$$

$$\begin{bmatrix} 1 & -2 & -1 & 5 \\ 0 & 1 & -5 & 4 \\ 0 & 0 & 0 & 0 \end{bmatrix}$$

$0x + 0y + 0z = 0$ or $0 = 0$

This equation, $0x + 0y + 0z = 0$ is *dependent* on the other two equations. Thus, it can be dropped from the system which can now be expressed in the form

$$\begin{bmatrix} 1 & -2 & -1 & 5 \\ 0 & 1 & -5 & 4 \end{bmatrix}$$

The original system is equivalent to the system

$x - 2y - z = 5$
$y - 5z = 4$

Solve for x and y in terms of z.

$y = 5z + 4$

Use back-substitution for y in the previous equation.

$x - 2(5z + 4) - z = 5$
$x - 10z - 8 - z = 5$
$x = 11z + 13$

Finally, letting $z = t$ (or any letter of your choice), the solutions to the system are all of the form $x = 11t + 13$, $y = 5t + 4$, $z = t$, where t is a real number. The solution set of the system with dependent equations can be written as $\{(11t + 13, 5t + 4, t)\}$.

3. $\begin{matrix} x + 2y + 3z = 70 \\ x + y + z = 60 \end{matrix} \rightarrow \begin{bmatrix} 1 & 2 & 3 & 70 \\ 1 & 1 & 1 & 60 \end{bmatrix}$

$$\begin{bmatrix} 1 & 2 & 3 & 70 \\ 1 & 1 & 1 & 60 \end{bmatrix} -1R_1 + R_2$$

$$\begin{bmatrix} 1 & 2 & 3 & 70 \\ 0 & -1 & -2 & -10 \end{bmatrix} -1R_2$$

$$\begin{bmatrix} 1 & 2 & 3 & 70 \\ 0 & 1 & 2 & 10 \end{bmatrix} \rightarrow \begin{matrix} x + 2y + 3z = 70 \\ y + 2z = 10 \end{matrix}$$

Express x and y in terms of z using back-substitution.

$y = -2z + 10$
$x + 2(-2z + 10) + 3z = 70$
$x - 4z + 20 + 3z = 70$
$x = z + 50$

With $z = t$, the ordered solution (x, y, z) enables us to express the system's solution set as $\{(t + 50, -2t + 10, t)\}$.

4. a. I_1: 10 + 5 = 15 cars enter I_1, and $x + w$ cars leave I_1, then $x + w = 15$.
I_2: 20 + 10 = 30 cars enter I_2 and $x + y$ cars leave I_2, then $x + y = 30$.
I_3: 15 + 30 = 45 cars enter I_3 and $y + z$ cars leave I_3, then $y + z = 45$.
I_4: 10 + 20 = 30 cars enter I_4 and $z + w$ cars leave I_4, then $z + w = 30$.
The system of equations that describes this situation is given by

$x + w = 15$
$x + y = 30$
$y + z = 45$
$z + w = 30.$

b.

$$\begin{bmatrix} 1 & 0 & 0 & 1 & 15 \\ 1 & 1 & 0 & 0 & 30 \\ 0 & 1 & 1 & 0 & 45 \\ 0 & 0 & 1 & 1 & 30 \end{bmatrix} -1R_2 + R_2$$

$$\begin{bmatrix} 1 & 0 & 0 & 1 & 15 \\ 0 & 1 & 0 & -1 & 15 \\ 0 & 1 & 1 & 0 & 45 \\ 0 & 0 & 1 & 1 & 30 \end{bmatrix} -1R_2 + R_3$$

$$\begin{bmatrix} 1 & 0 & 0 & 1 & 15 \\ 0 & 1 & 0 & -1 & 15 \\ 0 & 0 & 1 & 1 & 30 \\ 0 & 0 & 1 & 1 & 30 \end{bmatrix} -1R_3 + R_4$$

$$\begin{bmatrix} 1 & 0 & 0 & 1 & 15 \\ 0 & 1 & 0 & -1 & 15 \\ 0 & 0 & 1 & 1 & 30 \\ 0 & 0 & 0 & 0 & 0 \end{bmatrix}$$

$x + w = 15$
$y - w = 15$
$z + w = 30$

The last row of the matrix shows that the system has dependent equations and infinitely many solutions.
Let w be any real number.
Express x, y and z in terms of w:
$x = 15 - w$
$y = 15 + w$
$z = 30 - w$
With $w = t$, the ordered solution (x, y, z, w) enables us to express the system's solution set as
$\{(15-t, 15+t, 30-t, t)\}$

c. Because $w = t$, we replace 10 for t in the system's ordered solution:
$(15-t, 15+t, 30-t, t)$
$= (15-10, 15+10, 30-10, 10)$
$= (5, 25, 20, 10)$
Thus, $x = 5$, $y = 25$, $z = 20$.
With construction, this means that to keep traffic flowing, 5 cars per minute must be routed between I_1, and I_2, 25 cars per minute between I_2 and I_3 and 20 cars per minute between I_3 and I_4.

Exercise Set 6.2

1. $$\left[\begin{array}{ccc|c} 5 & 12 & 1 & 10 \\ 2 & 5 & 2 & -1 \\ 1 & 2 & -3 & 5 \end{array}\right] R_1 \leftrightarrow R_3$$

$$\left[\begin{array}{ccc|c} 1 & 2 & -3 & 5 \\ 2 & 5 & 2 & -1 \\ 5 & 12 & 1 & 10 \end{array}\right] \begin{array}{l} \\ -2R_1 + R_2 \\ -5R_1 + R_3 \end{array}$$

$$\left[\begin{array}{ccc|c} 1 & 2 & -3 & 5 \\ 0 & 1 & 8 & -11 \\ 0 & 2 & 16 & -15 \end{array}\right] -2R_2 + R_3$$

$$\left[\begin{array}{ccc|c} 1 & 2 & 3 & 5 \\ 0 & 1 & 8 & -11 \\ 0 & 0 & 0 & 7 \end{array}\right]$$

From the last row, we see that the system has no solution. The solution set is Ø, the empty set.

3. $$\left[\begin{array}{ccc|c} 5 & 8 & -6 & 14 \\ 3 & 4 & -2 & 8 \\ 1 & 2 & -2 & 3 \end{array}\right] R_1 \leftrightarrow R_3$$

$$\left[\begin{array}{ccc|c} 1 & 2 & -2 & 3 \\ 3 & 4 & -2 & 8 \\ 5 & 8 & -6 & 14 \end{array}\right] \begin{array}{l} -3R_1 + R_2 \\ -5R_1 + R_3 \end{array}$$

$$\left[\begin{array}{ccc|c} 1 & 2 & -2 & 3 \\ 0 & -2 & 4 & -1 \\ 0 & -2 & 4 & -1 \end{array}\right] -1R_2 + R_3$$

$$\left[\begin{array}{ccc|c} 1 & 2 & -2 & 3 \\ 0 & -2 & 4 & -1 \\ 0 & 0 & 0 & 0 \end{array}\right] -\frac{1}{2}R_2$$

$$\left[\begin{array}{ccc|c} 1 & 2 & -2 & 3 \\ 0 & 1 & -2 & \frac{1}{2} \\ 0 & 0 & 0 & 0 \end{array}\right]$$

The system $\begin{aligned} x + 2y - 2z &= 3 \\ y - 2z &= \frac{1}{2} \end{aligned}$ has no unique solution. Express x and y in terms of z:

$$y = 2z + \frac{1}{2}$$
$$x + 2\left(2z + \frac{1}{2}\right) - 2z = 3$$
$$x + 4z + 1 - 2z = 3$$
$$x + 2z + 1 = 3$$
$$x = -2z + 2$$

With $z = t$, the complete solution to the system is $\left\{\left(-2t + 2, 2t + \frac{1}{2}, t\right)\right\}$.

5. $$\left[\begin{array}{ccc|c} 3 & 4 & 2 & 3 \\ 4 & -2 & -8 & -4 \\ 1 & 1 & -1 & 3 \end{array}\right] R_1 \leftrightarrow R_3$$

$$\left[\begin{array}{ccc|c} 1 & 1 & -1 & 3 \\ 4 & -2 & -8 & -4 \\ 3 & 4 & 2 & 3 \end{array}\right] \begin{array}{l} -4R_1 + R_2 \\ -3R_1 + R_3 \end{array}$$

$$\left[\begin{array}{ccc|c} 1 & 1 & -1 & 3 \\ 0 & -6 & -4 & -16 \\ 0 & 1 & 5 & -6 \end{array}\right] R_2 \leftrightarrow R_3$$

$$\left[\begin{array}{ccc|c} 1 & 1 & -1 & 3 \\ 0 & 1 & 5 & -6 \\ 0 & -6 & -4 & -16 \end{array}\right] 6R_2 + R_3$$

$$\left[\begin{array}{ccc|c} 1 & 1 & 1 & 3 \\ 0 & 1 & 5 & -6 \\ 0 & 0 & 26 & -52 \end{array}\right] \frac{1}{26}R_3$$

$$\left[\begin{array}{ccc|c} 1 & 1 & -1 & 3 \\ 0 & 1 & 5 & -6 \\ 0 & 0 & 1 & -2 \end{array}\right]$$

This corresponds to the system

$x + y - z = 3$
$y + 5z = -6$
$z = -2$

Use back-substitution to find the values of x and y:

$y + 5(-2) = -6$
$y - 10 = -6$
$y = 4$
$x + 4 + 2 = 3$
$x + 6 = 3$
$x = -3$

The solution to the system is $\{(-3, 4, -2)\}$.

7. $$\left[\begin{array}{ccc|c} 8 & 5 & 11 & 30 \\ -1 & -4 & 2 & 3 \\ 2 & -1 & 5 & 12 \end{array}\right] R_1 \leftrightarrow R_2$$

$$\left[\begin{array}{ccc|c} -1 & -4 & 2 & 3 \\ 8 & 5 & 11 & 30 \\ 2 & -1 & 5 & 12 \end{array}\right] -1R_1$$

$$\left[\begin{array}{ccc|c} 1 & 4 & -2 & -3 \\ 8 & 5 & 11 & 30 \\ 2 & -1 & 5 & 12 \end{array}\right] \begin{array}{l} -8R_1 + R_2 \\ -2R_1 + R_3 \end{array}$$

$$\left[\begin{array}{ccc|c} 1 & 4 & -2 & -3 \\ 0 & -27 & 27 & 54 \\ 0 & -9 & 9 & 18 \end{array}\right] -\frac{1}{27}R_2$$

$$\left[\begin{array}{ccc|c} 1 & 4 & -2 & -3 \\ 0 & 1 & -1 & -2 \\ 0 & -9 & 9 & 18 \end{array}\right] 9R_2 + R_3$$

$$\left[\begin{array}{ccc|c} 1 & 4 & -2 & -3 \\ 0 & 1 & -1 & -2 \\ 0 & 0 & 0 & 0 \end{array}\right]$$

The system $\begin{array}{r} x + 4y - 2z = -3 \\ y - z = -2 \end{array}$ has no unique solution. Express x and y in terms of z:

$y = -2 + z$
$x + 4(-2 + z) - 2z = -3$
$x - 8 + 4z - 2z = -3$
$x - 8 + 2z = -3$
$x = 5 - 2z$

With $z = t$, the complete solution to the system is $\{(5 - 2t, -2 + t, t)\}$.

9. $$\left[\begin{array}{cccc|c} 1 & -2 & -1 & -3 & -9 \\ 1 & 1 & -1 & 0 & 0 \\ 3 & 4 & 0 & 1 & 6 \\ 0 & 2 & -2 & 1 & 3 \end{array}\right] \begin{array}{l} -1R_1 + R_2 \\ -3R_1 + R_3 \end{array}$$

$$\left[\begin{array}{cccc|c} 1 & -2 & -1 & -3 & -9 \\ 0 & 3 & 0 & 3 & 9 \\ 0 & 10 & 3 & 10 & 33 \\ 0 & 2 & -2 & 1 & 3 \end{array}\right] \tfrac{1}{3}R_2$$

$$\left[\begin{array}{cccc|c} 1 & -2 & -1 & -3 & -9 \\ 0 & 1 & 0 & 1 & 3 \\ 0 & 10 & 3 & 10 & 33 \\ 0 & 2 & -2 & 1 & 3 \end{array}\right] \begin{array}{l} -10R_2 + R_3 \\ -2R_2 + R_4 \end{array}$$

$$\left[\begin{array}{cccc|c} 1 & -2 & -1 & -3 & -9 \\ 0 & 1 & 0 & 1 & 3 \\ 0 & 0 & 3 & 0 & 3 \\ 0 & 0 & -2 & -1 & -3 \end{array}\right] \tfrac{1}{3}R_3$$

$$\left[\begin{array}{cccc|c} 1 & -2 & -1 & -3 & -9 \\ 0 & 1 & 0 & 1 & 3 \\ 0 & 0 & 1 & 0 & 1 \\ 0 & 0 & -2 & -1 & -3 \end{array}\right] 2R_3 + R_4$$

$$\left[\begin{array}{cccc|c} 1 & -2 & -1 & -3 & -9 \\ 0 & 1 & 0 & 1 & 3 \\ 0 & 0 & 1 & 0 & 1 \\ 0 & 0 & 0 & -1 & -1 \end{array}\right] -1R_4$$

$$\left[\begin{array}{cccc|c} 1 & -2 & -1 & -3 & -9 \\ 0 & 1 & 0 & 1 & 3 \\ 0 & 0 & 1 & 0 & 1 \\ 0 & 0 & 0 & 1 & 1 \end{array}\right]$$

This corresponds to the system

$$x - 2y - z - 3w = -9$$
$$y + w = 3$$
$$z = 1$$
$$w = 1$$

Use back-substitution to find the values of x and y:

$$y + 1 = 3$$
$$y = 2$$
$$x - 2(2) - 1 - 3(1) = -9$$
$$x - 4 - 1 - 3 = -9$$
$$x - 8 = -9$$
$$x = -1$$

The solution to the system is $\{(-1, 2, 1, 1)\}$.

11. $$\left[\begin{array}{cccc|c} 2 & 1 & -1 & 0 & 3 \\ 1 & -3 & 2 & 0 & -4 \\ 3 & 1 & -3 & 1 & 1 \\ 1 & 2 & -4 & -1 & -2 \end{array}\right] R_1 \leftrightarrow R_2$$

$$\left[\begin{array}{cccc|c} 1 & -3 & 2 & 0 & -4 \\ 2 & 1 & -1 & 0 & 3 \\ 3 & 1 & -3 & 1 & 1 \\ 1 & 2 & -4 & -1 & -2 \end{array}\right] \begin{array}{l} -2R_1 + R_2 \\ -3R_1 + R_3 \\ -1R_1 + R_4 \end{array}$$

$$\left[\begin{array}{cccc|c} 1 & -3 & 2 & 0 & -4 \\ 0 & 7 & -5 & 0 & 11 \\ 0 & 10 & -9 & 1 & 13 \\ 0 & 5 & -6 & -1 & 2 \end{array}\right] \tfrac{1}{7}R_2$$

$$\left[\begin{array}{cccc|c} 1 & -3 & 2 & 0 & -4 \\ 0 & 1 & -\frac{5}{7} & 0 & \frac{11}{7} \\ 0 & 10 & -9 & 1 & 13 \\ 0 & 5 & -6 & -1 & 2 \end{array}\right] \begin{array}{l} -10R_2 + R_3 \\ -5R_2 + R_4 \end{array}$$

$$\left[\begin{array}{cccc|c} 1 & -3 & 2 & 0 & -4 \\ 0 & 1 & -\frac{5}{7} & 0 & \frac{11}{7} \\ 0 & 0 & -\frac{13}{7} & 1 & -\frac{19}{7} \\ 0 & 0 & -\frac{17}{7} & -1 & -\frac{41}{7} \end{array}\right] -\tfrac{7}{13}R_3$$

$$\left[\begin{array}{cccc|c} 1 & -3 & 2 & 0 & -4 \\ 0 & 1 & -\frac{5}{7} & 0 & \frac{11}{7} \\ 0 & 0 & 1 & -\frac{7}{13} & \frac{19}{13} \\ 0 & 0 & -\frac{17}{7} & -1 & -\frac{41}{7} \end{array}\right] \tfrac{17}{7}R_3 + R_4$$

$$\left[\begin{array}{cccc|c} 1 & -3 & 2 & 0 & -4 \\ 0 & 1 & -\frac{5}{7} & 0 & \frac{11}{7} \\ 0 & 0 & 1 & -\frac{7}{13} & \frac{19}{13} \\ 0 & 0 & 0 & -\frac{30}{13} & -\frac{30}{13} \end{array}\right] -\tfrac{13}{30}R_4$$

$$\left[\begin{array}{cccc|c} 1 & -3 & 2 & 0 & -4 \\ 0 & 1 & -\frac{5}{7} & 0 & \frac{11}{7} \\ 0 & 0 & 1 & -\frac{7}{13} & \frac{19}{13} \\ 0 & 0 & 0 & 1 & 1 \end{array}\right]$$

This corresponds to the system

$$x - 3y + 2z = -4$$
$$y - \frac{5}{7}z = \frac{11}{7}$$
$$z - \frac{7}{13}w = \frac{19}{13}$$
$$w = 1$$

Use back-substitution to find the values of x, y, and z:

$$z - \frac{7}{13} = \frac{19}{13}$$
$$z = 2$$
$$y - \frac{5}{7}(2) = \frac{11}{7}$$
$$y - \frac{10}{7} = \frac{11}{7}$$
$$y = 3$$
$$x - 3(3) + 2(2) = -4$$
$$x - 9 + 4 = -4$$
$$x - 5 = -4$$
$$x = 1$$

The solution to the system is $\{(1, 3, 2, 1)\}$.

13. $\left[\begin{array}{cccc|c} 1 & -3 & 1 & -4 & 4 \\ -2 & 1 & 2 & 0 & -2 \\ 3 & -2 & 1 & -6 & 2 \\ -1 & 3 & 2 & -1 & -6 \end{array}\right] \begin{array}{l} 2R_1 + R_2 \\ -3R_1 + R_3 \\ R_1 + R_4 \end{array}$

$\left[\begin{array}{cccc|c} 1 & -3 & 1 & -4 & 4 \\ 0 & -5 & 4 & -8 & 6 \\ 0 & 7 & -2 & 6 & -10 \\ 0 & 0 & 3 & -5 & -2 \end{array}\right] -\frac{1}{5}R_2$

$\left[\begin{array}{cccc|c} 1 & -3 & 1 & -4 & 4 \\ 0 & 1 & -\frac{4}{5} & \frac{8}{5} & -\frac{6}{5} \\ 0 & 7 & -2 & 6 & -10 \\ 0 & 0 & 3 & -5 & -2 \end{array}\right] -7R_2 + R_3$

$\left[\begin{array}{cccc|c} 1 & -3 & 1 & -4 & 4 \\ 0 & 1 & -\frac{4}{5} & \frac{8}{5} & -\frac{6}{5} \\ 0 & 0 & \frac{18}{5} & -\frac{26}{5} & -\frac{8}{5} \\ 0 & 0 & 3 & -5 & -2 \end{array}\right] \frac{5}{18}R_3$

$\left[\begin{array}{cccc|c} 1 & -3 & 1 & -4 & 4 \\ 0 & 1 & -\frac{4}{5} & \frac{8}{5} & -\frac{6}{5} \\ 0 & 0 & 1 & -\frac{13}{9} & -\frac{4}{9} \\ 0 & 0 & 3 & -5 & -2 \end{array}\right] -3R_3 + R_4$

$\left[\begin{array}{cccc|c} 1 & -3 & 1 & -4 & 4 \\ 0 & 1 & -\frac{4}{5} & \frac{8}{5} & -\frac{6}{5} \\ 0 & 0 & 1 & -\frac{13}{9} & -\frac{4}{9} \\ 0 & 0 & 0 & -\frac{2}{3} & -\frac{2}{3} \end{array}\right] -\frac{3}{2}R_4$

$\left[\begin{array}{cccc|c} 1 & -3 & 1 & -4 & 4 \\ 0 & 1 & -\frac{4}{5} & \frac{8}{5} & -\frac{6}{5} \\ 0 & 0 & 1 & -\frac{13}{9} & -\frac{4}{9} \\ 0 & 0 & 0 & 1 & 1 \end{array}\right]$

This corresponds to the system

$$x - 3y + z - 4w = 4$$
$$y - \frac{4}{5}z + \frac{8}{5}w = -\frac{6}{5}$$
$$z - \frac{13}{9}w = -\frac{4}{9}$$
$$w = 1$$

Use back-substitution to find the values of x, y, and z:

$$z - \frac{13}{9} = -\frac{4}{9}$$
$$z = 1$$
$$y - \frac{4}{5} + \frac{8}{5} = -\frac{6}{5}$$
$$y + \frac{4}{5} = -\frac{6}{5}$$
$$y = -2$$
$$x - 3(-2) + 1 - 4 = 4$$
$$x + 6 - 3 = 4$$
$$x = 1$$

The solution to the system is $\{(1, -2, 1, 1)\}$.

15. $\left[\begin{array}{ccc|c} 2 & 1 & -1 & 2 \\ 3 & 3 & -2 & 3 \end{array}\right] \frac{1}{2}R_1$

$\left[\begin{array}{ccc|c} 1 & \frac{1}{2} & -\frac{1}{2} & 1 \\ 3 & 3 & -2 & 3 \end{array}\right] -3R_1 + R_2$

$\left[\begin{array}{ccc|c} 1 & \frac{1}{2} & -\frac{1}{2} & 1 \\ 0 & \frac{3}{2} & -\frac{1}{2} & 0 \end{array}\right] \frac{2}{3}R_2$

$\left[\begin{array}{ccc|c} 1 & \frac{1}{2} & -\frac{1}{2} & 1 \\ 0 & 1 & -\frac{1}{3} & 0 \end{array}\right]$

The system $x + \frac{1}{2}y - \frac{1}{2}z = 1$, $y - \frac{1}{3}z = 0$ has no unique solution. Express x and y in terms of z:

$$y = \frac{1}{3}z$$
$$x + \frac{1}{2}\left(\frac{1}{3}z\right) - \frac{1}{2}z = 1$$
$$x + \frac{1}{6}z - \frac{1}{2}z = 1$$
$$x - \frac{1}{3}z = 1$$
$$x = 1 + \frac{1}{3}z$$

With $z = t$, the complete solution to the system is $\left\{\left(1 + \frac{1}{3}t, \frac{1}{3}t, t\right)\right\}$.

17. The system $\begin{array}{r} x+2y+3z=5 \\ y-5z=0 \end{array}$ has no unique solution. Express x and y in terms of z:

$y = 5z$
$x + 2(5z) + 3z = 5$
$x + 10z + 3z = 5$
$x = -13z + 5$

With $z = t$, the complete solution to the system is $\{(-13t + 5, 5t, t)\}$.

19. $\left[\begin{array}{ccc|c} 1 & 1 & -2 & 2 \\ 3 & -1 & -6 & -7 \end{array}\right] -3R_1 + R_2$

$\left[\begin{array}{ccc|c} 1 & 1 & -2 & 2 \\ 0 & -4 & 0 & -13 \end{array}\right] -\frac{1}{4}R_2$

$\left[\begin{array}{ccc|c} 1 & 1 & -2 & 2 \\ 0 & 1 & 0 & \frac{13}{4} \end{array}\right]$

The system $\begin{array}{r} x+y-2z=2 \\ y=\frac{13}{4} \end{array}$ has no unique solution. Express x in terms of z:

$x + \frac{13}{4} - 2z = 2$

$x = 2z - \frac{5}{4}$

With $z = t$, the complete solution to the system is $\left\{\left(2t - \frac{5}{4}, \frac{13}{4}, t\right)\right\}$.

21. $\left[\begin{array}{cccc|c} 1 & 1 & -1 & 1 & -2 \\ 2 & -1 & 2 & -1 & 7 \\ -1 & 2 & 1 & 2 & -1 \end{array}\right] \begin{array}{l} -2R_1 + R_2 \\ 1R_1 + R_3 \end{array}$

$\left[\begin{array}{cccc|c} 1 & 1 & -1 & 1 & -2 \\ 0 & -3 & 4 & -3 & 11 \\ 0 & 3 & 0 & 3 & -3 \end{array}\right] R_2 \leftrightarrow R_3$

$\left[\begin{array}{cccc|c} 1 & 1 & -1 & 1 & -2 \\ 0 & 3 & 0 & 3 & -3 \\ 0 & -3 & 4 & -3 & 11 \end{array}\right] \frac{1}{3}R_2$

$\left[\begin{array}{cccc|c} 1 & 1 & -1 & 1 & -2 \\ 0 & 1 & 0 & 1 & -1 \\ 0 & -3 & 4 & -3 & 11 \end{array}\right] 3R_2 + R_3$

$\left[\begin{array}{cccc|c} 1 & 1 & -1 & 1 & -2 \\ 0 & 1 & 0 & 1 & -1 \\ 0 & 0 & 4 & 0 & 8 \end{array}\right] \frac{1}{4}R_3$

$\left[\begin{array}{cccc|c} 1 & 1 & -1 & 1 & -2 \\ 0 & 1 & 0 & 1 & -1 \\ 0 & 0 & 1 & 0 & 2 \end{array}\right]$

The system $\begin{array}{r} x+y-z+w=-2 \\ y+w=-1 \\ z=2 \end{array}$ has no unique solution. Express x and y in terms of w:

$y = -w - 1$
$x + (-w - 1) - 2 + w = -2$
$x - w + 1 - 2 + w = -2$
$x = 1$

With $w = t$, the complete solution to the system is $\{(1, -t - 1, 2, t)\}$.

23. $\left[\begin{array}{cccc|c} 1 & 2 & 3 & -1 & 7 \\ 0 & 2 & -3 & 1 & 4 \\ 1 & -4 & 1 & 0 & 3 \end{array}\right] -1R_1 + R_3$

$\left[\begin{array}{cccc|c} 1 & 2 & 3 & -1 & 7 \\ 0 & 2 & -3 & 1 & 4 \\ 0 & -6 & -2 & 1 & -4 \end{array}\right] \frac{1}{2}R_2$

$\left[\begin{array}{cccc|c} 1 & 2 & 3 & -1 & 7 \\ 0 & 1 & -\frac{3}{2} & \frac{1}{2} & 2 \\ 0 & -6 & -2 & 1 & -4 \end{array}\right] 6R_2 + R_3$

$\left[\begin{array}{cccc|c} 1 & 2 & 3 & -1 & 7 \\ 0 & 1 & -\frac{3}{2} & \frac{1}{2} & 2 \\ 0 & 0 & -11 & 4 & 8 \end{array}\right] -\frac{1}{11}R_3$

$\left[\begin{array}{cccc|c} 1 & 2 & 3 & -1 & 7 \\ 0 & 1 & -\frac{3}{2} & \frac{1}{2} & 2 \\ 0 & 0 & 1 & -\frac{4}{11} & -\frac{8}{11} \end{array}\right]$

The system $\begin{aligned} x+2y+3z-w&=7 \\ y-\frac{3}{2}z+\frac{1}{2}w&=2 \\ z-\frac{4}{11}w&=-\frac{8}{11}\end{aligned}$ has no unique solution. Express x, y, and z in terms of w:

$$z=\frac{4}{11}w-\frac{8}{11}$$

$$y-\frac{3}{2}\left(\frac{4}{11}w-\frac{8}{11}\right)+\frac{1}{2}w=2$$

$$y-\frac{6}{11}w+\frac{12}{11}+\frac{1}{2}w=2$$

$$y-\frac{1}{22}w+\frac{12}{11}=2$$

$$y=\frac{1}{22}w+\frac{10}{11}$$

$$x+2\left(\frac{1}{22}w+\frac{10}{11}\right)+3\left(\frac{4}{11}w-\frac{8}{11}\right)-w=7$$

$$x+\frac{1}{11}w+\frac{20}{11}+\frac{12}{11}w-\frac{24}{11}-w=7$$

$$x+\frac{2}{11}w-\frac{4}{11}=7$$

$$x=-\frac{2}{11}w+\frac{81}{11}$$

With $w = t$, the complete solution to the system is

$$\left\{\left(-\frac{2}{11}t+\frac{81}{11},\ \frac{1}{22}t+\frac{10}{11},\ \frac{4}{11}t-\frac{8}{11},\ t\right)\right\}.$$

25. $z + 12 = x + 6$

27. $x-y=4$
$x-z=6$
$y-z=2$

$$\left[\begin{array}{ccc|c} 1 & -1 & 0 & 4 \\ 1 & 0 & -1 & 6 \\ 0 & 1 & -1 & 2 \end{array}\right] -1R_1+R_2$$

$$\begin{bmatrix} 1 & -1 & 0 & 4 \\ 0 & -1 & 1 & -2 \\ 0 & 1 & -1 & 2 \end{bmatrix} -1R_2$$

$$\begin{bmatrix} 1 & -1 & 0 & 4 \\ 0 & 1 & -1 & 2 \\ 0 & 1 & -1 & 2 \end{bmatrix} \begin{matrix} \\ -1R_2+R_3 \\ 1R_2+R_1 \end{matrix}$$

$$\begin{bmatrix} 1 & 0 & -1 & 6 \\ 0 & 1 & -1 & 2 \\ 0 & 0 & 0 & 0 \end{bmatrix}$$

The system has no unique solution. Express x and y in terms of z:
$x-z=6$
$y-z=2$
$x=z+6$
$y=z+2$
With $z = t$, the complete solution to the system is $\{(t + 6, t + 2, t)\}$.

29. a. From left to right along Palm Drive, then along Sunset Drive, we get the equations
$x + w = 200 + 180 = 380;$
$x + y = 400 + 200 = 600;$
$w + 70 = z + 20$ or $z - w = 50;$
$z + 200 = y + 30$ or $y - z = 170.$
The system is
$x + w = 380$
$x + y = 600$
$z - w = 50$
$y - z = 170$

b.

$$\left[\begin{array}{cccc|c} 1 & 0 & 0 & 1 & 380 \\ 0 & 1 & 0 & -1 & 220 \\ 0 & 0 & 1 & -1 & 50 \\ 0 & 1 & -1 & 0 & 170 \end{array}\right] -1R_2+R_4$$

$$\left[\begin{array}{cccc|c} 1 & 0 & 0 & 1 & 380 \\ 0 & 1 & 0 & -1 & 220 \\ 0 & 0 & 1 & -1 & 50 \\ 0 & 0 & -1 & 1 & -50 \end{array}\right] 1R_3+R_4$$

$$\left[\begin{array}{cccc|c} 1 & 0 & 0 & 1 & 380 \\ 0 & 1 & 0 & -1 & 220 \\ 0 & 0 & 1 & -1 & 50 \\ 0 & 0 & 0 & 0 & 0 \end{array}\right]$$

The system $\begin{matrix} x+w=380 \\ y-w=220 \\ z-w=50 \end{matrix}$ has no unique solution. Express x and y and z in terms of w:

$x = 380 - w$
$y = 220 + w$
$z = 50 + w$

With $w = t$, the complete solution to the system is $\{(380 - t, 220 + t, 50 + t, t)\}$.

c. Letting $w = 50$, the solution is $x = 330$, $y = 270$, $z = 100$, $w = 50$.

31. Let x = the amount of Food 1, y = the amount of Food 2, and z = the amount of Food 3, in ounces. The amount of vitamin A is $20x + 30y + 10z$; the amount of iron is $20x + 10y + 10z$; the amount of calcium is $10x + 10y + 30z$.

a. Not having Food 1 means that all x terms are left out. The vitamin A requirement can then be represented by $30y + 10z = 220$; the iron requirement is $10y + 10z = 180$; the calcium requirement is $10y + 30z = 340$.

The corresponding system is

$30y + 10z = 220$
$10y + 10z = 180$
$10y + 30z = 340$.

Dividing all of the numbers by 10, the matrix for this system is

$$\left[\begin{array}{cc|c} 3 & 1 & 22 \\ 1 & 1 & 18 \\ 1 & 3 & 34 \end{array}\right] R_1 \leftrightarrow R_2$$

$$\left[\begin{array}{cc|c} 1 & 1 & 18 \\ 3 & 1 & 22 \\ 1 & 3 & 34 \end{array}\right] \begin{matrix} -3R_1 + R_2 \\ -1R_1 + R_3 \end{matrix}$$

$$\left[\begin{array}{cc|c} 1 & 1 & 18 \\ 0 & -2 & -32 \\ 0 & 2 & 16 \end{array}\right] 1R_2 + R_3$$

$$\left[\begin{array}{cc|c} 1 & 1 & 18 \\ 0 & -2 & -32 \\ 0 & 0 & -16 \end{array}\right]$$

From the last row, we see that the system has no solution, so there is no way to satisfy these dietary requirements with no Food 1 available.

b. With Food 1 available, and dropping the vitamin A requirement, the system is

$20x + 10y + 10z = 180$
$10x + 10y + 30z = 340$.

Dividing all of the numbers by 10, the matrix for this system is

$$\left[\begin{array}{ccc|c} 2 & 1 & 1 & 18 \\ 1 & 1 & 3 & 34 \end{array}\right] R_1 \leftrightarrow R_2$$

$$\left[\begin{array}{ccc|c} 1 & 1 & 3 & 34 \\ 2 & 1 & 1 & 18 \end{array}\right] -2R_1 + R_2$$

$$\left[\begin{array}{ccc|c} 1 & 1 & 3 & 34 \\ 0 & -1 & -5 & -50 \end{array}\right] -1R_2$$

$$\left[\begin{array}{ccc|c} 1 & 1 & 3 & 34 \\ 0 & 1 & 5 & 50 \end{array}\right].$$

The system $\begin{matrix} x+y+3z=34 \\ y+5z=50 \end{matrix}$ has no unique solution. Express x and y in terms of z:

$y = -5z + 50$
$x + (-5z + 50) + 3z = 34$
$x - 2z + 50 = 34$
$x = 2z - 16$

Now we can choose a value for z, i.e., an amount of Food 3, and find the corresponding values of x and y. Note that negative amounts of food are not realistic, so $z \geq 0$, $y = -5z + 50 \geq 0$, and $x = 2z - 16 \geq 0$. These conditions are equivalent to $8 \leq z \leq 10$.

Using $z = 8$ and $z = 10$, two possibilities are 0 ounces of Food 1, 10 ounces of Food 2, and 8 ounces of Food 3 or 4 ounces of Food 1, 0 ounces of Food 2, and 10 ounces of Food 3. (Other answers are possible.)

33.–35. Answers may vary.

37. $\left[\begin{array}{ccc|c} 1 & 3 & 1 & a^2 \\ 2 & 5 & 2a & 0 \\ 1 & 1 & a^2 & -9 \end{array}\right] \begin{array}{l} -2R_1 + R_2 \\ -1R_1 + R_3 \end{array}$

$\left[\begin{array}{ccc|c} 1 & 3 & 1 & a^2 \\ 0 & -1 & 2a-2 & -2a^2 \\ 0 & -2 & a^2-1 & -9-a^2 \end{array}\right] -1R_2$

$\left[\begin{array}{ccc|c} 1 & 3 & 1 & a^2 \\ 0 & 1 & 2-2a & 2a^2 \\ 0 & -2 & a^2-1 & -9-a^2 \end{array}\right] 2R_2 + R_3$

$\left[\begin{array}{ccc|c} 1 & 3 & 1 & a^2 \\ 0 & 1 & 2-2a & 2a^2 \\ 0 & 0 & a^2-4a+3 & -9+3a^2 \end{array}\right]$

The system will be inconsistent when $a^2 - 4a + 3 = 0$ but $-9 + 3a^2 \neq 0$.
$a^2 - 4a + 3 = (a-1)(a-3) = 0$ when $a = 1$ or $a = 3$. $-9 + 3a^2 = 0$ when $a = \pm\sqrt{3}$.
Thus, the system is inconsistent when $a = 1$ or $a = 3$.

Section 6.3

Check Point Exercises

1. a. The matrix $A = \begin{bmatrix} 5 & -2 \\ -3 & \pi \\ 1 & 6 \end{bmatrix}$ has 3 rows and 2 columns, so it is of order 3×2.

b. The element a_{12} is in the first row and second column. Thus, $a_{12} = -2$. The element a_{31} is in the third row and first column. Thus, $a_{31} = 1$.

2. a. $\begin{bmatrix} -4 & 3 \\ 7 & -6 \end{bmatrix} + \begin{bmatrix} 6 & -3 \\ 2 & -4 \end{bmatrix}$

$= \begin{bmatrix} -4+6 & 3+(-3) \\ 7+2 & -6+(-4) \end{bmatrix} = \begin{bmatrix} 2 & 0 \\ 9 & -10 \end{bmatrix}$

b. $\begin{bmatrix} 5 & 4 \\ -3 & 7 \\ 0 & 1 \end{bmatrix} - \begin{bmatrix} -4 & 8 \\ 6 & 0 \\ -5 & 3 \end{bmatrix}$

$= \begin{bmatrix} 5-(-4) & 4-8 \\ -3-6 & 7-0 \\ 0-(-5) & 1-3 \end{bmatrix} = \begin{bmatrix} 9 & -4 \\ -9 & 7 \\ 5 & -2 \end{bmatrix}$

3. a. $-6B = -6\begin{bmatrix} -1 & -2 \\ 8 & 5 \end{bmatrix}$

$= \begin{bmatrix} -6(-1) & -6(-2) \\ -6(8) & -6(5) \end{bmatrix}$

$= \begin{bmatrix} -6 & 12 \\ -48 & -30 \end{bmatrix}$

b. $3A + 2B =$

$3\begin{bmatrix} -4 & 1 \\ 3 & 0 \end{bmatrix} + 2\begin{bmatrix} -1 & -2 \\ 8 & 5 \end{bmatrix}$

$= \begin{bmatrix} 3(-4) & 3(1) \\ 3(3) & 3(0) \end{bmatrix} + \begin{bmatrix} 2(-1) & 2(-2) \\ 2(8) & 2(5) \end{bmatrix}$

$= \begin{bmatrix} -12 & 3 \\ 9 & 0 \end{bmatrix} + \begin{bmatrix} -2 & -4 \\ 16 & 10 \end{bmatrix}$

$= \begin{bmatrix} -12+(-2) & 3+(-4) \\ 9+16 & 0+10 \end{bmatrix}$

$= \begin{bmatrix} -14 & -1 \\ 25 & 10 \end{bmatrix}$

4. Given $A = \begin{bmatrix} 1 & 3 \\ 2 & 5 \end{bmatrix}$ and $B = \begin{bmatrix} 4 & 6 \\ 1 & 0 \end{bmatrix}$,

$AB = \begin{bmatrix} 1 & 3 \\ 2 & 5 \end{bmatrix}\begin{bmatrix} 4 & 6 \\ 1 & 0 \end{bmatrix}$

$= \begin{bmatrix} 1(4)+3(1) & 1(6)+3(0) \\ 2(4)+5(1) & 2(6)+5(0) \end{bmatrix}$

$= \begin{bmatrix} 7 & 6 \\ 13 & 12 \end{bmatrix}.$

5. If $A = \begin{bmatrix} 2 & 0 & 4 \end{bmatrix}$ and $B = \begin{bmatrix} 1 \\ 3 \\ 7 \end{bmatrix}$, then

$$\begin{aligned} AB &= \begin{bmatrix} 2 & 0 & 4 \end{bmatrix} \begin{bmatrix} 1 \\ 3 \\ 7 \end{bmatrix} \\ &= [2(1)+0(3)+4(7)] \\ &= [2+0+28] \\ &= [30] \end{aligned}$$

$$\begin{aligned} \text{and } BA &= \begin{bmatrix} 1 \\ 3 \\ 7 \end{bmatrix} \begin{bmatrix} 2 & 0 & 4 \end{bmatrix} \\ &= \begin{bmatrix} 1(2) & 1(0) & 1(4) \\ 3(2) & 3(0) & 3(4) \\ 7(2) & 7(0) & 7(4) \end{bmatrix} \\ &= \begin{bmatrix} 2 & 0 & 4 \\ 6 & 0 & 12 \\ 14 & 0 & 28 \end{bmatrix}. \end{aligned}$$

6. a. $\begin{bmatrix} 1 & 3 \\ 0 & 2 \end{bmatrix} \begin{bmatrix} 2 & 3 & -1 & 6 \\ 0 & 5 & 4 & 1 \end{bmatrix} = \begin{bmatrix} 1(2)+3(0) & 1(3)+3(5) & 1(-1)+3(4) & 1(6)+3(1) \\ 0(2)+2(0) & 0(3)+2(5) & 0(-1)+2(4) & 0(6)+2(1) \end{bmatrix} = \begin{bmatrix} 2 & 18 & 11 & 9 \\ 0 & 10 & 8 & 2 \end{bmatrix}$

b. $\begin{bmatrix} 2 & 3 & -1 & 6 \\ 0 & 5 & 4 & 1 \end{bmatrix} \begin{bmatrix} 1 & 3 \\ 0 & 2 \end{bmatrix}$

The number of columns in the first matrix does not equal the number of rows in the second matrix. Thus, the product of these two matrcies is undefined.

7. Because the *T* is dark gray and the background is light gray, a digital photograph of Figure 6.7 can be represented by the matrix

$$\begin{bmatrix} 2 & 2 & 2 \\ 1 & 2 & 1 \\ 1 & 2 & 1 \end{bmatrix}.$$

We can make the *T* light gray by decreasing each 2 in the above matrix to 1. We can make the background black by increasing each 1 in the matrix to 3. This is accomplished using the following matrix addition.

$$\begin{bmatrix} 2 & 2 & 2 \\ 1 & 2 & 1 \\ 1 & 2 & 1 \end{bmatrix} + \begin{bmatrix} -1 & -1 & -1 \\ 2 & -1 & 2 \\ 2 & -1 & 2 \end{bmatrix} = \begin{bmatrix} 1 & 1 & 1 \\ 3 & 1 & 3 \\ 3 & 1 & 3 \end{bmatrix}.$$

8. The gas station's total sales is represented in the first column of the product matrix $\begin{bmatrix} 836 & 117.40 \\ 791 & 111.80 \\ 921 & 129.70 \end{bmatrix}$.
The gas station's total sales for Monday, Tuesday, and Wednesday is 836 + 791 + 921 or \$2548.

Exercise Set 6.3

1. a. 2×3

b. a_{32} does not exist (A only has 2 rows).
$a_{23} = -1$

3. a. 3×4

b. $a_{32} = \frac{1}{2}$; $a_{23} = -6$

5. $\begin{bmatrix} x \\ 4 \end{bmatrix} = \begin{bmatrix} 6 \\ y \end{bmatrix}$
$x = 6$
$y = 4$

7. $\begin{bmatrix} x & 2y \\ z & 9 \end{bmatrix} = \begin{bmatrix} 4 & 12 \\ 3 & 9 \end{bmatrix}$
$x = 4$
$2y = 12$
$y = 6$
$z = 3$

9. a. $A + B = \begin{bmatrix} 4+5 & 1+9 \\ 3+0 & 2+7 \end{bmatrix} = \begin{bmatrix} 9 & 10 \\ 3 & 9 \end{bmatrix}$

b. $A - B = \begin{bmatrix} 4-5 & 1-9 \\ 3-0 & 2-7 \end{bmatrix} = \begin{bmatrix} -1 & -8 \\ 3 & -5 \end{bmatrix}$

c. $-4A = \begin{bmatrix} -16 & -4 \\ -12 & -8 \end{bmatrix}$

d. $3A + 2B = \begin{bmatrix} 12+10 & 3+18 \\ 9+0 & 6+14 \end{bmatrix} = \begin{bmatrix} 22 & 21 \\ 9 & 20 \end{bmatrix}$

11. a. $A + B = \begin{bmatrix} 1+2 & 3+(-1) \\ 3+3 & 4+(-2) \\ 5+0 & 6+1 \end{bmatrix} = \begin{bmatrix} 3 & 2 \\ 6 & 2 \\ 5 & 7 \end{bmatrix}$

b. $A - B = \begin{bmatrix} 1-2 & 3-(-1) \\ 3-3 & 4-(-2) \\ 5-0 & 6-1 \end{bmatrix} = \begin{bmatrix} -1 & 4 \\ 0 & 6 \\ 5 & 5 \end{bmatrix}$

c. $-4A = \begin{bmatrix} -4 & -12 \\ -12 & -16 \\ -20 & -24 \end{bmatrix}$

d. $3A + 2B = \begin{bmatrix} 3+4 & 9-2 \\ 9+6 & 12-4 \\ 15+0 & 18+2 \end{bmatrix} = \begin{bmatrix} 7 & 7 \\ 15 & 8 \\ 15 & 20 \end{bmatrix}$

13. a. $A + B = \begin{bmatrix} 2+(-5) \\ -4+3 \\ 1+(-1) \end{bmatrix} = \begin{bmatrix} -3 \\ -1 \\ 0 \end{bmatrix}$

b. $A - B = \begin{bmatrix} 2-(-5) \\ -4-3 \\ 1-(-1) \end{bmatrix} = \begin{bmatrix} 7 \\ -7 \\ 2 \end{bmatrix}$

c. $-4A = \begin{bmatrix} -8 \\ 16 \\ -4 \end{bmatrix}$

d. $3A + 2B = \begin{bmatrix} 6-10 \\ -12+6 \\ 3-2 \end{bmatrix} = \begin{bmatrix} -4 \\ -6 \\ 1 \end{bmatrix}$

15. **a.** $A+B=\begin{bmatrix} 2+6 & -10+10 & -2+(-2) \\ 14+0 & 12+(-12) & 10+(-4) \\ 4+(-5) & -2+2 & 2+(-2) \end{bmatrix}$

$=\begin{bmatrix} 8 & 0 & -4 \\ 14 & 0 & 6 \\ -1 & 0 & 0 \end{bmatrix}$

b. $A-B=\begin{bmatrix} 2-6 & -10-10 & -2-(-2) \\ 14-0 & 12-(-12) & 10-(-4) \\ 4-(-5) & -2-2 & 2-(-2) \end{bmatrix}$

$=\begin{bmatrix} -4 & -20 & 0 \\ 14 & 24 & 14 \\ 9 & -4 & 4 \end{bmatrix}$

c. $-4A=\begin{bmatrix} -8 & 40 & 8 \\ -56 & -48 & -40 \\ -16 & 8 & -8 \end{bmatrix}$

d. $3A+2B=\begin{bmatrix} 6+12 & -30+20 & -6-4 \\ 42+0 & 36-24 & 30-8 \\ 12-10 & -6+4 & 6-4 \end{bmatrix}$

$=\begin{bmatrix} 18 & -10 & -10 \\ 42 & 12 & 22 \\ 2 & -2 & 2 \end{bmatrix}$

17. **a.** $AB=\begin{bmatrix} 1 & 3 \\ 5 & 3 \end{bmatrix}\begin{bmatrix} 3 & -2 \\ -1 & 6 \end{bmatrix}=\begin{bmatrix} (1)(3)+(3)(-1) & (1)(-2)+(3)(6) \\ (5)(3)+(3)(-1) & (5)(-2)+(3)(6) \end{bmatrix}=\begin{bmatrix} 3-3 & -2+18 \\ 15-3 & -10+18 \end{bmatrix}=\begin{bmatrix} 0 & 16 \\ 12 & 8 \end{bmatrix}$

b. $BA=\begin{bmatrix} 3 & -2 \\ -1 & 6 \end{bmatrix}\begin{bmatrix} 1 & 3 \\ 5 & 3 \end{bmatrix}=\begin{bmatrix} (3)(1)+(-2)(5) & (3)(3)+(-2)(3) \\ (-1)(1)+(6)(5) & (-1)(3)+(6)(3) \end{bmatrix}=\begin{bmatrix} 3-10 & 9-6 \\ -1+30 & -3+18 \end{bmatrix}=\begin{bmatrix} -7 & 3 \\ 29 & 15 \end{bmatrix}$

19. **a.** $AB=[1 \quad 2 \quad 3 \quad 4]\begin{bmatrix} 1 \\ 2 \\ 3 \\ 4 \end{bmatrix}$

$=[(1)(1)+(2)(2)+(3)(3)+(4)(4)]$
$=[1+4+9+16]=[30]$

b. $BA = \begin{bmatrix} 1 \\ 2 \\ 3 \\ 4 \end{bmatrix} [1 \quad 2 \quad 3 \quad 4] = \begin{bmatrix} (1)(1) & (1)(2) & (1)(3) & (1)(4) \\ (2)(1) & (2)(2) & (2)(3) & (2)(4) \\ (3)(1) & (3)(2) & (3)(3) & (3)(4) \\ (4)(1) & (4)(2) & (4)(3) & (4)(4) \end{bmatrix} = \begin{bmatrix} 1 & 2 & 3 & 4 \\ 2 & 4 & 6 & 8 \\ 3 & 6 & 9 & 12 \\ 4 & 8 & 12 & 16 \end{bmatrix}$

21. a. $AB = \begin{bmatrix} 1 & -1 & 4 \\ 4 & -1 & 3 \\ 2 & 0 & -2 \end{bmatrix} \begin{bmatrix} 1 & 1 & 0 \\ 1 & 2 & 4 \\ 1 & -1 & 3 \end{bmatrix}$

$$= \begin{bmatrix} (1)(1)+(-1)(1)+(4)(1) & (1)(1)+(-1)(2)+(4)(-1) & (1)(0)+(-1)(4)+(4)(3) \\ (4)(1)+(-1)(1)+(3)(1) & (4)(1)+(-1)(2)+(3)(-1) & (4)(0)+(-1)(4)+(3)(3) \\ (2)(1)+(0)(1)+(-2)(1) & (2)(1)+(0)(2)+(-2)(-1) & (2)(0)+(0)(4)+(-2)(3) \end{bmatrix}$$

$$= \begin{bmatrix} 1-1+4 & 1-2-4 & 0-4+12 \\ 4-1+3 & 4-2-3 & 0-4+9 \\ 2+0-2 & 2+0+2 & 0+0-6 \end{bmatrix} = \begin{bmatrix} 4 & -5 & 8 \\ 6 & -1 & 5 \\ 0 & 4 & -6 \end{bmatrix}$$

b. $BA = \begin{bmatrix} 1 & 1 & 0 \\ 1 & 2 & 4 \\ 1 & -1 & 3 \end{bmatrix} \begin{bmatrix} 1 & -1 & 4 \\ 4 & -1 & 3 \\ 2 & 0 & -2 \end{bmatrix}$

$$= \begin{bmatrix} (1)(1)+(1)(4)+(0)(2) & (1)(-1)+(1)(-1)+(0)(0) & (1)(4)+(1)(3)+(0)(-2) \\ (1)(1)+(2)(4)+(4)(2) & (1)(-1)+(2)(-1)+(4)(0) & (1)(4)+(2)(3)+(4)(-2) \\ (1)(1)+(-1)(4)+(3)(2) & (1)(-1)+(-1)(-1)+(3)(0) & (1)(4)+(-1)(3)+(3)(-2) \end{bmatrix}$$

$$= \begin{bmatrix} 1+4+0 & -1-1+0 & 4+3+0 \\ 1+8+8 & -1-2+0 & 4+6-8 \\ 1-4+6 & -1+1+0 & 4-3-6 \end{bmatrix} = \begin{bmatrix} 5 & -2 & 7 \\ 17 & -3 & 2 \\ 3 & 0 & -5 \end{bmatrix}$$

23. a. $AB = \begin{bmatrix} 4 & 2 \\ 6 & 1 \\ 3 & 5 \end{bmatrix} \begin{bmatrix} 2 & 3 & 4 \\ -1 & -2 & 0 \end{bmatrix} = \begin{bmatrix} (4)(2)+(2)(-1) & (4)(3)+(2)(-2) & (4)(4)+(2)(0) \\ (6)(2)+(1)(-1) & (6)(3)+(1)(-2) & (6)(4)+(1)(0) \\ (3)(2)+(5)(-1) & (3)(3)+(5)(-2) & (3)(4)+(5)(0) \end{bmatrix}$

$$= \begin{bmatrix} 8-2 & 12-4 & 16+0 \\ 12-1 & 18-2 & 24+0 \\ 6-5 & 9-10 & 12+0 \end{bmatrix} = \begin{bmatrix} 6 & 8 & 16 \\ 11 & 16 & 24 \\ 1 & -1 & 12 \end{bmatrix}$$

b. $BA = \begin{bmatrix} 2 & 3 & 4 \\ -1 & -2 & 0 \end{bmatrix} \begin{bmatrix} 4 & 2 \\ 6 & 1 \\ 3 & 5 \end{bmatrix} = \begin{bmatrix} (2)(4)+(3)(6)+(4)(3) & (2)(2)+(3)(1)+(4)(5) \\ (-1)(4)+(-2)(6)+(0)(3) & (-1)(2)+(-2)(1)+(0)(5) \end{bmatrix}$

$$= \begin{bmatrix} 8+18+12 & 4+3+20 \\ -4-12+0 & -2-2+0 \end{bmatrix} = \begin{bmatrix} 38 & 27 \\ -16 & -4 \end{bmatrix}$$

25. a. $AB=\begin{bmatrix}2 & -3 & 1 & -1\\ 1 & 1 & -2 & 1\end{bmatrix}\begin{bmatrix}1 & 2\\ -1 & 1\\ 5 & 4\\ 10 & 5\end{bmatrix}$

$$=\begin{bmatrix}(2)(1)+(-3)(-1)+(1)(5)+(-1)(10) & (2)(2)+(-3)(1)+(1)(4)+(-1)(5)\\ (1)(1)+(1)(-1)+(-2)(5)+(1)(10) & (1)(2)+(1)(1)+(-2)(4)+(1)(5)\end{bmatrix}$$

$$=\begin{bmatrix}2+3+5-10 & 4-3+4-5\\ 1-1-10+10 & 2+1-8+5\end{bmatrix}=\begin{bmatrix}0 & 0\\ 0 & 0\end{bmatrix}$$

b. $BA=\begin{bmatrix}1 & 2\\ -1 & 1\\ 5 & 4\\ 10 & 5\end{bmatrix}\begin{bmatrix}2 & -3 & 1 & -1\\ 1 & 1 & -2 & 1\end{bmatrix}$

$$=\begin{bmatrix}(1)(2)+(2)(1) & (1)(-3)+(2)(1) & (1)(1)+(2)(-2) & (1)(-1)+(2)(1)\\ (-1)(2)+(1)(1) & (-1)(-3)+(1)(1) & (-1)(1)+(1)(-2) & (-1)(-1)+(1)(1)\\ (5)(2)+(4)(1) & (5)(-3)+(4)(1) & (5)(1)+(4)(-2) & (5)(-1)+(4)(1)\\ (10)(2)+(5)(1) & (10)(-3)+(5)(1) & (10)(1)+(5)(-2) & (10)(-1)+(5)(1)\end{bmatrix}$$

$$=\begin{bmatrix}2+2 & -3+2 & 1-4 & -1+2\\ -2+1 & 3+1 & -1-2 & 1+1\\ 10+4 & -15+4 & 5-8 & -5+4\\ 20+5 & -30+5 & 10-10 & -10+5\end{bmatrix}=\begin{bmatrix}4 & -1 & -3 & 1\\ -1 & 4 & -3 & 2\\ 14 & -11 & -3 & -1\\ 25 & -25 & 0 & -5\end{bmatrix}$$

27. $4B-3C=\begin{bmatrix}20 & 4\\ -8 & -8\end{bmatrix}-\begin{bmatrix}3 & -3\\ -3 & 3\end{bmatrix}=\begin{bmatrix}20-3 & 4-(-3)\\ -8-(-3) & -8-3\end{bmatrix}=\begin{bmatrix}17 & 7\\ -5 & -11\end{bmatrix}$

29. $BC+CB=\begin{bmatrix}5-1 & -5+1\\ -2+2 & 2-2\end{bmatrix}+\begin{bmatrix}5+2 & 1+2\\ -5-2 & -1-2\end{bmatrix}=\begin{bmatrix}4 & -4\\ 0 & 0\end{bmatrix}+\begin{bmatrix}7 & 3\\ -7 & -3\end{bmatrix}=\begin{bmatrix}11 & -1\\ -7 & -3\end{bmatrix}$

31. $A-C$ is not defined because A is 3×2 and C is 2×2.

33. $A(BC)=\begin{bmatrix}4 & 0\\ -3 & 5\\ 0 & 1\end{bmatrix}\begin{bmatrix}5-1 & -5+1\\ -2+2 & 2-2\end{bmatrix}=\begin{bmatrix}4 & 0\\ -3 & 5\\ 0 & 1\end{bmatrix}\begin{bmatrix}4 & -4\\ 0 & 0\end{bmatrix}$

$$=\begin{bmatrix}16+0 & -16+0\\ -12+0 & 12+0\\ 0+0 & 0+0\end{bmatrix}=\begin{bmatrix}16 & -16\\ -12 & 12\\ 0 & 0\end{bmatrix}$$

35. $\begin{bmatrix} 1 & 3 & 1 \\ 3 & 3 & 3 \\ 1 & 3 & 1 \end{bmatrix} + \begin{bmatrix} -1 & -1 & -1 \\ -1 & -1 & -1 \\ -1 & -1 & -1 \end{bmatrix} = \begin{bmatrix} 0 & 2 & 0 \\ 2 & 2 & 2 \\ 0 & 2 & 0 \end{bmatrix}$

37. $\begin{bmatrix} 1 & 3 & 1 \\ 3 & 3 & 3 \\ 1 & 3 & 1 \end{bmatrix} + \begin{bmatrix} 1 & -2 & 1 \\ -2 & -2 & -2 \\ 1 & -2 & 1 \end{bmatrix} = \begin{bmatrix} 2 & 1 & 2 \\ 1 & 1 & 1 \\ 2 & 1 & 2 \end{bmatrix}$

39. a. $A = \begin{bmatrix} 0 & 3 & 0 \\ 0 & 3 & 0 \\ 0 & 3 & 0 \end{bmatrix}$

b. $B = \begin{bmatrix} 1 & 0 & 1 \\ 1 & 0 & 1 \\ 1 & 0 & 1 \end{bmatrix}$

41. a. $AB = \begin{bmatrix} 0.15 & 0.25 & 0.20 & 0.10 \\ 0.35 & 0.40 & 0.35 & 0.70 \\ 0.50 & 0.35 & 0.45 & 0.20 \end{bmatrix} \begin{bmatrix} 820 & 640 \\ 950 & 1020 \\ 680 & 720 \\ 930 & 910 \end{bmatrix} = \begin{bmatrix} 589.5 & 586 \\ 1556 & 1521 \\ 1234.5 & 1183 \end{bmatrix}$

b. AB represents the distribution of students by gender and state of health. On this campus, there are 1521 females who are sick.

c. There are 1235 male carriers.

43. a. System 1: The midterm and final both count for 50% of the course grade.
System 2: The midterm counts for 30% of the course grade and the final counts for 70%

b. $AB = \begin{bmatrix} 84 & 87.2 \\ 79 & 81 \\ 90 & 88.4 \\ 73 & 68.6 \\ 69 & 73.4 \end{bmatrix}$

System 1 grades are listed first (if different).
Student 1: B; Student 2: C or B;
Student 3: A or B; Student 4: C or D;
Student 5: D or C

45.–57. Answers may vary.

59. $AB = \begin{bmatrix} 0 & -1 \\ 1 & 0 \end{bmatrix}\begin{bmatrix} 0 & -1 \\ 1 & 0 \end{bmatrix} = \begin{bmatrix} 0 & 1 \\ 1 & 0 \end{bmatrix}$

$-BA = \begin{bmatrix} 1 & 0 \\ 0 & -1 \end{bmatrix}\begin{bmatrix} 0 & -1 \\ 1 & 0 \end{bmatrix} = -\begin{bmatrix} 0 & -1 \\ -1 & 0 \end{bmatrix} = \begin{bmatrix} 0 & 1 \\ 1 & 0 \end{bmatrix}$

$AB = -BA$ so they are anticommutative.

Section 6.4

Check Point Exercises

1. We must show that: $AB = I_2 = \begin{bmatrix} 1 & 0 \\ 0 & 1 \end{bmatrix}$, and

$BA = I_2 = \begin{bmatrix} 1 & 0 \\ 0 & 1 \end{bmatrix}$.

$AB = \begin{bmatrix} 2 & 1 \\ 1 & 1 \end{bmatrix}\begin{bmatrix} 1 & -1 \\ -1 & 2 \end{bmatrix}$

$= \begin{bmatrix} 2(1)+1(-1) & 2(-1)+1(2) \\ 1(1)+1(-1) & 1(-1)+1(2) \end{bmatrix}$

$= \begin{bmatrix} 1 & 0 \\ 0 & 1 \end{bmatrix}$

$BA = \begin{bmatrix} 1 & -1 \\ -1 & 2 \end{bmatrix}\begin{bmatrix} 2 & 1 \\ 1 & 1 \end{bmatrix}$

$= \begin{bmatrix} 1(2)+-1(1) & 1(1)+-1(1) \\ -1(2)+2(1) & -1(1)+2(1) \end{bmatrix}$

$= \begin{bmatrix} 1 & 0 \\ 0 & 1 \end{bmatrix}$

Both products (AB and BA) give the multiplicative identity matrix, I_2. Thus, B is the mulpilicative inverse of A.

2. Let us denote the multiplicative inverse of A by $A^{-1} = \begin{bmatrix} x & y \\ z & w \end{bmatrix}$. Because A is a 2×2 matrix, we use the equation $AA^{-1} = I_2$ to find values for x, y, z and w.

$\begin{bmatrix} 5 & 7 \\ 2 & 3 \end{bmatrix}\begin{bmatrix} x & y \\ z & w \end{bmatrix} = \begin{bmatrix} 1 & 0 \\ 0 & 1 \end{bmatrix}$

$\begin{bmatrix} 5x+7z & 5y+7w \\ 2x+3z & 2y+3w \end{bmatrix} = \begin{bmatrix} 1 & 0 \\ 0 & 1 \end{bmatrix}$

$5x + 7z = 1$ and $5y + 7w = 0$

$2x + 3z = 0$ $\qquad 2y + 3w = 1$

Each of these systems can be solved using the addition method.

Multiply by –2:

$5x + 7z = 1 \rightarrow -10x - 14z = -2$

Multiply by 5:

$2x + 3z = 0 \rightarrow 10x + 15z = 0$

$z = -2$

Use back substitution: $x = 3$

Multiply by –2:

$5y + 7w = 0 \rightarrow -10y - 14w = 0$

Multiply by 5:

$2y + 3w = 1 \rightarrow 10y + 15w = 5$

$w = 5$

Use back substitution: $y = -7$

Using these values, we have

$A^{-1} = \begin{bmatrix} x & y \\ z & w \end{bmatrix} = \begin{bmatrix} 3 & -7 \\ -2 & 5 \end{bmatrix}$.

3. $A^{-1} = \dfrac{1}{ad - bc}\begin{bmatrix} d & -b \\ -c & a \end{bmatrix}$

$= \dfrac{1}{3(1)-(-2)(-1)}\begin{bmatrix} 1 & -(-2) \\ -(-1) & 3 \end{bmatrix}$

$= \dfrac{1}{3-2}\begin{bmatrix} 1 & 2 \\ 1 & 3 \end{bmatrix}$

$= \dfrac{1}{1}\begin{bmatrix} 1 & 2 \\ 1 & 3 \end{bmatrix}$

$= \begin{bmatrix} 1 & 2 \\ 1 & 3 \end{bmatrix}$

4. The augmented matrix $[A \mid I_3]$ is

$\left[\begin{array}{rrr|rrr} 1 & 0 & 2 & 1 & 0 & 0 \\ -1 & 2 & 3 & 0 & 1 & 0 \\ 1 & -1 & 0 & 0 & 0 & 1 \end{array}\right]$.

Perform row transformations on $[A \mid I_3]$ to obtain a matrix of the form $[I_3 | B]$.

$\left[\begin{array}{rrr|rrr} 1 & 0 & 2 & 1 & 0 & 0 \\ -1 & 2 & 3 & 0 & 1 & 0 \\ 1 & -1 & 0 & 0 & 0 & 1 \end{array}\right] \; 1R_1 / R_2$

$= \left[\begin{array}{rrr|rrr} 1 & 0 & 2 & 1 & 0 & 0 \\ 0 & 2 & 5 & 1 & 1 & 0 \\ 1 & -1 & 0 & 0 & 0 & 1 \end{array}\right] - 1R_3$

$$= \left[\begin{array}{ccc|ccc} 1 & 0 & 2 & 1 & 0 & 0 \\ 0 & 2 & 5 & 1 & 1 & 0 \\ -1 & 1 & 0 & 0 & 0 & -1 \end{array}\right] R_1 + R_3$$

$$= \left[\begin{array}{ccc|ccc} 1 & 0 & 2 & 1 & 0 & 0 \\ 0 & 2 & 5 & 1 & 1 & 0 \\ 0 & 1 & 2 & 1 & 0 & -1 \end{array}\right] \tfrac{1}{2}R_2$$

$$= \left[\begin{array}{ccc|ccc} 1 & 0 & 2 & 1 & 0 & 0 \\ 0 & 1 & \frac{5}{2} & \frac{1}{2} & \frac{1}{2} & 0 \\ 0 & 1 & 2 & 1 & 0 & -1 \end{array}\right] -1R_2 + R_3$$

$$= \left[\begin{array}{ccc|ccc} 1 & 0 & 2 & 1 & 0 & 0 \\ 0 & 1 & \frac{5}{2} & \frac{1}{2} & \frac{1}{2} & 0 \\ 0 & 0 & -\frac{1}{2} & \frac{1}{2} & -\frac{1}{2} & -1 \end{array}\right] -2R_3$$

$$= \left[\begin{array}{ccc|ccc} 1 & 0 & 2 & 1 & 0 & 0 \\ 0 & 1 & \frac{5}{2} & \frac{1}{2} & \frac{1}{2} & 0 \\ 0 & 0 & 1 & -1 & 1 & 2 \end{array}\right] \begin{array}{l} -2R_3 + R_1 \\ -\frac{5}{2}R_3 + R_2 \end{array}$$

$$= \left[\begin{array}{ccc|ccc} 1 & 0 & 0 & 3 & -2 & -4 \\ 0 & 1 & 0 & 3 & -2 & -5 \\ 0 & 0 & 1 & 1 & 1 & 2 \end{array}\right]$$

Thus, the multiplicative inverse of A is

$$A^{-1} = \begin{bmatrix} 3 & -2 & -4 \\ 3 & -2 & -5 \\ -1 & 1 & 2 \end{bmatrix}.$$

5. The linear system can be written as $AX = B$.

$$\begin{bmatrix} 1 & 0 & 2 \\ -1 & 2 & 3 \\ 1 & -1 & 0 \end{bmatrix}\begin{bmatrix} x \\ y \\ z \end{bmatrix} = \begin{bmatrix} 6 \\ -5 \\ 6 \end{bmatrix}.$$

$$X = A^{-1}B = \begin{bmatrix} 3 & -2 & -4 \\ 3 & -2 & -5 \\ -1 & 1 & 2 \end{bmatrix}\begin{bmatrix} 6 \\ -5 \\ 6 \end{bmatrix}$$

$$= \begin{bmatrix} 3(6) + -2(-5) + -4(6) \\ 3(6) + -2(-5) + -5(6) \\ -1(6) + 1(-5) + 2(6) \end{bmatrix}$$

$$= \begin{bmatrix} 18 + 10 - 24 \\ 18 + 10 - 30 \\ -6 - 5 + 12 \end{bmatrix} = \begin{bmatrix} 4 \\ -2 \\ 1 \end{bmatrix}$$

Thus, $x = 4$, $y = -2$, and $z = 1$. The solution set is $\{(4, -2, 1)\}$.

6. The numerical representation of the word BASE is 2, 1, 19, 5. The 2×2 matrix formed is $\begin{bmatrix} 2 & 19 \\ 1 & 5 \end{bmatrix}$.

$$\begin{bmatrix} -2 & -3 \\ 3 & 4 \end{bmatrix}\begin{bmatrix} 2 & 19 \\ 1 & 5 \end{bmatrix}$$

$$= \begin{bmatrix} -2(2) + -3(1) & -2(19) + -3(5) \\ 3(2) + 4(1) & 3(19) + 4(5) \end{bmatrix}$$

$$= \begin{bmatrix} -4 - 3 & -38 - 15 \\ 6 + 4 & 57 + 20 \end{bmatrix} = \begin{bmatrix} -7 & -53 \\ 10 & 77 \end{bmatrix}$$

The encoded message is –7, 10, –53, 77.

7. Use the multiplicative inverse of the coding matrix. It is $\begin{bmatrix} 4 & 3 \\ -3 & -2 \end{bmatrix}$.

$$\begin{bmatrix} 4 & 3 \\ -3 & -2 \end{bmatrix}\begin{bmatrix} -7 & -53 \\ 10 & 77 \end{bmatrix}$$

$$= \begin{bmatrix} 4(-7) + 3(10) & 4(-53) + 3(77) \\ -3(-7) + -2(10) & -3(-53) + -2(77) \end{bmatrix}$$

$$= \begin{bmatrix} -28 + 30 & -212 + 231 \\ 21 - 20 & 159 - 154 \end{bmatrix} = \begin{bmatrix} 2 & 19 \\ 1 & 5 \end{bmatrix}$$

The numbers are 2, 1, 19, and 5. Using letters, the decoded message is BASE.

Exercise Set 6.4

1. $A = \begin{bmatrix} 4 & -3 \\ -5 & 4 \end{bmatrix}$ $B = \begin{bmatrix} 4 & 3 \\ 5 & 4 \end{bmatrix}$

$$AB = \begin{bmatrix} 16 - 15 & 12 - 12 \\ -20 + 20 & -15 + 16 \end{bmatrix} = \begin{bmatrix} 1 & 0 \\ 0 & 1 \end{bmatrix}$$

$$BA = \begin{bmatrix} 16 - 15 & -12 + 12 \\ 20 - 20 & -15 + 16 \end{bmatrix} = \begin{bmatrix} 1 & 0 \\ 0 & 1 \end{bmatrix}$$

Since $AB = I_2$ $BA = I_2$, $B = A^{-1}$.

3. $AB = \begin{bmatrix} 8+0 & -16+0 \\ -2+0 & 4+3 \end{bmatrix} = \begin{bmatrix} 8 & -16 \\ -2 & 7 \end{bmatrix}$

$BA = \begin{bmatrix} 8+4 & 0+12 \\ 0+1 & 0+3 \end{bmatrix} = \begin{bmatrix} 12 & 12 \\ 1 & 3 \end{bmatrix}$

If B is the multiplicative inverse of A, both products (AB and BA) will be the multiplicative identity matrix, I_2. Therefore, B is not the multiplicative inverse of A. That is, $B \neq A^{-1}$.

5. $AB = \begin{bmatrix} -2+3 & -4+4 \\ \frac{3}{2}-\frac{3}{2} & 3-2 \end{bmatrix} = \begin{bmatrix} 1 & 0 \\ 0 & 1 \end{bmatrix}$

$BA = \begin{bmatrix} -2+3 & 1-1 \\ -6+6 & 3-2 \end{bmatrix} = \begin{bmatrix} 1 & 0 \\ 0 & 1 \end{bmatrix}$

Since $AB = I_2$ and $BA = I_2$, $B = A^{-1}$.

7. $A = \begin{bmatrix} 0 & 1 & 0 \\ 0 & 0 & 1 \\ 1 & 0 & 0 \end{bmatrix}$ $B = \begin{bmatrix} 0 & 0 & 1 \\ 1 & 0 & 0 \\ 0 & 1 & 0 \end{bmatrix}$

$AB = \begin{bmatrix} 0+1+0 & 0+0+0 & 0+0+0 \\ 0+0+0 & 0+0+1 & 0+0+0 \\ 0+0+0 & 0+0+0 & 1+0+0 \end{bmatrix} = \begin{bmatrix} 1 & 0 & 0 \\ 0 & 1 & 0 \\ 0 & 0 & 1 \end{bmatrix}$

$BA = \begin{bmatrix} 0+0+1 & 0+0+0 & 0+0+0 \\ 0+0+0 & 1+0+0 & 0+0+0 \\ 0+0+0 & 0+0+0 & 0+1+0 \end{bmatrix} = \begin{bmatrix} 1 & 0 & 0 \\ 0 & 1 & 0 \\ 0 & 0 & 1 \end{bmatrix}$

Since $AB = I_3$ and $BA = I_3$, $B = A^{-1}$.

9. $AB = \begin{bmatrix} \frac{7}{2}-1-\frac{3}{2} & -3+0+3 & \frac{1}{2}+1-\frac{3}{2} \\ \frac{7}{2}-\frac{3}{2}-2 & -3+0+4 & \frac{1}{2}+\frac{3}{2}-2 \\ \frac{7}{2}-2-\frac{3}{2} & -3+0+3 & \frac{1}{2}+2-\frac{3}{2} \end{bmatrix} = \begin{bmatrix} 1 & 0 & 0 \\ 0 & 1 & 0 \\ 0 & 0 & 1 \end{bmatrix}$

$BA = \begin{bmatrix} \frac{7}{2}-3+\frac{1}{2} & 7-9+2 & \frac{21}{2}-12+\frac{3}{2} \\ -\frac{1}{2}+0+\frac{1}{2} & -1+0+2 & -\frac{3}{2}+0+\frac{3}{2} \\ -\frac{1}{2}+1-\frac{1}{2} & -1+3-2 & -\frac{3}{2}+4-\frac{3}{2} \end{bmatrix} = \begin{bmatrix} 1 & 0 & 0 \\ 0 & 1 & 0 \\ 0 & 0 & 1 \end{bmatrix}$

Since $AB = I_3$ and $BA = I_3$, $B = A^{-1}$.

11. $AB = \begin{bmatrix} 0+0+0+1 & 0+0-2+2 & 0+0+0+0 & 0+0-2+2 \\ -1+0+0+1 & -2+0+1+2 & 0+0+0+0 & -3+0+1+2 \\ 0+0+0+0 & 0+1-1+0 & 0+1+0+0 & 0+1-1+0 \\ 1+0+0-1 & 2+0+0-2 & 0+0+0+0 & 3+0+0-2 \end{bmatrix} = \begin{bmatrix} 1 & 0 & 0 & 0 \\ 0 & 1 & 0 & 0 \\ 0 & 0 & 1 & 0 \\ 0 & 0 & 0 & 1 \end{bmatrix}$

$BA = \begin{bmatrix} 0-2+0+3 & 0+0+0+0 & -2+2+0+0 & 1+2+0-3 \\ 0-1+0+1 & 0+0+1+0 & 0+1-1+0 & 0+1+0-1 \\ 0-1+0+1 & 0+0+0+0 & 0+1+0+0 & 0+1+0-1 \\ 0-2+0+2 & 0+0+0+0 & -2+2+0+0 & 1+2+0-2 \end{bmatrix} = \begin{bmatrix} 1 & 0 & 0 & 0 \\ 0 & 1 & 0 & 0 \\ 0 & 0 & 1 & 0 \\ 0 & 0 & 0 & 1 \end{bmatrix}$

Since $AB = I_4$ and $BA = I_4$, $B = A^{-1}$.

13. $ad - bc = (2)(2) - (3)(-1) = 4 + 3 = 7$

$A^{-1} = \frac{1}{7}\begin{bmatrix} 2 & -3 \\ 1 & 2 \end{bmatrix} = \begin{bmatrix} \frac{2}{7} & -\frac{3}{7} \\ \frac{1}{7} & \frac{2}{7} \end{bmatrix}$

$AA^{-1} = \begin{bmatrix} \frac{4}{7}+\frac{3}{7} & -\frac{6}{7}+\frac{6}{7} \\ -\frac{2}{7}+\frac{2}{7} & \frac{3}{7}+\frac{4}{7} \end{bmatrix} = \begin{bmatrix} 1 & 0 \\ 0 & 1 \end{bmatrix}$

$A^{-1}A = \begin{bmatrix} \frac{4}{7}+\frac{3}{7} & \frac{6}{7}-\frac{6}{7} \\ \frac{2}{7}-\frac{2}{7} & \frac{3}{7}+\frac{4}{7} \end{bmatrix} = \begin{bmatrix} 1 & 0 \\ 0 & 1 \end{bmatrix}$

15. $ad - bc = (3)(2) - (-1)(-4) = 6 - 4 = 2$

$A^{-1} = \frac{1}{2}\begin{bmatrix} 2 & 1 \\ 4 & 3 \end{bmatrix} = \begin{bmatrix} 1 & \frac{1}{2} \\ 2 & \frac{3}{2} \end{bmatrix}$

$AA^{-1} = \begin{bmatrix} 3-2 & \frac{3}{2}-\frac{3}{2} \\ -4+4 & -\frac{4}{2}+\frac{6}{2} \end{bmatrix} = \begin{bmatrix} 1 & 0 \\ 0 & 1 \end{bmatrix}$

$A^{-1}A = \begin{bmatrix} 3-\frac{4}{2} & -1+\frac{2}{2} \\ 6-\frac{12}{2} & -2+\frac{6}{2} \end{bmatrix} = \begin{bmatrix} 1 & 0 \\ 0 & 1 \end{bmatrix}$

17. $ad - bc = (10)(1) - (-2)(-5) = 10 - 10 = 0$
Since division by zero is undefined, A does not have an inverse.
For Problems 19–24, verification that $AA^{-1} = I$ and $A^{-1}A = I$ is left to the student.

19. $\left[\begin{array}{rrr|rrr} 2 & 2 & -1 & 1 & 0 & 0 \\ 0 & 3 & -1 & 0 & 1 & 0 \\ -1 & -2 & 1 & 0 & 0 & 1 \end{array}\right] R_1 \leftrightarrow R_3$

$\left[\begin{array}{rrr|rrr} -1 & -2 & 1 & 0 & 0 & 1 \\ 0 & 3 & -1 & 0 & 1 & 0 \\ 2 & 2 & -1 & 1 & 0 & 0 \end{array}\right] -1R_1$

$\left[\begin{array}{rrr|rrr} 1 & 2 & -1 & 0 & 0 & -1 \\ 0 & 3 & -1 & 0 & 1 & 0 \\ 2 & 2 & -1 & 1 & 0 & 0 \end{array}\right] -2R_1 + R_3$

$\left[\begin{array}{rrr|rrr} 1 & 2 & -1 & 0 & 0 & -1 \\ 0 & 3 & -1 & 0 & 1 & 0 \\ 0 & -2 & 1 & 1 & 0 & 2 \end{array}\right] \frac{1}{3}R_2$

$\left[\begin{array}{rrr|rrr} 1 & 2 & -1 & 0 & 0 & -1 \\ 0 & 1 & -\frac{1}{3} & 0 & \frac{1}{3} & 0 \\ 0 & -2 & 1 & 1 & 0 & 2 \end{array}\right] \begin{array}{l} -2R_2 + R_1 \\ 2R_2 + R_3 \end{array}$

$\left[\begin{array}{rrr|rrr} 1 & 0 & -\frac{1}{3} & 0 & -\frac{2}{3} & -1 \\ 0 & 1 & -\frac{1}{3} & 0 & \frac{1}{3} & 0 \\ 0 & 0 & \frac{1}{3} & 1 & \frac{2}{3} & 2 \end{array}\right] \begin{array}{l} 1R_3 + R_1 \\ 1R_2 + R_1 \end{array}$

$\left[\begin{array}{rrr|rrr} 1 & 0 & 0 & 1 & 0 & 1 \\ 0 & 1 & 0 & 1 & 1 & 2 \\ 0 & 0 & \frac{1}{3} & 1 & \frac{2}{3} & 2 \end{array}\right] 3R_3$

$\left[\begin{array}{rrr|rrr} 1 & 0 & 0 & 1 & 0 & 1 \\ 0 & 1 & 0 & 1 & 1 & 2 \\ 0 & 0 & 1 & 3 & 2 & 6 \end{array}\right]$

$A^{-1} = \begin{bmatrix} 1 & 0 & 1 \\ 1 & 1 & 2 \\ 3 & 2 & 6 \end{bmatrix}$

21. $\left[\begin{array}{rrr|rrr} 5 & 0 & 2 & 1 & 0 & 0 \\ 2 & 2 & 1 & 0 & 1 & 0 \\ -3 & 1 & -1 & 0 & 0 & 1 \end{array}\right] \frac{1}{5}R_1$

$\left[\begin{array}{rrr|rrr} 1 & 0 & \frac{2}{5} & \frac{1}{5} & 0 & 0 \\ 2 & 2 & 1 & 0 & 1 & 0 \\ -3 & 1 & -1 & 0 & 0 & 1 \end{array}\right] \begin{array}{l} -2R_1 + R_2 \\ 3R_1 + R_3 \end{array}$

$\left[\begin{array}{rrr|rrr} 1 & 0 & \frac{2}{5} & \frac{1}{5} & 0 & 0 \\ 0 & 2 & \frac{1}{5} & -\frac{2}{5} & 1 & 0 \\ 0 & 1 & \frac{1}{5} & \frac{3}{5} & 0 & 1 \end{array}\right] R_2 \leftrightarrow R_3$

$\left[\begin{array}{rrr|rrr} 1 & 0 & \frac{2}{5} & \frac{1}{5} & 0 & 0 \\ 0 & 1 & \frac{1}{5} & \frac{3}{5} & 0 & 1 \\ 0 & 2 & \frac{1}{5} & -\frac{2}{5} & 1 & 0 \end{array}\right] -2R_2 + R_3$

$\left[\begin{array}{rrr|rrr} 1 & 0 & \frac{2}{5} & \frac{1}{5} & 0 & 0 \\ 0 & 1 & \frac{1}{5} & \frac{3}{5} & 0 & 1 \\ 0 & 0 & -\frac{1}{5} & -\frac{8}{5} & 1 & -2 \end{array}\right] \begin{array}{l} 2R_3 + R_1 \\ 1R_3 + R_2 \end{array}$

$\left[\begin{array}{rrr|rrr} 1 & 0 & 0 & -3 & 2 & -4 \\ 0 & 1 & 0 & -1 & 1 & -1 \\ 0 & 0 & -\frac{1}{5} & -\frac{8}{5} & 1 & -2 \end{array}\right] -5R_3$

$\left[\begin{array}{rrr|rrr} 1 & 0 & 0 & -3 & 2 & -4 \\ 0 & 1 & 0 & -1 & 1 & -1 \\ 0 & 0 & 1 & 8 & -5 & 10 \end{array}\right]$

$A^{-1} = \begin{bmatrix} -3 & 2 & -4 \\ -1 & 1 & -1 \\ 8 & -5 & 10 \end{bmatrix}$

23. $\left[\begin{array}{cccc|cccc} 1 & 0 & 0 & 0 & 1 & 0 & 0 & 0 \\ 0 & -1 & 0 & 0 & 0 & 1 & 0 & 0 \\ 0 & 0 & 3 & 0 & 0 & 0 & 1 & 0 \\ 1 & 0 & 0 & 1 & 0 & 0 & 0 & 1 \end{array}\right] -1R_1 + R_4$

$\left[\begin{array}{cccc|cccc} 1 & 0 & 0 & 0 & 1 & 0 & 0 & 0 \\ 0 & -1 & 0 & 0 & 0 & 1 & 0 & 0 \\ 0 & 0 & 3 & 0 & 0 & 0 & 1 & 0 \\ 0 & 0 & 0 & 1 & -1 & 0 & 0 & 1 \end{array}\right] -1R_2$

$\left[\begin{array}{cccc|cccc} 1 & 0 & 0 & 0 & 1 & 0 & 0 & 0 \\ 0 & 1 & 0 & 0 & 0 & -1 & 0 & 0 \\ 0 & 0 & 3 & 0 & 0 & 0 & 1 & 0 \\ 0 & 0 & 0 & 1 & -1 & 0 & 0 & 1 \end{array}\right] \frac{1}{3}R_3$

$\left[\begin{array}{cccc|cccc} 1 & 0 & 0 & 0 & 1 & 0 & 0 & 0 \\ 0 & 1 & 0 & 0 & 0 & -1 & 0 & 0 \\ 0 & 0 & 1 & 0 & 0 & 0 & \frac{1}{3} & 0 \\ 0 & 0 & 0 & 1 & -1 & 0 & 0 & 1 \end{array}\right]$

$A^{-1} = \begin{bmatrix} 1 & 0 & 0 & 0 \\ 0 & -1 & 0 & 0 \\ 0 & 0 & \frac{1}{3} & 0 \\ -1 & 0 & 0 & 1 \end{bmatrix}$

25. $\begin{bmatrix} 6 & 5 \\ 5 & 4 \end{bmatrix}\begin{bmatrix} x \\ y \end{bmatrix} = \begin{bmatrix} 13 \\ 10 \end{bmatrix}$

27. $\begin{bmatrix} 1 & 3 & 4 \\ 1 & 2 & 3 \\ 1 & 4 & 3 \end{bmatrix}\begin{bmatrix} x \\ y \\ z \end{bmatrix} = \begin{bmatrix} -3 \\ -2 \\ -6 \end{bmatrix}$

29. $4x - 7y = -3$
$2x - 3y = 1$

31. $2x - z = 6$
$3y = 9$
$x + y = 5$

33. a. $\begin{bmatrix} 2 & 6 & 6 \\ 2 & 7 & 6 \\ 2 & 7 & 7 \end{bmatrix}\begin{bmatrix} x \\ y \\ z \end{bmatrix} = \begin{bmatrix} 8 \\ 10 \\ 9 \end{bmatrix}$

b. $\begin{bmatrix} \frac{7}{2} & 0 & -3 \\ -1 & 1 & 0 \\ 0 & -1 & 1 \end{bmatrix}\begin{bmatrix} 8 \\ 10 \\ 9 \end{bmatrix} = \begin{bmatrix} 28+0-27 \\ -8+10+0 \\ 0-10+9 \end{bmatrix} = \begin{bmatrix} 1 \\ 2 \\ -1 \end{bmatrix}$

The solution to the system is $\{(1, 2, -1)\}$.

35. a. $\begin{bmatrix} 1 & -1 & 1 \\ 0 & 2 & -1 \\ 2 & 3 & 0 \end{bmatrix}\begin{bmatrix} x \\ y \\ z \end{bmatrix} = \begin{bmatrix} 8 \\ -7 \\ 1 \end{bmatrix}$

b. $\begin{bmatrix} 3 & 3 & -1 \\ -2 & -2 & 1 \\ -4 & -5 & 2 \end{bmatrix}\begin{bmatrix} 8 \\ -7 \\ 1 \end{bmatrix}$

$= \begin{bmatrix} 24-21-1 \\ -16+14+1 \\ -32+35+2 \end{bmatrix} = \begin{bmatrix} 2 \\ -1 \\ 5 \end{bmatrix}$

The solution to the system is $\{(2, -1, 5)\}$.

37. a. $\begin{bmatrix} 1 & -1 & 2 & 0 \\ 0 & 1 & -1 & 1 \\ -1 & 1 & -1 & 2 \\ 0 & -1 & 1 & -2 \end{bmatrix}\begin{bmatrix} x \\ y \\ z \\ w \end{bmatrix} = \begin{bmatrix} -3 \\ 4 \\ 2 \\ -4 \end{bmatrix}$

b. $\begin{bmatrix} 0 & 0 & -1 & -1 \\ 1 & 4 & 1 & 3 \\ 1 & 2 & 1 & 2 \\ 0 & -1 & 0 & -1 \end{bmatrix}\begin{bmatrix} -3 \\ 4 \\ 2 \\ -4 \end{bmatrix}$

$= \begin{bmatrix} 0+0-2+4 \\ -3+16+2-12 \\ -3+8+2-8 \\ 0-4+0+4 \end{bmatrix} = \begin{bmatrix} 2 \\ 3 \\ -1 \\ 0 \end{bmatrix}$

The solution to the system is $\{(2, 3, -1, 0)\}$.

39. The numerical equivalent of HELP is 8, 5, 12, 16.

$$\begin{bmatrix} 4 & -1 \\ -3 & 1 \end{bmatrix}\begin{bmatrix} 8 \\ 5 \end{bmatrix}=\begin{bmatrix} 27 \\ -19 \end{bmatrix},$$

$$\begin{bmatrix} 4 & -1 \\ -3 & 1 \end{bmatrix}\begin{bmatrix} 12 \\ 16 \end{bmatrix}=\begin{bmatrix} 32 \\ -20 \end{bmatrix}$$

The encoded message is 27, –19, 32, –20.

$$\begin{bmatrix} 1 & 1 \\ 3 & 4 \end{bmatrix}\begin{bmatrix} 27 \\ -19 \end{bmatrix}=\begin{bmatrix} 8 \\ 5 \end{bmatrix}, \begin{bmatrix} 1 & 1 \\ 3 & 4 \end{bmatrix}\begin{bmatrix} 32 \\ -20 \end{bmatrix}=\begin{bmatrix} 12 \\ 16 \end{bmatrix}$$

The decoded message is 8, 5, 12, 16 or HELP.

41. $$\begin{bmatrix} 1 & -1 & 0 \\ 3 & 0 & 2 \\ -1 & 0 & -1 \end{bmatrix}\begin{bmatrix} 19 & 4 & 1 \\ 5 & 0 & 19 \\ 14 & 3 & 8 \end{bmatrix}$$

$$=\begin{bmatrix} 19-5+0 & 4+0+0 & 1-19+0 \\ 57+0+28 & 12+0+6 & 3+0+16 \\ -19+0-14 & -4+0-3 & -1+0-8 \end{bmatrix}$$

$$=\begin{bmatrix} 14 & 4 & -18 \\ 85 & 18 & 19 \\ -33 & -7 & -9 \end{bmatrix}$$

The encoded message is 14, 85, –33, 4, 18, –7, –18, 19, –9.

$$\begin{bmatrix} 0 & 1 & 2 \\ -1 & 1 & 2 \\ 0 & -1 & -3 \end{bmatrix}\begin{bmatrix} 14 & 4 & -18 \\ 85 & 18 & 19 \\ -33 & -7 & -9 \end{bmatrix}$$

$$=\begin{bmatrix} 0+85-66 & 0+18-14 & 0+19-18 \\ -14+85-66 & -4+18-14 & 18+19-18 \\ 0-85+99 & 0-18+21 & 0-19+27 \end{bmatrix}$$

$$=\begin{bmatrix} 19 & 4 & 1 \\ 5 & 0 & 19 \\ 14 & 3 & 8 \end{bmatrix}$$

The decoded message is 19, 5, 14, 4, 0, 3, 1, 19, 8 or SEND_CASH

43.–51. Answers may vary.

53. Enter the matrix $\begin{bmatrix} 3 & -1 \\ -2 & 1 \end{bmatrix}$ as $[A]$, then use $[A]^{-1}$.

$$[A]^{-1}=\begin{bmatrix} 1 & 1 \\ 2 & 3 \end{bmatrix}$$

Verify this result by showing that $[A][A]^{-1}=I_2$ and $[A]^{-1}[A]=I_2$.

55. Enter the matrix $\begin{bmatrix} -2 & 1 & -1 \\ -5 & 2 & -1 \\ 3 & -1 & 1 \end{bmatrix}$ as $[A]$, then use $[A]^{-1}$.

$$[A]^{-1}=\begin{bmatrix} 1 & 0 & 1 \\ 2 & 1 & 3 \\ -1 & 1 & 1 \end{bmatrix}$$

Verify this result by showing that $[A][A]^{-1}=I_3$ and $[A]^{-1}[A]=I_3$.

57. Enter the matrix $\begin{bmatrix} 7 & -3 & 0 & 2 \\ -2 & 1 & 0 & -1 \\ 4 & 0 & 1 & -2 \\ -1 & 1 & 0 & -1 \end{bmatrix}$ as $[A]$,

then use $[A]^{-1}$. $[A]^{-1}=\begin{bmatrix} 0 & -1 & 0 & 1 \\ -1 & -5 & 0 & 3 \\ -2 & -4 & 1 & -2 \\ -1 & -4 & 0 & 1 \end{bmatrix}$

Verify this result by showing that $[A][A]^{-1}=I_4$ and $[A]^{-1}[A]=I_4$.

For Problems 46–50, enter the matrix A as $[A]$ and the matrix B as $[B]$ in your graphing utility, then calculate $[A]^{-1}[B]$ to find X.

59. The system is $AX = B$ where

$$A=\begin{bmatrix}1 & -1 & 1\\ 4 & 2 & 1\\ 4 & -2 & 1\end{bmatrix},\ X=\begin{bmatrix}x\\ y\\ z\end{bmatrix},\text{ and } B=\begin{bmatrix}-6\\ 9\\ -3\end{bmatrix}.$$

$X=\begin{bmatrix}2\\ 3\\ -5\end{bmatrix}$, so the solution to the system is $\{(2, 3, -5)\}$.

61. The system is $AX = B$ where

$$A=\begin{bmatrix}3 & -2 & 1\\ 4 & -5 & 3\\ 2 & -1 & 5\end{bmatrix},\ X=\begin{bmatrix}x\\ y\\ z\end{bmatrix},\text{ and } B=\begin{bmatrix}-2\\ -9\\ -5\end{bmatrix}.$$

$X=\begin{bmatrix}1\\ 2\\ -1\end{bmatrix}$ so the solution to the system is $\{(1, 2, -1)\}$.

63. The system is $AX = B$ where

$$A=\begin{bmatrix}1 & 0 & -3 & 0 & 1\\ 0 & 1 & 0 & 1 & 0\\ 0 & 0 & 1 & 0 & 1\\ 1 & 1 & -1 & 4 & 0\\ 1 & 1 & 1 & 1 & 1\end{bmatrix},\ X=\begin{bmatrix}x\\ y\\ z\\ w\\ v\end{bmatrix},\text{ and}$$

$B=\begin{bmatrix}-3\\ -1\\ 7\\ -8\\ 8\end{bmatrix}$. $X=\begin{bmatrix}2\\ 1\\ 3\\ -2\\ 4\end{bmatrix}$, so the solution to the system is $\{(2, 1, 3, -2, 4)\}$.

65. Answers may vary.

67. a. False; only square matrices have inverses.

b. False; $\begin{bmatrix}3 & 6\\ 2 & 4\end{bmatrix}$ does not have an inverse since $(3)(4) - (6)(2) = 12 - 12 = 0$ and division by zero is undefined.

c. True; $\begin{bmatrix}1 & 2\\ 2 & 3\end{bmatrix}+\begin{bmatrix}2 & 4\\ 0 & 1\end{bmatrix}=\begin{bmatrix}3 & 6\\ 2 & 4\end{bmatrix}$ and

$\begin{bmatrix}1 & 2\\ 2 & 3\end{bmatrix}^{-1}=\begin{bmatrix}-3 & 2\\ 2 & -1\end{bmatrix}$,

$\begin{bmatrix}2 & 4\\ 0 & 1\end{bmatrix}^{-1}=\begin{bmatrix}\frac{1}{2} & -2\\ 0 & 1\end{bmatrix}$ while $\begin{bmatrix}3 & 6\\ 2 & 4\end{bmatrix}$ does not have an inverse. [See part (b).]

d. False; to solve the matrix equation for X, multiply the inverse of A and B $(A^{-1}B)$ provided the inverse of A exists.

(c) is true.

69. Answers may vary.

71. Using the statement before problems 9–14, we want to find values for a such that $(1)(4) - (a + 1)(a - 2) = 0$.

$$\begin{aligned}(1)(4)-(a+1)(a-2)&=4-(a^2-a-2)\\ &=-a^2+a+6\\ 0&=-a^2+a+6\\ 0&=a^2-a-6\\ 0&=(a-3)(a+2)\\ a&=3,\ -2\end{aligned}$$

Section 6.5

Check Point Exercises

1. a. $\begin{vmatrix}10 & 9\\ 6 & 5\end{vmatrix}=10\cdot 5-6\cdot 9=50-54=-4$

b. $\begin{vmatrix}4 & 3\\ -5 & -8\end{vmatrix}=4\cdot(-8)-(-5)\cdot(3)$

$=-32+15=-17$

2. $5x + 4y = 12$
$3x - 6y = 24$

$$D = \begin{vmatrix} 5 & 4 \\ 3 & -6 \end{vmatrix} = 5 \cdot (-6) - 3 \cdot 4$$
$$= -30 - 12 = -42$$
$$D_x = \begin{vmatrix} 12 & 4 \\ 24 & -6 \end{vmatrix} = 12(-6) - 24(4)$$
$$= -72 - 96 = -168$$
$$D_y = \begin{vmatrix} 5 & 12 \\ 3 & 24 \end{vmatrix} = 5(24) - 3(12)$$
$$= 120 - 36 = 84$$

Thus, $x = \frac{D_x}{D} = \frac{-168}{-42} = 4$

$y = \frac{D_y}{D} = \frac{84}{-42} = -2$

The solution set is $\{(4, -2)\}$.

3. $\begin{bmatrix} 2 & 1 & 7 \\ -5 & 6 & 0 \\ -4 & 3 & 1 \end{bmatrix}$

The minor for 2 is $\begin{vmatrix} 6 & 0 \\ 3 & 1 \end{vmatrix}$.

The minor for –5 is $\begin{vmatrix} 1 & 7 \\ 3 & 1 \end{vmatrix}$.

The minor for –4 is $\begin{vmatrix} 1 & 7 \\ 6 & 0 \end{vmatrix}$.

$$\begin{bmatrix} 2 & 1 & 7 \\ -5 & 6 & 0 \\ -4 & 3 & 1 \end{bmatrix} = 2\begin{vmatrix} 6 & 0 \\ 3 & 1 \end{vmatrix} - (-5)\begin{vmatrix} 1 & 7 \\ 3 & 1 \end{vmatrix} - 4\begin{vmatrix} 1 & 7 \\ 6 & 0 \end{vmatrix}$$
$$= 2(6 \cdot 1 - 3 \cdot 0) + 5(1 \cdot 1 - 3 \cdot 7) - 4(1 \cdot 0 - 6 \cdot 7)$$
$$= 2(6 - 0) + 5(1 - 21) - 4(0 - 42)$$
$$= 12 - 100 + 168$$
$$= 80$$

4. $$\begin{vmatrix} 6 & 4 & 0 \\ -3 & -5 & 3 \\ 1 & 2 & 0 \end{vmatrix} = 0\begin{vmatrix} -3 & -5 \\ 1 & 2 \end{vmatrix} - 3\begin{vmatrix} 6 & 4 \\ 1 & 2 \end{vmatrix} + 0\begin{vmatrix} 6 & 4 \\ -3 & -5 \end{vmatrix}$$
$$= 0 - 3(6 \cdot 2 - 1 \cdot 4) + 0$$
$$= -3(12 - 4)$$
$$= -3(8)$$
$$= -24$$

5. $3x - 2y + z = 16$
$2x + 3y - z = -9$
$x + 4y + 3z = 2$

$$D = \begin{vmatrix} 3 & -2 & 1 \\ 2 & 3 & -1 \\ 1 & 4 & 3 \end{vmatrix};\ D_x = \begin{vmatrix} 16 & -2 & 1 \\ -9 & 3 & -1 \\ 2 & 4 & 3 \end{vmatrix};\ D_y = \begin{vmatrix} 3 & 16 & 1 \\ 2 & -9 & -1 \\ 1 & 2 & 3 \end{vmatrix};\ D_z = \begin{vmatrix} 3 & -2 & 16 \\ 2 & 3 & -9 \\ 1 & 4 & 2 \end{vmatrix}$$

$$D = \begin{vmatrix} 3 & -2 & 1 \\ 2 & 3 & -1 \\ 1 & 4 & 3 \end{vmatrix} = 3\begin{vmatrix} 3 & -1 \\ 4 & 3 \end{vmatrix} - 2\begin{vmatrix} -2 & 1 \\ 4 & 3 \end{vmatrix} + 1\begin{vmatrix} -2 & 1 \\ 3 & -1 \end{vmatrix}$$
$= 3[(3)\cdot 3 - 4\cdot(-1)] - 2[(-2)\cdot 3 - 4\cdot 1] + 1[(-2)\cdot(-1) - (3)\cdot 1]$
$= 3(9+4) - 2(-6-4) + 1(2-3)$
$= 39 + 20 - 1$
$= 58$

$$D_x = \begin{vmatrix} 16 & -2 & 1 \\ -9 & 3 & -1 \\ 2 & 4 & 3 \end{vmatrix} = 1\begin{vmatrix} -9 & 3 \\ 2 & 4 \end{vmatrix} - (-1)\begin{vmatrix} 16 & -2 \\ 2 & 4 \end{vmatrix} + 3\begin{vmatrix} 16 & -2 \\ -9 & 3 \end{vmatrix}$$
$= 1[(-9)\cdot 4 - 2\cdot(3)] + 1[16\cdot 4 - 2(-2)] + 3[16\cdot(3) - (-9)\cdot(-2)]$
$= 1(-36-6) + 1(64+4) + 3(48-18)$
$= -42 + 68 + 90$
$= 116$

$$D_y = \begin{vmatrix} 3 & 16 & 1 \\ 2 & -9 & -1 \\ 1 & 2 & 3 \end{vmatrix} = 3\begin{vmatrix} -9 & -1 \\ 2 & 3 \end{vmatrix} - 2\begin{vmatrix} 16 & 1 \\ 2 & 3 \end{vmatrix} + 1\begin{vmatrix} 16 & 1 \\ -9 & -1 \end{vmatrix}$$
$= 3[(-9)\cdot 3 - 2\cdot(-1)] - 2[16\cdot 3 - 2\cdot 1] + 1[16(-1) - (-9)\cdot 1]$
$= 3(-27+2) - 2(48-2) + 1(-16+9)$
$= -75 - 92 - 7$
$= -174$

$$D_z = \begin{vmatrix} 3 & -2 & 16 \\ 2 & 3 & -9 \\ 1 & 4 & 2 \end{vmatrix} = 3\begin{vmatrix} 3 & -9 \\ 4 & 2 \end{vmatrix} - 2\begin{vmatrix} -2 & 16 \\ 4 & 2 \end{vmatrix} + 1\begin{vmatrix} -2 & 16 \\ 3 & -9 \end{vmatrix}$$
$= 3[(3)2 - 4(-9)] - 2[(-2)2 - 4\cdot 16] + 1[(-2)(-9) - (3)\cdot 16]$
$= 3(6+36) - 2(-4-64) + 1(18-48)$
$= 126 + 136 - 30$
$= 232$

$$x = \frac{D_x}{D} = \frac{116}{58} = 2$$
$$y = \frac{D_y}{D} = \frac{-174}{58} = -3$$
$$z = \frac{D_z}{D} = \frac{232}{58} = 4$$

The solution to the system is $\{(2, -3, 4)\}$.

6. $|A| = \begin{vmatrix} 0 & 4 & 0 & -3 \\ -1 & 1 & 5 & 2 \\ 1 & -2 & 0 & 6 \\ 3 & 0 & 0 & 1 \end{vmatrix} = (-1)^{2+3} 5 \begin{vmatrix} 0 & 4 & -3 \\ 1 & -2 & 6 \\ 3 & 0 & 1 \end{vmatrix} = -5 \begin{vmatrix} 0 & 4 & -3 \\ 1 & -2 & 6 \\ 3 & 0 & 1 \end{vmatrix}$

Evaluate the third-order determinant to get $|A| = -5(50) = -250$.

Exercise Set 6.5

1. $\begin{vmatrix} 5 & 7 \\ 2 & 3 \end{vmatrix} = 5 \cdot 3 - 2 \cdot 7 = 15 - 14 = 1$

3. $\begin{vmatrix} -4 & 1 \\ 5 & 6 \end{vmatrix} = (-4)6 - 5 \cdot 1 = -24 - 5 = -29$

5. $\begin{vmatrix} -7 & 14 \\ 2 & -4 \end{vmatrix} = (-7)(-4) - 2(14) = 28 - 28 = 0$

7. $\begin{vmatrix} -5 & -1 \\ -2 & -7 \end{vmatrix} = (-5)(-7) - (-2)(-1) = 35 - 2 = 33$

9. $\begin{vmatrix} \frac{1}{2} & \frac{1}{2} \\ \frac{1}{8} & -\frac{3}{4} \end{vmatrix} = \frac{1}{2}\left(-\frac{3}{4}\right) - \frac{1}{8} \cdot \frac{1}{2} = -\frac{3}{8} - \frac{1}{16} = -\frac{7}{16}$

11. $D = \begin{vmatrix} 1 & 1 \\ 1 & -1 \end{vmatrix} = -1 - 1 = -2$

$D_x = \begin{vmatrix} 7 & 1 \\ 3 & -1 \end{vmatrix} = -7 - 3 = -10$

$D_y = \begin{vmatrix} 1 & 7 \\ 1 & 3 \end{vmatrix} = 3 - 7 = -4$

$x = \frac{D_x}{D} = \frac{-10}{-2} = 5$

$y = \frac{D_y}{D} = \frac{-4}{-2} = 2$

The solution set is $\{(5, 2)\}$.

13. $D=\begin{vmatrix} 12 & 3 \\ 2 & -3 \end{vmatrix}=-36-6=-42$

$D_x=\begin{vmatrix} 15 & 3 \\ 13 & -3 \end{vmatrix}=-45-39=-84$

$D_y=\begin{vmatrix} 12 & 15 \\ 2 & 13 \end{vmatrix}=156-30=126$

$x=\frac{D_x}{D}=\frac{-84}{-42}=2$

$y=\frac{D_y}{D}=\frac{126}{-42}=-3$

The solution set is $\{(2, -3)\}$.

15. $D=\begin{vmatrix} 4 & -5 \\ 2 & 3 \end{vmatrix}=12-(-10)=22$

$D_x=\begin{vmatrix} 17 & -5 \\ 3 & 3 \end{vmatrix}=51-(-15)=66$

$D_y=\begin{vmatrix} 4 & 17 \\ 2 & 3 \end{vmatrix}=12-34=-22$

$x=\frac{D_x}{D}=\frac{66}{22}=3$

$y=\frac{D_y}{D}=\frac{-22}{22}=-1$

The solution set is $\{(3, -1)\}$.

17. $D=\begin{vmatrix} 1 & 2 \\ 5 & 10 \end{vmatrix}=10-10=0$

$D_x=\begin{vmatrix} 3 & 2 \\ 15 & 10 \end{vmatrix}=30-30=0$

$D_y=\begin{vmatrix} 1 & 3 \\ 5 & 15 \end{vmatrix}=15-15=0$

Because all 3 determinants equal zero, the system is dependent.

19. $D=\begin{vmatrix} 3 & -4 \\ 2 & 2 \end{vmatrix}=6-(-8)=14$

$D_x=\begin{vmatrix} 4 & -4 \\ 12 & 2 \end{vmatrix}=8-(-48)=56$

$D_y=\begin{vmatrix} 3 & 4 \\ 2 & 12 \end{vmatrix}=36-8=28$

$x=\frac{D_x}{D}=\frac{56}{14}=4$

$y=\frac{D_y}{D}=\frac{28}{14}=2$

The solution set is $\{(4, 2)\}$.

21. $D=\begin{vmatrix} 2 & -3 \\ 5 & 4 \end{vmatrix}=8-(-15)=23$

$D_x=\begin{vmatrix} 2 & -3 \\ 51 & 4 \end{vmatrix}=8-(-153)=161$

$D_y=\begin{vmatrix} 2 & 2 \\ 5 & 51 \end{vmatrix}=102-10=92$

$x=\frac{D_x}{D}=\frac{161}{23}=7$

$y=\frac{D_y}{D}=\frac{92}{23}=4$

The solution set is $\{(7, 4)\}$.

23. $D=\begin{vmatrix} 3 & 3 \\ 2 & 2 \end{vmatrix}=6-6=0$

$D_x=\begin{vmatrix} 2 & 3 \\ 3 & 2 \end{vmatrix}=4-9=-5$

$D_y=\begin{vmatrix} 3 & 2 \\ 2 & 3 \end{vmatrix}=9-4=5$

Because $D = 0$ but D_x or $D_y \neq 0$, the system is inconsistent.

25. $D = \begin{vmatrix} 3 & 4 \\ 5 & 3 \end{vmatrix} = 9 - 20 = -11$

$D_x = \begin{vmatrix} 16 & 4 \\ 12 & 3 \end{vmatrix} = 48 - 48 = 0$

$D_y = \begin{vmatrix} 3 & 16 \\ 5 & 12 \end{vmatrix} = 36 - 80 = -44$

$x = \dfrac{D_x}{D} = \dfrac{0}{-11} = 0$

$y = \dfrac{D_y}{D} = \dfrac{-44}{-11} = 4$

The solution set is {(0, 4)}.

27. $\begin{vmatrix} 3 & 0 & 0 \\ 2 & 1 & -5 \\ -2 & 5 & -1 \end{vmatrix} = 3\begin{vmatrix} 1 & -5 \\ 5 & -1 \end{vmatrix} - 0\begin{vmatrix} 2 & -5 \\ -2 & -1 \end{vmatrix} + 0\begin{vmatrix} 2 & 1 \\ -2 & 5 \end{vmatrix}$

$= 3[(1)(-1) - (5)(-5)]$
$= 3(-1 + 25) = 3(24)$
$= 72$

29. $\begin{vmatrix} 3 & 1 & 0 \\ -3 & 4 & 0 \\ -1 & 3 & -5 \end{vmatrix} = 0\begin{vmatrix} -3 & 4 \\ -1 & 3 \end{vmatrix} - 0\begin{vmatrix} 3 & 1 \\ -1 & 3 \end{vmatrix} + (-5)\begin{vmatrix} 3 & 1 \\ -3 & 4 \end{vmatrix}$

$= -5[3 \cdot 4 - (-3)(1)]$
$= -5(12 + 3) = -5(15)$
$= -75$

31. $\begin{vmatrix} 1 & 1 & 1 \\ 2 & 2 & 2 \\ -3 & 4 & -5 \end{vmatrix} -2R_1 + R_2$

$\begin{vmatrix} 1 & 1 & 1 \\ 0 & 0 & 0 \\ -3 & 4 & -5 \end{vmatrix} = 0$

33. $D = \begin{vmatrix} 1 & 1 & 1 \\ 2 & -1 & 1 \\ -1 & 3 & -1 \end{vmatrix}$

$= \begin{vmatrix} -1 & 1 \\ 3 & -1 \end{vmatrix} - \begin{vmatrix} 2 & 1 \\ -1 & -1 \end{vmatrix} + \begin{vmatrix} 2 & -1 \\ -1 & 3 \end{vmatrix}$

$= (1 - 3) - [-2 - (-1)] + (6 - 1)$
$= -2 - (-1) + 5 = -2 + 1 + 5 = 4$

$D_x = \begin{vmatrix} 0 & 1 & 1 \\ -1 & -1 & 1 \\ -8 & 3 & -1 \end{vmatrix} = (-1)\begin{vmatrix} -1 & 1 \\ -8 & -1 \end{vmatrix} + \begin{vmatrix} -1 & -1 \\ -8 & 3 \end{vmatrix}$

$= (-1)[1 - (-8)] + (-3 - 8) = (-1)(9) - 11$
$= -20$

$D_y = \begin{vmatrix} 1 & 0 & 1 \\ 2 & -1 & 1 \\ -1 & -8 & -1 \end{vmatrix} = \begin{vmatrix} -1 & 1 \\ -8 & -1 \end{vmatrix} + \begin{vmatrix} 2 & -1 \\ -1 & -8 \end{vmatrix}$

$= 1 - (-8) + (-16 - 1) = 1 + 8 - 17 = -8$

$D_z = \begin{vmatrix} 1 & 1 & 0 \\ 2 & -1 & -1 \\ -1 & 3 & -8 \end{vmatrix} = 1\begin{vmatrix} -1 & -1 \\ 3 & -8 \end{vmatrix} - 1\begin{vmatrix} 2 & -1 \\ -1 & -8 \end{vmatrix}$

$= 8 - (-3) - 1(-16 - 1) = 11 + 17 = 28$

$x = \dfrac{D_x}{D} = \dfrac{-20}{4} = -5$

$y = \dfrac{D_y}{D} = \dfrac{-8}{4} = -2$

$z = \dfrac{D_z}{D} = \dfrac{28}{4} = 7$

The solution to the system is {(–5, –2, 7)}.

35. $D=\begin{vmatrix}4 & -5 & -6\\ 1 & -2 & -5\\ 2 & -1 & 0\end{vmatrix}=2\begin{vmatrix}-5 & -6\\ -2 & -5\end{vmatrix}-(-1)\begin{vmatrix}4 & -6\\ 1 & -5\end{vmatrix}$

$= 2(25-12)+[-20-(-6)] = 2(13)+(-14)$
$= 26-14 = 12$

$D_x=\begin{vmatrix}-1 & -5 & -6\\ -12 & -2 & -5\\ 7 & -1 & 0\end{vmatrix}$

$=7\begin{vmatrix}-5 & -6\\ -2 & -5\end{vmatrix}-(-1)\begin{vmatrix}-1 & -6\\ -12 & -5\end{vmatrix}$

$= 7(25-12)+(5-72) = 7(13)-67$
$= 91-67 = 24$

$D_y=\begin{vmatrix}4 & -1 & -6\\ 1 & -12 & -5\\ 2 & 7 & 0\end{vmatrix}=2\begin{vmatrix}-1 & -6\\ -12 & -5\end{vmatrix}-7\begin{vmatrix}4 & -6\\ 1 & -5\end{vmatrix}$

$= 2(5-72)-7[-20-(-6)]$
$= 2(-67)-7(-14) = -134+98 = -36$

$D_z=\begin{vmatrix}4 & -5 & -1\\ 1 & -2 & -12\\ 2 & -1 & 7\end{vmatrix}$

$=4\begin{vmatrix}-2 & -12\\ -1 & 7\end{vmatrix}-(-5)\begin{vmatrix}1 & -12\\ 2 & 7\end{vmatrix}+(-1)\begin{vmatrix}1 & -2\\ 2 & -1\end{vmatrix}$

$= 4(-14-12)+5[7-(-24)]-[-1-(-4)]$
$= 4(-26)+5(31)-(3) = -104+155-3 = 48$

$x=\dfrac{D_x}{D}=\dfrac{24}{12}=2,\ y=\dfrac{D_y}{D}=\dfrac{-36}{12}=-3,$

$z=\dfrac{D_z}{D}=\dfrac{48}{12}=4$

The solution set is {(2, −3, 4)}.

37. $D=\begin{vmatrix}1 & 1 & 1\\ 1 & -2 & 1\\ 1 & 3 & 2\end{vmatrix}=1\begin{vmatrix}-2 & 1\\ 3 & 2\end{vmatrix}-1\begin{vmatrix}1 & 1\\ 1 & 2\end{vmatrix}+1\begin{vmatrix}1 & -2\\ 1 & 3\end{vmatrix}$

$= -4-3-(2-1)+[3-(-2)]$
$= -7-1+5 = -3$

$D_x=\begin{vmatrix}4 & 1 & 1\\ 7 & -2 & 1\\ 4 & 3 & 2\end{vmatrix}=4\begin{vmatrix}-2 & 1\\ 3 & 2\end{vmatrix}-1\begin{vmatrix}7 & 1\\ 4 & 2\end{vmatrix}+1\begin{vmatrix}7 & -2\\ 4 & 3\end{vmatrix}$

$= 4(-4-3)-(14-4)+[21-(-8)]$
$= 4(-7)-10+29 = -28+19 = -9$

$D_y=\begin{vmatrix}1 & 4 & 1\\ 1 & 7 & 1\\ 1 & 4 & 2\end{vmatrix}=1\begin{vmatrix}7 & 1\\ 4 & 2\end{vmatrix}-1\begin{vmatrix}4 & 1\\ 4 & 2\end{vmatrix}+1\begin{vmatrix}4 & 1\\ 7 & 1\end{vmatrix}$

$= 14-4-(8-4)+(4-7) = 10-4-3 = 3$

$D_z=\begin{vmatrix}1 & 1 & 4\\ 1 & -2 & 7\\ 1 & 3 & 4\end{vmatrix}=1\begin{vmatrix}-2 & 7\\ 3 & 4\end{vmatrix}-1\begin{vmatrix}1 & 4\\ 3 & 4\end{vmatrix}+1\begin{vmatrix}1 & 4\\ -2 & 7\end{vmatrix}$

$= -8-21-(4-12)+[7-(-8)]$
$= -29+8+15 = -6$

$x=\dfrac{D_x}{D}=\dfrac{-9}{-3}=3,\ y=\dfrac{D_y}{D}=\dfrac{3}{-3}=-1,$

$z=\dfrac{D_z}{D}=\dfrac{-6}{-3}=2$

The solution set is {3, −1, 2}.

39. $D=\begin{vmatrix}1 & 0 & 2\\ 0 & 2 & -1\\ 2 & 3 & 0\end{vmatrix}=\begin{vmatrix}2 & -1\\ 3 & 0\end{vmatrix}+2\begin{vmatrix}0 & 2\\ 2 & 3\end{vmatrix}$

$= 0-(-3)+2(0-4) = 3-8 = -5$

$D_x=\begin{vmatrix}4 & 0 & 2\\ 5 & 2 & -1\\ 13 & 3 & 0\end{vmatrix}=4\begin{vmatrix}2 & -1\\ 3 & 0\end{vmatrix}+2\begin{vmatrix}5 & 2\\ 13 & 3\end{vmatrix}$

$= 4[0-(-3)]+2(15-26)$
$= 4(3)+2(-11) = 12-22 = -10$

$D_y=\begin{vmatrix}1 & 4 & 2\\ 0 & 5 & -1\\ 2 & 13 & 0\end{vmatrix}=\begin{vmatrix}5 & -1\\ 13 & 0\end{vmatrix}+2\begin{vmatrix}4 & 2\\ 5 & -1\end{vmatrix}$

$= 0-(-13)+2(-4-10)$
$= 13+2(-14) = 13-28 = -15$

$D_z=\begin{vmatrix}1 & 0 & 4\\ 0 & 2 & 5\\ 2 & 3 & 13\end{vmatrix}=\begin{vmatrix}2 & 5\\ 3 & 13\end{vmatrix}+4\begin{vmatrix}0 & 2\\ 2 & 3\end{vmatrix}$

$= 26-15+4(0-4) = 11+4(-4)$
$= 11-16 = -5$

$x=\dfrac{D_x}{D}=\dfrac{-10}{-5}=2,\ y=\dfrac{D_y}{D}=\dfrac{-15}{-5}=3,$

$z=\dfrac{D_z}{D}=\dfrac{-5}{-5}=1$

The solution set is {(2, 3, 1)}.

41. $\begin{vmatrix} 4 & 2 & 8 & -7 \\ -2 & 0 & 4 & 1 \\ 5 & 0 & 0 & 5 \\ 4 & 0 & 0 & -1 \end{vmatrix} = -2\begin{vmatrix} -2 & 4 & 1 \\ 5 & 0 & 5 \\ 4 & 0 & -1 \end{vmatrix} + 0\begin{vmatrix} 4 & 8 & -7 \\ 5 & 0 & 5 \\ 4 & 0 & -1 \end{vmatrix} - 0\begin{vmatrix} 4 & 8 & -7 \\ -2 & 4 & 1 \\ 4 & 0 & -1 \end{vmatrix} + 0\begin{vmatrix} 4 & 8 & -7 \\ -2 & 4 & 1 \\ 5 & 0 & 5 \end{vmatrix}$

$= (-2)\left[(-4)\begin{vmatrix} 5 & 5 \\ 4 & -1 \end{vmatrix} + 0\begin{vmatrix} -2 & 1 \\ 4 & -1 \end{vmatrix} - 0\begin{vmatrix} -2 & 1 \\ 5 & 5 \end{vmatrix}\right] = (-2)(-4)[5(-1) - 4 \cdot 5] = 8(-5-20) = 8(-25) = -200$

43. $\begin{vmatrix} -2 & -3 & 3 & 5 \\ 1 & -4 & 0 & 0 \\ 1 & 2 & 2 & -3 \\ 2 & 0 & 1 & 1 \end{vmatrix} = -1\begin{vmatrix} -3 & 3 & 5 \\ 2 & 2 & -3 \\ 0 & 1 & 1 \end{vmatrix} + (-4)\begin{vmatrix} -2 & 3 & 5 \\ 1 & 2 & -3 \\ 2 & 1 & 1 \end{vmatrix} - 0\begin{vmatrix} -2 & -3 & 5 \\ 1 & 2 & -3 \\ 2 & 0 & 1 \end{vmatrix} + 0\begin{vmatrix} -2 & -3 & 3 \\ 1 & 2 & 2 \\ 2 & 0 & 1 \end{vmatrix}$

$= (-1)\left[0\begin{vmatrix} 3 & 5 \\ 2 & -3 \end{vmatrix} - 1\begin{vmatrix} -3 & 5 \\ 2 & -3 \end{vmatrix} + 1\begin{vmatrix} -3 & 3 \\ 2 & 2 \end{vmatrix}\right] - 4\left[2\begin{vmatrix} 3 & 5 \\ 2 & -3 \end{vmatrix} - 1\begin{vmatrix} -2 & 5 \\ 1 & -3 \end{vmatrix} + 1\begin{vmatrix} -2 & 3 \\ 1 & 2 \end{vmatrix}\right] = (-1)$

$\{(-1)[(-3)(-3) - 2 \cdot 5] + [(-3)(2) - 2 \cdot 3]\} - 4\{2[3(-3) - 2 \cdot 5] - [(-2)(-3) - 1 \cdot 5] + [(-2)(2) - 1 \cdot 3]\}$
$= (-1)[(-1)(9-10) + (-6-6)] - 4[2(-9-10) - (6-5) + (-4-3)]$
$= (-1)[(-1)(-1) - 12] - 4[2(-19) - 1 - 7]$
$= (-1)(1-12) - 4(-38-8) = (-1)(-11) - 4(-46) = 11 + 184 = 195$

45. a. Area $= \pm\frac{1}{2}\begin{vmatrix} 3 & -5 & 1 \\ 2 & 6 & 1 \\ -3 & 5 & 1 \end{vmatrix} = \pm\frac{1}{2}\begin{vmatrix} 3 & -5 & 1 \\ -1 & 11 & 0 \\ -6 & 10 & 0 \end{vmatrix} = \pm\frac{1}{2}\begin{vmatrix} -1 & 11 \\ -6 & 10 \end{vmatrix} = \pm\frac{1}{2}[-10-(-66)] = \pm\frac{1}{2}(56) = 28$

The area is 28 square units.

b.

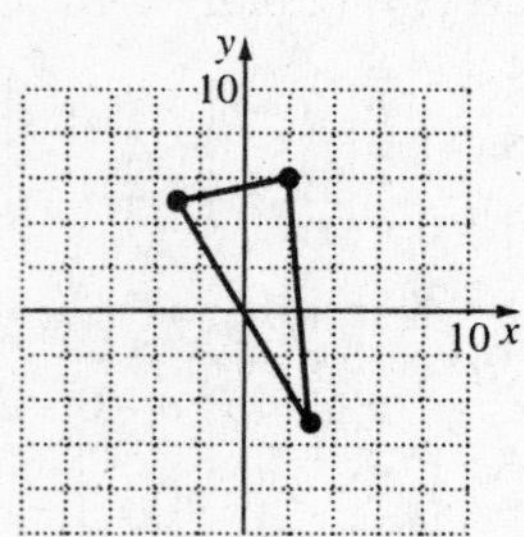

The slope of the line through (3, –5) and (–3, 5) is $m = \frac{5-(-5)}{-3-3} = \frac{10}{-6} = -\frac{5}{3}$.

The equation of the line is $y-(-5) = -\frac{5}{3}(x-3)$ or $y = -\frac{5}{3}x$.

The line perpendicular to $y = -\frac{5}{3}x$ through (2, 6) has equation $y - 6 = \frac{3}{5}(x-2)$ or $y = \frac{3}{5}x + \frac{24}{5}$.

These lines intersect where $-\frac{5}{3}x = \frac{3}{5}x + \frac{24}{5}$.

$$-\frac{24}{5}=\frac{34}{15}x$$

$$-\frac{36}{17}=x \text{ and } y=-\frac{5}{3}\left(-\frac{36}{17}\right)=\frac{60}{17}$$

Using the side connecting (3, –5) and (–3, 5) as the base, the height is the distance from (2, 6) to $\left(-\frac{36}{17}, \frac{60}{17}\right)$.

$$b=\sqrt{[3-(-3)]^2+(-5-5)^2}$$
$$=\sqrt{36+100}=\sqrt{136}=2\sqrt{34}$$

$$h=\sqrt{\left[2-\left(-\frac{36}{17}\right)\right]^2+\left(6-\frac{60}{17}\right)^2}$$
$$=\sqrt{\frac{4900}{289}+\frac{1764}{289}}=\frac{14\sqrt{34}}{17}$$

$$\frac{1}{2}bh=\frac{1}{2}\left(2\sqrt{34}\right)\left(\frac{14\sqrt{34}}{17}\right)=\frac{14(34)}{17}$$
$$=14(2)=28 \text{ square units}$$

47. $\begin{vmatrix}3 & -1 & 1\\ 0 & -3 & 1\\ 12 & 5 & 1\end{vmatrix}=\begin{vmatrix}3 & -1 & 1\\ -3 & -2 & 0\\ 9 & 6 & 0\end{vmatrix}=\begin{vmatrix}-3 & -2\\ 9 & 6\end{vmatrix}$

$=-18-(-18)=0$

Yes, the points are collinear.

49. $\begin{vmatrix}x & y & 1\\ 3 & -5 & 1\\ -2 & 6 & 1\end{vmatrix}=x\begin{vmatrix}-5 & 1\\ 6 & 1\end{vmatrix}-y\begin{vmatrix}3 & 1\\ -2 & 1\end{vmatrix}+\begin{vmatrix}3 & -5\\ -2 & 6\end{vmatrix}$

$=x(-5-6)-y[3-(-2)]+(18-10)$

$=-11x-5y+8$

The equation of the line is $-11x-5y+8=0$.

The equation of the line in slope-intercept form is $y=-\frac{11}{5}x+\frac{8}{5}$.

51.–57. Answers may vary.

59. Exercise 1 and 3

```
det([[5,7][2,3]]
)
                  1
det([[-4,1][5,6]
])
                -29
```

Exercises 5 and 7

```
det([[-7,14][2,-
4]])
                  0
det([[-5,-1][-2,
-7]])
                 33
```

Exericse 9

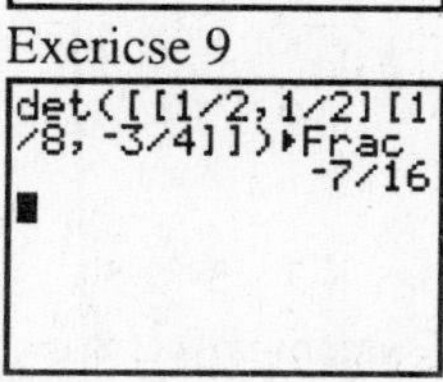

```
det([[1/2,1/2][1
/8,-3/4]])▸Frac
              -7/16
```

61. Input the matrix as $[A]$, then use det$[A]$ to find the determinant.

$$\begin{vmatrix}8 & 2 & 6 & -1 & 0\\ 2 & 0 & -3 & 4 & 7\\ 2 & 1 & -3 & 6 & -5\\ -1 & 2 & 1 & 5 & -1\\ 4 & 5 & -2 & 3 & -8\end{vmatrix}=13,200$$

63. **a.** $\begin{vmatrix}a & a\\ 0 & a\end{vmatrix}=a^2-0=a^2$

b. $\begin{vmatrix}a & a & a\\ 0 & a & a\\ 0 & 0 & a\end{vmatrix}=a\begin{vmatrix}a & a\\ 0 & a\end{vmatrix}-0+0$

$=a\left(a^2\right)=a^3$

c. $\begin{vmatrix}a & a & a & a\\ 0 & a & a & a\\ 0 & 0 & a & a\\ 0 & 0 & 0 & a\end{vmatrix}=a\begin{vmatrix}a & a & a\\ 0 & a & a\\ 0 & 0 & a\end{vmatrix}-0+0-0$

$=a\left(a^3\right)=a^4$

d. Each determinant has zeros below the main diagonal and a's everywhere else.

e. Each determinant equals a raised to the power equal to the order of the determinant.

65. The sign of the value is changed when 2 columns are interchanged in a 2nd order determinant.

Review Exercises

1.
$$\begin{aligned} x+y+3z &= 12\\ y-2z &= -4\\ z &= 3\\ y-2(3) &= -4\\ y-6 &= -4\\ y &= 2\\ x+2+3(3) &= 12\\ x+11 &= 12\\ x &= 1 \end{aligned}$$
The solution to the system is {(1, 2, 3)}.

2.
$$\begin{aligned} x-2z+2w &= 1\\ y+z-w &= 0\\ z-\frac{7}{3}w &= -\frac{1}{3}\\ w &= 1\\ z-\frac{7}{3}(1) &= -\frac{1}{3}\\ z-\frac{7}{3} &= -\frac{1}{3}\\ z &= \frac{6}{3}\\ z &= 2\\ y+2-1 &= 0\\ y+1 &= 0\\ y &= -1\\ x-2(2)+2(1) &= 1\\ x-2 &= 1\\ x &= 3 \end{aligned}$$
The solution to the system is {(3, –1, 2, 1)}.

3.
$$\left[\begin{array}{ccc|c} 1 & 2 & 2 & 2\\ 0 & 1 & -1 & 2\\ 0 & 5 & 4 & 1 \end{array}\right] -5R_2+R_3$$
$$\left[\begin{array}{ccc|c} 1 & 2 & 2 & 2\\ 0 & 1 & -1 & 2\\ 0 & 0 & 9 & -9 \end{array}\right]$$

4.
$$\left[\begin{array}{ccc|c} 2 & -2 & 1 & -1\\ 1 & 2 & -1 & 2\\ 6 & 4 & 3 & 5 \end{array}\right] \frac{1}{2}R_1$$
$$\left[\begin{array}{ccc|c} 1 & -1 & \frac{1}{2} & -\frac{1}{2}\\ 1 & 2 & -1 & 2\\ 6 & 4 & 3 & 5 \end{array}\right]$$

5.
$$\left[\begin{array}{ccc|c} 1 & 2 & 3 & -5\\ 2 & 1 & 1 & 1\\ 1 & 1 & -1 & 8 \end{array}\right] \begin{array}{l} -2R_1+R_2\\ -1R_1+R_3 \end{array}$$
$$\left[\begin{array}{ccc|c} 1 & 2 & 3 & -5\\ 0 & -3 & -5 & 11\\ 0 & -1 & -4 & 13 \end{array}\right] R_2 \leftrightarrow R_3$$
$$\left[\begin{array}{ccc|c} 1 & 2 & 3 & -5\\ 0 & -1 & -4 & 13\\ 0 & -3 & -5 & 11 \end{array}\right] -1R_2$$
$$\left[\begin{array}{ccc|c} 1 & 2 & 3 & -5\\ 0 & 1 & 4 & -13\\ 0 & -3 & -5 & 11 \end{array}\right] 3R_2+R_3$$
$$\left[\begin{array}{ccc|c} 1 & 2 & 3 & -5\\ 0 & 1 & 4 & -13\\ 0 & 0 & 7 & -28 \end{array}\right] \frac{1}{7}R_3$$
$$\left[\begin{array}{ccc|c} 1 & 2 & 3 & -5\\ 0 & 1 & 4 & -13\\ 0 & 0 & 1 & -4 \end{array}\right] -2R_2+R_1$$
$$\left[\begin{array}{ccc|c} 1 & 0 & -5 & 21\\ 0 & 1 & 4 & -13\\ 0 & 0 & 1 & -4 \end{array}\right] \begin{array}{l} 5R_3+R_1\\ -4R_3+R_2 \end{array}$$
$$\left[\begin{array}{ccc|c} 1 & 0 & 0 & 1\\ 0 & 1 & 0 & 3\\ 0 & 0 & 1 & -4 \end{array}\right]$$
The solution set is {(1, 3, –4)}.

6. $\left[\begin{array}{ccc|c} 1 & -2 & 1 & 0 \\ 0 & 1 & -3 & -1 \\ 0 & 2 & 5 & -2 \end{array}\right] -2R_2 + R_3$

$\left[\begin{array}{ccc|c} 1 & -2 & 1 & 0 \\ 0 & 1 & -3 & -1 \\ 0 & 0 & 11 & 0 \end{array}\right] \frac{1}{11}R_3$

$\left[\begin{array}{ccc|c} 1 & -2 & 1 & 0 \\ 0 & 1 & -3 & -1 \\ 0 & 0 & 1 & 0 \end{array}\right] 2R_2 + R_1$

$\left[\begin{array}{ccc|c} 1 & 0 & -5 & -2 \\ 0 & 1 & -3 & -1 \\ 0 & 0 & 1 & 0 \end{array}\right] \begin{matrix} 3R_3 + R_2 \\ 5R_3 + R_1 \end{matrix}$

$\left[\begin{array}{ccc|c} 1 & 0 & 0 & -2 \\ 0 & 1 & 0 & -1 \\ 0 & 0 & 1 & 0 \end{array}\right]$

$x = -2; y = -1; z = 0$

The solution set is $\{(-2, -1, 0)\}$.

7. $\left[\begin{array}{cccc|c} 3 & 5 & -8 & 5 & -8 \\ 1 & 2 & -3 & 1 & -7 \\ 2 & 3 & -7 & 3 & -11 \\ 4 & 8 & -10 & 7 & -10 \end{array}\right] R_1 \leftrightarrow R_2$

$\left[\begin{array}{cccc|c} 1 & 2 & -3 & 1 & -7 \\ 3 & 5 & -8 & 5 & -8 \\ 2 & 3 & -7 & 3 & -11 \\ 4 & 8 & -10 & 7 & -10 \end{array}\right] \begin{matrix} -3R_1 + R_2 \\ -2R_1 + R_3 \\ -4R_1 + R_4 \end{matrix}$

$\left[\begin{array}{cccc|c} 1 & 2 & -3 & 1 & -7 \\ 0 & -1 & 1 & 2 & 13 \\ 0 & -1 & -1 & 1 & 3 \\ 0 & 0 & 2 & 3 & 18 \end{array}\right] -1R_2$

$\left[\begin{array}{cccc|c} 1 & 2 & -3 & 1 & -7 \\ 0 & 1 & -1 & -2 & -13 \\ 0 & -1 & -1 & 1 & 3 \\ 0 & 0 & 2 & 3 & 18 \end{array}\right] \begin{matrix} -2R_2 + R_1 \\ 1R_2 + R_3 \end{matrix}$

$\left[\begin{array}{cccc|c} 1 & 0 & -1 & 5 & 19 \\ 0 & 1 & -1 & -2 & -13 \\ 0 & 0 & -2 & -1 & -10 \\ 0 & 0 & 2 & 3 & 18 \end{array}\right] -\frac{1}{2}R_3$

$\left[\begin{array}{cccc|c} 1 & 0 & -1 & 5 & 19 \\ 0 & 1 & -1 & -2 & -13 \\ 0 & 0 & 1 & \frac{1}{2} & 5 \\ 0 & 0 & 2 & 3 & 18 \end{array}\right] \begin{matrix} 1R_3 + R_1 \\ 1R_3 + R_2 \\ -2R_3 + R_4 \end{matrix}$

$\left[\begin{array}{cccc|c} 1 & 0 & 0 & \frac{11}{2} & 24 \\ 0 & 1 & 0 & -\frac{3}{2} & -8 \\ 0 & 0 & 1 & \frac{1}{2} & 5 \\ 0 & 0 & 0 & 2 & 8 \end{array}\right] \frac{1}{2}R_4$

$\left[\begin{array}{cccc|c} 1 & 0 & 0 & \frac{11}{2} & 24 \\ 0 & 1 & 0 & -\frac{3}{2} & -8 \\ 0 & 0 & 1 & \frac{1}{2} & 5 \\ 0 & 0 & 0 & 1 & 4 \end{array}\right] \begin{matrix} -\frac{11}{2}R_4 + R_1 \\ \frac{3}{2}R_4 + R_2 \\ -\frac{1}{2}R_4 + R_3 \end{matrix}$

$\left[\begin{array}{cccc|c} 1 & 0 & 0 & 0 & 2 \\ 0 & 1 & 0 & 0 & -2 \\ 0 & 0 & 1 & 0 & 3 \\ 0 & 0 & 0 & 1 & 4 \end{array}\right]$

The solution set is $\{(2, -2, 3, 4)\}$.

8. a. The function must satisfy:

$98 = 4a = 2b + c$
$138 = 16a + 4b + c$
$162 = 100a + 10b + c.$

$\left[\begin{array}{ccc|c} 4 & 2 & 1 & 98 \\ 16 & 4 & 1 & 138 \\ 100 & 10 & 1 & 162 \end{array}\right] \frac{1}{4}R_1$

$\left[\begin{array}{ccc|c} 1 & \frac{1}{2} & \frac{1}{4} & \frac{49}{2} \\ 16 & 4 & 1 & 138 \\ 100 & 10 & 1 & 162 \end{array}\right] \begin{matrix} -16R_1 + R_2 \\ -100R_1 + R_3 \end{matrix}$

$\left[\begin{array}{ccc|c} 1 & \frac{1}{2} & \frac{1}{4} & \frac{49}{2} \\ 0 & -4 & -3 & -254 \\ 0 & -40 & -24 & -2288 \end{array}\right] -\frac{1}{4}R_2$

$$\left[\begin{array}{ccc|c} 1 & \frac{1}{2} & \frac{1}{4} & \frac{49}{2} \\ 0 & 1 & \frac{3}{4} & \frac{127}{2} \\ 0 & -40 & -24 & -2288 \end{array}\right] 40R_2 + R_3$$

$$\left[\begin{array}{ccc|c} 1 & \frac{1}{2} & \frac{1}{4} & \frac{49}{2} \\ 0 & 1 & \frac{3}{4} & \frac{127}{2} \\ 0 & 0 & 6 & 252 \end{array}\right] \frac{1}{6}R_3$$

$$\left[\begin{array}{ccc|c} 1 & \frac{1}{2} & \frac{1}{4} & \frac{49}{2} \\ 0 & 1 & \frac{3}{4} & \frac{127}{2} \\ 0 & 0 & 1 & 42 \end{array}\right] \begin{array}{l} -\frac{1}{4}R_3 + R_1 \\ -\frac{3}{4}R_3 + R_2 \end{array}$$

$$\left[\begin{array}{ccc|c} 1 & \frac{1}{2} & 0 & 14 \\ 0 & 1 & 0 & 32 \\ 0 & 0 & 1 & 42 \end{array}\right] -\frac{1}{2}R_3 + R_1$$

$$\left[\begin{array}{ccc|c} 1 & 0 & 0 & -2 \\ 0 & 1 & 0 & 32 \\ 0 & 0 & 1 & 42 \end{array}\right]$$

The function is $y = -2x^2 + 32x + 42$ and $a = -2$, $b = 32$ and $c = 42$.

b. $y = -2x^2 + 32x + 42$ is a parabola.
The maximum occurs when
$x = \frac{-32}{2(-2)} = \frac{-32}{-4} = 8.$
The air pollution level is a maximum 8 hours after 6 A.M., which is 2 P.M.
The maximum level is
$y = -2(64) + 32(8) + 42$
$= -128 + 256 + 42.$
170 parts per million.

9. $$\left[\begin{array}{ccc|c} 2 & -3 & 1 & 1 \\ 1 & -2 & 3 & 2 \\ 3 & -4 & -1 & 1 \end{array}\right] R_1 \leftrightarrow R_2$$

$$\left[\begin{array}{ccc|c} 1 & -2 & 3 & 2 \\ 2 & -3 & 1 & 1 \\ 3 & -4 & -1 & 1 \end{array}\right] \begin{array}{l} -2R_1 + R_2 \\ -3R_1 + R_3 \end{array}$$

$$\left[\begin{array}{ccc|c} 1 & -2 & 3 & 2 \\ 0 & 1 & -5 & -3 \\ 0 & 2 & -10 & -5 \end{array}\right] -2R_2 + R_3$$

$$\left[\begin{array}{ccc|c} 1 & -2 & 3 & 2 \\ 0 & 1 & -5 & -3 \\ 0 & 0 & 0 & 1 \end{array}\right]$$

From the last line, we see that the system has no solution.Thus, the solution set is Ø.

10. $$\left[\begin{array}{ccc|c} 1 & -3 & 1 & 1 \\ -2 & 1 & 3 & -7 \\ 1 & -4 & 2 & 0 \end{array}\right] \begin{array}{l} 2R_1 + R_2 \\ -1R_1 + R_3 \end{array}$$

$$\left[\begin{array}{ccc|c} 1 & -3 & 1 & 1 \\ 0 & -5 & 5 & -5 \\ 0 & -1 & 1 & -1 \end{array}\right] -\frac{1}{5}R_2$$

$$\left[\begin{array}{ccc|c} 1 & -3 & 1 & 1 \\ 0 & 1 & -1 & 1 \\ 0 & -1 & 1 & -1 \end{array}\right] 1R_2 + R_3$$

$$\left[\begin{array}{ccc|c} 1 & -3 & 1 & 1 \\ 0 & 1 & -1 & 1 \\ 0 & 0 & 0 & 0 \end{array}\right]$$

The system $\begin{array}{r} x - 3y + z = 1 \\ y - z = 1 \end{array}$ has no unique solution. Express x and y in terms of z:
$y = z + 1$
$x - 3(z + 1) + z = 1$
$x - 3z - 3 + z = 1$
$x = 2z + 4$
With $z = t$, the complete solution to the system is $\{(2t + 4, t + 1, t)\}$.

11. $$\left[\begin{array}{cccc|c} 1 & 4 & 3 & -6 & 5 \\ 1 & 3 & 1 & -4 & 3 \\ 2 & 8 & 7 & -5 & 11 \\ 2 & 5 & 0 & -6 & 4 \end{array}\right] \begin{array}{l} -1R_1 + R_2 \\ -2R_1 + R_3 \\ -2R_1 + R_4 \end{array}$$

$$\left[\begin{array}{cccc|c} 1 & 4 & 3 & -6 & 5 \\ 0 & -1 & -2 & 2 & -2 \\ 0 & 0 & 1 & 7 & 1 \\ 0 & -3 & -6 & 6 & -6 \end{array}\right] -1R_2$$

$$\left[\begin{array}{cccc|c} 1 & 4 & 3 & -6 & 5 \\ 0 & 1 & 2 & -2 & 2 \\ 0 & 0 & 1 & 7 & 1 \\ 0 & -3 & -6 & 6 & -6 \end{array}\right] 3R_2 + R_4$$

$$\begin{bmatrix} 1 & 4 & 3 & -6 & | & 5 \\ 0 & 1 & 2 & -2 & | & 2 \\ 0 & 0 & 1 & 7 & | & 1 \\ 0 & 0 & 0 & 0 & | & 0 \end{bmatrix}$$

The system $\begin{aligned} x_1 + 4x_2 + 3x_3 - 6x_4 &= 5 \\ x_2 + 2x_3 - 2x_4 &= 2 \\ x_3 + 7x_4 &= 1 \end{aligned}$

does not have a unique solution.
Express x_1, x_2, and x_3 in terms of x_4:

$$x_3 = -7x_4 + 1$$
$$x_2 + 2(-7x_4 + 1) - 2x_4 = 2$$
$$x_2 - 14x_4 + 2 - 2x_4 = 2$$
$$x_2 = 16x_4$$
$$x_1 + 4(16x_4) + 3(-7x_4 + 1) - 6x_4 = 5$$
$$x_1 + 64x_4 - 21x_4 + 3 - 6x_4 = 5$$
$$x_1 = -37x_4 + 2$$

With $x_4 = t$, the complete solution to the system is $\{(-37t + 2, 16t, -7t + 1, t)\}$.

12. $\begin{bmatrix} 2 & 3 & -5 & | & 15 \\ 1 & 2 & -1 & | & 4 \end{bmatrix} R_1 \leftrightarrow R_2$

$\begin{bmatrix} 1 & 2 & -1 & | & 4 \\ 2 & 3 & -5 & | & 15 \end{bmatrix} -2R_1 + R_2$

$\begin{bmatrix} 1 & 2 & -1 & | & 4 \\ 0 & -1 & -3 & | & 7 \end{bmatrix} -1R_2$

$\begin{bmatrix} 1 & 2 & -1 & | & 4 \\ 0 & 1 & 3 & | & -7 \end{bmatrix}$

The system $\begin{aligned} x + 2y - z &= 4 \\ y + 3z &= -7 \end{aligned}$ has no unique solution. Express x and y in terms of z:

$y = -3z - 7$
$x + 2(-3z - 7) - z = 4$
$x - 6z - 14 - z = 4$
$x = 7z + 18$

With $z = t$, the complete solution to the system is $\{(7t + 18, -3t - 7, t)\}$.

13. a. $350 + 400 = x + z$
$450 + z = y + 700$
$x + y = 300 + 200$
or
$x + z = 750$
$y - z = -250$
$x + y = 500$

b. $\begin{bmatrix} 1 & 0 & 1 & | & 750 \\ 0 & 1 & -1 & | & -250 \\ 1 & 1 & 0 & | & 500 \end{bmatrix} -1R_1 + R_3$

$\begin{bmatrix} 1 & 0 & 1 & | & 750 \\ 0 & 1 & -1 & | & -250 \\ 0 & 1 & -1 & | & -250 \end{bmatrix} -1R_2 + R_3$

$\begin{bmatrix} 1 & 0 & 1 & | & 750 \\ 0 & 1 & -1 & | & -250 \\ 0 & 0 & 0 & | & 0 \end{bmatrix}$

The system $\begin{aligned} x + z &= 750 \\ y - z &= -250 \end{aligned}$ has no unique solution.
Express x and y in terms of z:
$y = z - 250$
$x = -z + 750$
With $z = t$, the complete solution to the system is $\{(-t + 750, t - 250, t)\}$.

c. $x = -400 + 750 = 350$
$y = 400 - 250 = 150$

14. $2x = -10$
$x = -5$
$y + 7 = 13$
$y = 6$
$z = 6$
$x = -5; y = 6; z = 6$

15. $A + D = \begin{bmatrix} 2-2 & -1+3 & 2+1 \\ 5+3 & 3-2 & -1+4 \end{bmatrix} = \begin{bmatrix} 0 & 2 & 3 \\ 8 & 1 & 3 \end{bmatrix}$

16. $2B = \begin{bmatrix} 2(0) & 2(-2) \\ 2(3) & 2(2) \\ 2(1) & 2(-5) \end{bmatrix} = \begin{bmatrix} 0 & -4 \\ 6 & 4 \\ 2 & -10 \end{bmatrix}$

17. $D - A = \begin{bmatrix} -2-2 & 3+1 & 1-2 \\ 3-5 & -2-3 & 4+1 \end{bmatrix} = \begin{bmatrix} -4 & 4 & -1 \\ -2 & -5 & 5 \end{bmatrix}$

18. Not possible since B is 3×2 and C is 3×3.

19. $3A+2D=\begin{bmatrix} 6 & -3 & 6 \\ 15 & 9 & -3 \end{bmatrix}+\begin{bmatrix} -4 & 6 & 2 \\ 6 & -4 & 8 \end{bmatrix}=\begin{bmatrix} 2 & 3 & 8 \\ 21 & 5 & 5 \end{bmatrix}$

20. $-2A+4D=\begin{bmatrix} -4 & 2 & -4 \\ -10 & -6 & 2 \end{bmatrix}+\begin{bmatrix} -8 & 12 & 4 \\ 12 & -8 & 16 \end{bmatrix}=\begin{bmatrix} -12 & 14 & 0 \\ 2 & -14 & 18 \end{bmatrix}$

21. $-5(A+D)=-5\left(\begin{bmatrix} 0 & 2 & 3 \\ 8 & 1 & 3 \end{bmatrix}\right)=\begin{bmatrix} 0 & -10 & -15 \\ -40 & -5 & -15 \end{bmatrix}$

22. $AB=\begin{bmatrix} 0-3+2 & -4-2-10 \\ 0+9-1 & -10+6+5 \end{bmatrix}=\begin{bmatrix} -1 & -16 \\ 8 & 1 \end{bmatrix}$

23. $BA=\begin{bmatrix} 0-10 & 0-6 & 0+2 \\ 6+10 & -3+6 & 6-2 \\ 2-25 & -1-15 & 2+5 \end{bmatrix}=\begin{bmatrix} -10 & -6 & 2 \\ 16 & 3 & 4 \\ -23 & -16 & 7 \end{bmatrix}$

24. $BD=\begin{bmatrix} 0-6 & 0+4 & 0-8 \\ -6+6 & 9-4 & 3+8 \\ -2-15 & 3+10 & 1-20 \end{bmatrix}=\begin{bmatrix} -6 & 4 & -8 \\ 0 & 5 & 11 \\ -17 & 13 & -19 \end{bmatrix}$

25. $DB=\begin{bmatrix} 0+9+1 & 4+6-5 \\ 0-6+4 & -6-4-20 \end{bmatrix}=\begin{bmatrix} 10 & 5 \\ -2 & -30 \end{bmatrix}$

26. Not possible since *AB* is 2 × 2 and *BA* is 3 × 3.

27. $(A-D)C=\begin{bmatrix} 4 & -4 & 1 \\ 2 & 5 & -5 \end{bmatrix}\begin{bmatrix} 1 & 2 & 3 \\ -1 & 1 & 2 \\ -1 & 2 & 1 \end{bmatrix}=\begin{bmatrix} 4+4-1 & 8-4+2 & 12-8+1 \\ 2-5+5 & 4+5-10 & 6+10-5 \end{bmatrix}=\begin{bmatrix} 7 & 6 & 5 \\ 2 & -1 & 11 \end{bmatrix}$

28. $B(AC)=\begin{bmatrix} 0 & -2 \\ 3 & 2 \\ 1 & -5 \end{bmatrix}\begin{bmatrix} 2+1-2 & 4-1+4 & 6-2+2 \\ 5-3+1 & 10+3-2 & 15+6-1 \end{bmatrix}$

$=\begin{bmatrix} 0 & -2 \\ 3 & 2 \\ 1 & -5 \end{bmatrix}\begin{bmatrix} 1 & 7 & 6 \\ 3 & 11 & 20 \end{bmatrix}=\begin{bmatrix} 0-6 & 0-22 & 0-40 \\ 3+6 & 21+22 & 18+40 \\ 1-15 & 7-55 & 6-100 \end{bmatrix}$

$=\begin{bmatrix} -6 & -22 & -40 \\ 9 & 43 & 58 \\ -14 & -48 & -94 \end{bmatrix}$

29. $\begin{bmatrix} 2 & 1 & 1 \\ 2 & 1 & 1 \\ 2 & 2 & 2 \end{bmatrix}$

30. $B = \begin{bmatrix} 1 & -1 & -1 \\ 1 & -1 & -1 \\ 1 & 1 & 1 \end{bmatrix}$

31. a. $AB = \begin{bmatrix} 192,000+84,000+84,000 & 228,000+105,000+111,000 \\ 340,000+96,000+140,000 & 380,000+120,000+185,000 \\ 112,000+24,000+42,000 & 133,000+30,000+55,500 \end{bmatrix} = \begin{bmatrix} 360,000 & 444,000 \\ 556,000 & 685,000 \\ 178,000 & 218,500 \end{bmatrix}$

b. The rows of AB correspond to the outlets, the columns represent the wholesale and retail prices. The entries tell how much value in wholesale or retail is at each outlet.

c. \$360,000

d. \$685,000

e. Profit = retail price – wholesale price = \$218,500 – \$178,000 = \$40,500

32.

$AB = \begin{bmatrix} 8-7 & -14+21 \\ 4-4 & -7+12 \end{bmatrix} = \begin{bmatrix} 1 & 7 \\ 0 & 5 \end{bmatrix}$

$BA = \begin{bmatrix} 8-7 & 28-28 \\ -2+3 & -7+12 \end{bmatrix} = \begin{bmatrix} 1 & 0 \\ 1 & 5 \end{bmatrix}$

If B is the multiplicative inverse of A, both products (AB and BA) will be the multiplicative identity matrix, I_2. Therefore, B is not the multiplicative inverse of A. That is, $B \neq A^{-1}$.

33. $AB = \begin{bmatrix} 1+0+0 & 0+0+0 & 0+0+0 \\ 0+0+0 & 0+8-7 & 0+14-14 \\ 0+0+0 & 0-4+4 & 0-7+8 \end{bmatrix} = \begin{bmatrix} 1 & 0 & 0 \\ 0 & 1 & 0 \\ 0 & 0 & 1 \end{bmatrix}$

$BA = \begin{bmatrix} 1+0+0 & 0+0+0 & 0+0+0 \\ 0+0+0 & 1+8-7 & 0-28+28 \\ 0+0+0 & 0+2-2 & 0-7+8 \end{bmatrix} = \begin{bmatrix} 1 & 0 & 0 \\ 0 & 1 & 0 \\ 0 & 0 & 1 \end{bmatrix}$

Since $AB = I_3$ and $BA = I_3$, $B = A^{-1}$.

34. $A^{-1}=\dfrac{1}{3-2}\begin{bmatrix}3&1\\2&1\end{bmatrix}$

$=1\begin{bmatrix}3&1\\2&1\end{bmatrix}=\begin{bmatrix}3&1\\2&1\end{bmatrix}$

$AA^{-1}=\begin{bmatrix}1&-1\\-2&3\end{bmatrix}\begin{bmatrix}3&1\\2&1\end{bmatrix}$

$=\begin{bmatrix}3-2&1-1\\-6+6&-2+3\end{bmatrix}=\begin{bmatrix}1&0\\0&1\end{bmatrix}$

$A^{-1}A=\begin{bmatrix}3&1\\2&1\end{bmatrix}\begin{bmatrix}1&-1\\-2&3\end{bmatrix}$

$=\begin{bmatrix}3-2&3+3\\2-2&-2+3\end{bmatrix}=\begin{bmatrix}1&0\\0&1\end{bmatrix}$

35. $A^{-1}=\dfrac{1}{0-5}\begin{bmatrix}3&-1\\-5&0\end{bmatrix}$

$=\dfrac{-1}{5}\begin{bmatrix}3&-1\\-5&0\end{bmatrix}=\begin{bmatrix}-\frac{3}{5}&\frac{1}{5}\\1&0\end{bmatrix}$

$AA^{-1}=\begin{bmatrix}0&1\\5&3\end{bmatrix}\begin{bmatrix}-\frac{3}{5}&\frac{1}{5}\\1&0\end{bmatrix}$

$=\begin{bmatrix}0+1&0+0\\-3+3&1+0\end{bmatrix}=\begin{bmatrix}1&0\\0&1\end{bmatrix}$

$A^{-1}A=\begin{bmatrix}-\frac{3}{5}&\frac{1}{5}\\1&0\end{bmatrix}\begin{bmatrix}0&1\\5&3\end{bmatrix}$

$=\begin{bmatrix}0+1&-\frac{3}{5}+\frac{3}{5}\\0+0&1+0\end{bmatrix}=\begin{bmatrix}1&0\\0&1\end{bmatrix}$

36. $\left[\begin{array}{ccc|ccc}1&0&-2&1&0&0\\2&1&0&0&1&0\\1&0&-3&0&0&1\end{array}\right]\begin{matrix}-2R_1+R_2\\-1R_1+R_3\end{matrix}$

$\left[\begin{array}{ccc|ccc}1&0&-2&1&0&0\\0&1&4&-2&1&0\\0&0&-1&-1&0&1\end{array}\right]-1R_3$

$\left[\begin{array}{ccc|ccc}1&0&-2&1&0&0\\0&1&4&-2&1&0\\0&0&1&1&0&-1\end{array}\right]\begin{matrix}2R_3+R_1\\-4R_3+R_2\end{matrix}$

$\left[\begin{array}{ccc|ccc}1&0&0&3&0&-2\\0&1&0&-6&1&4\\0&0&1&1&0&-1\end{array}\right]$

$A^{-1}=\begin{bmatrix}3&0&-2\\-6&1&4\\1&0&-1\end{bmatrix}$

Verification is left to the student.

37. $\left[\begin{array}{ccc|ccc}1&3&-2&1&0&0\\4&13&-7&0&1&0\\5&16&-8&0&0&1\end{array}\right]\begin{matrix}-4R_1+R_2\\-5R_1+R_3\end{matrix}$

$=\left[\begin{array}{ccc|ccc}1&3&-2&1&0&0\\0&1&1&-4&1&0\\0&1&2&-5&0&1\end{array}\right]\begin{matrix}-1R_2+R_3\\-3R_2+R_1\end{matrix}$

$=\left[\begin{array}{ccc|ccc}1&0&-5&13&-3&0\\0&1&1&-4&1&0\\0&0&1&-1&-1&1\end{array}\right]\begin{matrix}-1R_3+R_2\\5R_3+R_1\end{matrix}$

$=\left[\begin{array}{ccc|ccc}1&0&0&8&-8&5\\0&1&0&-3&2&-1\\0&0&1&-1&-1&1\end{array}\right]$

$A^{-1}=\begin{bmatrix}8&-8&5\\-3&2&-1\\-1&-1&1\end{bmatrix}$

$$AA^{-1}=\begin{bmatrix}1 & 3 & -2\\ 4 & 13 & -7\\ 5 & 16 & -8\end{bmatrix}\begin{bmatrix}8 & -8 & 5\\ -3 & 2 & -1\\ -1 & -1 & 1\end{bmatrix}=\begin{bmatrix}8-9+2 & -8+6+2 & 5-3-2\\ 32-39+7 & -32+26+7 & 20-13-7\\ 40-48+8 & -40+32+8 & 25-16-8\end{bmatrix}=\begin{bmatrix}1 & 0 & 0\\ 0 & 1 & 0\\ 0 & 0 & 1\end{bmatrix}$$

$$A^{-1}A=\begin{bmatrix}8 & -8 & 5\\ -3 & 2 & -1\\ -1 & -1 & -1\end{bmatrix}\begin{bmatrix}1 & 3 & -2\\ 4 & 13 & -7\\ 5 & 16 & -8\end{bmatrix}=\begin{bmatrix}8-32+25 & 24-104+80 & -16+56-40\\ -3+8-5 & -9+26-16 & 6-14+8\\ -1-4+5 & -3-13+16 & 2+7-8\end{bmatrix}=\begin{bmatrix}1 & 0 & 0\\ 0 & 1 & 0\\ 0 & 0 & 1\end{bmatrix}$$

38. a. $\begin{bmatrix}1 & 1 & 2\\ 0 & 1 & 3\\ 3 & 0 & -2\end{bmatrix}\begin{bmatrix}x\\ y\\ z\end{bmatrix}=\begin{bmatrix}7\\ -2\\ 0\end{bmatrix}.$

b. The solution to the system is $A^{-1}B$.

$$A^{-1}B=\begin{bmatrix}-2 & 2 & 1\\ 9 & -8 & -3\\ -3 & 3 & 1\end{bmatrix}\begin{bmatrix}7\\ -2\\ 0\end{bmatrix}=\begin{bmatrix}-14-4+0\\ 63+16+0\\ -21-6+0\end{bmatrix}=\begin{bmatrix}-18\\ 79\\ -27\end{bmatrix}$$

The solution to the system is $\{(-18, 79, -27)\}$.

39. a. $\begin{bmatrix}1 & -1 & 2\\ 0 & 1 & -1\\ 1 & 0 & 2\end{bmatrix}\begin{bmatrix}x\\ y\\ z\end{bmatrix}=\begin{bmatrix}12\\ -5\\ 10\end{bmatrix}$

b. $\begin{bmatrix}x\\ y\\ z\end{bmatrix}=\begin{bmatrix}2 & 2 & -1\\ -1 & 0 & 1\\ -1 & -1 & 1\end{bmatrix}\begin{bmatrix}12\\ -5\\ 10\end{bmatrix}$

$$\begin{bmatrix}x\\ y\\ z\end{bmatrix}=\begin{bmatrix}24-10-10\\ -12+10\\ -12+5+10\end{bmatrix}=\begin{bmatrix}4\\ -2\\ 3\end{bmatrix}$$

The solution to the system is $\{(4, -2, 3)\}$.

40. R U L E has a numerical equivalent of 18, 21, 12, 5.

$$\begin{bmatrix}3 & 2\\ 4 & 3\end{bmatrix}\begin{bmatrix}18 & 12\\ 21 & 5\end{bmatrix}=\begin{bmatrix}54+42 & 36+10\\ 72+63 & 48+15\end{bmatrix}=\begin{bmatrix}96 & 46\\ 135 & 63\end{bmatrix}$$

The encoded message is 96, 135, 46, 63.

$$\begin{bmatrix}3 & -2\\ -4 & 3\end{bmatrix}\begin{bmatrix}96 & 46\\ 135 & 63\end{bmatrix}=\begin{bmatrix}288-270 & 138-126\\ -384+405 & -184+189\end{bmatrix}=\begin{bmatrix}18 & 12\\ 21 & 5\end{bmatrix}$$

The decoded message is 18, 21, 12, 5 or RULE.

41. $\begin{vmatrix}3 & 2\\ -1 & 5\end{vmatrix}=15-(-2)=17$

42. $\begin{vmatrix} -2 & -3 \\ -4 & -8 \end{vmatrix} = 16 - 12 = 4$

43. $\begin{vmatrix} 2 & 4 & -3 \\ 1 & -1 & 5 \\ -2 & 4 & 0 \end{vmatrix} = 2\begin{vmatrix} 2 & 4 & -3 \\ 1 & -1 & 5 \\ -1 & 2 & 0 \end{vmatrix}$

$= 2\left[(-1)\begin{vmatrix} 4 & -3 \\ -1 & 5 \end{vmatrix} - 2\begin{vmatrix} 2 & -3 \\ 1 & 5 \end{vmatrix}\right]$

$= 2\{(-1)(20 - 3) - 2[10 - (-3)]\}$

$= 2[-17 - 2(13)] = 2(-17 - 26) = 2(-43)$

$= -86$

44. $\begin{vmatrix} 4 & 7 & 0 \\ -5 & 6 & 0 \\ 3 & 2 & -4 \end{vmatrix} = 4\begin{vmatrix} 6 & 0 \\ 2 & -4 \end{vmatrix} + 5\begin{vmatrix} 7 & 0 \\ 2 & -4 \end{vmatrix} + 3\begin{vmatrix} 7 & 0 \\ 6 & 0 \end{vmatrix}$

$4(-24 - 0) + 5(-28 - 0) + 3(0 - 0)$

$4(-24) + 5(-28) + 0$

$= -236$

45. $\begin{vmatrix} 1 & 1 & 0 & 2 \\ 0 & 3 & 2 & 1 \\ 0 & -2 & 4 & 0 \\ 0 & 3 & 0 & 1 \end{vmatrix} = \begin{vmatrix} 3 & 2 & 1 \\ -2 & 4 & 0 \\ 3 & 0 & 1 \end{vmatrix} = 3\begin{vmatrix} 2 & 1 \\ 4 & 0 \end{vmatrix} + \begin{vmatrix} 3 & 2 \\ -2 & 4 \end{vmatrix}$

$= 3(0 - 4) + [12 - (-4)]$

$= 3(-4) + 16 = -12 + 16 = 4$

46. $\begin{vmatrix} 2 & 2 & 2 & 2 \\ 0 & 2 & 2 & 2 \\ 0 & 0 & 2 & 2 \\ 0 & 0 & 0 & 2 \end{vmatrix} = 2\begin{vmatrix} 2 & 2 & 2 \\ 0 & 2 & 2 \\ 0 & 0 & 2 \end{vmatrix}$

$= 2(2)\begin{vmatrix} 2 & 2 \\ 0 & 2 \end{vmatrix} = 2(2)(20)$

$= 16$

47. $D = \begin{vmatrix} 1 & -2 \\ 3 & 2 \end{vmatrix} = 2 - (-6) = 2 + 6 = 8$

$D_x = \begin{vmatrix} 8 & -2 \\ -1 & 2 \end{vmatrix} = 16 - 2 = 14$

$D_y = \begin{vmatrix} 1 & 8 \\ 3 & -1 \end{vmatrix} = -1 - 24 = -25$

$x = \frac{D_x}{D} = \frac{14}{8} = \frac{7}{4},\ y = \frac{D_y}{D} = \frac{-25}{8} = -\frac{25}{8}$

The solution to the system is $\left\{\left(\frac{7}{4}, -\frac{25}{8}\right)\right\}$.

48. $D = \begin{vmatrix} 7 & 2 \\ 2 & 1 \end{vmatrix} = 7 - 4 = 3$

$D = \begin{vmatrix} 7 & 2 \\ 2 & 1 \end{vmatrix} = 7 - 4 = 3$

$D_x = \begin{vmatrix} 0 & 2 \\ -3 & 1 \end{vmatrix} = 0 - (-6) = 6$

$D_y = \begin{vmatrix} 7 & 0 \\ 2 & -3 \end{vmatrix} = -21 - 0 = -21$

$x = \frac{6}{3} = 2$

$y = \frac{-21}{3} = -7$

The solution to the system is $\{(2, -7)\}$.

49. $D = \begin{vmatrix} 1 & 2 & 2 \\ 2 & 4 & 7 \\ -2 & -5 & -2 \end{vmatrix} = \begin{vmatrix} 1 & 2 & 2 \\ 0 & 0 & 3 \\ 0 & -1 & 2 \end{vmatrix}$

$= \begin{vmatrix} 0 & 3 \\ -1 & 2 \end{vmatrix} = 0 - (-3) = 3$

$D_x = \begin{vmatrix} 5 & 2 & 2 \\ 19 & 4 & 7 \\ 8 & -5 & -2 \end{vmatrix}$

$= 5\begin{vmatrix} 4 & 7 \\ -5 & -2 \end{vmatrix} - 2\begin{vmatrix} 19 & 7 \\ 8 & -2 \end{vmatrix} + 2\begin{vmatrix} 19 & 4 \\ 8 & -5 \end{vmatrix}$

$= 5[-8 - (-35)] - 2(-38 - 56) + 2(-95 - 32)$

$= 5(27) - 2(-94) - 2(127)$

$= 135 + 188 - 254 = 69$

$D_y = \begin{vmatrix} 1 & 5 & 2 \\ 2 & 19 & 7 \\ -2 & 8 & -2 \end{vmatrix} = \begin{vmatrix} 1 & 5 & 2 \\ 0 & 9 & 3 \\ 0 & 18 & 2 \end{vmatrix}$

$= \begin{vmatrix} 9 & 3 \\ 18 & 2 \end{vmatrix} = 18 - 54 = -36$

$$D_z = \begin{vmatrix} 1 & 2 & 5 \\ 2 & 4 & 19 \\ -2 & -5 & 8 \end{vmatrix} = \begin{vmatrix} 1 & 2 & 5 \\ 0 & 0 & 9 \\ 0 & -1 & 18 \end{vmatrix}$$

$$= \begin{vmatrix} 0 & 9 \\ -1 & 18 \end{vmatrix} = 0-(-9) = 9$$

$$x = \frac{D_x}{D} = \frac{69}{3} = 23,\ y = \frac{D_y}{D} = \frac{-36}{3} = -12,$$

$$z = \frac{D_z}{D} = \frac{9}{3} = 3$$

The solution to the system is $\{(23, -12, 3)\}$.

50. $$D = \begin{vmatrix} 2 & 1 & 0 \\ 0 & 1 & -2 \\ 3 & 0 & -2 \end{vmatrix} = 2\begin{vmatrix} 1 & -2 \\ 0 & -2 \end{vmatrix} + 3\begin{vmatrix} 1 & 0 \\ 1 & -2 \end{vmatrix}$$

$$= 2(-2-0)+3(-2-0)$$
$$= 2(-2)+3(-2)$$
$$= -4-6$$
$$= -10$$

$$D_x = \begin{vmatrix} -4 & 1 & 0 \\ 0 & 1 & -2 \\ -11 & 0 & -2 \end{vmatrix} = -1\begin{vmatrix} 0 & -2 \\ -11 & -2 \end{vmatrix} + 1\begin{vmatrix} -4 & 0 \\ -11 & -2 \end{vmatrix}$$

$$= -1(0-22)+1(8-0)$$
$$= 22+8$$
$$= 30$$

$$D_y = \begin{vmatrix} 2 & -4 & 0 \\ 0 & 0 & -2 \\ 3 & -11 & -2 \end{vmatrix} = 2\begin{vmatrix} 0 & -2 \\ -11 & -2 \end{vmatrix} + 3\begin{vmatrix} -4 & 0 \\ 0 & -2 \end{vmatrix}$$

$$= 2(0-22)+3(8-0)$$
$$= 2(-22)+3(8)$$
$$= -44+24$$
$$= -20$$

$$D_z = \begin{vmatrix} 2 & 1 & -4 \\ 0 & 1 & 0 \\ 3 & 0 & -11 \end{vmatrix} = 2\begin{vmatrix} 1 & 0 \\ 0 & -11 \end{vmatrix} + 3\begin{vmatrix} 1 & -4 \\ 1 & 0 \end{vmatrix}$$

$$= 2(-11-0)+3(0+4)$$
$$= 2(-11)+3(+4) = -22+12$$
$$= -10$$

$$x = \frac{30}{-10} = -3$$
$$y = \frac{-20}{-10} = 2$$
$$z = \frac{-10}{-10} = 1$$

The solution to the system is $\{(-3, 2, 1)\}$.

51. The quadratic function must satisfy
$f(20) = 400 = 400a + 20b + c$
$f(40) = 150 = 1600a + 40b + c$
$f(60) = 400 = 3600a + 60b + c$

$$D = \begin{vmatrix} 400 & 20 & 1 \\ 1600 & 40 & 1 \\ 3600 & 60 & 1 \end{vmatrix} = (400)(20)\begin{vmatrix} 1 & 1 & 1 \\ 4 & 2 & 1 \\ 9 & 3 & 1 \end{vmatrix}$$

$$= 8000\begin{vmatrix} 1 & 1 & 1 \\ 3 & 1 & 0 \\ 8 & 2 & 0 \end{vmatrix} = 8000\begin{vmatrix} 3 & 1 \\ 8 & 2 \end{vmatrix}$$

$$= 8000(6-8)$$
$$= 8000(-2) = -16{,}000$$

$$D_a = \begin{vmatrix} 400 & 20 & 1 \\ 150 & 40 & 1 \\ 400 & 60 & 1 \end{vmatrix} = (50)(20)\begin{vmatrix} 8 & 1 & 1 \\ 3 & 2 & 1 \\ 8 & 3 & 1 \end{vmatrix}$$

$$= 1000\begin{vmatrix} 8 & 1 & 1 \\ -5 & 1 & 0 \\ 0 & 2 & 0 \end{vmatrix} = 1000\begin{vmatrix} -5 & 1 \\ 0 & 2 \end{vmatrix}$$

$$= 1000(-10-0) = -10{,}000$$

$$D_b = \begin{vmatrix} 400 & 400 & 1 \\ 1600 & 150 & 1 \\ 3600 & 400 & 1 \end{vmatrix} = (400)(50)\begin{vmatrix} 1 & 8 & 1 \\ 4 & 3 & 1 \\ 9 & 8 & 1 \end{vmatrix}$$

$$= 20{,}000\begin{vmatrix} 1 & 8 & 1 \\ 3 & -5 & 0 \\ 8 & 0 & 0 \end{vmatrix} = 20{,}000\begin{vmatrix} 3 & -5 \\ 8 & 0 \end{vmatrix}$$

$$= 20{,}000[0-(-40)] = 20{,}000(40)$$
$$= 800{,}000$$

$$D_c = \begin{vmatrix} 400 & 20 & 400 \\ 1600 & 40 & 150 \\ 3600 & 60 & 400 \end{vmatrix}$$
$$= (400)(20)(50)\begin{vmatrix} 1 & 1 & 8 \\ 4 & 2 & 3 \\ 9 & 3 & 8 \end{vmatrix}$$
$$= 400{,}000\begin{vmatrix} 1 & 0 & 0 \\ 4 & -2 & -29 \\ 2 & -6 & -64 \end{vmatrix}$$
$$= 400{,}000\begin{vmatrix} -2 & -29 \\ -6 & -64 \end{vmatrix}$$
$= 400{,}000(128 - 174)$
$= 400{,}000(-46)$
$= -18{,}400{,}000$

$$a = \frac{D_a}{D} = \frac{-10{,}000}{-16{,}000} = \frac{5}{8},$$
$$b = \frac{D_b}{D} = \frac{800{,}000}{-16{,}000} = -50,$$
$$c = \frac{D_c}{D} = \frac{-18{,}400{,}000}{-16{,}000} = 1150$$

The model is $f(x) = \frac{5}{8}x^2 - 50x + 1150.$

$f(30) = \frac{5}{8}(900) - 50(30) + 1150$
$= 562.5 - 1500 + 1150$
$= 212.5$

$f(50) = \frac{5}{8}(2500) - 50(50) + 1150$
$= 1562.8 - 2500 + 1150$
$= 212.5$

30- and 50-year-olds are involved in an average of 212.5 automobile accidents per day.

Chapter 6 Test

1. $\left[\begin{array}{ccc|c} 1 & 2 & -1 & -3 \\ 2 & -4 & 1 & -7 \\ -2 & 2 & -3 & 4 \end{array}\right] \begin{array}{l} -2R_1 + R_2 \\ 2R_1 + R_3 \end{array}$

$\left[\begin{array}{ccc|c} 1 & 2 & -1 & -3 \\ 0 & -8 & 3 & -1 \\ 0 & 6 & -5 & -2 \end{array}\right] -\frac{1}{8}R_2$

$\left[\begin{array}{ccc|c} 1 & 2 & -1 & -3 \\ 0 & 1 & -\frac{3}{8} & \frac{1}{8} \\ 0 & 6 & -5 & -2 \end{array}\right] -6R_2 + R_3$

$\left[\begin{array}{ccc|c} 1 & 2 & -1 & -3 \\ 0 & 1 & -\frac{3}{8} & \frac{1}{8} \\ 0 & 0 & -\frac{11}{4} & -\frac{11}{4} \end{array}\right] -\frac{4}{11}R_3$

$\left[\begin{array}{ccc|c} 1 & 2 & -1 & -3 \\ 0 & 1 & -\frac{3}{8} & \frac{1}{8} \\ 0 & 0 & 1 & 1 \end{array}\right]$

$x + 2y - z = -3$
$y - \frac{3}{8}z = \frac{1}{8}$
$z = 1$

Using back substitution,
$y - \frac{3}{8}(1) = \frac{1}{8}$ and $x + 2\left(\frac{1}{2}\right) - 1 = -3.$
$y = \frac{1}{2}$ $\quad x + 1 - 1 = -3$
$x = -3$

The solution to the system is $\left\{\left(-3, \frac{1}{2}, 1\right)\right\}$.

2. $\left[\begin{array}{ccc|c} 1 & -2 & 1 & 2 \\ 2 & -1 & -1 & 1 \end{array}\right] -2R_1 + R_2$

$\left[\begin{array}{ccc|c} 1 & -2 & 1 & 2 \\ 0 & 3 & -3 & -3 \end{array}\right] \frac{1}{3}R_2$

$\left[\begin{array}{ccc|c} 1 & -2 & 1 & 2 \\ 0 & 1 & -1 & -1 \end{array}\right]$

The system $\begin{array}{r} x - 2y + z = 2 \\ y - z = -1 \end{array}$ has no unique solution. Express x and y in terms of z:
$y = z - 1$
$x - 2(z - 1) + z = 2$
$x - 2z + 2 + z = 2$
$x = z$

With $z = t$, the complete solution to the system is $\{(t, t - 1, t)\}$.

3. $2B + 3C = \begin{bmatrix} 2 & -2 \\ 4 & 2 \end{bmatrix} + \begin{bmatrix} 3 & 6 \\ -3 & 9 \end{bmatrix} = \begin{bmatrix} 5 & 4 \\ 1 & 11 \end{bmatrix}$

4. $AB = \begin{bmatrix} 3+2 & -3+1 \\ 1+0 & -1+0 \\ 2+2 & -2+1 \end{bmatrix} = \begin{bmatrix} 5 & -2 \\ 1 & -1 \\ 4 & -1 \end{bmatrix}$

5. $C^{-1} = \frac{1}{(1)(3)-(2)(-1)} \begin{bmatrix} 3 & -2 \\ 1 & 1 \end{bmatrix} = \frac{1}{3+2} \begin{bmatrix} 3 & -2 \\ 1 & 1 \end{bmatrix} = \begin{bmatrix} \frac{3}{5} & -\frac{2}{5} \\ \frac{1}{5} & \frac{1}{5} \end{bmatrix}$

6. $BC = \begin{bmatrix} 1+1 & 2-3 \\ 2-1 & 4+3 \end{bmatrix} = \begin{bmatrix} 2 & -1 \\ 1 & 7 \end{bmatrix}$

$BC - 3B = \begin{bmatrix} 2 & -1 \\ 1 & 7 \end{bmatrix} - \begin{bmatrix} 3 & -3 \\ 6 & 3 \end{bmatrix} = \begin{bmatrix} -1 & 2 \\ -5 & 4 \end{bmatrix}$

7. $AB = \begin{bmatrix} -3+14-10 & 2-8+6 & 0+2-2 \\ -6+21-15 & 4-12+9 & 0+3-3 \\ -3-7+10 & 2+4-6 & 0-1+2 \end{bmatrix} = \begin{bmatrix} 1 & 0 & 0 \\ 0 & 1 & 0 \\ 0 & 0 & 1 \end{bmatrix} = I_3$

$BA = \begin{bmatrix} -3+4+0 & -6+6+0 & -6+6+0 \\ 7-8+1 & 14-12-1 & 14-12-2 \\ -5+6-1 & -10+9+1 & -10+9+2 \end{bmatrix} = \begin{bmatrix} 1 & 0 & 0 \\ 0 & 1 & 0 \\ 0 & 0 & 1 \end{bmatrix} = I_3$

8. a. $\begin{bmatrix} 3 & 5 \\ 2 & -3 \end{bmatrix} \begin{bmatrix} x \\ y \end{bmatrix} = \begin{bmatrix} 9 \\ -13 \end{bmatrix}$

b. $A^{-1} = \frac{1}{(3)(-3)-(5)(2)} \begin{bmatrix} -3 & -5 \\ -2 & 3 \end{bmatrix}$

$= \frac{1}{-19} \begin{bmatrix} -3 & -5 \\ -2 & 3 \end{bmatrix} = \begin{bmatrix} \frac{3}{19} & \frac{5}{19} \\ \frac{2}{19} & -\frac{3}{19} \end{bmatrix}$

c. The solution is $A^{-1}B = \begin{bmatrix} \frac{3}{19} & \frac{5}{19} \\ \frac{2}{19} & -\frac{3}{19} \end{bmatrix} \begin{bmatrix} 9 \\ -13 \end{bmatrix} = \begin{bmatrix} \frac{27}{19} - \frac{65}{19} \\ \frac{18}{19} + \frac{39}{19} \end{bmatrix} = \begin{bmatrix} -2 \\ 3 \end{bmatrix}$

The solution to the system is {(–2, 3)}.

9. $\begin{vmatrix} 4 & -1 & 3 \\ 0 & 5 & -1 \\ 5 & 2 & 4 \end{vmatrix} = 4\begin{vmatrix} 5 & -1 \\ 2 & 4 \end{vmatrix} + 5\begin{vmatrix} -1 & 3 \\ 5 & -1 \end{vmatrix}$

$= 4[20-(-2)] + 5(1-15)$
$= 4(22) + 5(-14)$
$= 88 - 70$
$= 18$

10. $D = \begin{vmatrix} 3 & 1 & -2 \\ 2 & 7 & 3 \\ 4 & -3 & -1 \end{vmatrix} = 3\begin{vmatrix} 7 & 3 \\ -3 & -1 \end{vmatrix} - 1\begin{vmatrix} 2 & 3 \\ 4 & -1 \end{vmatrix} - 2\begin{vmatrix} 2 & 7 \\ 4 & -3 \end{vmatrix}$

$= 3[-7-(-9)] - 1(-2-12) - 2(-6-28)$

$= 3(2) - 1(-14) - 2(-34)$

$= 6 + 14 + 68$

$= 88$

$D_x = \begin{vmatrix} -3 & 1 & -2 \\ 9 & 7 & 3 \\ 7 & -3 & -1 \end{vmatrix} - 3\begin{vmatrix} 7 & 3 \\ -3 & -1 \end{vmatrix} - 1\begin{vmatrix} 9 & 3 \\ 7 & -1 \end{vmatrix} - 2\begin{vmatrix} 9 & 7 \\ 7 & -3 \end{vmatrix}$

$= -3[-7-(-9)] - 1(-9-21) - 2(-27-49)$

$= -3(2) - 1(-30) - 2(-76)$

$= -6 + 30 + 152$

$= 176$

$x = \frac{D_x}{D} = \frac{176}{88} = 2$

Cumulative Review Exercises (Chapters 1–6)

1. $2x^2 = 4 - x$

$2x^2 + x - 4 = 0$

$x = \frac{-1 \pm \sqrt{1^2 - 4(2)(-4)}}{2(2)}$

$x = \frac{-1 \pm \sqrt{1-32}}{4}$

$x = \frac{-1 \pm \sqrt{33}}{4}$

The solution set is $\left\{\frac{-1+\sqrt{33}}{4}, \frac{-1-\sqrt{33}}{4}\right\}$.

2. $5x + 8 \le 7(1 + x)$

$5x + 8 \le 7 + 7x$

$-2x \le -1$

$x \ge \frac{1}{2}$

The solution set is $\left\{x \middle| x \ge \frac{1}{2}\right\}$ or $\left[\frac{1}{2}, \infty\right)$.

3. $\sqrt{2x+4}-\sqrt{x+3}-1=0$
$\sqrt{2x+4}=\sqrt{x+3}+1$
$2x+4=x+3+2\sqrt{x+3}+1$
$x=2\sqrt{x+3}$
$x^2=4(x+3)$
$x^2=4x+12$
$x^2-4x-12=0$
$(x-6)(x+2)=0$
$x=6$ or $x=-2$
$x=-2$ is an extraneous solution. The solution set is $\{6\}$.

4. $3x^3+8x^2-15x+4=0$
$p=\pm1,\pm2,\pm4$
$q=\pm1,\pm3$
$\frac{p}{q}=\pm1,\pm\frac{1}{3},\pm2,\pm\frac{2}{3},\pm4,\pm\frac{4}{3}$

–4	3	8	–15	4
		–12	16	–4
	3	–4	1	0

$(x+4)(3x^2-4x+1)=0$
$(x+4)(3x-1)(x-1)=0$
$x=-4,\ x=\frac{1}{3},\ x=1$
The solution set is $\left\{4,\frac{1}{3},1\right\}$.

5. $e^{2x}-14e^x+45=0\ \ le+t=e^x$
$t^2-14t+45=0$
$(t-5)(t-9)=0$
$t=5\ \ t=9$
$e^x=5\ \ e^x=9$
$\ln e^x=\ln 5\ \ \ln e^x=\ln 9$
$x=e^x=\ln 5\ \ x=\ln 9$
The solution set is $\{\ln 5, \ln 9\}$.

6. $\log_3 x+\log_3(x+2)=1$
$\log_3 x^2+2x=1$
$3^1=x^2+2x$
$x^2+2x-3=0$
$(x-1)(x+3)=0$
$x=1,\ x=-3$
$x=-3$ is an extraneous solution. The solution set is $\{1\}$.

7. $\left[\begin{array}{rrr|r}1&-1&1&17\\2&3&1&8\\-4&1&5&-2\end{array}\right]\begin{array}{l}\\-2R_1+R_2\\4R_1+R_3\end{array}$

$\left[\begin{array}{rrr|r}1&-1&1&17\\0&5&-1&-26\\0&-3&9&66\end{array}\right]-\frac{1}{3}R_3$

$\left[\begin{array}{rrr|r}1&-1&1&17\\0&1&-3&-22\\0&5&-1&-26\end{array}\right]\begin{array}{l}\\-5R_2+R_3\\1R_2+R_1\end{array}$

$\left[\begin{array}{rrr|r}1&0&-2&-5\\0&1&-3&-22\\0&0&14&84\end{array}\right]\frac{1}{14}R_3$

$\left[\begin{array}{rrrr}1&0&-2&-5\\0&1&-3&-22\\0&0&1&6\end{array}\right]\begin{array}{l}\\3R_3+R_2\\2R_3+R_1\end{array}$

$\left[\begin{array}{rrrr}1&0&0&7\\0&1&0&-4\\0&0&1&6\end{array}\right]$

$x=7\ \ y=-4\ \ z=6$
The solution set is $\{(7,-4,6)\}$.

8. $D = \begin{vmatrix} 1 & -2 & 1 \\ 2 & 1 & -1 \\ 3 & 2 & -2 \end{vmatrix}$

$$\begin{aligned}
&= 1\begin{vmatrix} 1 & -1 \\ 2 & -2 \end{vmatrix} - 2\begin{vmatrix} -2 & 1 \\ 2 & -2 \end{vmatrix} + 3\begin{vmatrix} -2 & 1 \\ 1 & 1 \end{vmatrix} \\
&= 1(-2+2) - 2(4-2) + 3(2-1) \\
&= 0 - 4 + 3 \\
&= -1
\end{aligned}$$

$$\begin{aligned}
D_x &= \begin{vmatrix} 7 & -2 & 1 \\ 0 & 1 & -1 \\ -2 & 2 & -2 \end{vmatrix} = 7\begin{vmatrix} 1 & -1 \\ 2 & -2 \end{vmatrix} - 2\begin{vmatrix} -2 & 1 \\ 1 & -1 \end{vmatrix} \\
&= 7(-2+2) - 2(2-1) \\
&= 0 - 2 = -2
\end{aligned}$$

$$\begin{aligned}
D_y &= \begin{vmatrix} 1 & 7 & 1 \\ 2 & 0 & -1 \\ 3 & -2 & -2 \end{vmatrix} = 7\begin{vmatrix} 2 & -1 \\ 3 & -2 \end{vmatrix} - 2\begin{vmatrix} 1 & 1 \\ 2 & -1 \end{vmatrix} \\
&= 7(-4+3) - 2(-1-2) \\
&= -7 + 6 = 1
\end{aligned}$$

$$\begin{aligned}
D_z &= \begin{vmatrix} 1 & -2 & 7 \\ 2 & 1 & 0 \\ 3 & 2 & -2 \end{vmatrix} = 7\begin{vmatrix} 2 & 1 \\ 3 & 2 \end{vmatrix} - 2\begin{vmatrix} 1 & -2 \\ 2 & 1 \end{vmatrix} \\
&= 7(4-3) - 2(1+4) \\
&= 7 - 10 = -3
\end{aligned}$$

$$x = \frac{-2}{-1} = 2$$

$$y = \frac{1}{-1} = -1$$

$$z = \frac{-3}{-1} = 3$$

The solution set is $\{(2, -1, 3)\}$. Therefore, $y = -1$.

9. $y = \sqrt{4x-7}$

$x = \sqrt{4y-7}$

$x^2 = 4y - 7$

$x^2 + 7 - 4y$

$\dfrac{x^2+7}{4} = y$

$f^{-1}(x) = \dfrac{x^2+7}{4} \; (x \geq 0)$

10. $f(x) = \dfrac{x}{x^2-16}$

$f(0) = \dfrac{0}{-16} = 0$

y - intercept at 0

$0 = \dfrac{x}{x^2-16}$

$0 = x$

x - intercept at 0

$f(x) = \dfrac{x}{(x+4)(x-4)}$

vertical asymptotes at 4, –4

horizontal asymptote at 0

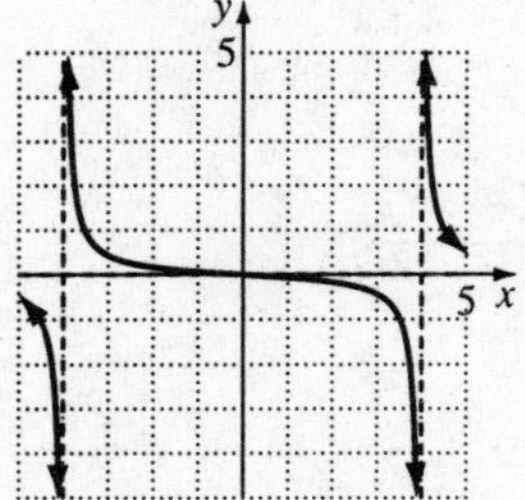

11. $f(x) = 4x^4 - 4x^3 - 25x^2 + x + 6$

–2	4	–4	–25	1	6
		–8	24	2	–6
3	4	–12	–1	3	0
		12	0	–3	
	4	0	–1	0	

$f(x) = (x+2)(x-3)(4x^2-1)$

$f(x) = (x+2)(x-3)(2x+1)(2x-1)$

12. $y = \log_2 x$
$2^y = x$

x	y
1	0
2	1
$\frac{1}{2}$	−1

$y = \log_2(x+1)$
shift graph left one

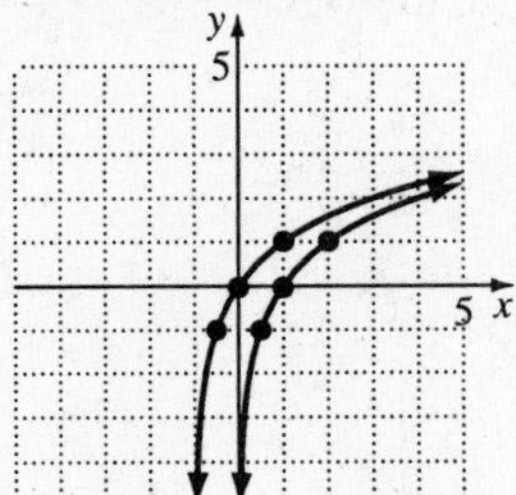

13. a. $A = A_0e^{kt}$
$450 = 900e^{k(40)}$
$\frac{1}{2} = e^{40k}$
$\ln\left(\frac{1}{2}\right) = 40k$
$k = \frac{\ln\frac{1}{2}}{40} \approx -0.017$
$A = A_0e^{-0.017t}$

b. $A = 900e^{-0.017(10)}$
$A = 900e^{-0.17}$
$A \approx 759.30$ grams

14. $$\begin{bmatrix}1 & -1 & 0\\ 2 & 1 & 3\end{bmatrix}\begin{bmatrix}4 & -1\\ 2 & 0\\ 1 & 1\end{bmatrix} = \begin{bmatrix}4-2+0 & -1+0+0\\ 8+2+3 & -2+0+3\end{bmatrix} = \begin{bmatrix}2 & -1\\ 13 & 1\end{bmatrix}$$

15. $\dfrac{3x^2+17x-38}{(x-3)(x-2)(x+2)} = \dfrac{A}{x-3} + \dfrac{B}{x-2} + \dfrac{C}{x+2}$

$3x^2+17x-38 = A(x^2-4) + B(x^2-x-6) + C(x^2-5x+6)$

$3x^2+17x-38 = Ax^2 - 4A + Bx^2 - Bx - 6B + Cx^2 - 5Cx + 6c$

$3x^2+17x-38 = (A+B+C)x^2 + (-B-5C)x - (4A+6B-6C)$

$$\begin{aligned} A+B+C &= 3 \\ -B-5C &= 17 \\ 4A+6B-6C &= 38 \end{aligned}$$

$\left[\begin{array}{ccc|c} 1 & 1 & 1 & 3 \\ 0 & -1 & -5 & 17 \\ 4 & 6 & -6 & 38 \end{array}\right] -4R_1 + R_3$

$\left[\begin{array}{ccc|c} 1 & 1 & 1 & 3 \\ 0 & -1 & -5 & 17 \\ 0 & 2 & -10 & 26 \end{array}\right] -1R_2$

$\left[\begin{array}{ccc|c} 1 & 1 & 1 & 3 \\ 0 & 1 & 5 & -17 \\ 0 & 2 & -10 & 26 \end{array}\right] \begin{array}{l} \\ -2R_2 + R_3 \\ -1R_2 + R_1 \end{array}$

$\left[\begin{array}{ccc|c} 1 & 0 & -4 & 20 \\ 0 & 1 & 5 & -17 \\ 0 & 0 & -20 & 60 \end{array}\right] -\frac{1}{20}R_3$

$\left[\begin{array}{ccc|c} 1 & 0 & -4 & 20 \\ 0 & 1 & 5 & -17 \\ 0 & 0 & 1 & -3 \end{array}\right] \begin{array}{l} \\ -5R_3 + R_2 \\ 4R_3 + R_1 \end{array}$

$\left[\begin{array}{ccc|c} 1 & 0 & 0 & 8 \\ 0 & 1 & 0 & -2 \\ 0 & 0 & 1 & -3 \end{array}\right]$

$A = 8$
$B = -2$
$C = -3$

$\dfrac{8}{x-3} + \dfrac{-2}{x-2} + \dfrac{-3}{x+2}$

16.

x	y
0	−1
3	−3
−3	1

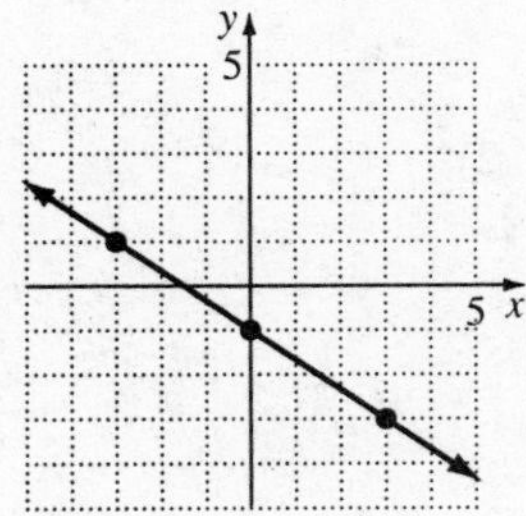

17. $3x - 5y < 15$
$-5y < -3x + 15$
$y > \frac{3}{5}x - 3$

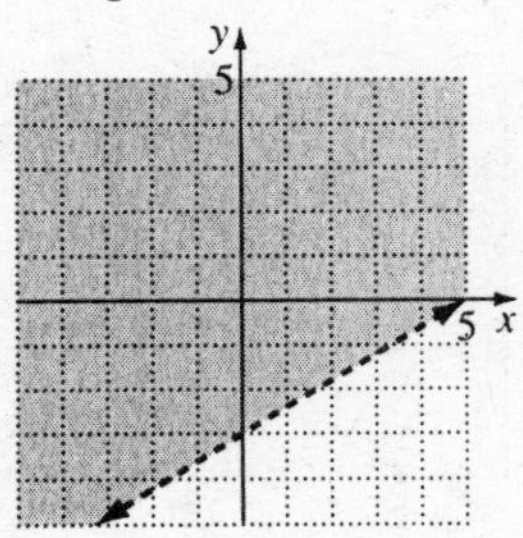

18. $f(x) = x^2 - 2x - 3$
$f(x) = (x^2 - 2x + 1) - 3 - 1$
$f(x) = (x - 1)^2 - 4$

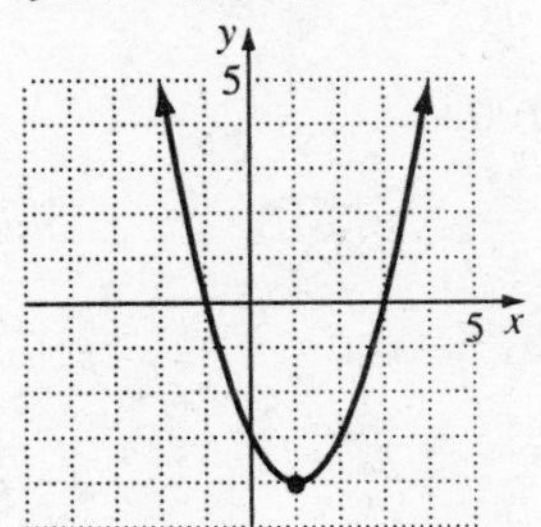

19. $(x - 1)^2 + (y + 1)^2 = 9$
center $(1, -1)$
radius = 3

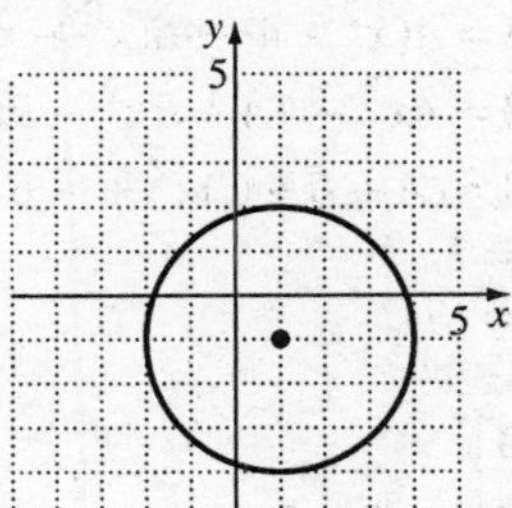

20.

2	1	0	−6	4
		2	4	−4
	1	2	−2	0

$= x^2 + 2x - 2$

Chapter 7

Section 7.1

Check Point Exercises

1. $\frac{x^2}{36}+\frac{y^2}{9}=1$

   $a^2=36,\ a=6$

   $b^2=9,\ b=3$

   $c^2=a^2-b^2=36-9=27$

   $c=\sqrt{27}=3\sqrt{3}$

   The foci are located at $(-3\sqrt{3},\ 0)$ and $(3\sqrt{3},\ 0)$.

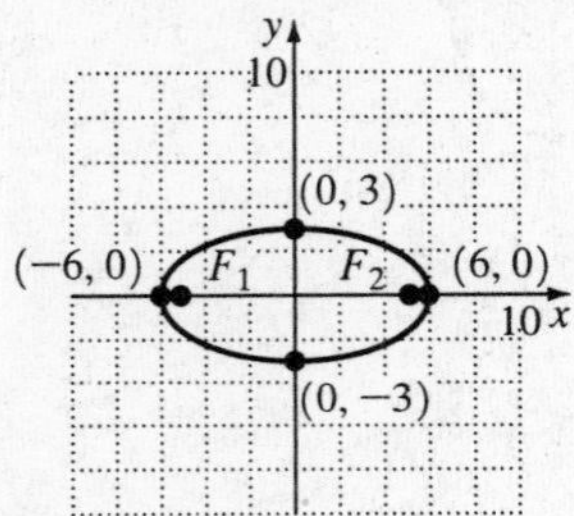

2. $16x^2+9y^2=144$

   $\frac{16x^2}{144}+\frac{9y^2}{144}=\frac{144}{144}$

   $\frac{x^2}{9}+\frac{y^2}{16}=1$

   $a^2=16,\ a=4$

   $b^2=9,\ b=3$

   $c^2=a^2-b^2=16-9=7$

   $c=\sqrt{7}$

   The foci are located at $(0,\ -\sqrt{7})$ and $(0,\ \sqrt{7})$.

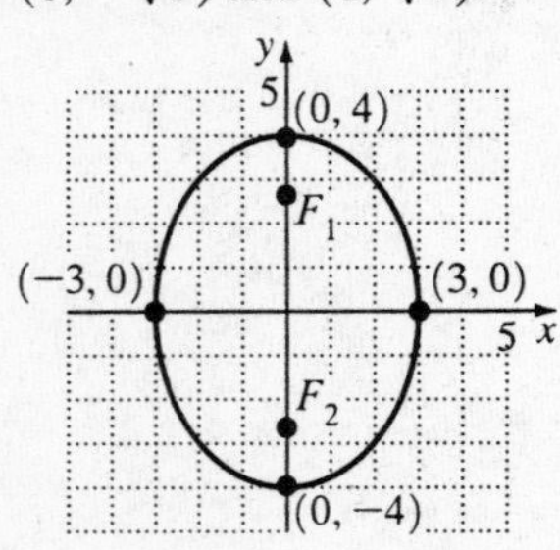

3. $c^2=4,\ a^2=9$

   $b^2=a^2-c^2=9-4=5$

   $\frac{x^2}{9}+\frac{y^2}{5}=1$

4. $\frac{(x+1)^2}{9}+\frac{(y-2)^2}{4}=1$

   $a^2=9,\ a=3$

   $b^2=4,\ b=2$

   center at $(-1,\ 27)$

   $c^2=a^2-b^2=9-4=5$

   $c=\sqrt{5}$

   The foci are located at $(-1-\sqrt{5},\ 2)$ and $(-1+\sqrt{5},\ 2)$.

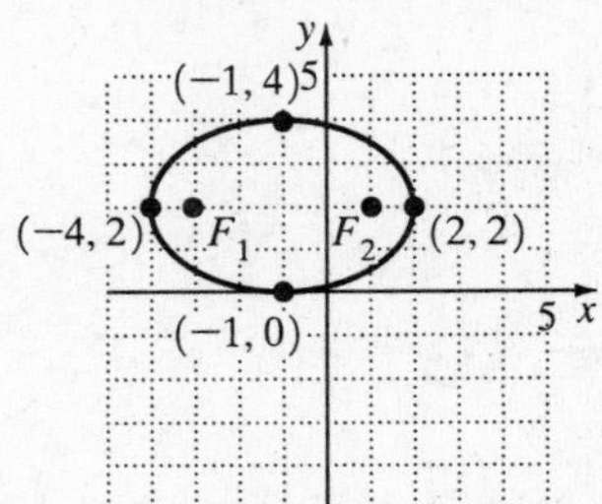

5. $a=20,\ b=10$

   $\frac{x^2}{400}+\frac{y^2}{100}=1$

   Let $x=6$

   $\frac{6^2}{400}+\frac{y^2}{100}=1$

   $400\left(\frac{36}{400}+\frac{y^2}{100}\right)=400(1)$

   $36+4y^2=400$

   $4y^2=364$

   $y^2=91$

   $y=\sqrt{91}\approx 9.54$

   Yes, the truck needs only 9 feet so it will clear.

Exercise Set 7.1

1. $\frac{x^2}{16}+\frac{y^2}{4}=1$

$a^2=16,\ a=4$

$b^2=4,\ b=2$

$c^2=a^2-b^2=16-4=12$

$c=\sqrt{12}=2\sqrt{3}$

The foci are located at $(-2\sqrt{3},\ 0)$ and $(2\sqrt{3},\ 0)$.

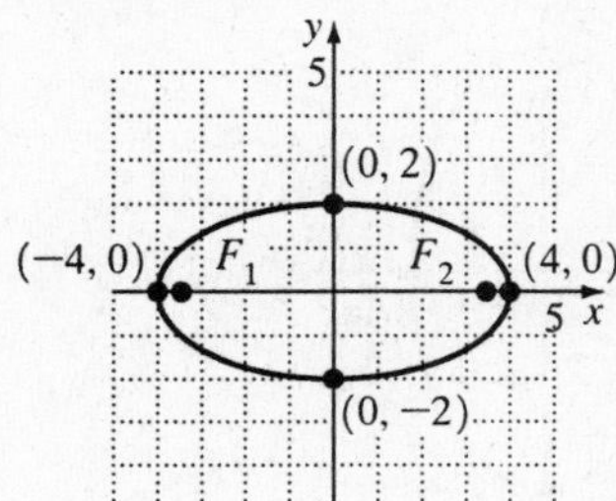

3. $\frac{x^2}{9}+\frac{y^2}{36}=1$

$a^2=36,\ a=6$

$b^2=9,\ b=3$

$c^2=a^2-b^2=36-9=27$

$c=\sqrt{27}=3\sqrt{3}$

The foci are located at $(0,\ -3\sqrt{3})$ and $(0,\ 3\sqrt{3})$.

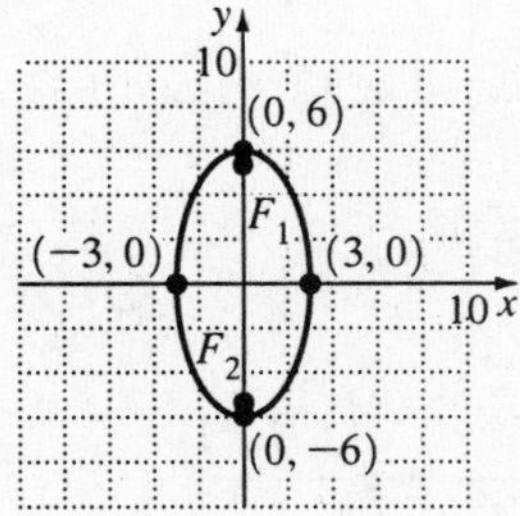

5. $\frac{x^2}{25}+\frac{y^2}{64}=1$

$a^2=64,\ a=8$

$b^2=25,\ b=5$

$c^2=a^2-b^2=64-25=39$

$c=\sqrt{39}$

The foci are located at $(0,\ -\sqrt{39})$ and $(0,\ \sqrt{39})$.

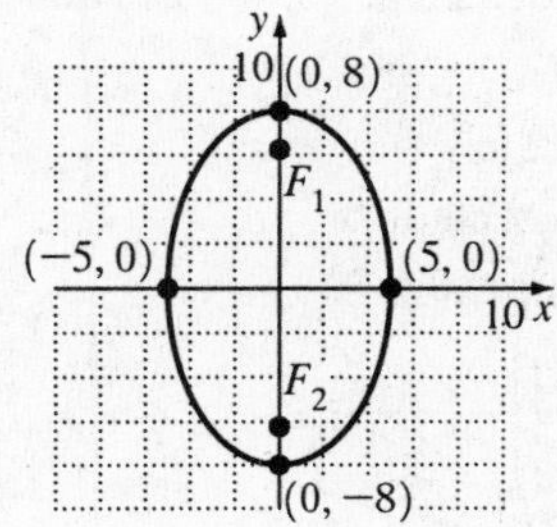

7. $\frac{x^2}{49}+\frac{y^2}{81}=1$

$a^2=81,\ a=9$

$b^2=49,\ b=7$

$c^2=a^2-b^2=81-49=32$

$c=\sqrt{32}=4\sqrt{2}$

The foci are located at $(0,\ -4\sqrt{2})$ and $(0,\ 4\sqrt{2})$.

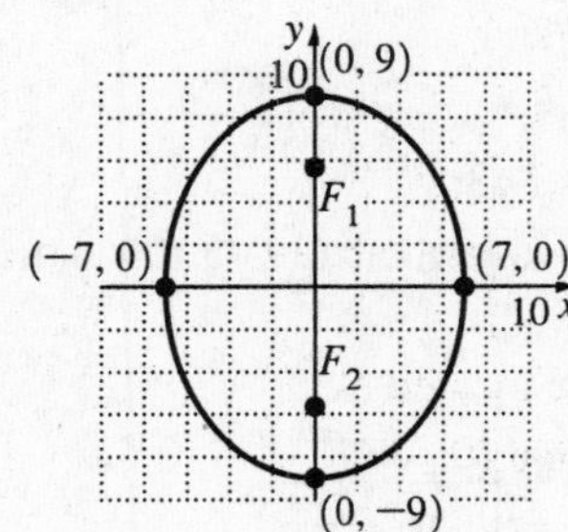

9. $25x^2 + 4y^2 = 100$

$$\frac{25x^2}{100} + \frac{4y^2}{100} = \frac{100}{100}$$

$$\frac{x^2}{4} + \frac{y^2}{25} = 1$$

$a^2 = 25,\ a = 5$

$b^2 = 4,\ b = 2$

$c^2 = a^2 = b^2 = 25 - 4 = 21$

The foci are located at $(0, -\sqrt{21})$ and $(0, \sqrt{21})$.

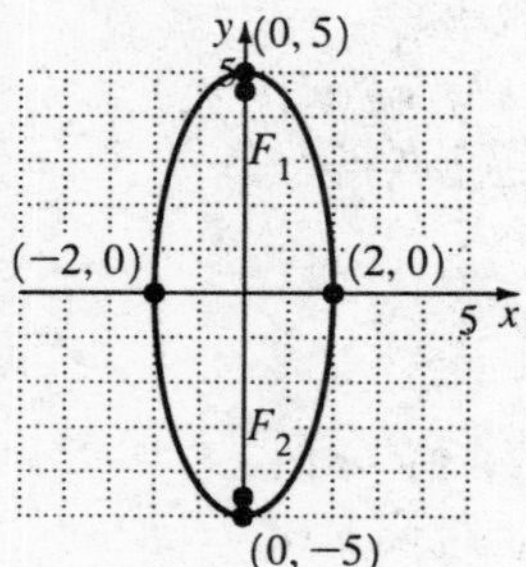

11. $4x^2 + 16y^2 = 64$

$$\frac{4x^2}{64} + \frac{16y^2}{64} = \frac{64}{64}$$

$$\frac{x^2}{16} + \frac{y^2}{4} = 1$$

$a^2 = 16,\ a = 4$

$b^2 = 4,\ b = 2$

$c^2 = a^2 - b^2 = 16 - 4 = 12$

$c = \sqrt{12} = 2\sqrt{3}$

The foci are located at $(-2\sqrt{3}, 0)$ and $(2\sqrt{3}, 0)$.

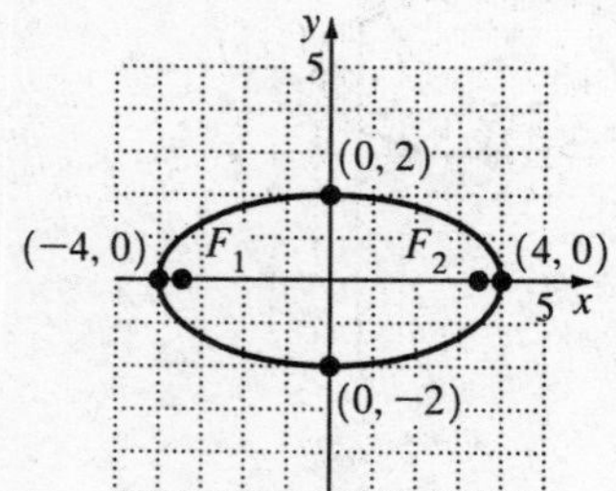

13. $25x^2 + 9y^2 = 225$

$$\frac{25x^2}{225} + \frac{9y^2}{225} = \frac{225}{225}$$

$$\frac{x^2}{9} + \frac{y^2}{25} = 1$$

$a^2 = 25,\ a = 5$

$b^2 = 9,\ b = 3$

$c^2 = a^2 - b^2 = 25 - 9 = 16$

$c = 4$

The foci are located at $(0, 4)$ and $(0, -4)$.

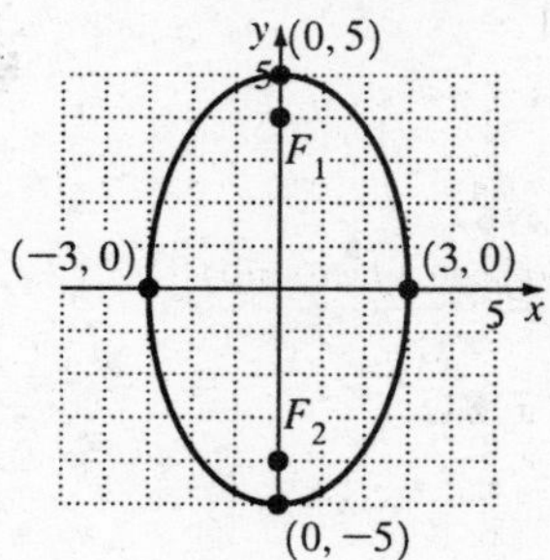

15. $x^2 + 2y^2 = 8$

$$\frac{x^2}{8} + \frac{2y^2}{8} = \frac{8}{8}$$

$$\frac{x^2}{8} + \frac{y^2}{4} = 1$$

$a^2 = 8,\ a = \sqrt{8} = 2\sqrt{2}$

$b^2 = 4,\ b = 2$

$c^2 = a^2 - b^2 = 8 - 4 = 4$

$c = 2$

The foci are located at $(2, 0)$ and $(-2, 0)$.

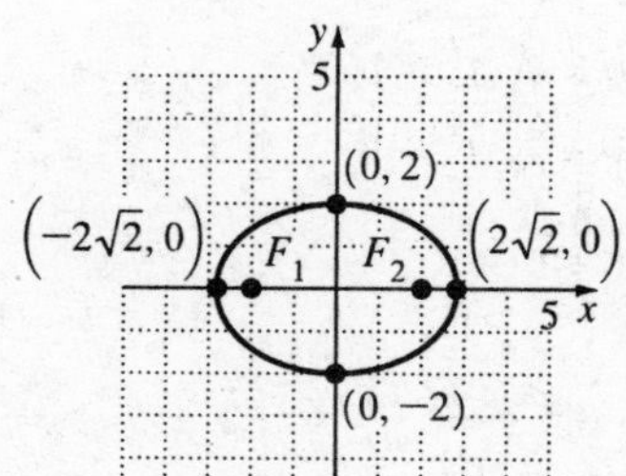

17. $a^2 = 4$, $b^2 = 1$, center at (0, 0)

$\frac{x^2}{4} + \frac{y^2}{1} = 1;$

$c^2 = a^2 - b^2 = 4 - 1 = 3$

$c = \sqrt{3}$

The foci are at $(-\sqrt{3}, 0)$ and $(\sqrt{3}, 0)$.

19. $a^2 = 4$, $b^2 = 1$,

center: (0, 0)

$\frac{x^2}{1} + \frac{y^2}{4} = 1;$

$c^2 = a^2 - b^2 = 4 - 1 = 3$

$c = \sqrt{3}$

The foci are at $(0, \sqrt{3})$ and $(0, -\sqrt{3})$.

21. $c^2 = 25$, $a^2 = 64$

$b^2 = a^2 - c^2 = 64 - 25 = 39$

$\frac{x^2}{64} + \frac{y^2}{39} = 1$

23. $c^2 = 16$, $a^2 = 49$

$b^2 = a^2 - c^2 = 49 - 16 = 33$

$\frac{x^2}{33} + \frac{y^2}{49} = 1$

25. $c^2 = 4$, $b^2 = 9$

$a^2 = b^2 + c^2 = 9 + 4 = 13$

$\frac{x^2}{13} + \frac{y^2}{9} = 1$

27. $2a = 8$, $a = 4$, $a^2 = 16$

$2b = 4$, $b = 2$, $b^2 = 4$

$\frac{x^2}{16} + \frac{y^2}{4} = 1$

29. $2a = 10$, $a = 5$, $a^2 = 25$

$2b = 4$, $b = 2$, $b^2 = 4$

$\frac{x^2}{4} + \frac{y^2}{25} = 1$

31. $\frac{(x-2)^2}{9} + \frac{(y-1)^2}{4} = 1$

$a^2 = 9$, $a = 3$

$b^2 = 4$, $b = 2$

center: (2, 1)

$c^2 = a^2 - b^2 = 9 - 4 = 5$

$c = \sqrt{5}$

The foci are at $(2 - \sqrt{5}, 1)$ and $(2 + \sqrt{5}, 1)$.

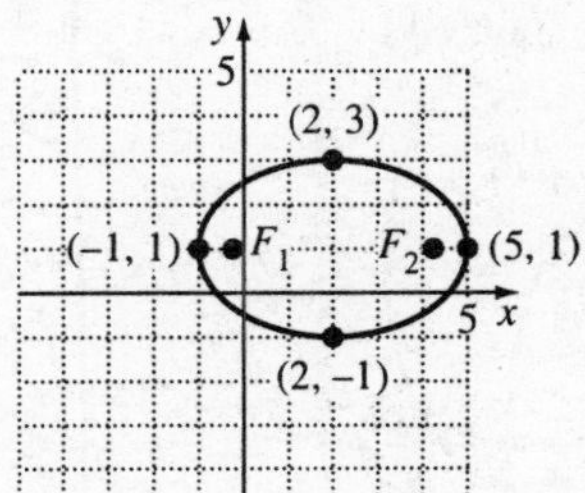

33. $(x+3)^2 + 4(y-2)^2 = 16$

$\frac{(x+3)^2}{16} + \frac{4(y-2)^2}{16} = \frac{16}{16}$

$\frac{(x+3)^2}{16} + \frac{(y-2)^2}{4} = 1$

$a^2 = 16$, $a = 4$

$b^2 = 4$, $b = 2$

center: (−3, 2)

$c^2 = a^2 - b^2 = 16 - 4 = 12$

$c = \sqrt{12} = 2\sqrt{3}$

The foci are at $(-3 - 2\sqrt{3}, 2)$ and $(-3 + 2\sqrt{3}, 2)$.

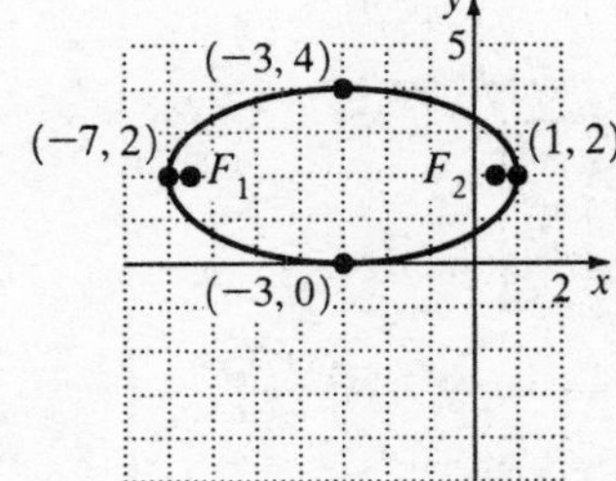

35. $\dfrac{(x-4)^2}{9}+\dfrac{(y+2)^2}{25}=1$

$a^2=25,\ a=5$

$b^2=9,\ b=3$

center: $(4,-2)$

$c^2=a^2-b^2=25-9=16$

$c=4$

The foci are at $(4, 2)$ and $(4, -6)$.

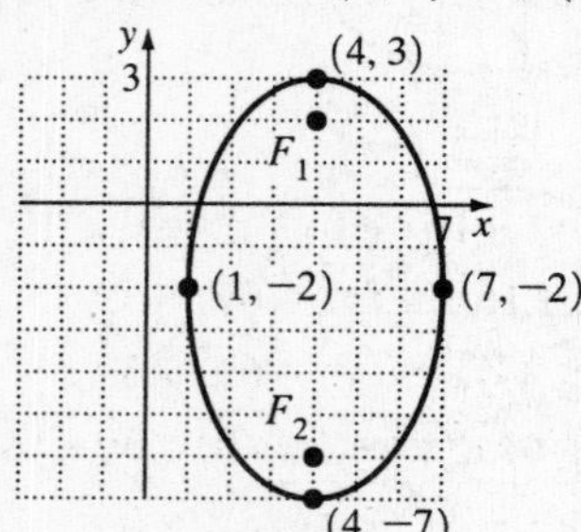

37. $\dfrac{x^2}{25}+\dfrac{(y-2)^2}{36}=1$

$a^2=36,\ a=6$

$b^2=25,\ b=5$

center: $(0, 2)$

$c^2=a^2-b^2=36-25=11$

$c=\sqrt{11}$

The foci are at $(0, 2+\sqrt{11})$ and $(0, 2-\sqrt{11})$.

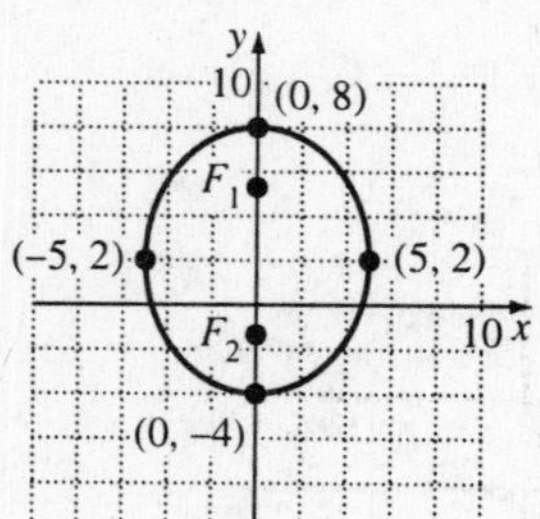

39. $\dfrac{(x+3)^2}{9}+(y-2)^2=1$

$a^2=9,\ a=3$

$b^2=1,\ b=1$

center: $(-3, 2)$

$c^2=a^2-b^2=9-1=8$

$c=\sqrt{8}=2\sqrt{2}$

The foci are at $(-3-2\sqrt{2},\ 2)$ and $(-3+2\sqrt{2},\ 2)$.

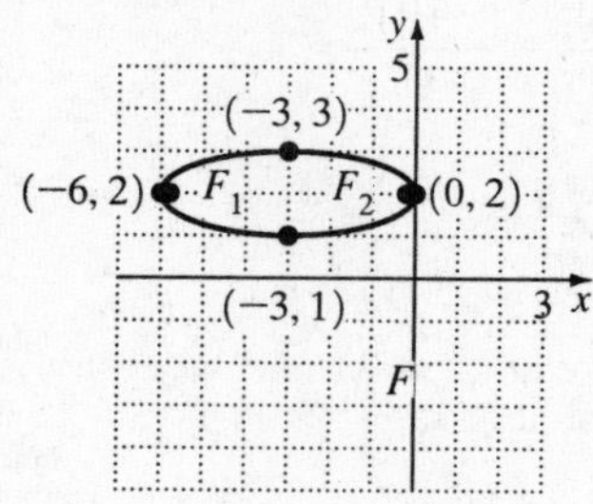

41. $9(x-1)^2+4(y+3)^2=36$

$\dfrac{9(x-1)^2}{36}+\dfrac{4(y+3)^2}{36}=\dfrac{36}{36}$

$\dfrac{(x-1)^2}{4}+\dfrac{(y+3)^2}{9}=1$

$a^2=9,\ a=3$

$b^2=4,\ b=2$

center: $(1, -3)$

$c^2=a^2-b^2=9-4=5$

$c=\sqrt{5}$

The foci are at $(1, -3+\sqrt{5})$ and $(1, -3-\sqrt{5})$.

43. $9x^2 + 25y^2 - 36x + 50y - 164 = 0$

$(9x^2 - 36x) + (25y^2 + 50y) = 164$

$9(x^2 - 4x) + 25(y^2 + 2y) = 164$

$9(x^2 - 4x + 4) + 25(y^2 + 2y + 1)$
$= 164 + 36 + 25$

$9(x-2)^2 + 25(y+1)^2 = 225$

$$\frac{9(x-2)^2}{225} + \frac{25(y+1)^2}{225} = \frac{225}{225}$$

$$\frac{(x-2)^2}{25} + \frac{(y+1)^2}{9} = 1;$$

center: $(2, -1)$
$a^2 = 25, a = 5$
$b^2 = 9, b = 3$
$c^2 = a^2 - b^2 = 25 - 9 = 16$
$c = 4$
The foci are at $(-2, -1)$ and $(6, -1)$.

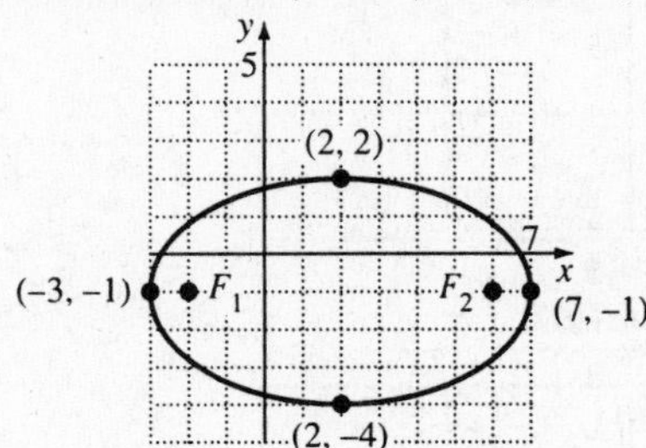

45. $9x^2 + 16y^2 - 18x + 64y - 71 = 0$

$(9x^2 - 18x) + (16y^2 + 64y) = 71$

$9(x^2 - 2x) + 16(y^2 + 4y) = 71$

$9(x^2 - 2x + 1) + 16(y^2 + 4y + 4)$
$= 71 + 9 + 64$

$9(x-1)^2 + 16(y+2)^2 = 144$

$$\frac{9(x-1)^2}{144} + \frac{16(y+2)^2}{144} = \frac{144}{144}$$

$$\frac{(x-1)^2}{16} + \frac{(y+2)^2}{9} = 1;$$

center: $(1, -2)$
$a^2 = 16, a = 4$
$b^2 = 9, b = 3$
$c^2 = a^2 - b^2 = 16 - 9 = 7$
$c = \sqrt{7}$

The foci are at
$(1 - \sqrt{7}, -2)$ and $(1 + \sqrt{7}, -2)$.

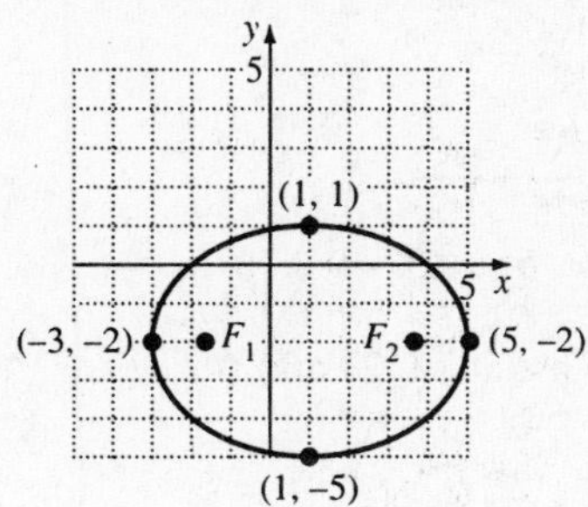

47. $4x^2 + y^2 + 16x - 6y - 39 = 0$

$(4x^2 + 16x) + (y^2 - 6y) = 39$

$4(x^2 + 4x) + (y^2 - 6y) = 39$

$4(x^2 + 4x + 4) + (y^2 - 6y + 9) = 39 + 16 + 9$

$4(x+2)^2 + (y-3)^2 = 64$

$$\frac{4(x+2)^2}{64} + \frac{(y-3)^2}{64} = \frac{64}{64}$$

$$\frac{(x+2)^2}{16} + \frac{(y-3)^2}{64} = 1;$$

center: $(-2, 3)$
$a^2 = 64, a = 8$
$b^2 = 16, b = 4$
$c^2 = a^2 - b^2 = 64 - 16 = 48$
$c = \sqrt{48} = 4\sqrt{3}$
The foci are at $(-2, 3 + 4\sqrt{3})$ and
$(-2, 3 - 4\sqrt{3})$.

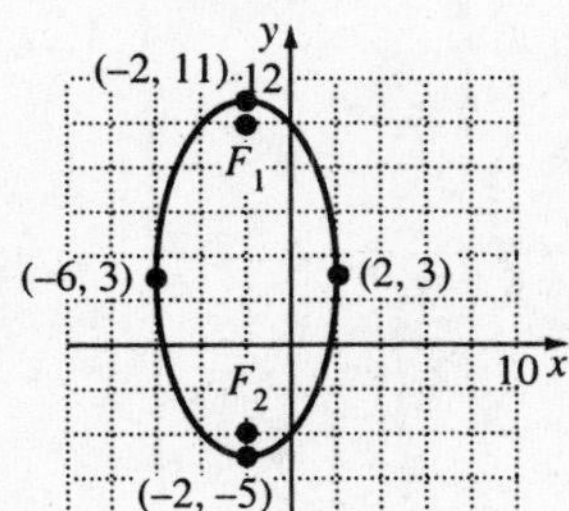

49. $a = 15, b = 10$

$$\frac{x^2}{225} + \frac{y^2}{100} = 1$$

Let $x = 4$

$$\frac{4^2}{225} + \frac{y^2}{100} = 1$$

$$900\left(\frac{16}{225} + \frac{y^2}{100}\right) = 900(1)$$

$$64 + 9y^2 = 900$$

$$9y^2 = 836$$

$$y = \sqrt{\frac{836}{9}} \approx 9.64$$

Yes, the truck only needs 7 feet so it will clear.

51. a. $a = 48, a^2 = 2304$
$b = 23, b^2 = 529$

$$\frac{x^2}{2304} + \frac{y^2}{529} = 1$$

b. $c^2 = a^2 - b^2 = 2304 - 529 = 1775$

$c = \sqrt{1775} \approx 42.13$

He situated his desk about 42 feet from the center of the ellipse, along the major axis.

53.–57. Answers may vary.

59. Exercise 1

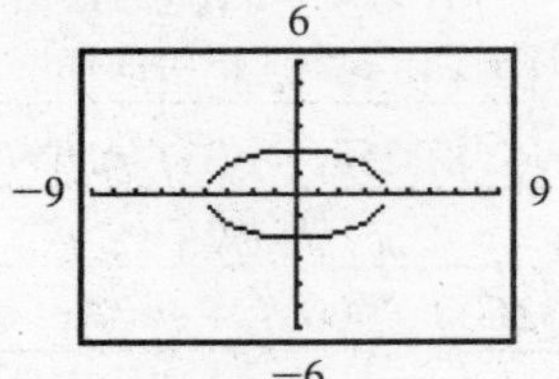

Exercise 3

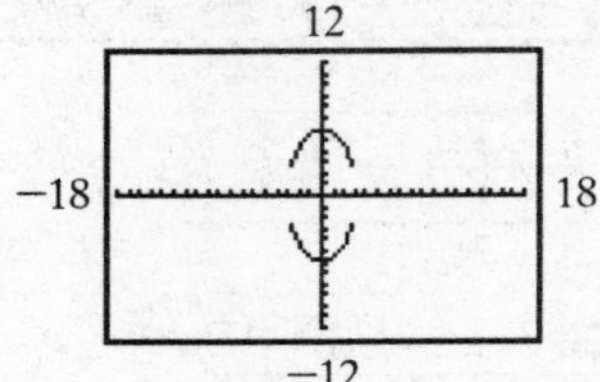

Exercise 5

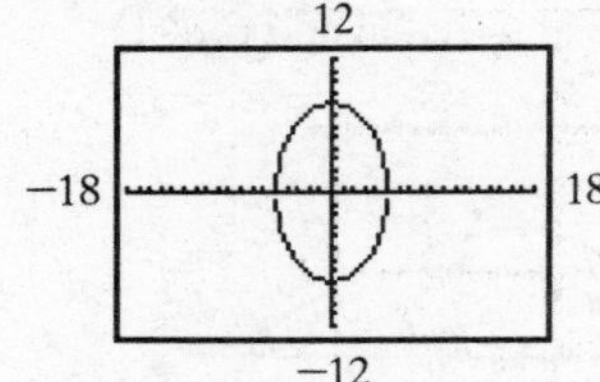

Exercise 7

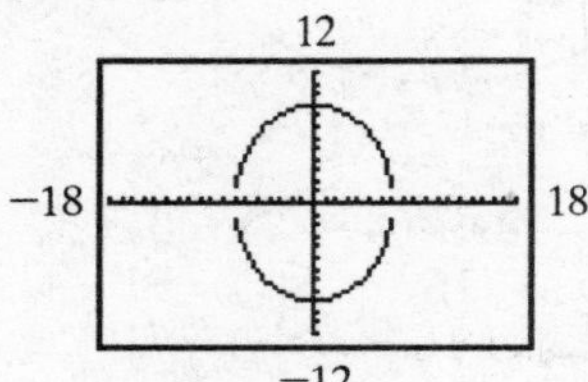

Exercise 9

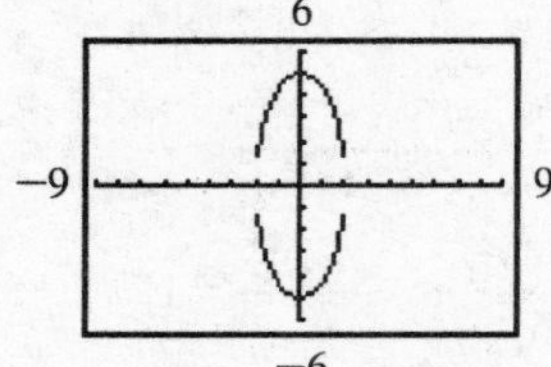

61. Exercise 43

$$25y^2 + 50y + 9x^2 - 36x - 164 = 0$$

$$y = \frac{-50 \pm \sqrt{(50)^2 - 4(25)(9x^2 - 36x - 164)}}{2(25)}$$

$$= \frac{-50 \pm \sqrt{2500 - 900x^2 + 3600x - 16,400}}{50}$$

$$= \frac{-50 \pm \sqrt{-900x^2 + 3600x + 18,900}}{50}$$

$$= \frac{-50 \pm \sqrt{900\left(-x^2 + 2x + 21\right)}}{50}$$

$$= \frac{-50 \pm 30\sqrt{-x^2 + 4x + 21}}{50}$$

$$y = \frac{-5 \pm 3\sqrt{-x^2 + 4x + 21}}{5};$$

63. $a = 6,\ a^2 = 36$

$$\frac{x^2}{b^2} + \frac{y^2}{36} = 1$$

When $x = 2$ and $y = -4$,

$$\frac{2^2}{b^2} + \frac{(-4)^2}{36} = 1$$

$$\frac{4}{b^2} + \frac{16}{36} = 1$$

$$\frac{4}{b^2} = \frac{5}{9}$$

$$36 = 5b^2$$

$$b^2 = \frac{36}{5}$$

$$\frac{x^2}{\frac{36}{5}} + \frac{y^2}{36} = 1$$

65. The large circle has radius 5 with center (0, 0). Its equation is $x^2 + y^2 = 25$. The small circle has radius 3 with center (0, 0). Its equation is $x^2 + y^2 = 9$.

Section 7.2

Check Point Exercises

1. a. $a^2 = 25,\ a = 5$

vertices: (–5, 0) and (5, 0)

$b^2 = 16$

$c^2 = a^2 + b^2 = 25 + 16 = 41$

$c = \sqrt{41}$

The foci are at $(\sqrt{41}, 0)$ and $(-\sqrt{41}, 0)$.

b. $a^2 = 25,\ a = 5$

vertices: (0, 5) and (0, –5)

$b^2 = 16$

$c^2 = a^2 + b^2 = 25 + 16 = 41$

$c = \sqrt{41}$

The foci are at $(0, \sqrt{41})$ and $(0, -\sqrt{41})$.

2. $a = 3,\ c = 5$

$b^2 = c^2 - a^2 = 25 - 9 = 16$

$$\frac{y^2}{9} - \frac{x^2}{16} = 1$$

3. $\frac{x^2}{36} - \frac{y^2}{9} = 1$

$a^2 = 36,\ a = 6$

The vertices are (6, 0) and (-6, 0).

$b^2 = 9,\ b = 3$

asymptotes: $y = \pm\frac{b}{a}x = \pm\frac{3}{6}x = \pm\frac{1}{2}x$

$c^2 = a^2 + b^2 = 36 + 9 = 45$

$c = \sqrt{45} = 3\sqrt{5}$

The foci are at $(-3\sqrt{5}, 0)$ and $(3\sqrt{5}, 0)$.

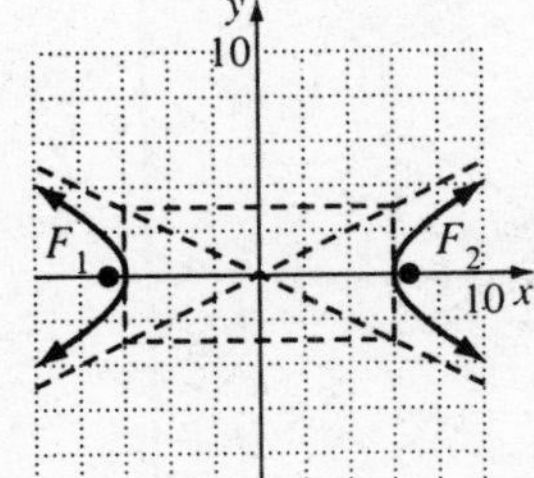

4. $y^2 - 4x^2 = 4$

$\frac{y^2}{4} - \frac{4x^2}{4} = \frac{4}{4}$

$\frac{y^2}{4} - x^2 = 1$

$a^2 = 4,\ a = 2$

The vertices are (0, 2) and (0, –2).

$b^2 = 1,\ b = 1$

asymptotes: $y = \pm\frac{a}{b}x = \pm 2x$

$c^2 = a^2 + b^2 = 4 + 1 = 5$

$c = \sqrt{5}$

The foci are at $(0, \sqrt{5})$ and $(0, -\sqrt{5})$.

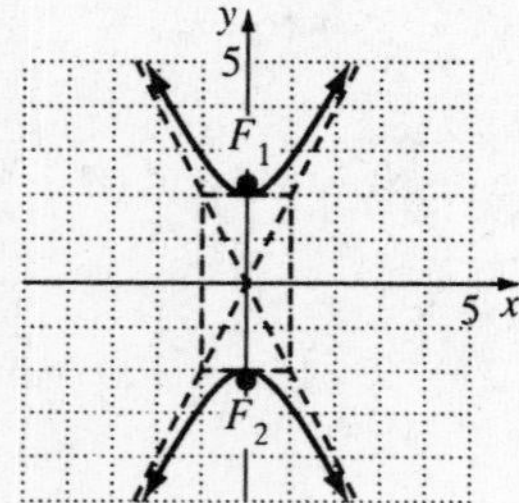

5. $\frac{(x-3)^2}{4} - \frac{(y-1)^2}{1} = 1$

center at (3, 1)

$a^2 = 4,\ a = 2$

$b^2 = 1,\ b = 1$

The vertices are (1, 1) and (5, 1).

asymptotes: $y - 1 = \pm\frac{1}{2}(x-3)$

$c^2 = a^2 + b^2 = 4 + 1 = 5$

$c = \sqrt{5}$

The foci are at $(3-\sqrt{5}, 1)$ and $(3+\sqrt{5}, 1)$.

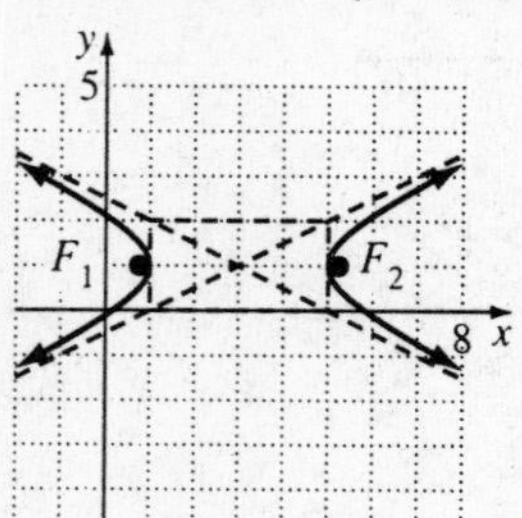

6. $c = 5280$

$2a = 3300, a = 1650$

$b^2 = c^2 - a^2 = 5280^2 - 1650^2 = 25,155,900$

The explosion occurred somewhere at the right branch of the hyperbola given by

$\frac{x^2}{2,722,500} - \frac{y^2}{25,155,900} = 1.$

Exercise Set 7.2

1. $a^2 = 4$, a = 2

The vertices are (2, 0) and (–2, 0).

$b^2 = 1$

$c^2 = a^2 + b^2 = 4 + 1 = 5$

$c = \sqrt{5}$

The foci are located at $(\sqrt{5}, 0)$ and $(-\sqrt{5}, 0)$.

graph (b)

3. $a^2 = 4,\ a = 2$

The vertices are (0, 2) and (0, –2).

$b^2 = 1$

$c^2 = a^2 + b^2 = 4 + 1 = 5$

$c = \sqrt{5}$

The foci are located at $(0, \sqrt{5})$ and $(0, -\sqrt{5})$.

graph (a)

5. $a = 1, c = 3$

$b^2 = c^2 - a^2 = 9 - 1 = 8$

$y^2 - \frac{x^2}{8} = 1$

7. $a = 3, c = 4$

$b^2 = c^2 - a^2 = 16 - 9 = 7$

$\frac{x^2}{9} - \frac{y^2}{7} = 1$

9. $\frac{x^2}{9} - \frac{y^2}{25} = 1$
$a^2 = 9, a = 3$
$b^2 = 25, b = 5$
vertices: (3, 0) and (–3, 0)
asymptotes: $y = \pm\frac{b}{a}x = \pm\frac{5}{3}x$
$c^2 = a^2 + b^2 = 9 + 25 = 34$
$c = \sqrt{34}$ on x-axis
The foci are at $(\sqrt{34}, 0)$ and $(-\sqrt{34}, 0)$.

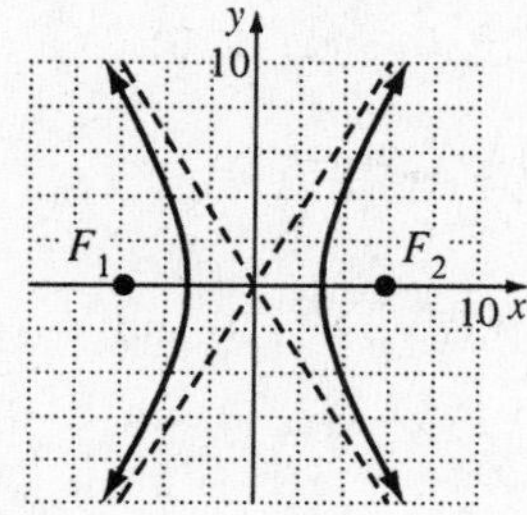

11. $\frac{x^2}{100} - \frac{y^2}{64} = 1$
$a^2 = 100, a = 10$
$b^2 = 64, b = 8$
vertices: (10, 0) and (–10, 0)
asymptotes: $y = \pm\frac{b}{a}x = \pm\frac{8}{10}x$
or $y = \pm\frac{4}{5}x$
$c^2 = a^2 + b^2 = 100 + 64 = 164$
$c = \sqrt{164} = 2\sqrt{41}$ on x-axis
The foci are at $(2\sqrt{41}, 0)$ and $(-2\sqrt{41}, 0)$.

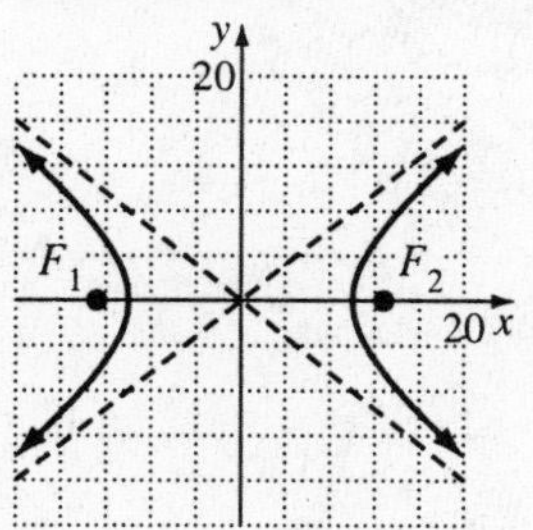

13. $\frac{y^2}{16} - \frac{x^2}{36} = 1$
$a^2 = 16, a = 4$
$b^2 = 36, b = 6$
vertices: (0, 4) and (0, –4)
asymptotes: $y = \pm\frac{a}{b}x = \pm\frac{4}{6}x$
or $y = \pm\frac{2}{3}x$
$c^2 = a^2 + b^2 = 16 + 36 = 52$
$c = \sqrt{52} = 2\sqrt{13}$ on y-axis
The foci are at $(0, 2\sqrt{13})$ and $(0, -2\sqrt{13})$.

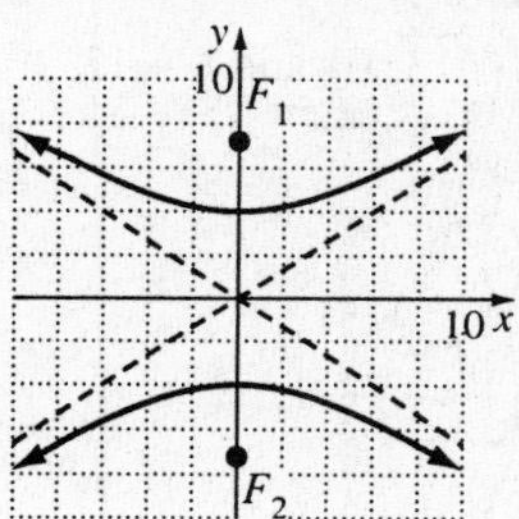

15. $\frac{y^2}{36} - \frac{x^2}{25} = 1$
$a^2 = 36, a = 6$
$b^2 = 25, b = 5$
vertices: (0, 6) and (0, –6)
asymptotes: $y = \pm\frac{a}{b}x = \pm\frac{6}{5}x$
$c^2 = a^2 + b^2 = 36 + 25 = 61$
$c = \sqrt{61}$ on y-axis
The foci are at $(0, \sqrt{61})$ and $(0, -\sqrt{61})$.

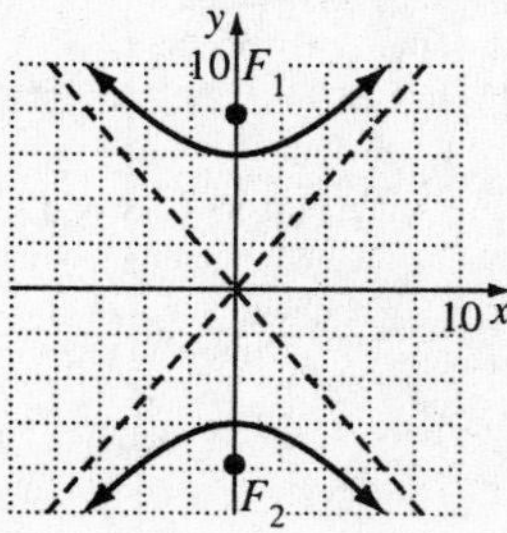

17. $9x^2 - 4y^2 = 36$

$\frac{9x^2}{36} - \frac{4y^2}{36} = \frac{36}{36}$

$\frac{x^2}{4} - \frac{y^2}{9} = 1$

$a^2 = 4,\ a = 2$

$b^2 = 9,\ b = 3$

vertices: (2, 0) and (–2, 0)

asymptotes: $y = \pm\frac{b}{a}x = \pm\frac{3}{2}x$

$c^2 = a^2 + b^2 = 4 + 9 = 13$

$c = \sqrt{13}$ on x-axis

The foci are at $(\sqrt{13},\ 0)$ and $(-\sqrt{13},\ 0)$.

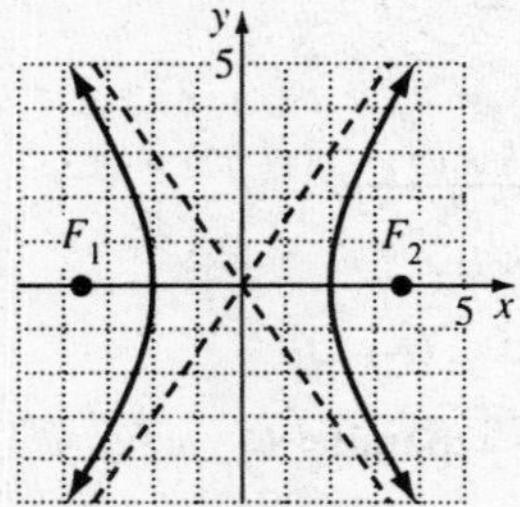

19. $9y^2 - 25x^2 = 225$

$\frac{9y^2}{225} - \frac{25x^2}{225} = \frac{225}{225}$

$\frac{y^2}{25} - \frac{x^2}{9} = 1$

$a^2 = 25,\ a = 5$

$b^2 = 9,\ b = 3$

vertices: (0, 5) and (0, –5)

asymptotes: $y = \pm\frac{a}{b}x = \pm\frac{5}{3}x$

$c^2 = a^2 + b^2 = 25 + 9 = 34$

$c = \sqrt{34}$ on y-axis

The foci are at $(0,\ \sqrt{34})$ and $(0,\ -\sqrt{34})$.

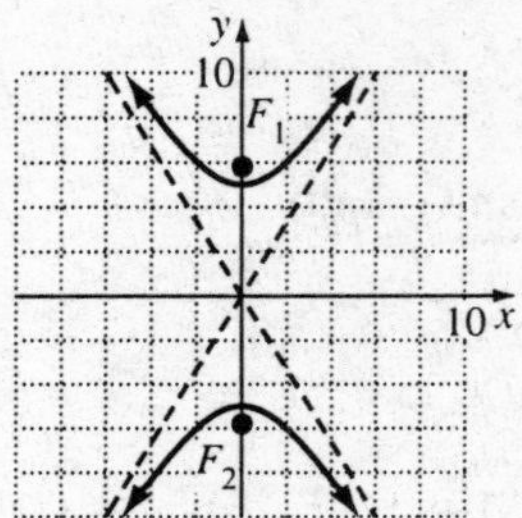

21. $4x^2 = 4 + y^2$

$4x^2 - y^2 = 4$

$\frac{4x^2}{4} - \frac{y^2}{4} = \frac{4}{4}$

$x^2 - \frac{y^2}{4} = 1$

$a^2 = 1,\ a = 1$

$b^2 = 4,\ b = 2$

vertices: (1, 0) and (–1, 0)

asymptotes: $y = \pm\frac{b}{a}x = \pm 2x$

$c^2 = a^2 + b^2 = 1 + 4 = 5$

$c = \sqrt{5}$ on x-axis

The foci are at $(\sqrt{5},\ 0)$ and $(-\sqrt{5},\ 0)$.

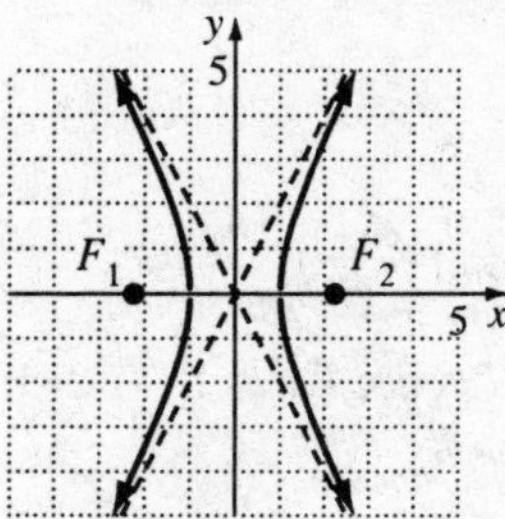

23. $a = 3,\ b = 5$

$\frac{x^2}{9} - \frac{y^2}{25} = 1$

25. $a = 2, b = 3$

$$\frac{y^2}{4} - \frac{x^2}{9} = 1$$

27. $$\frac{(x+4)^2}{9} - \frac{(y+3)^2}{16} = 1$$

center: $(-4, -3)$
$a^2 = 1, a = 3$
$b^2 = 16, b = 4$
vertices: $(-7, -3)$ and $(-1, -3)$
asymptotes: $y + 3 = \pm\frac{4}{3}(x+4)$
$c^2 = a^2 + b^2 = 9 + 16 = 25$
$c = \pm 5$ parallel to x-axis
The foci are at $(-9, -3)$ and $(1, -3)$.

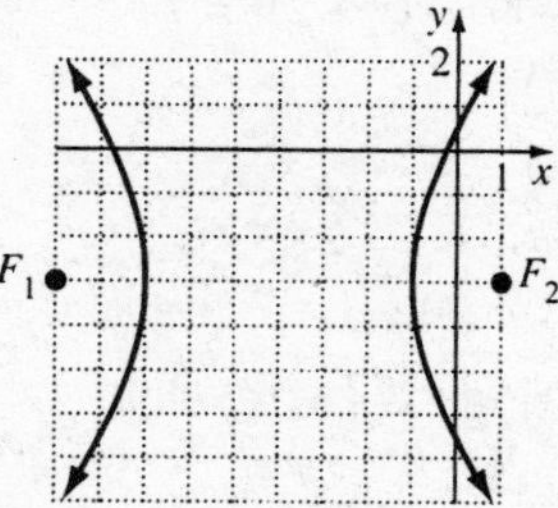

29. $$\frac{(x+3)^2}{25} - \frac{y^2}{16} = 1$$

center: $(-3, 0)$
$a^2 = 25, a = 5$
$b^2 = 16, b = 4$
vertices: $(2, 0)$ and $(-8, 0)$
asymptotes: $y = \pm\frac{4}{5}(x+3)$
$c^2 = a^2 + b^2 = 25 + 16 = 41$
$c = \sqrt{41}$

The foci are at $(-3+\sqrt{41}, 0)$ and $(-3-\sqrt{41}, 0)$.

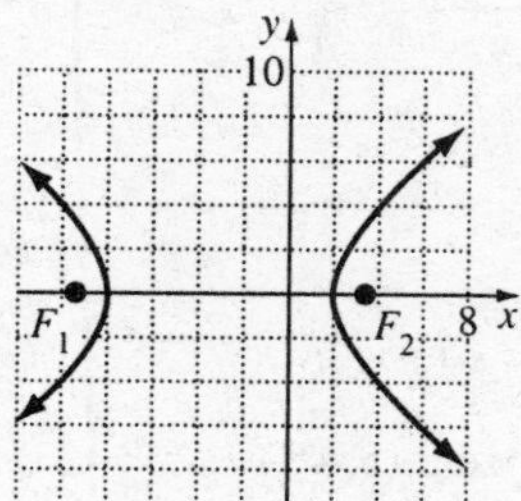

31. $$\frac{(y+2)^2}{4} - \frac{(x-1)^2}{16} = 1$$

center: $(1, -2)$
$a^2 = 4, a = 2$
$b^2 = 16, b = 4$
vertices: $(1, 0)$ and $(1, -4)$
asymptotes: $y + 2 = \pm\frac{1}{2}(x-1)$
$c^2 = a^2 + b^2 = 4 + 16 = 20$
$c = \sqrt{20} = 2\sqrt{5}$ parallel to y-axis
The foci are at $(1, -2+2\sqrt{5})$ and $(1, -2-2\sqrt{5})$.

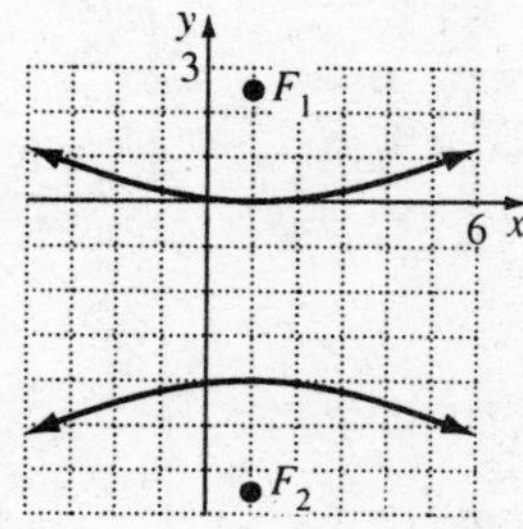

33. $(x-3)^2 - 4(y+3)^2 = 4$

$\frac{(x-3)^2}{4} - \frac{4(y+3)^2}{4} = \frac{4}{4}$

$\frac{(x-3)^2}{4} - (y-3)^2 = 1$

center: (3, –3)

$a^2 = 4, a = 2$

$b^2 = 1, b = 1$

vertices: (1, –3) and (5, –3)

asymptotes: $y+3 = \pm\frac{1}{2}(x-3)$

$c^2 = a^2 + b^2 = 4 + 1 = 5$

$c = \sqrt{5}$

The foci are at $(3+\sqrt{5}, -3)$ and $(3-\sqrt{5}, -3)$.

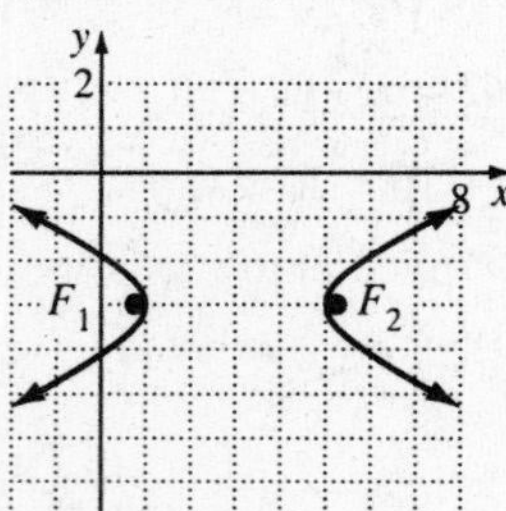

35. $(x-1)^2 - (y-2)^2 = 4$

$\frac{(x-1)^2}{4} - \frac{(y-2)^2}{4} = 1$

center: (1, 2)

$a^2 = 4, a = 2$

$b^2 = 4, b = 2$

vertices: (–1, 2) and (3, 2)

asymptotes: $y - 2 = \pm(x-1)$

$c^2 = a^2 + b^2 = 4 + 4 = 8$

$c = \sqrt{8} = 2\sqrt{2}$ parallel to *y*-axis

The foci are at $(1-2\sqrt{2}, 2)$ and $(1+2\sqrt{2}, 2)$.

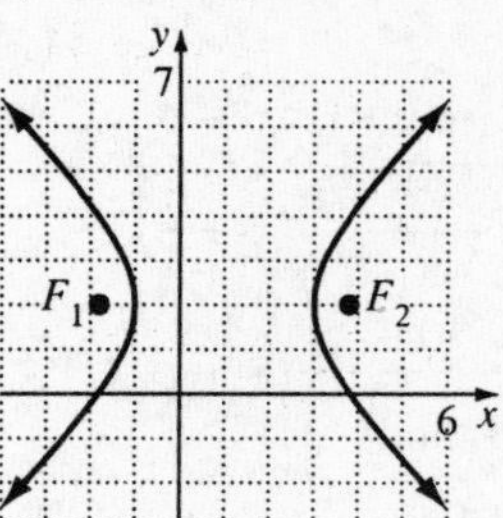

37. $x^2 - y^2 - 2x - 4y - 4 = 0$

$(x^2 - 2x) - (y^2 + 4y) = 4$

$(x^2 - 2x + 1) - (y^2 + 4y + 4) = 4 + 1 - 4$

$(x-1)^2 - (y+2)^2 = 1$

center: (1, –2)

$a^2 = 1, a = 1$

$b^2 = 1, b = 1$

$c^2 = a^2 + b^2 = 1 + 1 = 2$

$c = \sqrt{2}$

The foci are at $(1+\sqrt{2}, -2)$ and $(1-\sqrt{2}, -2)$.

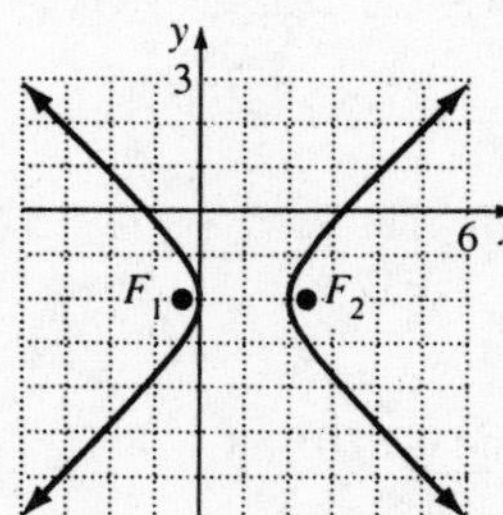

39. $16x^2 - y^2 + 64x - 2y + 67 = 0$

$$(16x^2 + 64x) - (y^2 + 2y) = -67$$

$$16(x^2 + 4x + 4) - (y^2 + 2y + 1) = -67 + 64 - 1$$

$$16(x+2)^2 - (y+1)^2 = -4$$

$$\frac{16(x+2)^2}{-4} - \frac{(y+1)^2}{-4} = \frac{-4}{-4}$$

$$\frac{(y+1)^2}{4} - \frac{(x+2)^2}{\frac{1}{4}} = 1;$$

center: $(-2, -1)$

$a^2 = 4, a = 2$

$b^2 = \frac{1}{4}, b = \frac{1}{2}$

$c^2 = a^2 + b^2 = 4 + \frac{1}{4} = \frac{17}{4}$

$c = \sqrt{\frac{17}{4}}$

The foci are at $\left(-2, -1 + \sqrt{\frac{17}{4}}\right)$ and $\left(-2, -1 - \sqrt{\frac{17}{4}}\right)$.

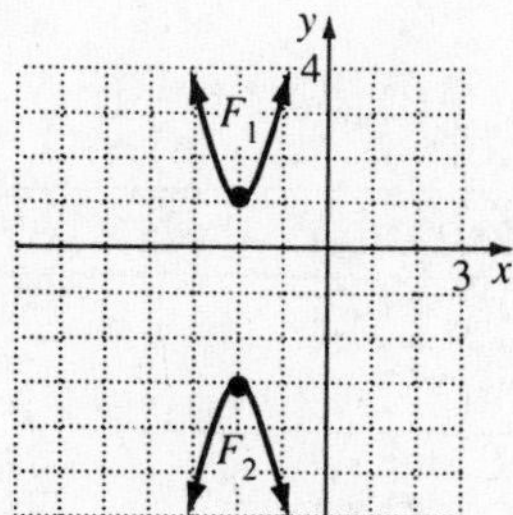

41. $4x^2 - 9y^2 - 16x + 54y - 101 = 0$

$$(4x^2 - 16x) - (9y^2 - 54y) = 101$$

$$4(x^2 - 4x + 4) - 9(y^2 - 6y + 9) = 101 + 16 - 81$$

$$4(x-2)^2 - 9(y-3)^2 = 36$$

$$\frac{(x-2)^2}{9} - \frac{(y-3)^2}{4} = 1;$$

center: $(2, 3)$

$a^2 = 9, a = 3$

$b^2 = 4, b = 2$

$c^2 = a^2 + b^2 = 9 + 4 = 13$

$c = \sqrt{13}$

The foci are at $(2 + \sqrt{13}, 3)$ and $(2 - \sqrt{13}, 3)$.

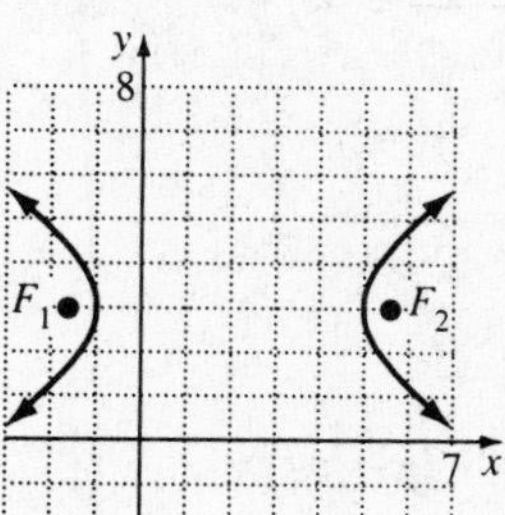

43. $4x^2 - 25y^2 - 32x + 164 = 0$

$$(4x^2 - 32x) - 25y^2 = -164$$

$$4(x^2 - 8x + 16) - 25y^2 = -164 + 64$$

$$4(x-4)^2 - 25y^2 = -100$$

$$\frac{4(x-4)^2}{-100} - \frac{25y^2}{-100} = \frac{-100}{-100}$$

$$\frac{y^2}{4} - \frac{(x-4)^2}{25} = 1;$$

center: $(4, 0)$

$a^2 = 4, a = 2$

$b^2 = 25, b = 5$

$c^2 = a^2 + b^2 = 4 + 25 = 29$

$c = \sqrt{29}$

The foci are at $(4, \sqrt{29})$ and $(4, -\sqrt{29})$.

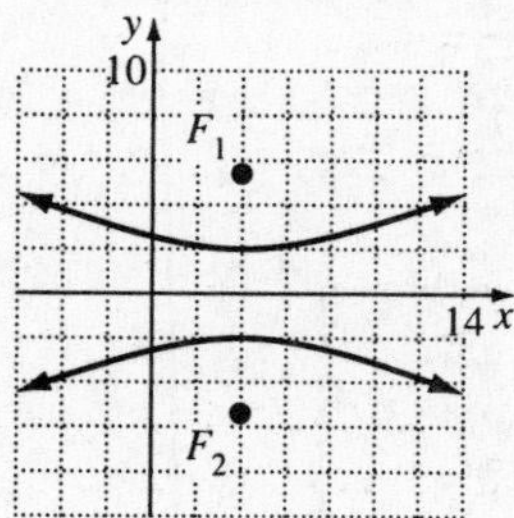

45. $|d_2 - d_1| = 2a = (2 \text{ s})(1100 \text{ ft / s}) = 2200 \text{ ft}$
$a = 1100 \text{ ft}$
$2c = 5280 \text{ ft}, c = 2640 \text{ ft}$
$b^2 = c^2 - a^2 = (2640)^2 - (1100)^2$
$= 5{,}759{,}600$

$$\frac{x^2}{(1100)^2} - \frac{y^2}{5{,}759{,}600} = 1$$

$$\frac{x^2}{1{,}210{,}000} - \frac{y^2}{5{,}759{,}600} = 1$$

If M_1 is located 2640 feet to the right of the origin on the x-axis, the explosion is located on the right branch of the hyperbola given by the equation above.

47.
$$625y^2 - 400x^2 = 250{,}000$$

$$\frac{625y^2}{250{,}000} - \frac{400x^2}{250{,}000} = \frac{250{,}000}{250{,}000}$$

$$\frac{y^2}{400} - \frac{x^2}{625} = 1$$

$a^2 = 400, a = \sqrt{400} = 20$
$2a = 40$
The houses are 40 yards apart at their closest point.

49.–55. Answers may vary.

57. Exercise 27

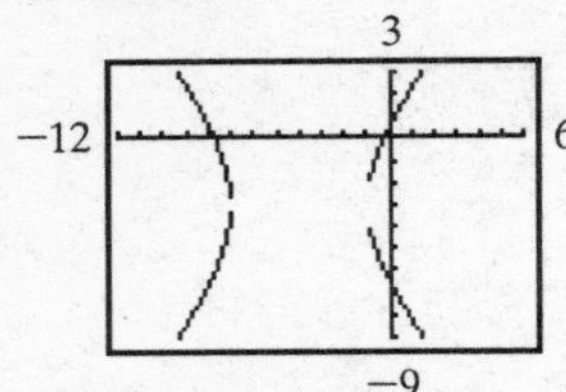

Exercise 29

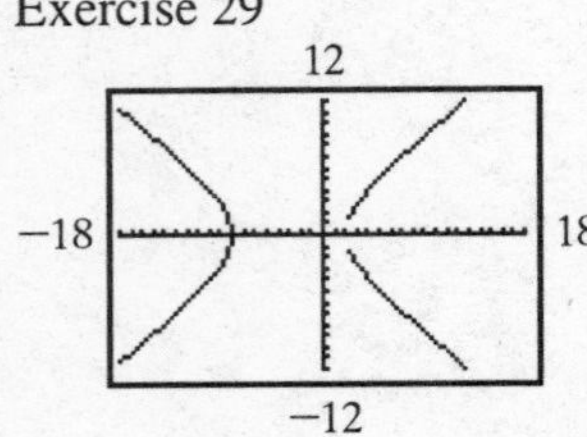

Exercise 31

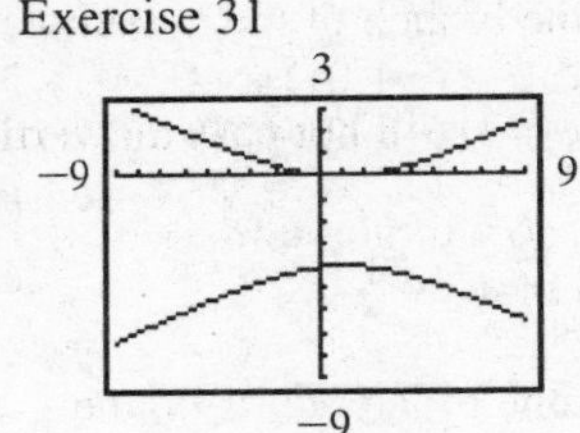

59. $\frac{x^2}{4} - \frac{y^2}{9} = 0$

$y^2 = \frac{9}{4}x^2$

$y = \pm\frac{3}{2}x$

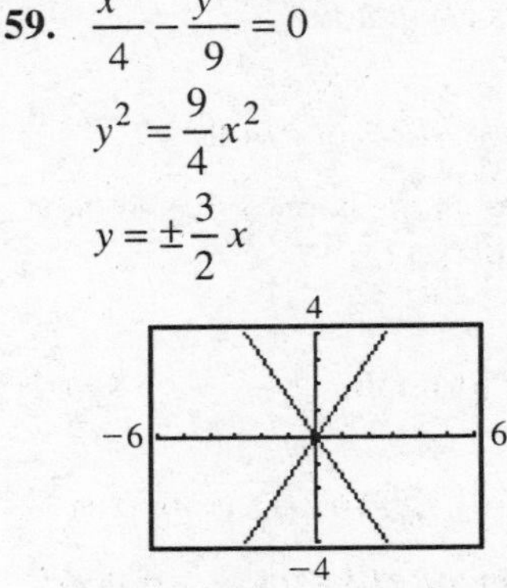

No. In general, the graph is two intersecting lines.

61. $4x^2 - 6xy + 2y^2 - 3x + 10y - 6 = 0$
$2y^2 + (10 - 6x)y + (4x^2 - 3x - 6) = 0$

$$y = \frac{6x - 10 \pm \sqrt{(10 - 6x)^2 - 8(4x^2 - 3x - 6)}}{4}$$

$$y = \frac{6x - 10 \pm \sqrt{4(x^2 - 24x + 37)}}{4}$$

$$y = \frac{3x - 5 \pm \sqrt{x^2 - 24x + 37}}{2}$$

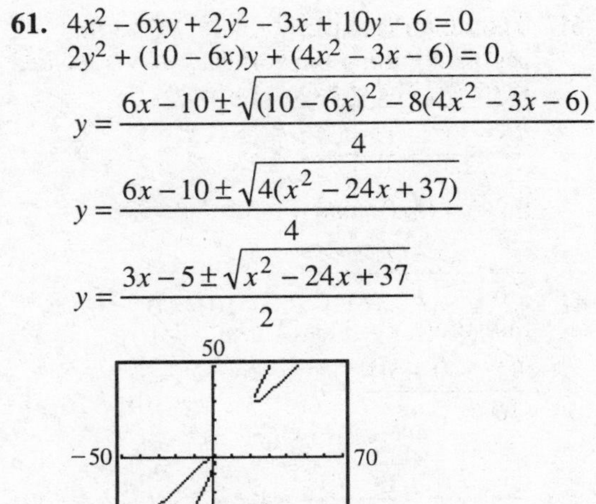

The xy term rotates the hyperbola. Separation of terms into ones containing only x or only y would be impossible.

63. a. False. One branch of the hyperbola $\frac{x^2}{a^2} - \frac{y^2}{b^2} = 1$ will not pass the vertical line test, so will not define y as a function of x.

b. False. None of the points on the asymptotes satisfy the hyperbola's equation, since the hyperbola never touches its asymptotes.

c. True. $y = -\frac{2}{3}x$ is one of the asymptotes of the hyperbola and they will not intersect.

d. False. For example, $\frac{x^2}{4} - \frac{y^2}{4} = 1$ and $\frac{y^2}{4} - \frac{x^2}{4} = 1$ each have asymptotes $y = \pm x$, but are different hyperbolas.

(c) is true.

65. The center is at the midpoint of the line segment joining the vertices, so it is located at (5, 0). The standard form is:

$$\frac{(y-k)^2}{a^2} - \frac{(x-h)^2}{b^2} = 1$$

$(h, k) = (5, 0)$, and $a = 6$, so $a^2 = 36$.

$$\frac{y^2}{36} - \frac{(x-5)^2}{b^2} = 1.$$

Substitute $x = 0$ and $y = 9$:

$$\frac{9^2}{36} - \frac{(0-5)^2}{b^2} = 1$$

$$-\frac{25}{b^2} = -\frac{5}{4}$$

$$-100 = -5b^2$$

$$b^2 = 20$$

Standard form: $\frac{y^2}{36} - \frac{(x-5)^2}{20} = 1$

Section 7.3

Check Point Exercises

1. $y^2 = 8x$
$4p = 8,\ p = 2$
foci: (2, 0)
directrix: $x = -2$

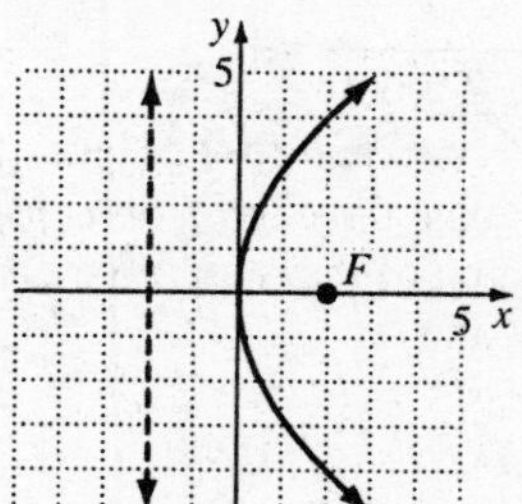

2. $x^2 = -12y$
$4p = -12,\ p = 3$
focus: (0, –3)
directrix: $y = 3$

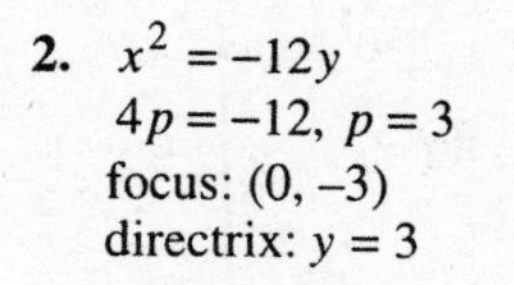

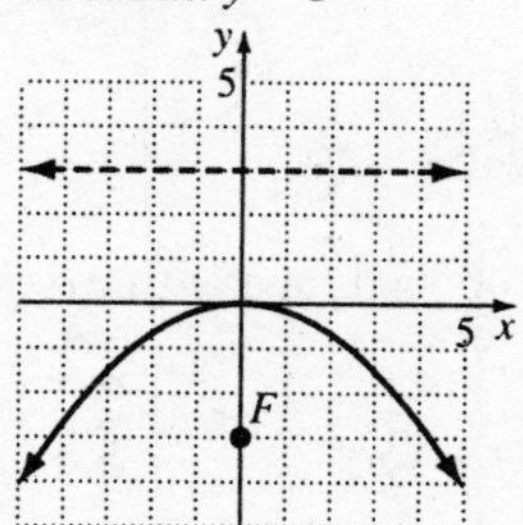

3. $p = 8$
$y^2 = 4 \cdot 8x$
$y^2 = 32x$

4. $(x-2)^2 = 4(y+1)$
$4p = 4,\ p = 1$
vertex: (2, –1)
focus: (2, 0)
directrix: $y = -2$

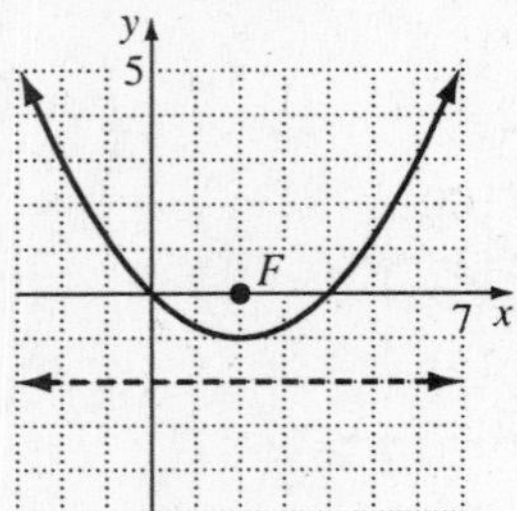

5. $y^2 + 2y + 4x - 7 = 0$
$y^2 + 2y = -4x + 7$
$y^2 + 2y + 1 = -4x + 7 + 1$
$(y+1)^2 = -4(x-2)$
$4p = -4,\ p = -1$
vertex: (2, –1)
focus: (1, –1)
directrix: $x = 3$

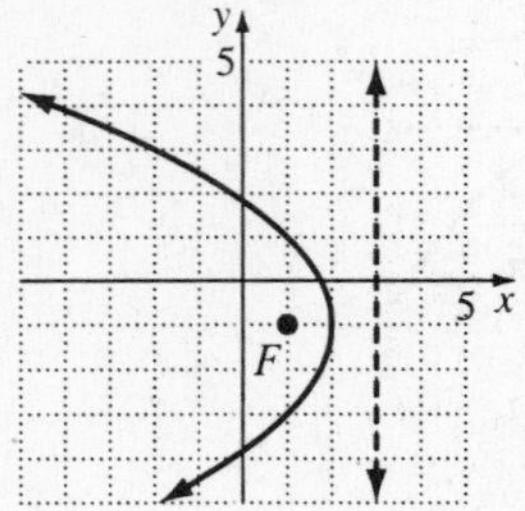

6. $x^2 = 4py$
Let $x = 3$ and $y = 4$.
$3^2 = 4p \cdot 4$
$9 = 16p$
$p = \frac{9}{16}$
$x^2 = \frac{9}{4}y$

The light should be placed at $\left(0, \frac{9}{16}\right)$ or $\frac{9}{16}$ inch above the vertex.

Exercise Set 7.3

1. $y^2 = 4x$
$4p = 4,\ p = 1$
vertex: (0, 0)
focus: (1, 0)
directrix: $x = -1$
graph (c)

3. $x^2 = -4y$
$4p = -4,\ p = -1$
vertex: (0, 0)
focus: (0, –1)
directrix: $y = 1$
graph (b)

5. $y^2 = 16x$
$4p = 16,\ p = 4$
vertex: (0, 0)
focus: (4, 0)
directrix: $x = -4$

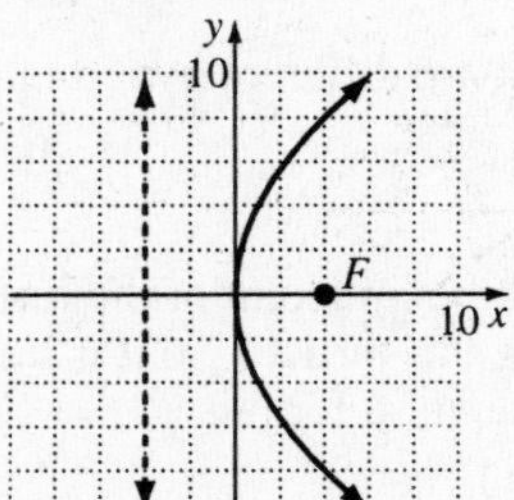

7. $y^2 = -8x$
$4p = -8,\ p = -2$
vertex: (0, 0)
focus: (–2, 0)
directrix: $x = 2$

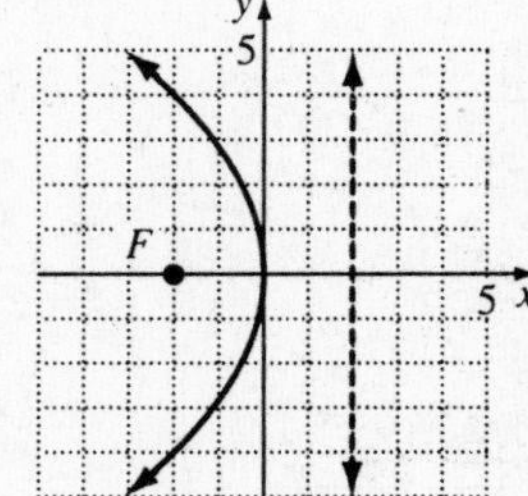

9. $x^2 = 12y$
$4p = 12, p = 3$
vertex: (0, 0)
focus: (0, 3)
directrix: $y = -3$

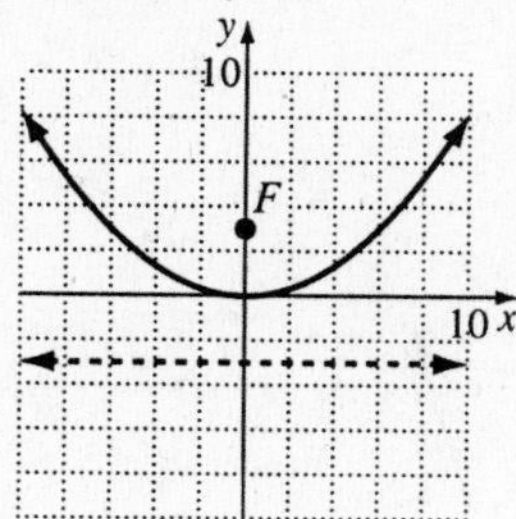

11. $x^2 = -16y$
$4p = -16, p = -4$
vertex: (0, 0)
focus: (0, –4)
directrix: $y = 4$

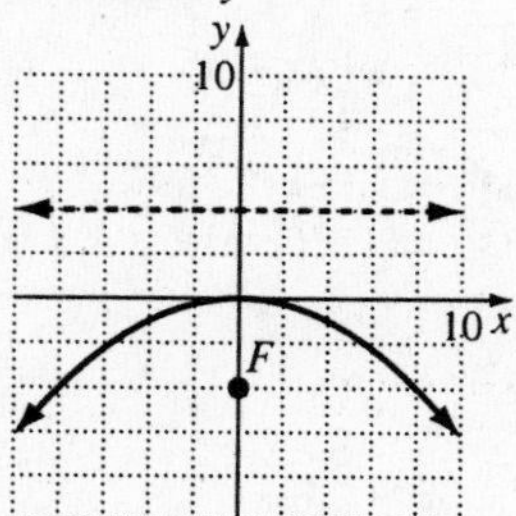

13. $y^2 - 6x = 0$
$y^2 = 6x$
$4p = 6, p = \frac{6}{4} = \frac{3}{2}$
vertex: (0, 0)
focus: $\left(\frac{3}{2}, 0\right)$
directrix: $x = -\frac{3}{2}$

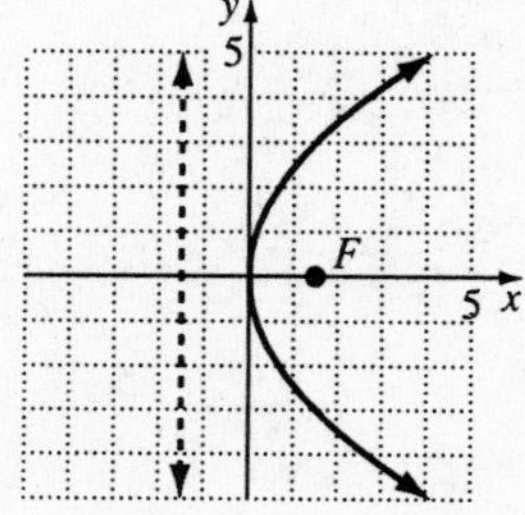

15. $p = 7, 4p = 28$
$y^2 = 28x$

17. $p = -5, 4p = -20$
$y^2 = -20x$

19. $p = 15, 4p = 60$
$x^2 = 60y$

21. $p = -25, 4p = -100$
$x^2 = -100y$

23. $(y-1)^2 = 4(x-1)$
$4p = 4, p = 1$
vertex: (1, 1)
focus: (2, 1)
directrix: $x = 0$
graph (c)

25. $(x+1)^2 = -4(y+1)$
$4p = -4, p = -1$
vertex: (–1, –1)
focus: (–1, –2)
directrix: $y = 0$
graph (d)

27. $(x-2)^2 = 8(y-1)$
$4p = 8, p = 2$
vertex: (2, 1)
focus: (2, 3)
directrix: $y = -1$

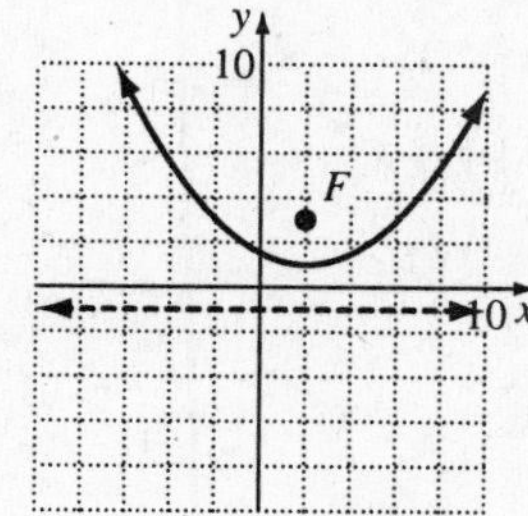

29. $(x+1)^2 = -8(y+1)$
$4p = -8, p = -2$
vertex: $(-1, -1)$
focus: $(-1, -3)$
directrix: $y = 1$

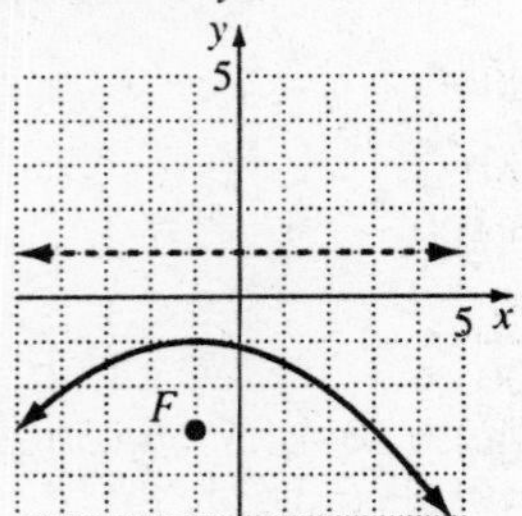

31. $(y+3)^2 = 12(x+1)$
$4p = 12, p = 3$
vertex: $(-1, -3)$
focus: $(2, -3)$
directrix: $x = -4$

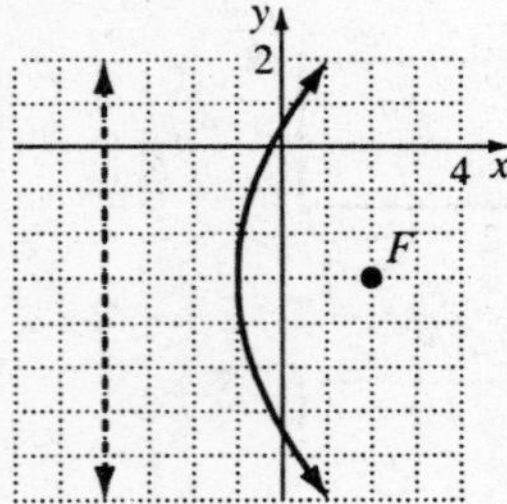

33. $(y+1)^2 = -8x$
$(y+1)^2 = -8(x-0)$
$4p = -8, p = -2$
vertex: $(0, -1)$
focus: $(-2, -1)$
directrix: $x = 2$

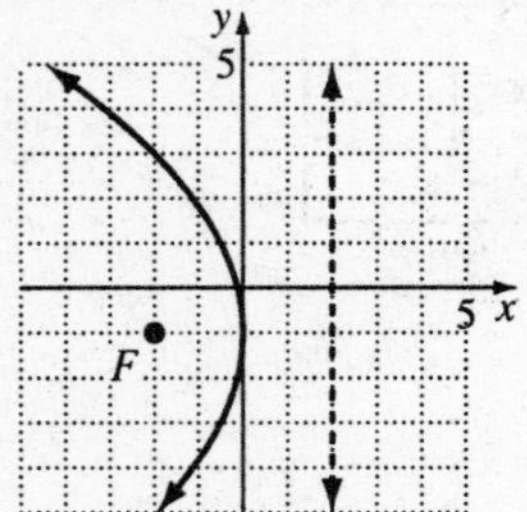

35. $x^2 - 2x - 4y + 9 = 0$
$x^2 - 2x = 4y - 9$
$x^2 - 2x + 1 = 4y - 9 + 1$
$(x-1)^2 = 4y - 8$
$(x-1)^2 = 4(y-2);$
$4p = 4, p = 1$
vertex: $(1, 2)$
focus: $(1, 3)$
directrix: $y = 1$

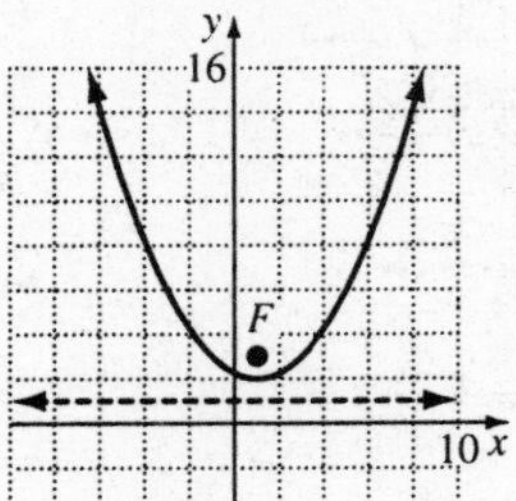

37. $y^2 - 2y + 12x - 35 = 0$
$y^2 - 2y = -12x + 35$
$y^2 - 2y + 1 = -12x + 35 + 1$
$(y-1)^2 = -12x + 36$
$(y-1)^2 = -12(x-3);$
$4p = -12, p = -3$
vertex: $(3, 1)$
focus: $(0, 1)$
directrix: $x = 6$

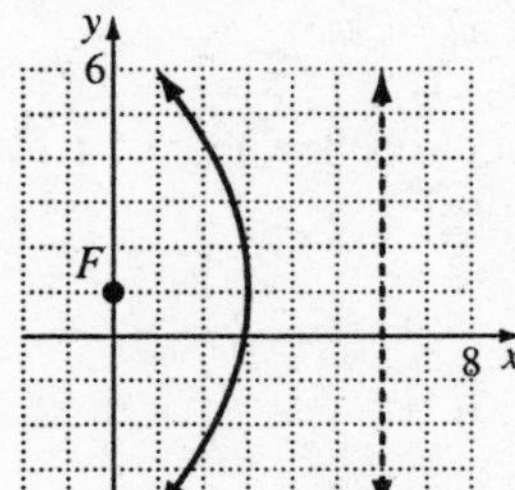

39. $x^2 + 6x - 4y + 1 = 0$
$x^2 + 6x = 4y - 1$
$x^2 + 6x + 9 = 4y - 1 + 9$
$(x+3)^2 = 4(y+2);$
$4p = 4, p = 1$
vertex: $(-3, -2)$
focus: $(-3, -1)$
directrix: $y = -3$

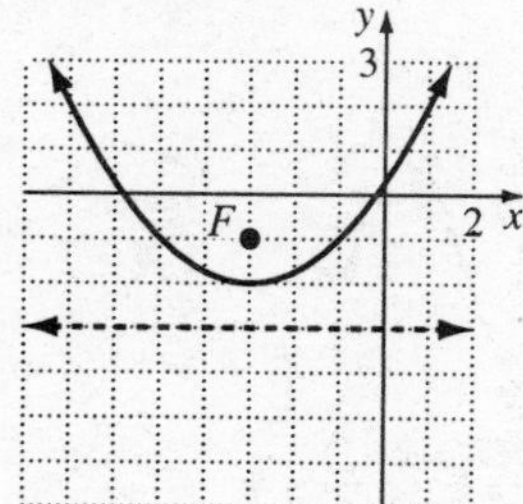

41. $x^2 = 4py$
$2^2 = 4p(1)$
$4 = 4p$
$p = 1$
The light bulb should be placed 1 inch above the vertex.

43. $x^2 = 4py$
$6^2 = 4p(2)$
$36 = 8p$
$p = \frac{36}{8} = \frac{9}{2} = 4.5$
The receiver should be located 4.5 feet from the base of the dish.

45. $x^2 = 4py$
$(640)^2 = 4p(160)$
$p = \frac{(640)^2}{640} = 640$
$x = 640 - 200 = 440$
$(440)^2 = 4(640)y$
$y = \frac{(440)^2}{4(640)} = 75.625$
The height is 75.625 meters.

47. $x^2 = 4py$
$\left(\frac{200}{2}\right)^2 = 4p(-50)$
$\frac{10,000}{-50} = 4p$
$4p = -200$
$x^2 = -200y$
$(30)^2 = -200y$
$y = \frac{900}{-200} = -4.5$
(height of bridge) = 50 – 4.5 = 45.5 feet.
Yes, the boat will clear the arch.

49.–53. Answers may vary.

55. Exercise 27

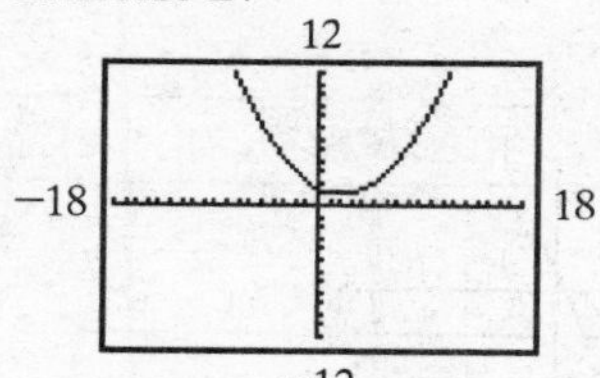

Exercise 29

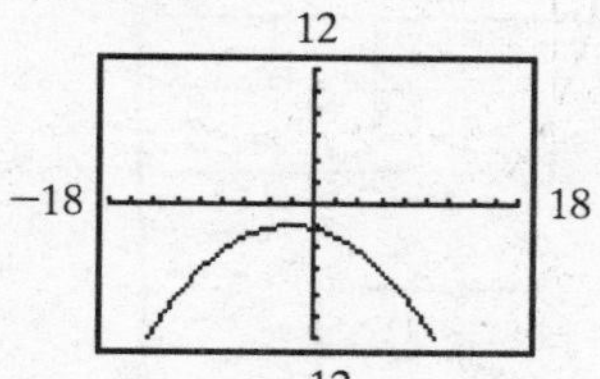

Exercise 31

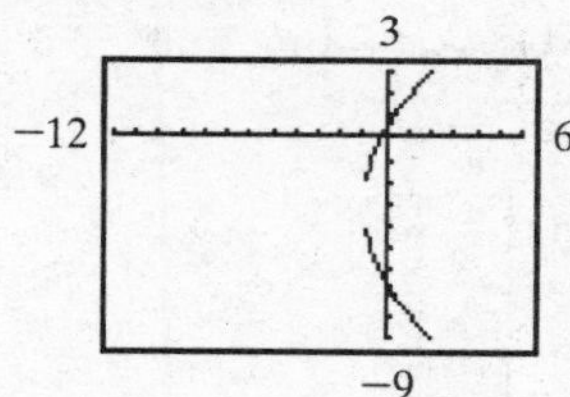

57. $y^2 + 10y - x + 25 = 0$

$y^2 + 10y + (-x + 25) = 0$

$y = \dfrac{-10 \pm \sqrt{10^2 - 4(-x+25)}}{2}$

$y = \dfrac{-10 \pm \sqrt{4x}}{2}$

$y = -5 \pm \sqrt{x}$

59. $x^2 + 2\sqrt{3}\,xy + 3y^2 + 8\sqrt{3}\,x - 8y + 32 = 0$

$3y^2 + (2\sqrt{3}\,x - 8)y + (x^2 + 8\sqrt{3}\,x + 32) = 0$

$y = \dfrac{-(2\sqrt{3}x - 8) \pm \sqrt{(2\sqrt{3}x - 8)^2 - 12(x^2 + 8\sqrt{3}x + 32)}}{6}$

$y = \dfrac{-2\sqrt{3}x + 8 \pm \sqrt{-128\sqrt{3}x - 320}}{6}$

$y = \dfrac{-2\sqrt{3}x + 8 \pm 8\sqrt{-2\sqrt{3}x - 5}}{6}$

$y = \dfrac{-\sqrt{3}x + 4 \pm 4\sqrt{-2\sqrt{3}x - 5}}{3}$

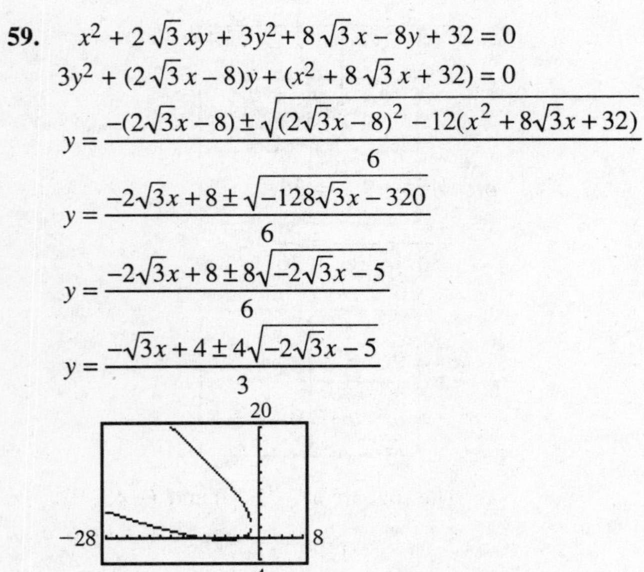

61. $p = 6,\ 4p = 24$

$x^2 = 24y$

$10^2 = 24y$

$y = \dfrac{100}{24} = \dfrac{25}{6}$

The dish should have a depth of $\dfrac{25}{6}$ feet.

Review Exercises

1. $\frac{x^2}{36}+\frac{y^2}{25}=1$
$a^2 = 36, a = 6$
$b^2 = 25, b = 5$
$c^2 = a^2 - b^2 = 36 - 25 = 11$
$c = \sqrt{11}$
The foci are at $(\sqrt{11}, 0)$ and $(-\sqrt{11}, 0)$.

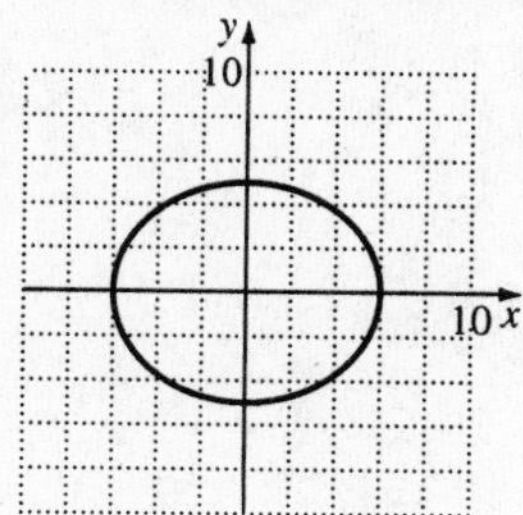

2. $\frac{y^2}{25}+\frac{x^2}{16}=1$
$a^2 = 25, a = 5$
$b^2 = 16, b = 4$
$c^2 = a^2 - b^2 = 25 - 16 = 9$
$c = 3$
The foci are at (0, 3) and (0, –3).

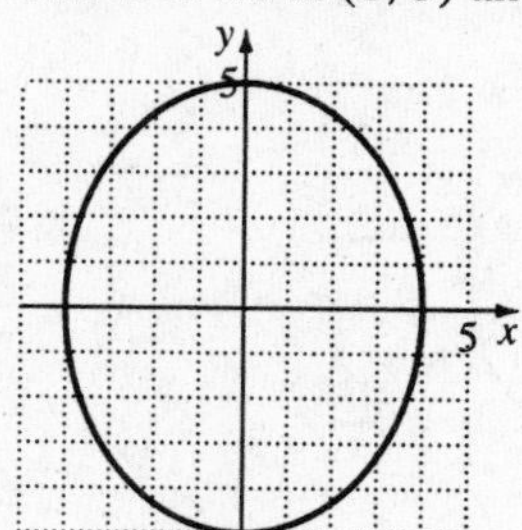

3. $4x^2 + y^2 = 16$
$\frac{4x^2}{16}+\frac{y^2}{16}=\frac{16}{16}$
$\frac{x^2}{4}+\frac{y^2}{16}=1$
$b^2 = 4, b = 2$
$a^2 = 16, a = 4$
$c^2 = a^2 - b^2 = 16 - 4 = 12$
$c = \sqrt{12} = 2\sqrt{3}$
The foci are at $(0, 2\sqrt{3})$ and $(0, -2\sqrt{3})$.

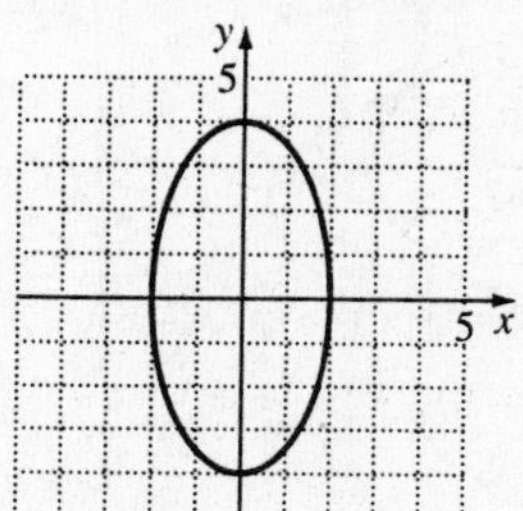

4. $4x^2 + 9y^2 = 36$
$\frac{4x^2}{36}+\frac{9y^2}{36}=\frac{36}{36}$
$\frac{x^2}{9}+\frac{y^2}{4}=1$
$a^2 = 9, a = 3$
$b^2 = 4, b = 2$
$c^2 = a^2 - b^2 = 9 - 4 = 5$
$c = \sqrt{5}$
The foci are at $(\sqrt{5}, 0)$ and $(-\sqrt{5}, 0)$.

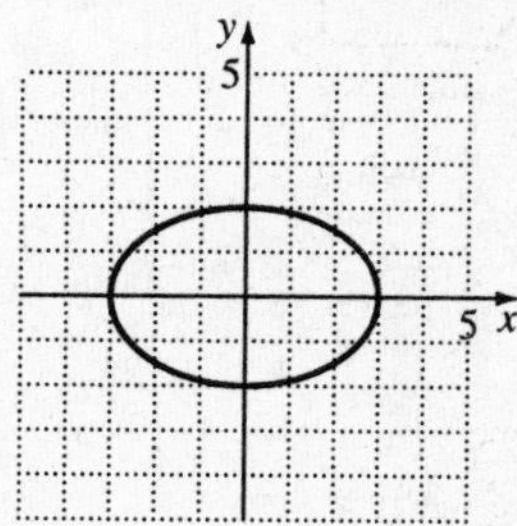

5. $\frac{(x-1)^2}{16}+\frac{(y+2)^2}{9}=1$
$a^2=16\ a=4$
$b^2=9\ b=3$
$c^2=16-9=7, c=\sqrt{7}$
center: (1, –2)
The foci are at
$(1+\sqrt{7},\,-2)$ and $(1-\sqrt{7},\,-2)$.

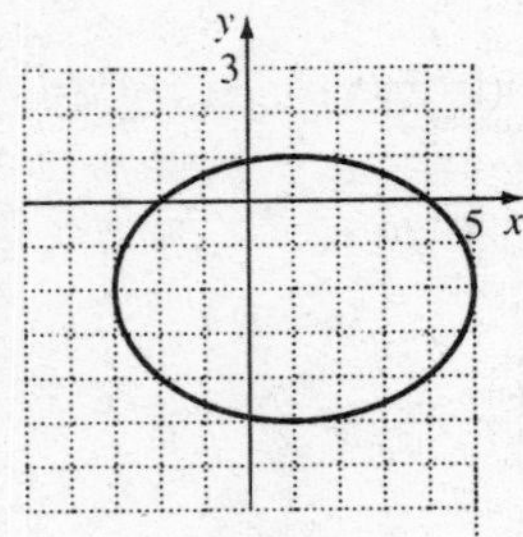

6. $\frac{(x+1)^2}{9}+\frac{(y-2)^2}{16}=1$
$a^2=16,\ a=4$
$b^2=9,\ b=3$
$c^2=a^2-b^2=16-9=7$
$c=\sqrt{7}$
center: (–1, 2)
The foci are at $(-1,\,2+\sqrt{7})$ and $(-1,\,2-\sqrt{7})$.

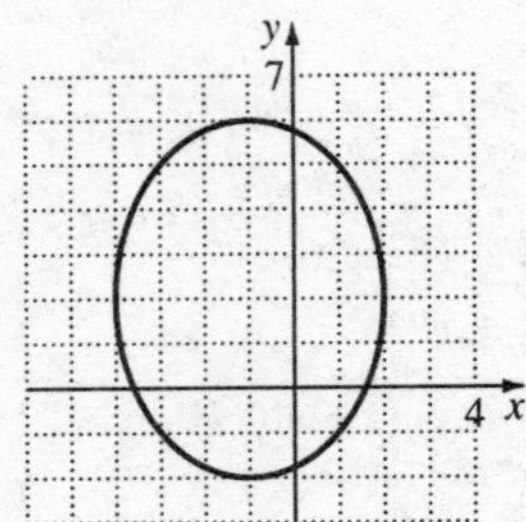

7. $4x^2+9y^2+24x-36y+36=0$
$4x^2+24x+9y^2-36y=-36$
$4(x^2+6x+9)+9(y^2-4y+4)$
$=-36+36+36$
$=4(x+3)^2+9(y-2)^2=36$
$\frac{(x+3)^2}{9}+\frac{(y-2)^2}{4}=1$
$c^2=a^2-b^2=5,\ c=\sqrt{5}$
center: (–3, 2)

The foci are at
$(-3+\sqrt{5},\,2)$ and $(-3-\sqrt{5},\,2)$.

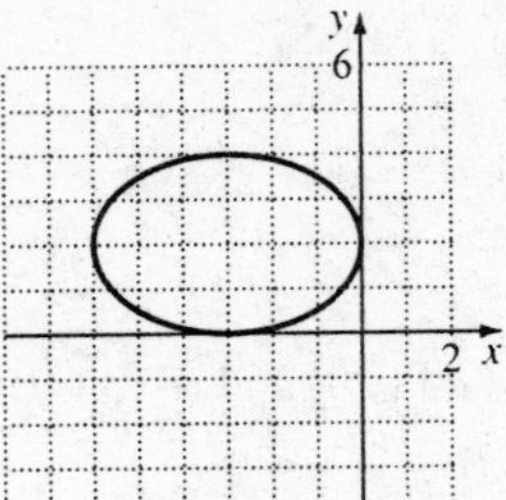

8. $9x^2+4y^2-18x+8y-23=0$
$9x^2-18x+4y^2+8y=23$
$9(x^2-2x+1)+4(y^2+2y+1)$
$=23+9+4$
$9(x-1)^2+4(y+1)^2=36$
$\frac{(x-1)^2}{4}+\frac{(y+1)^2}{9}=1$
$c^2=a^2-b^2=9-4=5$
$c=\sqrt{5}$
center: (1, –1)
The foci are at $(1,\,-1+\sqrt{5})$ and $(1,\,-1-\sqrt{5})$.

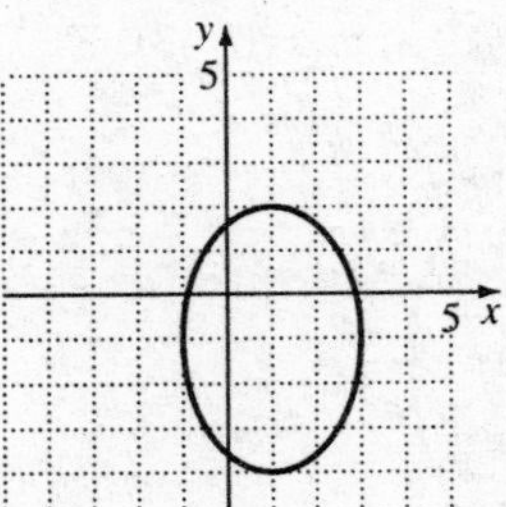

9. $c=4,\ c^2=16$
$a=5,\ a^2=25$
$b^2=a^2-c^2=25-16=9$
$\frac{x^2}{25}+\frac{y^2}{9}=1$

10. $c=3,\ c^2=9$
$a=6,\ a^2=36$
$b^2=a^2-c^2=36-9=27$
$\frac{x^2}{27}+\frac{y^2}{36}=1$

11. $2a = 12, a = 6, a^2 = 36$
$2b = 4, b = 2, b^2 = 4$
$$\frac{x^2}{36} + \frac{y^2}{4} = 1$$

12. $2a = 20, a = 10, a^2 = 100$
$b = 6, b^2 = 36$
$$\frac{x^2}{100} + \frac{y^2}{36} = 1$$

13. $2a = 50, a = 25$
$b = 15$
$$\frac{x^2}{625} + \frac{y^2}{225} = 1$$
Let $x = 14$
$$\frac{(14)^2}{625} + \frac{y^2}{225} = 1$$
$$y^2 = 225\left(1 - \frac{196}{625}\right)$$
$y \approx 15(0.8285) \approx 12.4 > 12$
Yes, the truck can drive under the archway.

14. The hit ball will collide with the other ball.

15. $\frac{x^2}{16} - y^2 = 1$
$c^2 = a^2 + b^2 = 16 + 1 = 17, c = \sqrt{17}$
The foci are at $(\sqrt{17}, 0)$ and $(-\sqrt{17}, 0)$.

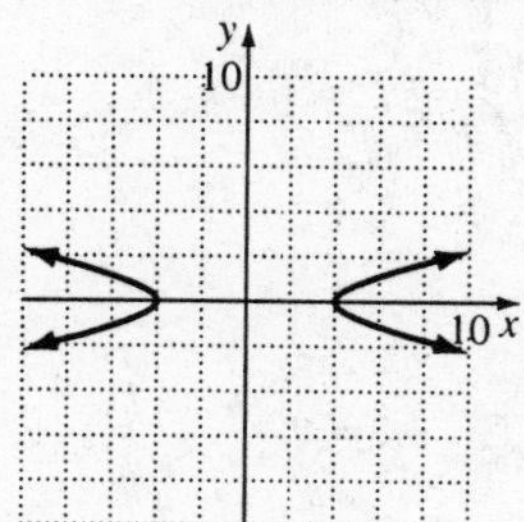

16. $\frac{y^2}{16} - x^2 = 1$
$c^2 = a^2 + b^2 = 16 + 1 = 17$
$c = \sqrt{17}$
The foci are at $(0, \sqrt{17})$ and $(0, -17)$.

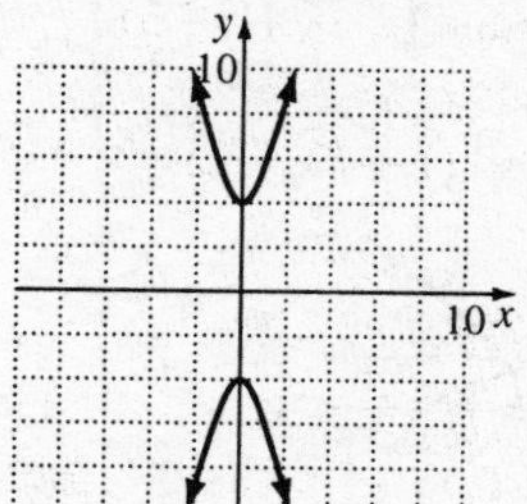

17. $9x^2 - 16y^2 = 144$
$$\frac{x^2}{16} - \frac{y^2}{9} = 1$$
$c^2 = a^2 + b^2 = 16 + 9 = 25, c = 5$
The foci are at $(5, 0)$ and $(-5, 0)$.

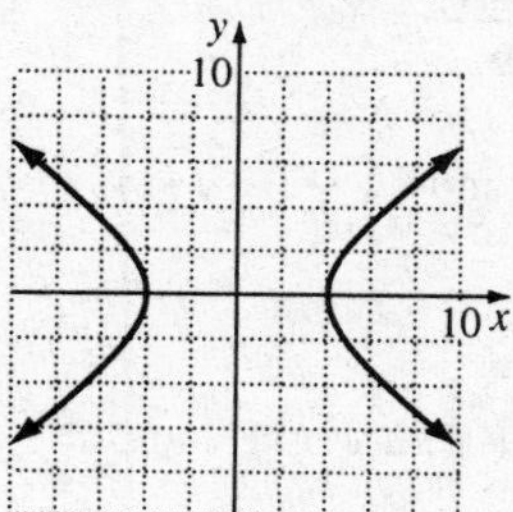

18. $4y^2 - x^2 = 16$
$$\frac{y^2}{4} - \frac{x^2}{16} = 1$$
$c^2 = a^2 + b^2 = 4 + 16 = 20$
$c = \sqrt{20} = 2\sqrt{5}$
The foci are at $(0, 2\sqrt{5})$ and $(0, -2\sqrt{5})$.

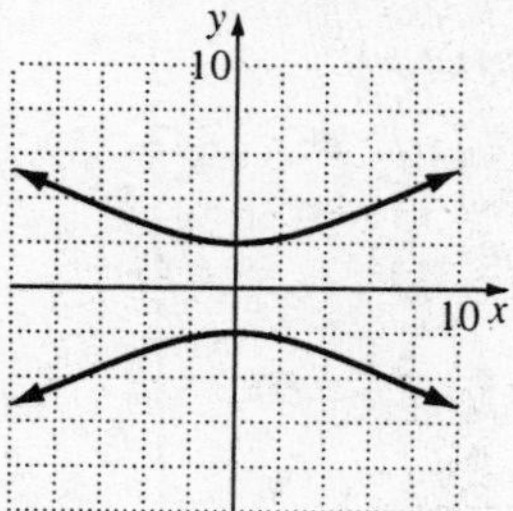

19. $\frac{(x-2)^2}{25} - \frac{(y+3)^2}{16} = 1$
$c^2 = a^2 + b^2 = 25 + 16 = 41,\ c = \sqrt{41}$
center: (2, –3)
The foci are at
$(2+\sqrt{41}, -3)$ and $(2-\sqrt{41}, -3)$.

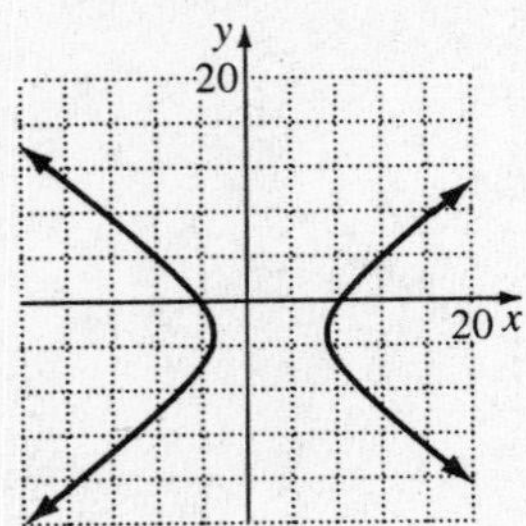

20. $\frac{(y+2)^2}{25} - \frac{(x-3)^2}{16} = 1$
$c^2 = a^2 + b^2 = 25 + 16 = 41$
$c = \sqrt{41}$
center: (3, –2)
The foci are at
$(3, -2+\sqrt{41})$ and $(3, -2-\sqrt{41})$.

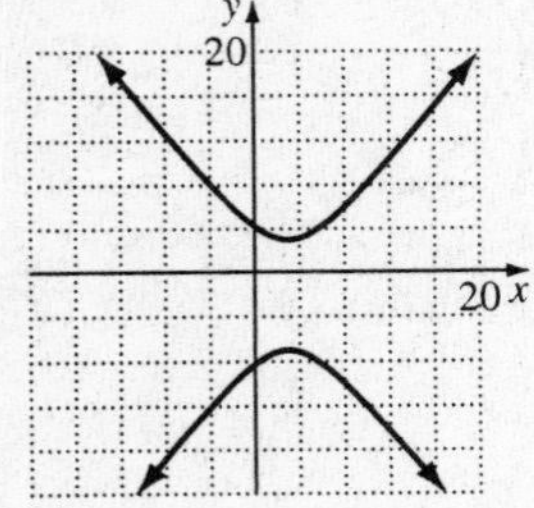

21. $y^2 - 4y - 4x^2 + 8x - 4 = 0$
$(y^2 - 4y + 4) - 4(x^2 - 2x + 1) = 4 + 4 - 4$
$(y-2)^2 - 4(x-1)^2 = 4$
$\frac{(y-2)^2}{4} - (x-1)^2 = 1$
$c^2 = a^2 + b^2 = 4 + 1 = 5,\ c = \sqrt{5}$
center: (1, 2)

The foci are at $(1, 2+\sqrt{5})$ and $(1, 2-\sqrt{5})$.

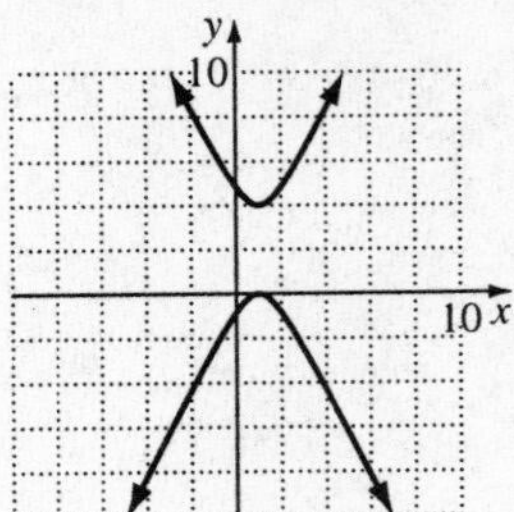

22. $x^2 - y^2 - 2x - 2y - 1 = 0$
$x^2 - 2x - y^2 - 2y = 1$
$(x^2 - 2x + 1) - (y^2 + 2y + 1) = 1 + 1 - 1$
$(x-1)^2 - (y+1)^2 = 1$
$c^2 = a^2 + b^2 = 1 + 1 = 2,\ c = \sqrt{2}$
center: (1, –1)
The foci are at
$(1+\sqrt{2}, -1)$ and $(1-\sqrt{2}, -1)$.

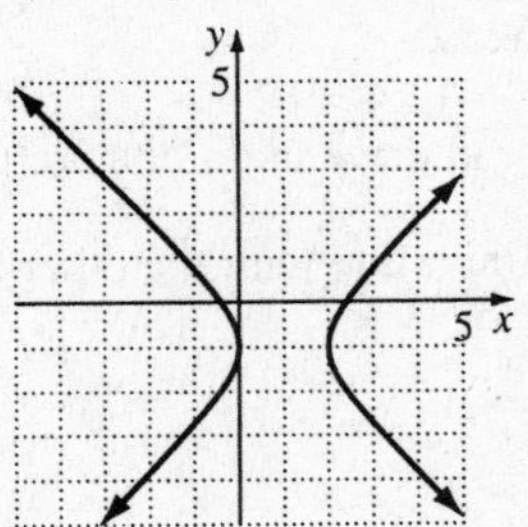

23. $c = 4,\ c^2 = 16$
$a = 2,\ a^2 = 4$
$b^2 = c^2 - a^2 = 16 - 4 = 12$
$\frac{y^2}{4} - \frac{x^2}{12} = 1$

24. $c = 8,\ c^2 = 64$
$a = 3,\ a^2 = 9$
$b^2 = c^2 - a^2 = 64 - 9 = 55$
$\frac{x^2}{9} - \frac{y^2}{55} = 1$

25. If the foci are at (0, –2) and (0, 2), then $c = 2$. If the vertices are at (0, –3) and (0, 3) then $a = 3$. This is not possible since c must be greater than a.

26. foci: (±100, 0), $c = 100$

$$|d_1 - d_2| = \left(0.186\frac{\text{mi}}{\mu\text{s}}\right)(500\mu\text{s})$$

$$= 93 \text{ mi} = 2a$$

$$a = \frac{93}{2}$$

$$b^2 = c^2 - a^2 = (100)^2 - \left(\frac{93}{2}\right)^2$$

$$= 7837.75$$

$$\frac{x^2}{\left(\frac{93}{2}\right)^2} - \frac{y^2}{7837.75} = 1$$

$$\frac{x^2}{2162.25} - \frac{y^2}{7837.75} = 1$$

27. $y^2 = 8x$

$4p = 8, p = 2$

vertex: (0, 0)

focus: (2, 0)

directrix: $x = -2$

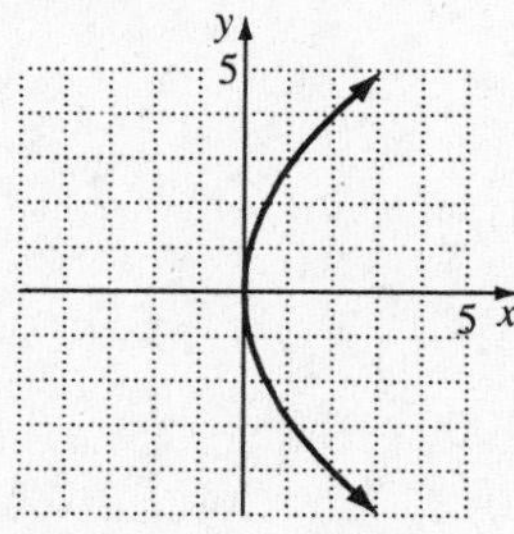

28. $x^2 + 16y = 0$

$x^2 = -16y$

$4p = -16$

$p = -4$

vertex: (0, 0)

focus: (0, –4)

directrix: $y = 4$

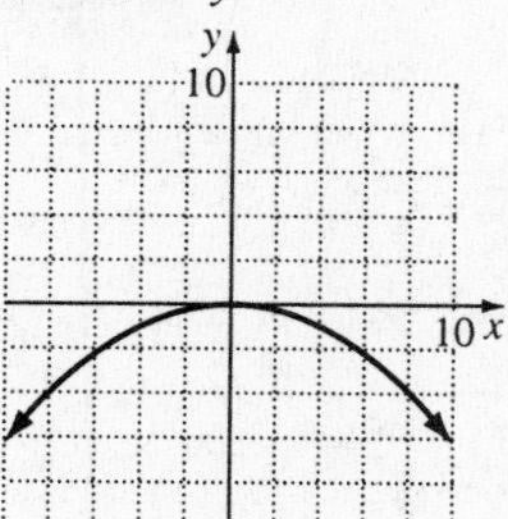

29. $(y-2)^2 = -16x$

$4p = -16$

$p = -4$

vertex: (0, 2)

focus: (–4, 2)

directrix: $x = 4$

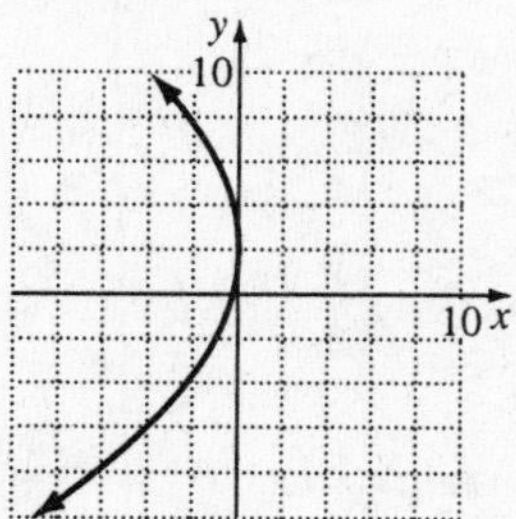

30. $(x-4)^2 = 4(y+1)$

$4p = 4, p = 1$

vertex: (4, –1)

focus: (4, 0)

directrix: $y = -2$

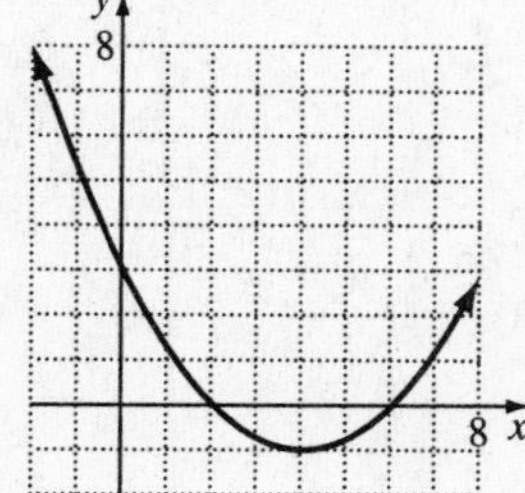

31. $x^2 + 4y = 4$
$x^2 = -4y + 4$
$x^2 = -4(y - 1)$
$4p = -4,\ p = -1$
vertex: (0, 1)
focus: (0, 0)
directrix: $y = 2$

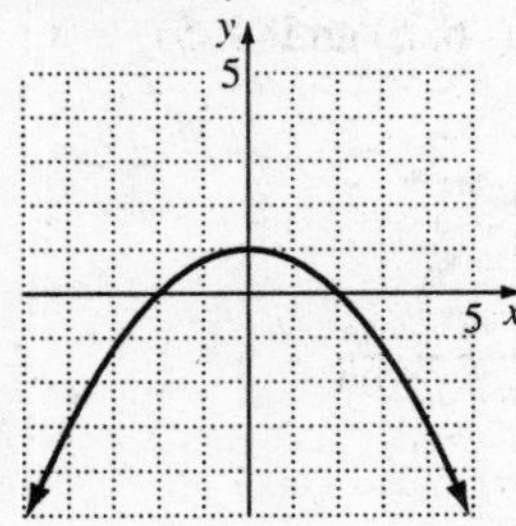

32. $y^2 - 4x - 10y + 21 = 0$
$y^2 - 10y = 4x - 21$
$y^2 - 10y + 25 = 4x - 21 + 25$
$(y-5)^2 = 4(x+1)$
$4p = 4,\ p = 1$
vertex: (–1, 5)
focus: (0, 5)
directrix: $x = -2$

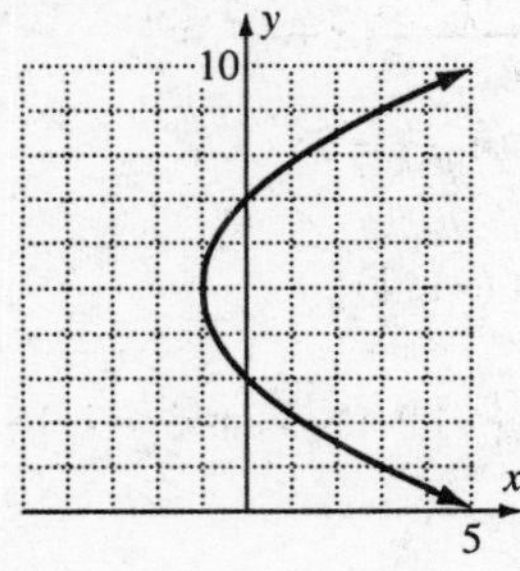

33. $x^2 - 4x - 2y = 0$
$x^2 - 4x = 2y$
$(x^2 - 4x + 4) = 2y + 4$
$(x - 2)^2 = 2(y + 2)$
$4p = 2,\ p = \frac{1}{2}$
vertex: (2, –2)
focus: $\left(2, -\frac{3}{2}\right)$
directrix: $y = -\frac{5}{2}$

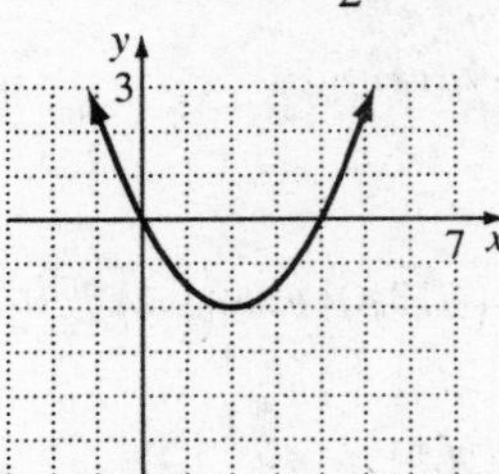

34. $p = 12$
$y^2 = 48x$

35. $p = -11$
$x^2 = -44y$

36. $x^2 = 4py$
$(6)^2 = 4p(3)$
$p = 3$
$x^2 = 12y$
Place the light 3 inches from the vertex at (0, 3).

37. $x^2 = 4py$
$(1750)^2 = 4p(316)$
$4p \approx 9691$
$x^2 = 9691y$
Let $x = 1750 - 1000 = 750$
$y = \frac{x^2}{9691} = \frac{(750)^2}{9691} \approx 58$
The height is approximately 58 feet.

38. $x^2 = 4py$
$(150)^2 = 4p(44)$
$22{,}500 = 176p$
$p \approx 128$
The receiver should be placed approximately 128 feet from the base of the dish.

Chapter 7 Test

1. $9x^2 - 4y^2 = 36$

$\frac{x^2}{4} - \frac{y^2}{9} = 1$

$c^2 = a^2 + b^2 = 4 + 9 = 13$

$c = \sqrt{13}$

hyperbola

The foci are at $(\sqrt{13}, 0)$ and $(-\sqrt{13}, 0)$.

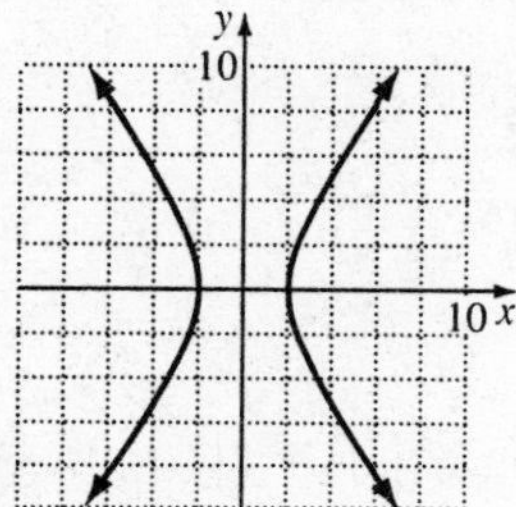

2. $x^2 = -8y$

$4p = -8,\ p = -2$

parabola

vertex: (0, 0)

focus: (0, –2)

directrix: $y = 2$

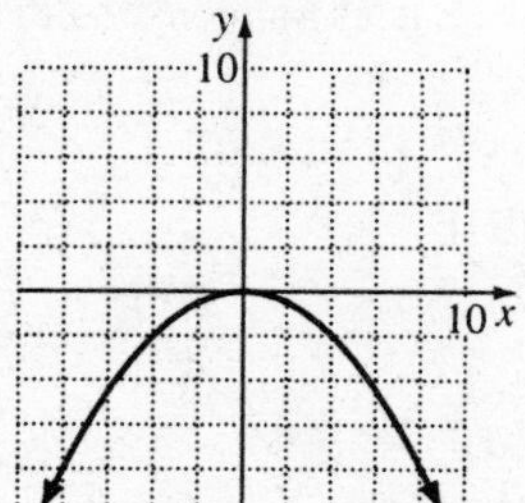

3. $\frac{(x+2)^2}{25} + \frac{(y-5)^2}{9} = 1$

The center is at (–2, 5).

$c^2 = a^2 - b^2 = 25 - 9 = 16$

$c = 4$

ellipse

The foci are at (–6, 5) and (2, 5).

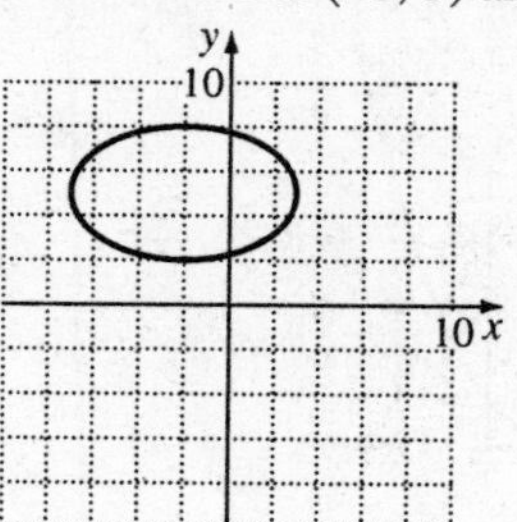

4.

$$4x^2 - y^2 + 8x + 2y + 7 = 0$$
$$(4x^2 + 8x) - (y^2 - 2y) = -7$$
$$4(x^2 + 2x + 1) - (y^2 - 2y + 1) = -7 + 4 - 1$$
$$4(x+1)^2 - (y-1)^2 = -4$$
$$(y-1)^2 - 4(x+1)^2 = 4$$
$$\frac{(y-1)^2}{4} - (x+1)^2 = 1$$

$c^2 = a^2 + b^2 = 4 + 1 = 5$

$c = \sqrt{5}$

The center is at (–1, 1).

hyperbola

The foci are at $(-1, 1+\sqrt{5})$ and $(-1, 1-\sqrt{5})$.

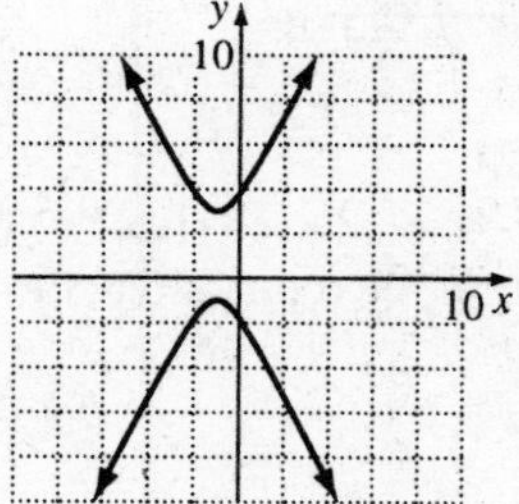

5. $(x+5)^2 = 8(y-1)$
$4p = 8, p = 2$
parabola
vertex: (–5, 1)
focus: (–5, 3)
directrix: $y = -1$

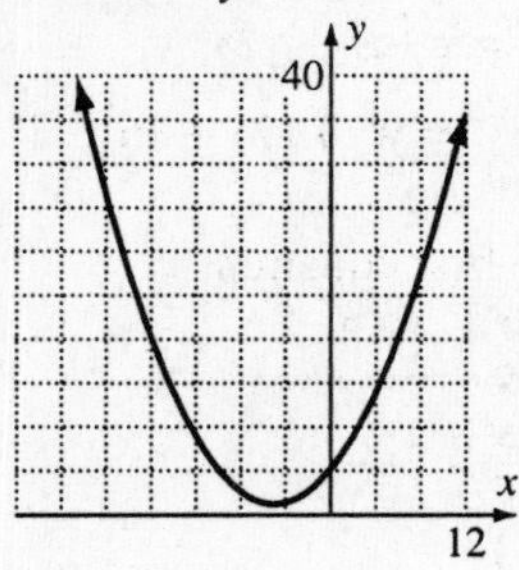

6. $c = 7, c^2 = 49$
$a = 10, a^2 = 100$
$b^2 = a^2 - c^2 = 100 - 49 = 51$
$$\frac{x^2}{100} + \frac{y^2}{51} = 1$$

7. $c = 10, c^2 = 100$
$a = 7, a^2 = 49$
$b^2 = c^2 - a^2 = 100 - 49 = 51$
$$\frac{y^2}{49} - \frac{x^2}{51} = 1$$

8. $p = 50$
$y^2 = 4px$
$y^2 = 200x$

9. $b = 24, b^2 = 576$
$2a = 80, a = 40, a^2 = 1600$
$c^2 = a^2 - b^2 = 1600 - 576 = 1024$
$c = \sqrt{1024} = 32$
The two people should each stand 32 feet from the center of the room, along the major axis.

10. a. $x^2 = 4py$
when $x = \pm 3, y = 3$
$9 = 4p(3)$
$4p = 3, p = \frac{3}{4}$
$x^2 = 3y$

b. focus: $\left(0, \frac{3}{4}\right)$
The light is placed $\frac{3}{4}$ inch above the vertex.

Cumulative Review Exercises (Chapters 1–7)

1. $2(x-3) + 5x = 8(x-1)$
$2x - 6 + 5x = 8x - 8$
$7x - 6 = 8x - 8$
$-x = -2$
$x = 2$
The solution set is $\{2\}$.

2. $-3(2x-4) > 2(6x-12)$
$-6x + 12 > 12x - 24$
$-18x > -36$
$x < 2$
The solution set is $\{x | x < 2\}$.

3. $x - 5 = \sqrt{x+7}$
$(x-5)^2 = x + 7$
$x^2 - 10x + 25 = x + 7$
$x^2 - 11x + 18 = 0$
$(x-2)(x-9) = 0$
$x = 2$ or $x = 9$
The solution $x = 2$ is extraneous, so the only solution is $x = 9$.
The solution set is $\{9\}$.

4. $(x-2)^2 = 20$
$x - 2 = \pm\sqrt{20}$
$x - 2 = \pm 2\sqrt{5}$
$x = 2 \pm 2\sqrt{5}$
The solution set is $\{2 + 2\sqrt{5}, 2 - 2\sqrt{5}\}$.

5. $|2x-1| \geq 7$
$2x - 1 \geq 7$ or $2x - 1 \leq -7$
$2x \geq 8$ $\quad 2x \leq -6$
$x \geq 4$ or $\quad x \leq -3$
The solution set is $\{x | x \leq -3 \text{ or } x \geq 4\}$.

6. $3x^3 + 4x^2 - 7x + 2 = 0$
$p: \pm 1, \pm 2$
$q: \pm 1, \pm 3$
$\frac{p}{q}: \pm 1, \pm 2, \pm\frac{1}{3}, \pm\frac{2}{3}$
Let $f(x) = 3x^3 + 4x^2 - 7x + 2.$
Evaluate f at the possible rational zeros to find $f\left(\frac{2}{3}\right) = 0.$

$$\begin{array}{r|rrrr} \frac{2}{3} & 3 & 4 & -7 & 2 \\ & & 2 & 4 & -2 \\ \hline & 3 & 6 & -3 & \end{array}$$

$\left(x - \frac{2}{3}\right)(3x^2 + 6x - 3) = 0$
$(3x - 2)(x^2 + 2x - 1) = 0$
$x = \frac{2}{3}$ or $x = \frac{-2 \pm \sqrt{(2)^2 - 4(1)(-1)}}{2}$
$x = \frac{-2 \pm \sqrt{8}}{2}$
$x = -1 \pm \sqrt{2}$
The solution set is $\left\{\frac{2}{3}, -1 \pm \sqrt{2}\right\}$.

7. $\log_2(x+1) + \log_2(x-1) = 3$
$\log_2(x^2 - 1) = 3$
$x^2 - 1 = 2^3$
$x^2 = 9$
$x = \pm 3$
$x = -3$ is not a solution of the original equation.
The solution set is $\{3\}$.

8. $3x + 4y = 2$
$2x + 5y = -1$
$6x + 8y = 4$
$-6x - 15y = 3$
$-7y = 7$
$y = -1$
$3x + 4(-1) = 2$
$3x = 6$
$x = 2$
The solution set is $\{(2, -1)\}$.

9. $2x^2 - y^2 = -8$
$x - y = 6$
$x - y = 6 \Rightarrow x = y + 6$
$\Rightarrow x^2 = (y+6)^2 = y^2 + 12y + 36$

Substitute into first equation.
$2(y^2 + 12y + 36) - y^2 = -8$
$2y^2 + 24y + 72 - y^2 = -8$
$y^2 + 24y + 80 = 0$
$y = -4$ or $y = -20$
$x = 2 \qquad x = -14$
The solution set is $\{(2, -4)$ and $(-14, -20)\}$.

10. Set up the augmented matrix and use Gauss-Jordan reduction.

$$\left[\begin{array}{rrr|r} 1 & -1 & 1 & 17 \\ -4 & 1 & 5 & -2 \\ 2 & 3 & 1 & 8 \end{array}\right]$$

$$\left[\begin{array}{rrr|r} 1 & -1 & 1 & 17 \\ 0 & -3 & 9 & 66 \\ 0 & 5 & -1 & -26 \end{array}\right] \begin{array}{l} 4R_1 + R_2 \\ -2R_1 + R_3 \end{array}$$

$$\left[\begin{array}{rrr|r} 1 & -1 & 1 & 17 \\ 0 & 1 & -3 & -22 \\ 0 & 5 & -1 & -26 \end{array}\right] -\frac{1}{3}R_2$$

$$\left[\begin{array}{rrr|r} 1 & 0 & -2 & -5 \\ 0 & 1 & -3 & -22 \\ 0 & 0 & 14 & 84 \end{array}\right] \begin{array}{l} R_2 + R_1 \\ -5R_2 + R_3 \end{array}$$

$$\left[\begin{array}{rrr|r} 1 & 0 & -2 & -5 \\ 0 & 1 & -3 & -22 \\ 0 & 0 & 1 & 6 \end{array}\right] \frac{1}{14}R_3$$

$$\left[\begin{array}{rrr|r} 1 & 0 & 0 & 7 \\ 0 & 1 & 0 & -4 \\ 0 & 0 & 1 & 6 \end{array}\right] \begin{array}{l} 2R_3 + R_1 \\ 3R_3 + R_2 \end{array}$$

$x = 7, y = -4, z = 6$
The solution set is $\{(7, -4, 6)\}$.

11. $f(x) = (x-1)^2 - 4$
Parabola with vertex at (1, –4).

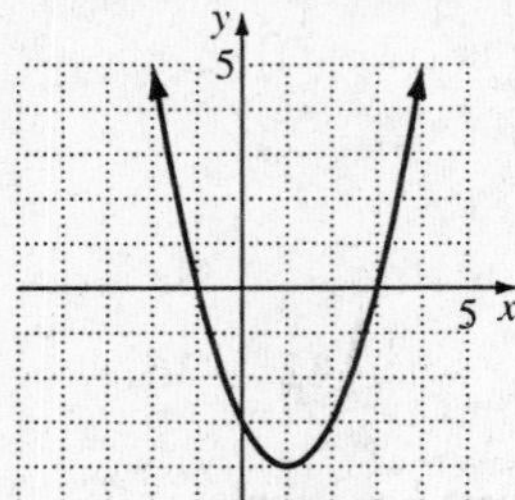

12. $\frac{x^2}{9} + \frac{y^2}{4} = 1$
Ellipse with center at (0, 0) and vertices at (3, 0) and (–3, 0).

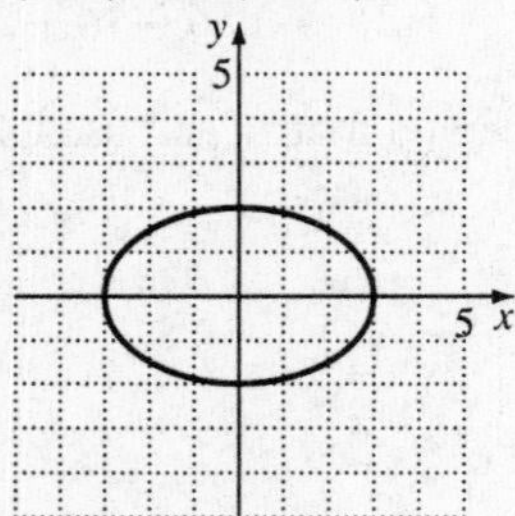

13. Graph solid 5*x* + *y* = 10 and $y = \frac{1}{4}x + 2$.
Shade the appropriate region. Then dash the solid lines that do not contain the solution set.

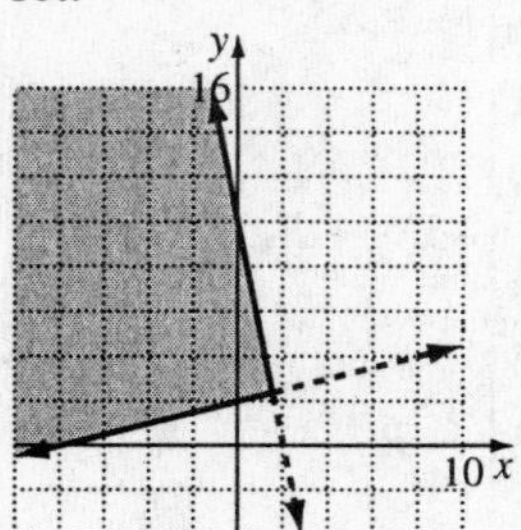

14. a. $p: \pm 1, \pm 3$
$q: \pm 1, \pm 2, \pm 4, \pm 8, \pm 16, \pm 32$
$\frac{p}{q}: \pm 1, \pm 3, \pm \frac{1}{2}, \pm \frac{3}{2}, \pm \frac{1}{4}, \pm \frac{3}{4}, \pm \frac{1}{8}, \pm \frac{3}{8}, \pm \frac{1}{16}, \pm \frac{3}{16}, \pm \frac{1}{32}, \pm \frac{3}{32}$

b. *x* = 1 appears to be a root.

1	32	–52	17	3
		32	–20	–3
	32	–20	–3	0

$32x^3 - 52x^2 + 17x + 3 = 0$
$(x-1)(32x^2 - 20x - 3) = 0$
$(x-1)(4x-3)(8x+1) = 0$
$x = 1 \text{ or } x = \frac{3}{4} \text{ or } x = -\frac{1}{8}$
The solution set is $\left\{-\frac{1}{8}, \frac{3}{4}, 1\right\}$.

15. a. 1980–1991

b. 1991–2025

c. 1950–1980

d. *f*(*x*) = 98

e. The scale is not uniformly spaced.

16. $f(x) = x^2 - 4, g(x) = x + 2$
$(g \circ f)(x) = x^2 - 4 + 2 = x^2 - 2$

17.
$$\log_5 \frac{x^3\sqrt{y}}{125} = \log_5 x^3\sqrt{y} - \log_5 125 = \log_5 x^3 + \log_5 \sqrt{y} - 3 = 3\log_5 x + \frac{1}{2}\log_5 y - 3$$

18. $m = \dfrac{y_2 - y_1}{x_2 - x_1} = \dfrac{8-(-4)}{-5-1} = \dfrac{12}{-6} = -2$

$y - y_1 = m(x - x_1)$
$y + 4 = -2(x - 1)$
$y = -2x - 2$

19. Let R = the cost of a rental at Rent-a-Truck and let A = the cost of a rental at Ace Truck Rentals.
$R = 39 + 0.16m$
$A = 25 + 0.24m$
where m is the number of miles.
$39 + 0.16m = 25 + 0.24m$
$14 = 0.08m$
$m = 175$
$R(175) = 39 + 0.16(175) = 67$
The cost will be the same when the number of miles driven is 175 miles. The cost will be $67.

20. Let x = the age of Richard Nixon, $x + 2$ = the age of Thomas Jefferson, and $x + 4$ = the age of James Madison. Then:
$x + x + 2 + x + 4 = 249$
$3x + 6 = 249$
$3x = 243$
$x = 81$
Richard Nixon lived 81 years, Thomas Jefferson lived 83 years, and James Madison lived 85 years.

Chapter 8

Section 8.1

Check Point Exercises

1. a. $a_n = 2n+5$

$a_1 = 2(1)+5 = 7$

$a_2 = 2(2)+5 = 9$

$a_3 = 2(3)+5 = 11$

$a_4 = 2(4)+5 = 13$

The first four terms are 7, 9, 11, and 13.

b. $a_n = \dfrac{(-1)^n}{2^n+1}$

$a_1 = \dfrac{(-1)^1}{2^1+1} = \dfrac{-1}{3} = -\dfrac{1}{3}$

$a_2 = \dfrac{(-1)^2}{2^2+1} = \dfrac{1}{5}$

$a_3 = \dfrac{(-1)^3}{2^3+1} = \dfrac{-1}{9} = -\dfrac{1}{9}$

$a_4 = \dfrac{(-1)^4}{2^4+1} = \dfrac{1}{17}$

The first four terms are $-\frac{1}{3}, \frac{1}{5}, -\frac{1}{9}$, and $\frac{1}{17}$.

2. $a_1 = 3$ and $a_n = 2a_{n-1}+5$ for $n \ge 2$

$a_2 = 2a_1 + 5$
$= 2(3)+5 = 11$

$a_3 = 2a_2 + 5$
$= 2(11)+5 = 27$

$a_4 = 2a_3 + 5$
$= 2(27)+5 = 59$

The first four terms are 3, 11, 27, and 59.

3. $a_n = \dfrac{20}{(n+1)!}$

$a_1 = \dfrac{20}{(1+1)!} = \dfrac{20}{2!} = 10$

$a_2 = \dfrac{20}{(2+1)!} = \dfrac{20}{3!} = \dfrac{20}{6} = \dfrac{10}{3}$

$a_3 = \dfrac{20}{(3+1)!} = \dfrac{20}{4!} = \dfrac{20}{24} = \dfrac{5}{6}$

$a_4 = \dfrac{20}{(4+1)!} = \dfrac{20}{5!} = \dfrac{20}{120} = \dfrac{1}{6}$

The first four terms are 10, $\frac{10}{3}$, $\frac{5}{6}$, and $\frac{1}{6}$.

4. a. $\dfrac{14!}{2!\,12!} = \dfrac{14\cdot 13\cdot 12!}{2!\,12!} = \dfrac{14\cdot 13}{2\cdot 1} = 91$

b. $\dfrac{n!}{(n-1)!} = \dfrac{n\cdot(n-1)!}{(n-1)!} = n$

5. a. $\displaystyle\sum_{i=1}^{6} 2i^2$

$= 2(1)^2 + 2(2)^2 + 2(3)^2$
$+ 2(4)^2 + 2(5)^2 + 2(6)^2$
$= 2+8+18+32+50+72$
$= 182$

b. $\displaystyle\sum_{k=3}^{5} \left(2^k - 3\right)$

$= \left(2^3-3\right)+\left(2^4-3\right)+\left(2^5-3\right)$
$= (8-3)+(16-3)+(32-3)$
$= 5+13+29$
$= 47$

c. $\displaystyle\sum_{i=1}^{5} 4 = 4+4+4+4+4 = 20$

6. a. The sum has nine terms, each of the form i^2, starting at $i=1$ and ending at $i=9$.

$$1^2+2^2+3^2+\cdots+9^2 = \sum_{i=1}^{9} i^2$$

b. The sum has n terms, each of the form $\frac{1}{2^{i-1}}$, starting at $i=1$ and ending at $i=n$.

$$1+\frac{1}{2}+\frac{1}{4}+\frac{1}{8}+\cdots+\frac{1}{2^{n-1}} = \sum_{i=1}^{n} \frac{1}{2^{i-1}}$$

Exercise Set 8.1

1. $a_n = 3n + 2$
$a_1 = 3(1) + 2 = 5$
$a_2 = 3(2) + 2 = 8$
$a_3 = 3(3) + 2 = 11$
$a_4 = 3(4) + 2 = 14$
The first four terms are 5, 8, 11, and 14.

3. $a_n = 3^n$
$a_1 = 3^1 = 3$
$a_2 = 3^2 = 9$
$a_3 = 3^3 = 27$
$a_4 = 3^4 = 81$
The first four terms are 3, 9, 27, and 81.

5. $a_n = (-3)^n$
$a_1 = (-3)^1 = -3$
$a_2 = (-3)^2 = 9$
$a_3 = (-3)^3 = -27$
$a_4 = (-3)^4 = 81$
The first four terms are –3, 9, –27, and 81.

7. $a_n = (-1)^n (n+3)$
$a_1 = (-1)^1 (1+3) = -4$
$a_2 = (-1)^2 (2+3) = 5$
$a_3 = (-1)^3 (3+3) = -6$
$a_4 = (-1)^4 (4+3) = 7$
The first four terms are –4, 5, –6, and 7.

9. $a_n = \dfrac{2n}{n+4}$
$a_1 = \dfrac{2(1)}{1+4} = \dfrac{2}{5}$
$a_2 = \dfrac{2(2)}{2+4} = \dfrac{4}{6} = \dfrac{2}{3}$
$a_3 = \dfrac{2(3)}{3+4} = \dfrac{6}{7}$
$a_4 = \dfrac{2(4)}{4+4} = \dfrac{8}{8} = 1$
The first four terms are $\frac{2}{5}, \frac{2}{3}, \frac{6}{7}$, and 1.

11. $a_n = \dfrac{(-1)^{n+1}}{2^n - 1}$
$a_1 = \dfrac{(-1)^{1+1}}{2^1 - 1} = \dfrac{1}{1}\ n = 1$
$a_2 = \dfrac{(-1)^{2+1}}{2^2 - 1} = -\dfrac{1}{3}$
$a_3 = \dfrac{(-1)^{3+1}}{2^3 - 1} = \dfrac{1}{7}$
$a_4 = \dfrac{(-1)^{4+1}}{2^4 - 1} = -\dfrac{1}{15}$
The first four terms are $1, -\frac{1}{3}, \frac{1}{7}$, and $-\frac{1}{15}$.

13. $a_1 = 7$ and $a_n = a_{n-1} + 5$ for $n \ge 2$
$a_2 = a_1 + 5 = 7 + 5 = 12$
$a_3 = a_2 + 5 = 12 + 5 = 17$
$a_4 = a_3 + 5 = 17 + 5 = 22$
The first four terms are 7, 12, 17, and 22.

15. $a_1 = 3$ and $a_n = 4a_{n-1}$ for $n \ge 2$
$a_2 = 4a_1 = 4(3) = 12$
$a_3 = 4a_2 = 4(12) = 48$
$a_4 = 4a_3 = 4(48) = 192$
The first four terms are 3, 12, 48, and 192.

17. $a_1 = 4$ and $a_n = 2a_{n-1} + 3$
$a_2 = 2(4) + 3 = 11$
$a_3 = 2(11) + 3 = 25$
$a_4 = 2(25) + 3 = 53$
The first four terms are 4, 11, 25, and 53.

19. $a_n = \dfrac{n^2}{n!}$
$a_1 = \dfrac{1^2}{1!} = 1$
$a_2 = \dfrac{2^2}{2!} = 2$
$a_3 = \dfrac{3^2}{3!} = \dfrac{9}{6} = \dfrac{3}{2}$
$a_4 = \dfrac{4^2}{4!} = \dfrac{16}{24} = \dfrac{2}{3}$
The first four terms are 1, 2, $\frac{3}{2}$, and $\frac{2}{3}$.

21. $a_n = 2(n+1)!$
$a_1 = 2(1+1)! = 2(2) = 4$
$a_2 = 2(2+1)! = 2(6) = 12$
$a_3 = 2(3+1)! = 2(24) = 48$
$a_4 = 2(4+1)! = 2(120) = 240$
The first four terms are 4, 12, 48, and 240.

23. $\frac{17!}{15!} = \frac{17\cdot 16\cdot 15!}{15!} = 17\cdot 16 = 272$

25. $\frac{16!}{2!\cdot 14!} = \frac{16\cdot 15\cdot 14!}{2!14!} = \frac{16\cdot 15}{2\cdot 1} = \frac{8\cdot 15}{1} = 120$

27. $\frac{(n+2)!}{n!} = \frac{(n+2)(n+1)n!}{n!} = (n+2)(n+1)$

29. $\sum_{i=1}^{6} 5i = 5\cdot 1 + 5\cdot 2 + 5\cdot 3 + 5\cdot 4 + 5\cdot 5 + 5\cdot 6$
$= 5+10+15+20+25+30$
$= 105$

31. $\sum_{i=1}^{4} 2i^2 = 2\cdot 1^2 + 2\cdot 2^2 + 2\cdot 3^2 + 2\cdot 4^2$
$= 2+8+18+32$
$= 60$

33. $\sum_{k=1}^{5} k(k+4) = 1(5)+2(6)+3(7)+4(8)+5(9)$
$= 5+12+21+32+45$
$= 115$

35. $\sum_{i=1}^{4} \left(\frac{-1}{2}\right)^i$
$= \left(-\frac{1}{2}\right)^1 + \left(-\frac{1}{2}\right)^2 + \left(-\frac{1}{2}\right)^3 + \left(-\frac{1}{2}\right)^4$
$= -\frac{1}{2} + \frac{1}{4} + -\frac{1}{8} + \frac{1}{16}$
$= -\frac{5}{16}$

37. $\sum_{i=5}^{9} 11 = 11+11+11+11+11 = 55$

39. $\sum_{i=0}^{4} \frac{(-1)^i}{i!}$
$= \frac{(-1)^0}{0!} + \frac{(-1)^1}{1!} + \frac{(-1)^2}{2!} + \frac{(-1)^3}{3!} + \frac{(-1)^4}{4!}$
$= 1 - 1 + \frac{1}{2} - \frac{1}{6} + \frac{1}{24}$
$= \frac{9}{24} = \frac{3}{8}$

41. $\sum_{i=1}^{5} \frac{i!}{(i-1)!} = \frac{1!}{0!} + \frac{2!}{1!} + \frac{3!}{2!} + \frac{4!}{3!} + \frac{5!}{4!}$
$= 1+2+3+4+5 = 15$

43. $1^2 + 2^2 + 3^2 + \cdots + 15^2 = \sum_{i=1}^{15} i^2$

45. $2 + 2^2 + 2^3 + 2^4 + \cdots + 2^{11} = \sum_{i=1}^{11} 2^i$

47. $1+2+3+\cdots+30 = \sum_{i=1}^{30} i$

49. $\frac{1}{2} + \frac{2}{3} + \frac{3}{4} + \cdots + \frac{14}{14+1} = \sum_{i=1}^{14} \frac{i}{i+1}$

51. $4 + \frac{4^2}{2} + \frac{4^3}{3} + \cdots + \frac{4^n}{n} = \sum_{i=1}^{n} \frac{4^i}{i}$

53. $1+3+5+\cdots+(2n-1) = \sum_{i=1}^{n} (2i-1)$

55. $5+7+9+11+\cdots+31$
Possible answer: $\sum_{k=1}^{14} (2k+3)$

57. $5+7+9+11+\cdots+31$
Possible answer: $\sum_{k=0}^{12} ar^k$

59. $a+(a+d)+(a+2d)+\cdots+(a+nd)$

Possible answer: $\sum_{k=0}^{n}(a+kd)$

61. a. $\sum_{i=2}^{7} a_i$
$= 470+588+735+800+920+1100$
$= 4613$
This represents the total number of home-educated children in the U.S. from 1992 to 1997, in thousands.

b. $\frac{1}{6}\sum_{i=2}^{7} a_i = \frac{4613}{6} \approx 769$
This represents the average number of children home-educated each year from 1992 to 1997, in thousands.

63. $a_n = 0.16n^2 - 1.04n + 7.39$
$a_1 = 0.16(1)^2 - 1.04(1) + 7.39 = 6.51$
$a_2 = 0.16(2)^2 - 1.04(2) + 7.39 = 5.95$
$a_3 = 0.16(3)^2 - 1.04(3) + 7.39 = 5.71$
$a_4 = 0.16(4)^2 - 1.04(4) + 7.39 = 5.79$
$a_5 = 0.16(5)^2 - 1.04(5) + 7.39 = 6.19$
$\sum_{i=1}^{5} a_i = 6.51+5.95+5.71+5.79+6.19 = 30.15$
Americans spent a total of \$30.15 billion on recreational boating from 1991 through 1995.

65. $a_n = 6000\left(1+\frac{0.06}{4}\right)^n,\ n = 1, 2, 3, \ldots$

$a_{20} = 6000\left(1+\frac{0.06}{4}\right)^{20} \approx 8081.13$
After five years, the balance is \$8081.13.

67.–73. Answers may vary.

75. $\frac{200!}{198!} = 39,800$

77. $\frac{20!}{300} = 8,109,673,360,588,800$

79. $\frac{54!}{(54-3)!3!} = 24,804$

81. Exercise 29

```
sum(seq(5X,X,1,6
,1))
                105
```

Exercise 31

```
sum(seq(2X²,X,1,
4,1))
                 60
```

Exercise 33

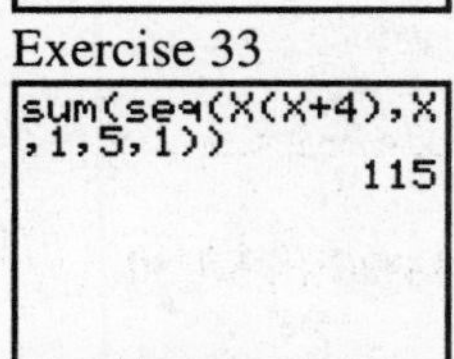

Exercise 35

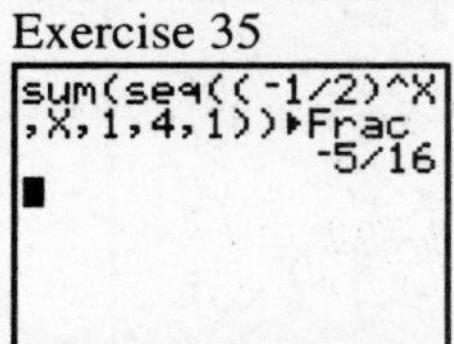

Exercise 37

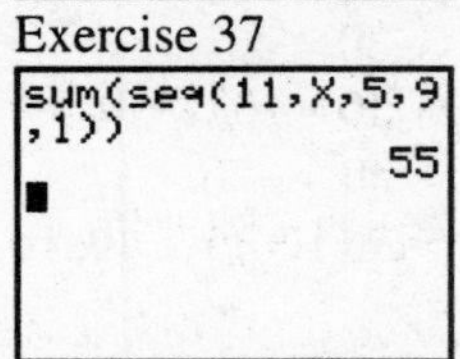

83. $a_n = \frac{n}{n+1}$

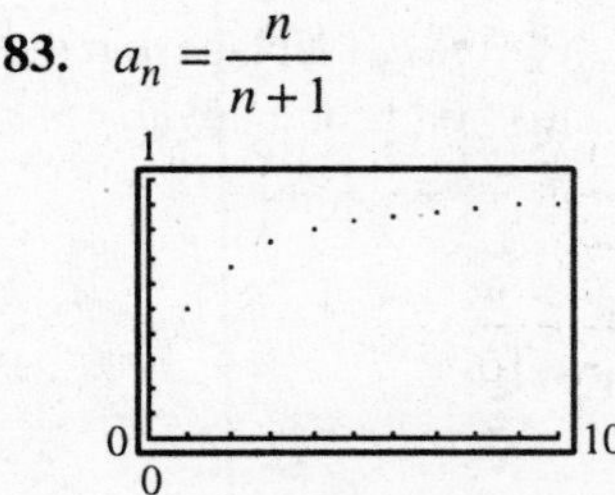

As n gets larger, a_n approaches 1.

85. $a_n = \dfrac{2n^2+5n-7}{n^3}$

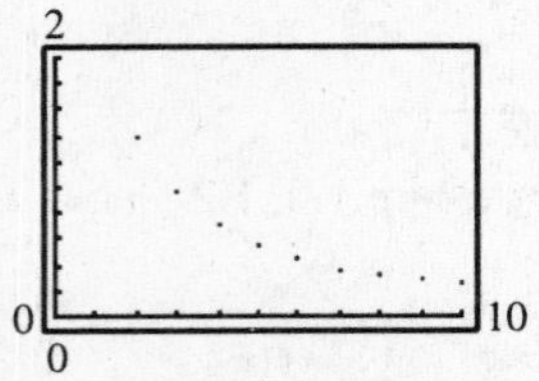

As n gets larger, a_n approaches 0.

87. a. False; $\dfrac{n!}{(n-1)!} = \dfrac{n\cdot(n-1)!}{(n-1)!} = n$

b. True

c. False; $\sum_{i=1}^{2}(-1)^i 2^i = -2+4=2$

d. False;
$a_1b_1 + a_2b_2 \neq (a_1+a_2)+(b_1+b_2)$

(b) is true.

Section 8.2

Check Point Exercises

1. $a_1 = 100,\ a_n = a_{n-1} - 30$
$a_2 = a_1 - 30 = 100 - 30 = 70$
$a_3 = a_2 - 30 = 70 - 30 = 40$
$a_4 = a_3 - 30 = 40 - 30 = 10$
$a_5 = a_4 - 30 = 10 - 30 = -20$
The first five terms are 100, 70, 40, 10, and –20.

2. $a_1 = 6,\ d = -5$
To find the ninth term, a_9, replace n in the formula with 9, a_1 with 6, and d with –5.
$a_n = a_1 + (n-1)d$
$a_9 = 6 + (9-1)(-5)$
$= 6 + 8(-5)$
$= 6 + (-40)$
$= -34$

3. a. The amounts spent can be expressed by the following arithmetic sequence:
12,808, 15,158, 17,508
In this sequence, a_1, the first term, represents the amount spent in 1984.
Each subsequent year, this amount increases by $2350, so $d = 2350$.
Thus, the nth term of the sequence that describes the amount spent n years after 1983 is:
$a_n = a_1 + (n-1)d$
$a_n = 12,808 + (n-1)2350$
$a_n = 12,808 + 2350n - 2350$
$a_n = 2350n + 10,458$

b. The year 2010 is 27 years after 1983.
So substitute 27 for n in
$a_n = 2350n + 10,458.$
$a_{27} = 2350(27) + 10,458 = 73,908$
In 2010, U.S. travelers will spend $73,908 million in other countries.

4. 3, 6, 9, 12, ...
To find the sum of the first 15 terms, S_{15}, replace n in the formuls with 15.

$S_n = \dfrac{n}{2}(a_1 + a_n)$

$S_{15} = \dfrac{15}{2}(a_1 + a_{15})$

Use the formula for the general term of a sequence to find a_{15}. The common difference, d, is 3, and the first term, a_1, is 3.
$a_n = a_1 + (n-1)d$
$a_{15} = 3 + (15-1)(3)$
$= 3 + 14(3)$
$= 3 + 42$
$= 45$
Thus, $S_{15} = \frac{15}{2}(3+45) = \frac{15}{2}(48) = 360$.

5. $\sum_{i=1}^{30}(6i-11) = (6\cdot1-11)+(6\cdot2-11)$
$+(6\cdot3-11)+\cdots+(6\cdot30-11)$
$= -5+1+7+\cdots+169$
So the first term, a_1, is –5; the common difference, d, is $1-(-5)=6$; the last term, a_{30}, is 169. Substitute $n=30$, $a_1=-5$, and $a_{30}=169$ in the formula $S_n = \frac{n}{2}(a_1+a_n)$.
$S_{30} = \frac{30}{2}(-5+169) = 15(164) = 2460$

Thus, $\sum_{i=1}^{30}(6i-11) = 2460$

6. Find the sum of the arithmetic sequence whose first term corresponds to costs in 2001 and whose last term corresponds to costs in 2010. Because the model describes costs n years after 2000, $n = 1$ describes the year 2001 and $n = 10$ describes the year 2010.

$$a_n = 1800n + 49,730$$
$$a_1 = 1800 \cdot 1 + 49,730 = 51,530$$
$$a_{10} = 1800 \cdot 10 + 49,730 = 67,730$$

To find the sum of the costs for all 10 years, find the sum of the ten terms of the arithmetic sequence 51,530, 53,330, . . . , 67,730.
There are 10 terms with first term 51,530 and last term 67,730 so $n = 10$, $a_1 = 51,530$, and $a_{10} = 67,730$.

$$S_n = \frac{n}{2}(a_1 + a_n)$$
$$S_{10} = \frac{10}{2}(51,530 + 67,730) = 5(119,260)$$
$$= 596,300$$

The total cost for the ten-year period is $596,300.

Exercise Set 8.2

1. $a_1 = 200,\ d = 20$
The first six terms are 200, 220, 240, 260, 280, and 300.

3. $a_1 = -7,\ d = 4$
The first six terms are –7, –3, 1, 5, 9, and 13.

5. $a_1 = 300,\ d = -90$
The first six terms are 300, 210, 120, 30, –60, and –150.

7. $a_1 = \frac{5}{2},\ d = -\frac{1}{2}$

The first six terms are $\frac{5}{2}, 2, \frac{3}{2}, 1, \frac{1}{2}$, and 0.

9. $a_n = a_{n-1} + 6,\ a_1 = -9$
The first six terms are –9, –3, 3, 9, 15, and 21.

11. $a_n = a_{n-1} - 10,\ a_1 = 30$
The first six terms are 30, 20, 10, 0, –10, and –20.

13. $a_n = a_{n-1} - 0.4,\ a_1 = 1.6$
The first six terms are 1.6, 1.2, 0.8, 0.4, 0, and –0.4.

15. $a_1 = 13,\ d = -4$
$$a_n = 13 + (n-1)4$$
$$a_6 = 13 + 5(4) = 13 + 20 = 33$$

17. $a_1 = 7,\ d = 5$
$$a_n = 7 + (n-1)2$$
$$a_{50} = 7 + 49(5) = 252$$

19. $a_1 = -40,\ d = 5$
$$a_n = -40 + (n-1)5$$
$$a_{200} = -40 + (199)5 = 955$$

21. $a_1 = 35,\ d = -3$
$$a_n = 35 - 3(n-1)$$
$$a_{60} = 35 - 3(59) = -142$$

23. 1, 5, 9, 13, …
$$d = 5 - 1,\ = 4$$
$$a_n = 1 + (n-1)4 = 1 + 4n - 4$$
$$a_n = 4n - 3$$
$$a_{20} = 4(20) - 3 = 77$$

25. 7, 3, –1, –5, …
$$d = 3 - 7 = -4$$
$$a_n = 7 + (n-1)(-4) = 7 - 4n + 4$$
$$a_n = 11 - 4n$$
$$a_{20} = 11 - 4(20) = -69$$

27. $a_1 = 9,\ d = 2$
$$a_n = 9 + (n-1)(2)$$
$$a_n = 7 + 2n$$
$$a_{20} = 7 + 2(20) = 47$$

29. $a_1 = -20,\ d = -4$
$$a_n = -20 + (n-1)(-4)$$
$$a_n = -20 - 4n + 4$$
$$a_n = -16 - 4n$$
$$a_{20} = -16 - 4(20) = -96$$

31. $a_n = a_{n-1} + 3,\ a_1 = 4$
$d = 3$
$a_n = 4 + (n-1)(3)$
$a_n = 1 + 3n$
$a_{20} = 1 + 3(20) = 61$

33. $a_n = a_{n-1} - 10,\ a_1 = 30,\ d = -10$
$a_n = 30 - 10(n-1) = 30 - 10n + 10$
$= 40 - 10n$
$a_{20} = 40 - 10(20) = -160$

35. 4, 10, 16, 22, . . .
$d = 10 - 4 = 6$
$a_n = 4 + (n-1)(6)$
$a_{20} = 4 + (19)(6) = 118$
$S_{20} = \frac{20}{2}(4 + 118) = 1220$

37. −10, −6, −2, 2, . . .
$d = -6 - (-10) = -6 + 10 = 4$
$a_n = -10 + (n-1)4$
$a_{50} = -10 + (49)4 = 186$
$S_{50} = \frac{50}{2}(-10 + 186) = 4400$

39. $1 + 2 + 3 + 4 + \cdots + 100$
$S_{100} = \frac{100}{2}(1 + 100) = 5050$

41. $2 + 4 + 6 + \cdots + 120$
$S_{60} = \frac{60}{2}(2 + 120) = 3660$

43. even integers between 21 and 45;
$22 + 24 + 26 + \cdots + 144$
$S_{12} = \frac{12}{2}(22 + 44) = 396$

45. $\sum_{i=1}^{17}(5i + 3)$
$= (5+3) + (10+3) + (15+3) + \cdots + (85+3)$
$= 8 + 13 + 18 + \cdots + 88$
$S_{17} = \frac{17}{2}(8 + 88) = 816$

47. $\sum_{i=1}^{30}(-3i + 5)$
$= (-3+5) + (-6+5) + (-9+5) + \cdots$
$+ (-90+5)$
$= 2 - 1 - 4 - \cdots - 85$
$S_{30} = \frac{30}{2}(2 - 85) = -1245$

49. $\sum_{i=1}^{100} 4i = 4 + 8 + 12 + \cdots + 400$
$S_{100} = \frac{100}{2}(4 + 400) = 20,200$

51. a. $a_n = 126,424,\ d = 1265$
$a_n = 126,424 + (n-1)(1265)$
$a_n = 125,159 + 1265n$

b. $n = 2005 - 1989 = 16$
$a_{16} = 125,159 + 1265(16) = 145,399$
In 2005, there will be 145,399 thousand employees.

53. Company A:
$a_n = 24,000 + (n-1)(1600)$
$a_{10} = 24,000 + 9(1600) = \$38,400$
Company B:
$a_n = 28,000 + (n-1)(1000)$
$a_{10} = 28,000 + 9(1000) = \$37,000$
Company A will pay $1400 more.

55. a. $a_1 = 3.78,\ d = 0.576$
$a_n = 3.78 + (n-1)(0.576)$
$a_n = 3.204 + 0.576n$

b. $a_1 = 3.78$
$a_{41} = 3.204 + 0.576(41) = 26.82$
$S_{41} = \frac{41}{2}(3.78 + 26.82) = 627.3$
The total amount is 627.3 million tons.

57. $a_n = 33,000 + (n-1)(2500)$
$a_{10} = 33,000 + 9(2500) = 55,500$
$S_n = \frac{10}{2}(33,000 + 55,500) = 442,500$
The total ten year salary is $442,500.

59. $a_n = 30 + (n-1)2$
$a_{26} = 30 + (25)2 = 80$
$S_{26} = \frac{26}{2}(30 + 80) = 1430$
The theater has 1430 seats.

61.–65. Answers may vary.

67. Answers may vary for Exercises 45, 47, and 49:
Exercise 45

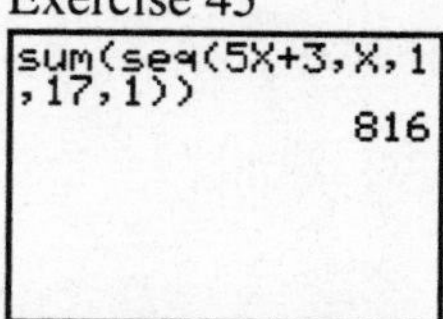

Exercise 47

```
sum(seq(-3X+5,X,
1,30,1))
                 -1245
```

Exercise 49

```
sum(seq(4X,X,1,1
00,1))
                 20200
```

69. 21,700, 23,172, 24,644, 26,166, . . . , 314,628
$d = 23{,}172 - 21{,}700 = 1472$
$314{,}628 = 1472n + 20{,}228$
$1472n = 294{,}400$
$n = 200$
It is the 200th term.

71. $1 + 3 + 5 + \cdots + (2n-1)$
$S_n = \frac{n}{2}(1 + 2n - 1)$
$= \frac{n}{2}(2n)$
$= n^2$

Section 8.3

Check Point Exercises

1. $a_1 = 12,\ r = \frac{1}{2}$
$a_2 = 12\left(\frac{1}{2}\right)^1 = 6$
$a_3 = 12\left(\frac{1}{2}\right)^2 = \frac{12}{4} = 3$
$a_4 = 12\left(\frac{1}{2}\right)^3 = \frac{12}{8} = \frac{3}{2}$
$a_5 = 12\left(\frac{1}{2}\right)^4 = \frac{12}{16} = \frac{3}{4}$
$a_6 = 12\left(\frac{1}{2}\right)^5 = \frac{12}{32} = \frac{3}{8}$

The first six terms are 12, 6, 3, $\frac{3}{2}$, $\frac{3}{4}$, and $\frac{3}{8}$.

2. $a_1 = 5,\ r = -3$
$a_n = 5r^{n-1}$
$a_7 = 5(-3)^{7-1} = 5(-3)^6 = 5(729) = 3645$
The seventh term is 3645.

3. 3, 6, 12, 24, 48, ...
$r = \frac{6}{3} = 2,\ a_1 = 3$
$a_n = 3(2)^{n-1}$
$a_8 = 3(2)^{8-1} = 3(2)^7 = 3(128) = 384$
The eighth term is 384.

4. $a_1 = 2,\ r = \frac{-6}{2} = -3$
$S_n = \frac{a_1(1 - r^r)}{1 - r}$
$S_9 = \frac{2\left(1 - (-3)^9\right)}{1 - (-3)} = \frac{2(19{,}684)}{4} = 9842$
The sum of the first nine terms is 9842.

5. $\sum_{i=1}^{8} 2 \cdot 3^i$

$a_1 = 2 \cdot (3)^1 = 6,\ r = 3$

$S_n = \frac{a_1(1-r^n)}{1-r}$

$S_8 = \frac{6\left(1-3^8\right)}{1-3} = \frac{6(-6560)}{-2} = 19,680$

Thus, $\sum_{i=1}^{8} 2 \cdot 3^i = 19,680.$

6. $a_1 = 30,000,\ r = 1.06$

$S_n = \frac{a_1(1-r^n)}{1-r}$

$S_{30} = \frac{30,000\left(1-(1.06)^{30}\right)}{1-1.06} \approx 2,371,746$

The total lifetime salary is \$2,371,746.

7. $A = P\frac{\left(1+\frac{r}{n}\right)^{nt}-1}{\frac{r}{n}}$

$P = 3000,\ r = 0.10,\ n = 1,\ t = 40$

$A = 3000\frac{(1+0.10)^{40}-1}{0.10} \approx 1,327,778$

The value of the IRA will be \$1,327,778.

8. $3+2+\frac{4}{3}+\frac{8}{9}+\cdots$

$a_1 = 3,\ r = \frac{2}{3}$

$S = \frac{a_1}{1-r}$

$S = \frac{3}{1-\frac{2}{3}} = \frac{3}{\frac{1}{3}} = 9$

The sum of this infinite geometric series is 9.

9. $0.\overline{9} = 0.9999\ldots = \frac{9}{10}+\frac{9}{100}+\frac{9}{1000}+\cdots$

$a_1 = \frac{9}{10},\ r = \frac{1}{10}$

$S = \frac{\frac{9}{10}}{1-\frac{1}{10}} = \frac{\frac{9}{10}}{\frac{9}{10}} = 1$

An equivalent fraction for $0.\overline{9}$ is 1.

10. $a_1 = 1000(0.8) = 800,\ r = 0.8$

$S = \frac{800}{1-0.8} = 4000$

The total amount spent is \$4000.

Exercise Set 8.3

1. $a_1 = 5,\ r = 3$

The first five terms are 5, 15, 45, 135, and 405.

3. $a_1 = 20,\ r = \frac{1}{2}$

The first five terms are 20, 10, 5, $\frac{5}{2}$, and $\frac{5}{4}$.

5. $a_n = -4a_{n-1},\ a_1 = 10$

The first five terms are 10, –40, 160, –640, and 2560.

7. $a_n = -5a_{n-1},\ a_1 = -6$

The first five terms are –6, 30, –150, 750, and –3750.

9. $a_1 = 6,\ r = 2$

$a_n = 6 \cdot 2^{n-1}$

$a_8 = 6 \cdot 2^7 = 768$

11. $a_1 = 5,\ r = -2$

$a_n = 5 \cdot (-2)^{n-1}$

$a_{12} = 5 \cdot (-2)^{11} = -10,240$

13. $a_1 = 1000,\ r = -\frac{1}{2}$

$$a_n = 1000\left(-\frac{1}{2}\right)^{n-1}$$

$$a_{40} = 1000\left(-\frac{1}{2}\right)^{39} \approx 0.000000002$$

15. $a_1 = 1,000,000,\ r = 0.1$

$$a_n = 1,000,000(0.1)^{n-1}$$

$$a_8 = 1,000,000(0.1)^7 = 0.1$$

17. 3, 12, 48, 192, . . .

$$r = \frac{12}{3} = 4$$

$$a_n = 3(4)^{n-1}$$

$$a_7 = 3(4)^6 = 12,288$$

19. $18,\ 6,\ 2,\ \frac{2}{3}, \ldots$

$$r = \frac{6}{18} = \frac{1}{3}$$

$$a_n = 18\left(\frac{1}{3}\right)^{n-1}$$

$$a_7 = 18\left(\frac{1}{3}\right)^6 = \frac{2}{81}$$

21. 1.5, –3, 6, –12, . . .

$$r = \frac{6}{-3} = -2$$

$$a_n = 1.5(-2)^{n-1}$$

$$a_7 = 1.5(-2)^6 = 96$$

23. 0.0004, –0.004, 0.04, –0.4, . . .

$$r = \frac{-0.004}{0.0004} = -10$$

$$a_n = 0.0004(-10)^{n-1}$$

$$a_7 = 0.0004(-10)^6 = 400$$

25. 2, 6, 18, 54, . . .

$$r = \frac{6}{2} = 3$$

$$S_{12} = \frac{2\left(1-3^{12}\right)}{1-3} = \frac{2(-531,440)}{-2} = 531,440$$

27. 3, –6, 12, –24, . . .

$$r = \frac{-6}{3} = -2$$

$$S_{11} = \frac{3\left[1-(-2)^{11}\right]}{1-(-2)} = \frac{3(2049)}{3} = 2049$$

29. $-\frac{3}{2},\ 3,\ -6,\ 12, \ldots$

$$r = \frac{3}{\frac{-3}{2}} = -2$$

$$S_{14} = \frac{-\frac{3}{2}\left[1-(-2)^{14}\right]}{1-(-2)} = \frac{-\frac{3}{2}(-16,383)}{3} = \frac{16,383}{2}$$

31. $\sum_{i=1}^{8} 3^i$

$r = 3,\ a_1 = 3$

$$S_8 = \frac{3\left(1-3^8\right)}{1-3} = \frac{3(-6560)}{-2} = 9840$$

33. $\sum_{i=1}^{10} 5 \cdot 2^i$

$r = 2,\ a_1 = 10$

$$S_{10} = \frac{10\left(1-2^{10}\right)}{1-2} = \frac{10(-1023)}{-1} = 10,230$$

35. $\sum_{i=1}^{6} \left(\frac{1}{2}\right)^{i+1}$

$r = \frac{1}{2},\ a_1 = \frac{1}{4}$

$$S_6 = \frac{\frac{1}{4}\left(1-\left(\frac{1}{2}\right)^6\right)}{1-\frac{1}{2}} = \frac{\frac{1}{4}\left(\frac{63}{64}\right)}{\frac{1}{2}} = \frac{63}{128}$$

37. $1+\frac{1}{3}+\frac{1}{9}+\frac{1}{27}+\cdots$

$r=\frac{1}{3}$

$S_\infty=\frac{1}{1-\frac{1}{3}}=\frac{1}{\frac{2}{3}}=\frac{3}{2}$

39. $3+\frac{3}{4}+\frac{3}{4^2}+\frac{3}{4^3}+\cdots$

$r=\frac{1}{4}$

$S_\infty=\frac{3}{1-\frac{1}{4}}=\frac{3}{\frac{3}{4}}=4$

41. $1-\frac{1}{2}-\frac{1}{4}-\frac{1}{8}+\cdots$

$r=-\frac{1}{2}$

$S_\infty=\frac{1}{1-\left(-\frac{1}{2}\right)}=\frac{1}{\frac{3}{2}}=\frac{2}{3}$

43. $\sum_{i=1}^{\infty}8(-0.3)^{i-1}=8-2.4+\cdots$

$r=-0.3$

$S_\infty=\frac{8}{1-(-0.3)}=\frac{8}{1.3}\approx 6.15385$

45. $0.\overline{5}=\frac{5}{10}+\frac{5}{100}+\frac{5}{1000}+\frac{5}{10,000}+\cdots$

$r=\frac{1}{10}$

$S_\infty=\frac{\frac{5}{10}}{1-\frac{1}{10}}=\frac{\frac{5}{10}}{\frac{9}{10}}=\frac{5}{9}$

47. $0.47=\frac{47}{100}+\frac{47}{10,000}+\frac{47}{1,000,000}+\cdots$

$r=\frac{1}{100}$

$S_\infty=\frac{\frac{47}{100}}{1-\frac{1}{100}}=\frac{\frac{47}{100}}{\frac{99}{100}}=\frac{47}{99}$

49. $0.\overline{257}=\frac{257}{1000}+\frac{257}{10^6}+\frac{257}{10^9}+\cdots$

$r=\frac{1}{1000}$

$S_\infty=\frac{\frac{257}{1000}}{1-\frac{1}{1000}}=\frac{\frac{257}{1000}}{\frac{999}{1000}}=\frac{257}{999}$

51. $a_n=n+5$

arithmetic, $d=1$

53. $a_n=2^n$

geometric, $r=2$

55. $a_n=n^2+5$

neither

57. 1, 2, 4, 8, . . .

$r=2$

$a_n=2^{n-1}$

$a_{15}=2^{14}=\$16,384$

59. $a_1=3,000,000$

$r=1.04$

$a_n=3,000,000(1.04)^{n-1}$

$a_7=3,000,000(1.04)^6=\$3,795,957$

61. a. $\frac{1996}{1995}\Rightarrow\frac{21.36}{20.60}\approx 1.04$

$\frac{1997}{1996}\Rightarrow\frac{22.19}{21.36}\approx 1.04$

$\frac{1998}{1997}\Rightarrow\frac{23.02}{22.19}\approx 1.04$

The population is increasing geometrically with $r = 1.04$.

b. $a_n=20.6(1.04)^{n-1}$

c. $2005-1994=11$

$a_{11}=20.6(1.04)^{10}$

≈ 30.49

In 2005, Iraq will have a population of 30.49 million.

63. $1, 2, 4, 8, \ldots$

$r = 2$

$$S_{15} = \frac{1(1-2^{15})}{1-2} = 32,767$$

The total savings is \$32,767.

65. $a_1 = 24,000,\ r = 1.05$

$$S_{20} = \frac{24,000\left[1-(1.05)^{20}\right]}{1-1.05} = 793,582.90$$

The total salary is \$793,582.90.

67. $20 + 0.9(20) + (0.9)^2(20) + \cdots$

$r = 0.9$

$$S_{10} = \frac{20(1-0.9^{10})}{1-0.9} \approx 130.26$$

The total length is 130.26 inches.

69. $A = 2500\dfrac{(1+0.09)^{40}-1}{0.09} \approx 844,706.11$

In 40 years, the value is \$844,706.11.

71. $A = 600\dfrac{\left(1+\frac{0.08}{4}\right)^{72}-1}{\frac{0.08}{4}} \approx 94,834.21$

After 18 years, the value is \$94,834.21.

73. $6(0.6) + 6(0.6)^2 + 6(0.6)^3 + \cdots$

$r = 0.6$

$$S_\infty = \frac{6(0.6)}{1-0.6} = 9$$

The total economic impact is \$9 million.

75. $\frac{1}{4} + \frac{1}{16} + \frac{1}{64} + \cdots$

$r = \frac{1}{4}$

$$S_\infty = \frac{\frac{1}{4}}{1-\frac{1}{4}} = \frac{1}{4}\cdot\frac{4}{3} = \frac{1}{3}$$

77.–83. Answers may vary.

85. Exercise 17

```
seq(3(4)^(X-1),X
,1,7,1)
...768 3072 12288}
```

Exercise 19

```
seq(18(1/3)^(X-1
),X,1,7,1)►Frac
... 2/9 2/27 2/81}
```

Exercise 21

```
seq(1.5(-2)^(X-1
),X,1,7,1)
... -12 24 -48 96}
```

87. $f(x) = \dfrac{2\left[1-\left(\frac{1}{3}\right)^x\right]}{1-\frac{1}{3}}$

10

−10 10

−10

Horizontal asymptote at $y = 3$

$$\sum_{n=0}^{\infty} 2\left(\tfrac{1}{3}\right)^n = \frac{2}{1-\frac{1}{3}} = 3$$

89. **a.** False; there is no common ratio.

b. False; the sum can be calculated exactly, since the series is geometric $\left(r = \frac{1}{2}\right)$.

c. False; $10 - 5 + \frac{5}{2} - \frac{5}{4} \cdots = \frac{10}{1+\frac{1}{2}}$

d. True; $r = 0.5 = \frac{1}{2}$

(d) is true.

91. $1,000,000 = P\dfrac{\left(1+\frac{0.1}{12}\right)^{360}-1}{\frac{0.1}{12}}$

$1,000,000 \approx 2260.49P$

$P \approx 442.38$

You must deposit \$442.38 monthly.

Section 8.4

Check Point Exercises

1. a.

$$S_1:\ 2 = 1(1+1)$$
$$S_k:\ 2+4+6+\cdots+2k = k(k+1)$$
$$S_{k+1}:\ 2+4+6+\cdots+2(k+1) = (k+1)(k+2)$$

b.

$$S_1:\ 1^3 = \frac{1^2(1+1)^2}{4}$$
$$S_k:\ 1^3+2^3+3^3+\cdots+k^3 = \frac{k^2(k+1)^2}{4}$$
$$S_{k+1}:\ 1^3+2^3+3^3+\cdots+(k+1)^3 = \frac{(k+1)^2(k+2)^2}{4}$$

2.

$S_1: 2 = 1(1+1)$
$2 = 2$ is true.
$S_k: 2+4+6+\cdots+2k = k(k+1)$
$S_{k+1}: 2+4+6+\cdots+2k+2(k+1) = (k+1)(k+2)$
Add $2(k+1)$ to both sides of S_k:
$2+4+6+\cdots+2k+2(k+1) = k(k+1)+2(k+1)$
Simplify the right-hand side:
$k(k+1)+2(k+1) = (k+1)(k+2)$
If S_k is true, then S_{k+1} is true. The statement is true for all n.

3.

$$S_1:\ 1^3 = \frac{1^2(1+1)^2}{4}$$
$$1 = \frac{4}{4}$$
$1 = 1$ is true.

$$S_k:\ 1^3+2^3+3^3+\cdots+k^3 = \frac{k^2(k+1)^2}{4}$$
$$S_{k+1}:\ 1^3+2^3+3^3+\cdots+k^3+(k+1)^3 = \frac{(k+1)^2(k+2)^2}{4}$$

Add $(k+1)^3$ to both sides of S_k:

$$1^3+2^3+3^3+\cdots+k^3+(k+1)^3 = \frac{k^2(k+1)^2}{4}+(k+1)^3$$

Simplify the right hand side:

$$\frac{k^2(k+1)^2}{4}+(k+1)^3 = \frac{k^2(k+1)^2+4(k+1)^3}{4} = \frac{(k+1)^2\left[k^2+4(k+1)\right]}{4} = \frac{(k+1)^2(k^2+4k+4)}{4}$$
$$= \frac{(k+1)^2(k+2)^2}{4}$$

If S_k is true, then S_{k+1} is true. The statement is true for all n.

4. S_1: 2 is a factor $1^2 + 1 = 2$, since $2 = 2 \cdot 1$.
S_k: 2 is a factor of $k^2 + k$
S_{k+1}: 2 is a factor of $(k + 1)^2 + (k + 1)$
Simplify:

$$\begin{aligned}(k+1)^2 + (k+1) &= k^2 + 2k + 1 + k + 1 \\ &= k^2 + 3k + 2 \\ &= k^2 + k + 2k + 2 \\ &= (k^2 + k) + 2(k+1)\end{aligned}$$

Because we assume S_k is true, we know 2 is a factor of $k^2 + k$. Since 2 is a factor of $2(k + 1)$, we conclude 2 is a factor of the sum $(k^2 + k) + 2(k + 1)$. If S_k is true, then S_{k+1} is true. The statement is true for all n.

Exercise Set 8.4

1. S_n: $1+3+5+\cdots+(n-1)=n^2$

S_1: $1=1^2$
$1=1$ true

S_2: $1+3=2^2$
$4=4$ true

S_3: $1+3+5=3^2$
$9=9$ true

3. S_n: 2 is a factor of n^2-n

S_1: 2 is a factor of $1^2-1=0$
$0=0\cdot 2$ so 2 is a factor of 0 is true.

S_2: 2 is a factor of $2^2-2=2$
$2=1\cdot 2$ so 2 is a factor of 2 is true.

S_3: 2 is a factor of $3^2-3=6$
$6=3\cdot 2$ so 2 is a factor of 6 is true.

5. S_n: $4+8+12+\cdots+4n=2n(n+1)$
S_k: $4+8+12+\cdots+4k=2k(k+1)$
S_{k+1}: $4+8+12+\cdots+4(k+1)=2(k+1)(k+1+1)$
$4+8+12+\cdots+(4k+4)=2(k+1)(k+2)$

7. S_n: $3+7+11+\cdots+(4n-1)=n(2n+1)$
S_k: $3+7+11+\cdots+(4k-1)=k(2k+1)$
S_{k+1}: $3+7+11+\cdots+\left[4(k+1)-1\right]=(k+1)\left[2(k+1)+1\right]$
$3+7+11+\cdots+(4k+3)=(k+1)(2k+3)$

9. S_n: 2 is a factor of $n^2 - n + 2$

S_k: 2 is a factor of $k^2 - k + 2$

S_{k+1}: 2 is a factor of $(\mathrm{k}+1)^2 - (k+1) + 2$

$k^2 + 2k + 1 - k - 1 + 2 = k^2 + k + 2$

S_{k+1}: 2 is a factor of $k^2 + k + 2$.

11. $S_1: 4 = 2(1)(1+1)$

$4 = 2(2)$

$4 = 4$ is true.

S_k: $4 + 8 + 12 + \cdots + 4k = 2k(k+1)$

S_{k+1}: $4 + 8 + 12 + \cdots + 4(k+1) = 2(k+1)(k+1+1)$

Add $4(k + 1)$ to both sides of S_k:

$4 + 8 + 12 + \cdots + 4k + 4(k+1) = 2k(k+1) + 4(k+1)$

Simplify the right-hand side:

$= 2k(k+1) + 4(k+1) = (2k+4)(k+1)$

$= 2(k+2)(k+1)$

$= 2(k+1)(k+1+1)$

If S_k is true, then S_{k+1} is true. The statement is true for all *n*.

13. $S_1: 1 = 1^2$

$1 = 1$ is true.

S_k: $1 + 3 + 5 + \cdots + (2k-1) = k^2$

S_{k+1}: $1 + 3 + 5 + \cdots + (2k-1) + (2(k+1)-1) = (k+1)^2$

$1 + 3 + 5 + \cdots + (2k-1) + (2k+1) = (k+1)^2$

Add $(2k + 1)$ to both sides of S_k:

$1 + 3 + 5 + \cdots + (2k-1) + (2k+1) = k^2 + (2k+1)$

Simplify the right-hand side:

$= k^2 + (2k + 1)$

$= (k + 1)^2$

If S_k is true, then S_{k+1} is true. The statement is true for all *n*.

15. $S_1: 3 = 1(2(1)+1)$

$3 = 3$ is true.

S_k: $3 + 7 + 11 + \cdots + (4k-1) = k(2k+1)$

S_{k+1}: $3 + 7 + 11 + \cdots + (4k-1) + [4(k+1)-1] = (k+1)[2(k+1)+1]$

$3 + 7 + 11 + \cdots + (4k-1) + (4k+3) = (k+1)(2k+3)$

Add $(4k + 3)$ to both sides of S_k:

$3 + 7 + 11 + \cdots + (4k - 1) + (4k - 3) = k(2k + 1) + 4(k + 3)$

Simplify the right-hand side:

$= k(2k+1) + (4k+3) = 2k^2 + k + 4k + 3$

$= 2k^2 + 5k + 3$

$= (k+1)(2k+3)$

If S_k is true, then S_{k+1} is true. The statement is true for all *n*.

17. $S_1: 1 = 2^1 - 1$

$1 = 1$ is true.

$S_k: 1+2+2^2+\cdots+2^{k-1} = 2^k - 1$

$S_{k+1}: 1+2+2^2+\cdots+2^{k-1}+2^{k+1-1} = 2^{k+1} - 1$

$1+2+2^2+\cdots+2^{k-1}+2^k = 2^{k+1} - 1$

Add 2^k to both sides of S_k:

$1+2+2^2+\cdots+2^{k-1}+2^k = 2^k + 2^k - 1$

Simplify the right-hand side:

$= 2^k + 2^k - 1 = 2\left(2^k\right) - 1$

$= 2^{k+1} - 1$

If S_k is true, then S_{k+1} is true. The statement is true for all n.

19. $S_1: 2 = 2^{1+1} - 2$

$2 = 4 - 2$

$2 = 2$ is true.

$S_k: 2+4+8+\cdots+2^k = 2^{k+1} - 2$

$S_{k+1}: 2+4+8+\cdots+2^k+2^{k+1} = 2^{k+2} - 2$

Add 2^{k+1} to both sides of S_k:

$2+4+8+\cdots+2^k+2^{k+1} = 2^{k+1} + 2^{k+1} - 2$

Simplify the right-hand side:

$= 2^{k+1} + 2^{k+1} - 1 = 2\left(2^{k+1}\right) - 2$

$= 2^{k+2} - 2$

If S_k is true, then S_{k+1} is true. The statement is true for all n.

21. $S_1: 1 \cdot 2 = \dfrac{1(1+1)(1+2)}{3}$

$2 = \dfrac{6}{3}$

$2 = 2$ is true.

$S_k: 1\cdot 2 + 2\cdot 3 + 3\cdot 4 + \cdots + k(k+1) = \dfrac{k(k+1)(k+2)}{3}$

$S_{k+1}: 1\cdot 2 + 2\cdot 3 + 3\cdot 4 + \cdots + k(k+1) + (k+1)(k+2) = \dfrac{(k+1)(k+2)(k+3)}{3}$

Add $(k+1)(k+2)$ to both sided of S_k:

$1\cdot 2 + 2\cdot 3 + 3\cdot 4 + \cdots + k(k+1) + (k+1)(k+2) = \dfrac{k(k+1)(k+2)}{3} + (k+1)(k+2)$

Simplify the right-hand side:

$= \dfrac{k(k+1)(k+2)}{3} + (k+1)(k+2) = \dfrac{k(k+1)(k+2) + 3(k+1)(k+2)}{3}$

$= \dfrac{(k+1)(k+2)(k+3)}{3}$

If S_k is true, then S_{k+1} is true. The statement is true for all n.

23. S_1: $\frac{1}{1\cdot 2}=\frac{1}{1+1}$

$\frac{1}{2}=\frac{1}{2}$ is true.

S_k: $\frac{1}{1\cdot 2}+\frac{1}{2\cdot 3}+\frac{1}{3\cdot 4}+\cdots+\frac{1}{k(k+1)}=\frac{k}{k+1}$

S_{k+1}: $\frac{1}{1\cdot 2}+\frac{1}{2\cdot 3}+\frac{1}{3\cdot 4}+\cdots+\frac{1}{k(k+1)}+\frac{1}{(k+1)(k+2)}=\frac{k+1}{k+2}$

Add $\frac{1}{(k+1)(k+2)}$ to both sides of S_k:

$$\frac{1}{1\cdot 2}+\frac{1}{2\cdot 3}+\frac{1}{3\cdot 4}+\cdots+\frac{1}{k(k+1)}+\frac{1}{(k+1)(k+2)}=\frac{k}{k+1}+\frac{1}{(k+1)(k+2)}$$

Simplify the right-hand side:

$$\frac{k}{(k+1)}+\frac{1}{(k+1)(k+2)}=\frac{k(k+2)+1}{(k+1)(k+2)}$$
$$=\frac{k^2+2k+1}{(k+1)(k+2)}$$
$$=\frac{(k+1)(k+1)}{(k+1)(k+2)}$$
$$=\frac{k+1}{k+2}$$

If S_k is true, then S_{k+1} is true. The statement is true for all n.

25. S_1: 2 is a factor of $1^2-1=0$, since $0=2\cdot 0$.

S_k: 2 is a factor of k^2-k

S_{k+1}: 2 is a factor of $(k+1)^2-(k+1)$

$$(k+1)^2-(k-1)=k^2+2k+1-k-1$$
$$=k^2+k$$
$$=k^2-k+2k$$
$$=(k^2-k)+2k$$

Because we assume S_k is true, we know 2 as a factor of k^2-k. Since 2 is a factor of 2*k*, we conclude 2 is factor of the sum $(k^2+k)+2k$. If S_k is true, then S_{k+1} is true. The statement is true for all n.

27. S_1: 6 is a factor of $1(1+1)(1+2)=6$, since $6=6\cdot 1$.

S_k: 6 is a factor of $k(k+1)(k+2)$

S_{k+1}: 6 is a factor of $(k+1)(k+2)(k+3)$

$$(k+1)(k+2)(k+3)=k(k+1)(k+2)+3(k+1)(k+2)$$

Because we assume S_k is true, we know 6 as a factor of $k(k+1)(k+2)$. Since either $k+1$ or $k+2$ must be even, the product $(k+1)(k+2)$ is even. Thus 2 is a factor of $(k+1)(k+2)$, and we can conclude that 6 is factor of $3(k+1)(k+2)$ If S_k is true, then S_{k+1} is true.

The statement is true for all n.

29. $S_1: (ab)^1 = a^1b^1$
$ab = ab$ is true.
$S_k: (ab)^k = a^k b^k$
$S_{k+1}: (ab)^{k+1} = a^{k+1}b^{k+1}$
Multiply both sides of S_k by ab:
$(ab)^k(ab) = a^k b^k(ab)$
$(ab)^{k+1} = a^{k+1}b^{k+1}$
If S_k is true, then S_{k+1} is true.
The statement is true for all n.

31. Answers may vary.

33. $n^2 > 2n + 1$ for $n \ge 3$
$S_3: 3^2 > 2 \cdot 3 + 1$
$9 > 7$
$S_k: k^2 > 2k + 1$ for $k \ge 3$
$S_{k+1}: (k + 1)^2 > 2k + 3.$
Add $2k + 1$ to both sides of S_k.
$k^2 + (2k+1) > 2k+1+(2k+1)$
Write the left side of the inequalities as the square of a binomial and simplify the right side. $(k+1)^2 > 4k+2$
Since $4k + 2 > 2k + 3$ for $k \ge 3$, we can conclude that $(k+1)^2 > 4k+2 > 2k+3$.
By the transitive property,
$(k+1)^2 > 2k+3$
$(k+1)^2 > 2(k+1)+1$
If S_k is true, then S_{k+1} is true.
The statement is true for all n.

35. S_1: $\frac{1}{4} = \frac{1}{4}$

S_2: $\frac{1}{4} + \frac{1}{12} = \frac{2}{6} = \frac{1}{3}$

S_3: $\frac{1}{4} + \frac{1}{12} + \frac{1}{24} = \frac{3}{8}$

S_4: $\frac{1}{4} + \frac{1}{12} + \frac{1}{24} + \frac{1}{40} = \frac{4}{10} = \frac{2}{5}$

S_5: $\frac{1}{4} + \frac{1}{12} + \frac{1}{24} + \frac{1}{40} + \frac{1}{60} = \frac{5}{12}$

S_n: $\frac{1}{4} + \frac{1}{12} + \frac{1}{24} + \cdots + \frac{1}{2n(n+1)} = \frac{n}{2n+2}$

S_k: $\frac{1}{4} + \frac{1}{12} + \frac{1}{24} + \cdots + \frac{1}{2k(k+1)} = \frac{k}{2k+2}$

S_{k+1}: $\frac{1}{4} + \frac{1}{12} + \frac{1}{24} + \cdots$
$+ \frac{1}{2k(k+1)} + \frac{1}{2(k+1)(k+2)}$
$= \frac{k+1}{2k+4}$

Add $\frac{1}{2(k+1)(k+2)}$ to both sides of S_k:

$\frac{1}{4} + \frac{1}{12} + \frac{1}{24} + \cdots + \frac{1}{2k(k+1)} + \frac{1}{2(k+1)(k+2)}$
$= \frac{k}{2k+2} + \frac{1}{2(k+1)(k+2)}$

Simplify the right-hand side:

$\frac{k}{2k+2} + \frac{1}{2(k+1)(k+2)}$
$= \frac{k(k+2)+1}{2(k+1)(k+2)}$
$= \frac{k^2+2k+1}{2(k+1)(k+2)}$
$= \frac{(k+1)^2}{2(k+1)(k+2)}$
$= \frac{k+1}{2k+4}$

If S_k is true, then S_{k+1} is true.
The conjecture is proven.

Section 8.5

Check Point Exercises

1. a. $\binom{6}{3} = \frac{6!}{3!(6-3)!} = \frac{6!}{3!3!} = \frac{5 \cdot 4}{1} = 20$

b. $\binom{6}{0} = \frac{6!}{0!(6-0)!} = \frac{6!}{6!} = 1$

c. $\binom{8}{2} = \frac{8!}{2!(8-2)!} = \frac{8!}{2!6!} = \frac{8 \cdot 7}{2} = 28$

d. $\binom{3}{3} = \frac{3!}{3!(3-3)!} = \frac{3!}{3!0!} = \frac{3!}{3!} = 1$

2. $(x+1)^4 = \binom{4}{0}x^4 + \binom{4}{1}x^3 + \binom{4}{2}x^2 + \binom{4}{1}x + \binom{4}{0} = x^4 + 4x^3 + 6x^2 + 4x + 1$

3. $(x-2y)^5$

$= \binom{5}{0}x^5(-2y)^0 + \binom{5}{1}x^4(-2y)^1 + \binom{5}{2}x^3(-2y)^2 + \binom{5}{3}x^2(-2y)^3 + \binom{5}{4}x(-2y)^4 + \binom{5}{5}x^0(-2y)^5$

$= x^5 - 5x^4(2y) + 10x^3(4y^2) - 10x^2(8y^3) + 5x(16y^4) - 32y^5$

$= x^5 - 10x^4y + 40x^3y^2 - 80x^2y^3 + 80xy^4 - 32y^5$

4. $(2x+y)^9$

fifth term $= \binom{9}{4}(2x)^5y^4 = \frac{9!}{4!5!}(32x^5)y^4 = 4032x^5y^4$

Exercise Set 8.5

1. $\binom{8}{3} = \frac{8!}{3!(8-3)!} = \frac{8 \cdot 7 \cdot 6}{3 \cdot 2 \cdot 1} = 56$

3. $\binom{12}{1} = \frac{12!}{1!11!} = 12$

5. $\binom{6}{6} = \frac{6!}{0!6!} = 1$

7. $\binom{100}{2} = \frac{100!}{2!98!} = \frac{100 \cdot 99}{2} = 4950$

9. $(x+2)^3 = \binom{3}{0}x^3 + \binom{3}{1}2x^2 + \binom{3}{2}4x + \binom{3}{3}8$
$= x^3 + 3x^2 \cdot 2 + 3x \cdot 4 + 8$
$= x^3 + 6x^2 + 12x + 8$

11. $(3x+y)^3 = \binom{3}{0}27x^3 + \binom{3}{1}9x^2y + \binom{3}{2}3xy^2 + \binom{3}{3}y^3$
$= 27x^3 + 27x^2y + 9xy^2 + y^3$

13. $(5x-1)^3 = \binom{3}{0}125x^3 - \binom{3}{1}25x^2 + \binom{3}{2}5x - \binom{3}{3}$
$= 125x^3 - 75x^2 + 15x - 1$

15. $(2x+1)^4 = \binom{4}{0}16x^4 - \binom{4}{1}8x^3 + \binom{4}{2}4x^2 + \binom{4}{3}2x + \binom{4}{4}$
$= 16x^4 + 32x^3 + 24x^2 + 8x + 1$

17. $(x^2+2y)^4 = \binom{4}{0}(x^2)^4 + \binom{4}{1}(x^2)^3(2y) + \binom{4}{2}(x^2)^2(2y)^2 + \binom{4}{3}(x^2)^1(2y)^3 + \binom{4}{4}(2y)^4$
$= 1(x^8) + 4(x^6)(2y) + 6(x^4)(4y^2) + 4x^2(8y^3) + 1(16y^4)$
$= x^8 + 8x^6y + 24x^4y^2 + 32x^2y^3 + 16y^4$

19. $(y-3)^4 = \binom{4}{0}y^4 + \binom{4}{1}y^3(-3) + \binom{4}{2}y^2(-3)^2 + \binom{4}{3}y(-3)^3 + \binom{4}{4}(-3)^4$
$= y^4 + 4(y^3)(-3) + 6(y^2)(9) + 4(y)(-27) + 81$
$= y^4 - 12y^3 + 54y^2 - 108y + 81$

21. $\left(2x^3-1\right)^4 = \binom{4}{0}\left(2x^3\right)^4 + \binom{4}{1}\left(2x^3\right)^3(-1) + \binom{4}{2}\left(2x^3\right)^2(-1)^2 + \binom{4}{3}\left(2x^3\right)(-1)^3 + \binom{4}{4}(-1)^4$
$= 16x^{12} - 4(8x^9) + 6(4x^6) - 4(2x^3) + 1$
$= 16x^{12} - 32x^9 + 24x^6 - 8x^3 + 1$

23. $(c+2)^5 = \binom{5}{0}c^5 + \binom{5}{1}c^4(2) + \binom{5}{2}c^3(2^2) + \binom{5}{3}c^2(2^3) + \binom{5}{4}c(2^4) + \binom{5}{5}(2^5)$
$= c^5 + 5c^4(2) + 10c^3(4) + 10c^2(8) + 5c(16) + 32$
$= c^5 + 10c^4 + 40c^3 + 80c^2 + 80c + 32$

25. $(x-1)^5 = \binom{5}{0}x^5 - \binom{5}{1}x^4 + \binom{5}{2}x^3 - \binom{5}{3}x^2 + \binom{5}{4}x - \binom{5}{5}$
$= x^5 - 5x^4 + 10x^3 - 10x^2 + 5x - 1$

27. $(x-2y)^5 = \binom{5}{0}x^5 - \binom{5}{1}x^4(2y) + \binom{5}{2}x^3(2y)^2 - \binom{5}{3}x^2(2y)^3 + \binom{5}{4}x(2y)^4 - \binom{5}{5}(2y)^5$
$= x^5 - 10x^4y + 40x^3y^2 - 80x^2y^3 + 80xy^4 - 32y^5$

29. $(2a+b)^6 = \binom{6}{0}(2a)^6 + \binom{6}{1}(2a)^5b + \binom{6}{2}(2a)^4b^2 + \binom{6}{3}(2a)^3b^3 + \binom{6}{4}(2a)^2b^4 + \binom{6}{5}(2a)b^5 + \binom{6}{6}b^6$
$= 64a^6 + 6(32a^5)b + 15(16a^4)b^2 + 20(8a^3)b^3 + 15(4a^2)b^4 + 6(2a)b^5 + b^6$
$= 64a^6 + 192a^5b + 240a^4b^2 + 160a^3b^3 + 60a^2b^4 + 12ab^5 + b^6$

31. $(x+2)^8 = \binom{8}{0}x^8 + \binom{8}{1}2x^7 + \binom{8}{2}2^2x^6 + \cdots$
$= x^8 + 16x^7 + 112x^6 + \cdots$

33. $(x-2y)^{10} = \binom{10}{0}x^{10} - \binom{10}{1}x^9(2y) + \binom{10}{2}x^8(2y)^2 - \cdots$
$= x^{10} - 20x^9y + 180x^8y^2 - \cdots$

35. $\left(x^2+1\right)^{16} = \binom{16}{0}\left(x^2\right)^{16} + \binom{16}{1}\left(x^2\right)^{15} + \binom{16}{2}\left(x^2\right)^{14} + \cdots$
$= x^{32} + 16x^{30} + 120x^{28} + \cdots$

37. $\left(y^3-1\right)^{20} = \binom{20}{0}\left(y^3\right)^{20} - \binom{20}{1}\left(y^3\right)^{19} + \binom{20}{2}\left(y^3\right)^{18} - \cdots$
$= y^{60} - 20y^{57} + 190y^{54} - \cdots$

39. $(2x+y)^6$

third term $= \binom{6}{2}(2x)^4(y)^2 = 15\left(16x^4y^2\right) = 240x^4y^2$

41. $(x-1)^9$

fifth term $= \binom{9}{4}x^5(-1)^4 = 126x^5$

43. $\left(x^2+y^3\right)^8$

sixth term $= \binom{8}{5}\left(x^2\right)^3\left(y^3\right)^5 = 56x^6y^{15}$

45. $\left(x-\frac{1}{2}\right)^9$

fourth term $= \binom{9}{3}x^6\left(-\frac{1}{2}\right)^3 = 84x^6\left(-\frac{1}{8}\right) = -\frac{21}{2}x^6$

47. $f(t)=0.002t^3-0.9t^2+1.27t+6.76,\ 0\le t\le 20$

$$g(t)=f(t+10)=0.002(t+10)^3-0.9(t+10)^2+1.27(t+10)+6.76$$

$$(t+10)^3=\binom{3}{0}t^3+\binom{3}{1}t^2\cdot 10+\binom{3}{2}t\cdot 10^2+\binom{3}{3}10^3=t^3+30t^2+300t+1000$$

$$(t+10)^2=\binom{2}{0}t^2+\binom{2}{1}t\cdot 10+\binom{2}{2}10^2=t^2+20t+100$$

$$\begin{aligned}g(t)&=0.002\left(t^3+30t^2+300t+1000\right)-0.9\left(t^2+20t+100\right)+1.27(t+10)+6.76\\&=0.002t^3+0.06t^2+0.6t+2-0.9t^2-18t-90+1.27t+12.7+6.76\\&=0.002t^3-0.84t^2-16.13t-68.54\end{aligned}$$

49.–57. Answers may vary.

59. Exercises 1 and 3   Exercises 5 and 7

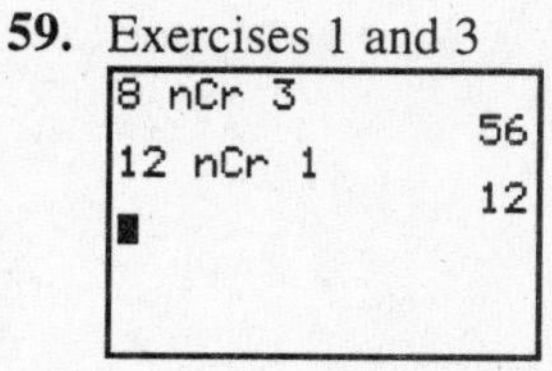

61. $f_1(x)=(x+1)^4$

$f_2(x)=x^4$

$f_3(x)=x^4+4x^3$

$f_4(x)=x^4+4x^3+6x^2$

$f_5(x)=x^4+4x^3+6x^2+4x$

$f_6(x)=x^4+4x^3+6x^2+4x+1$

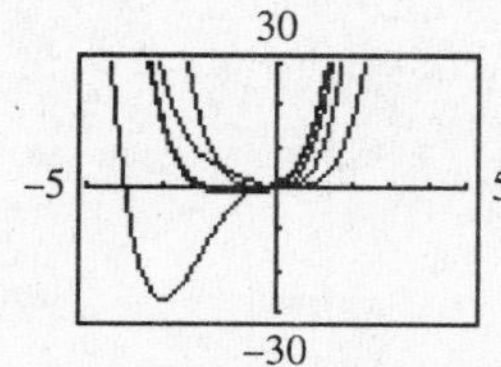

f_2, f_3, f_4, and f_5 are approaching $f_1=f_6$.

63. $f_1(x)=(x-2)^4$

$$\begin{aligned}&=\binom{4}{0}x^4+\binom{4}{1}x^3(-2)+\binom{4}{2}x^2(-2)^2+\binom{4}{3}x(-2)^3+\binom{4}{4}(-2)^4\\&=x^4+4x^3(-2)+6x^2(4)+4x(-8)+16\\&=x^4-8x^3+24x^2-32x+16\end{aligned}$$

65. Exercises 9, 11 and 13

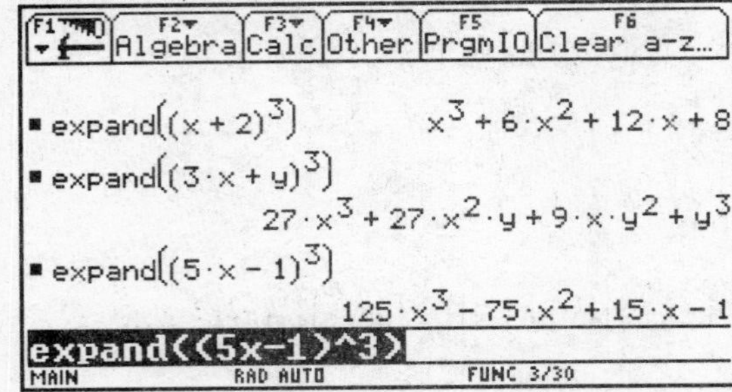

Exercises 15 and 17

F1 F2 Algebra F3 Calc F4 Other F5 PrgmIO F6 Clear a-z...
expand((2·x + 1)^4)
16·x^4 + 32·x^3 + 24·x^2 + 8·x + 1
expand((x^2 + 2·y)^4)
x^8 + 8·x^6·y + 24·x^4·y^2 + 32·x^2·y^3 + 16·y^4
expand((x^2+2y)^4)
MAIN RAD AUTO FUNC 2/30

67. $(x^2+x+1)^3 = \left[x^2+(x+1)\right]^3$

$$= \binom{3}{0}\left(x^2\right)^3 + \binom{3}{1}\left(x^2\right)^2(x+1) + \binom{3}{2}x^2(x+1)^2 + \binom{3}{3}(x+1)^3$$
$$= x^6 + 3x^4(x+1) + 3x^2\left(x^2+2x+1\right) + x^3 + 3x^2 + 3x + 1$$
$$= x^6 + 3x^5 + 3x^4 + 3x^4 + 6x^3 + 3x^2 + x^3 + 3x^2 + 3x + 1$$
$$= x^6 + 3x^5 + 6x^4 + 7x^3 + 6x^2 + 3x + 1$$

69. $\binom{n}{r} = \dfrac{n!}{r!(n-r)!}$

$$\binom{n}{n-r} = \frac{n!}{(n-r)!\left[n-(n-r)\right]!} = \frac{n!}{(n-r)!\,r!} = \binom{n}{r}$$

71. a. S_1: $(a+b)^1 = \binom{1}{0}a^1 + \binom{1}{1}a^{1-1}b = a+b$

b. S_k: $(a+b)^k = \binom{k}{0}a^k + \binom{k}{1}a^{k-1}b + \binom{k}{2}a^{k-2}b^2 + \cdots + \binom{k}{k-1}ab^{k-1} + \binom{k}{k}b^k$

S_{k+1}: $(a+b)^{k+1} = \binom{k+1}{0}a^{k+1} + \binom{k+1}{1}a^kb + \binom{k+1}{2}a^{k-1}b^2 + \cdots + \binom{k+1}{k}ab^k + \binom{k+1}{k+1}b^{k+1}$

c. $(a+b)(a+b)^k$

$$(a+b)^{k+1} = \binom{k}{0}a^{k+1} + \binom{k}{0}a^k b + \binom{k}{1}a^k b + \binom{k}{1}a^{k-1}b^2 + \binom{k}{2}a^{k-1}b^2 + \binom{k}{2}a^{k-2}b^3 + \cdots$$
$$+\binom{k}{k-1}a^2b^{k-1} + \binom{k}{k-1}ab^k + \binom{k}{k}ab^k + \binom{k}{k}b^{k+1}$$

d. $$(a+b)^{k+1} = \binom{k}{0}a^{k+1} + \left[\binom{k}{0}+\binom{k}{1}\right]a^k b + \left[\binom{k}{1}+\binom{k}{2}\right]a^{k-1}b^2 + \left[\binom{k}{2}+\binom{k}{3}\right]a^{k-2}b^3 + \cdots$$
$$+\left[\binom{k}{k-1}+\binom{k}{k}\right]ab^k + \binom{k}{k}b^{k+1}$$

e. $$(a+b)^{k+1} = \binom{k}{0}a^{k+1} + \binom{k+1}{1}a^k b + \binom{k+1}{2}a^{k-1}b^2 + \binom{k+1}{3}a^{k-2}b^3 + \cdots + \binom{k+1}{k}ab^k + \binom{k}{k}b^{k+1}$$

f. $\binom{k}{0} = \binom{k+1}{0}$ because both equal 1. $\binom{k}{k} = \binom{k+1}{k+1}$ also because both equal 1.

$$S_{k+1}\text{: } (a+b)^{k+1} = \binom{k+1}{0}a^{k+1} + \binom{k+1}{1}a^k b + \binom{k+1}{2}a^{k-1}b^2 + \cdots + \binom{k+1}{k}ab^k + \binom{k+1}{k+1}b^{k+1}$$

Section 8.6

Check Point Exercises

1. We use the Fundamental Counting Principal to find the number of ways a one-topping pizza can be ordered. Multiply the number of choices for each of the three groups. $3 \cdot 4 \cdot 6 = 72$ pizzas
There are 72 different ways of ordering a one-topping pizza.

2. We use the Fundamental Counting Principal to find the number of ways we can answer the questions. Multiply the number of choices, 3, for each of the six questions. $3 \cdot 3 \cdot 3 \cdot 3 \cdot 3 \cdot 3 = 3^6 = 729$ ways
There are 729 ways of answering the questions.

3. We use the Fundamental Counting Principal to find the number of different license plates that can be manufactured. Multiply the number of different letters, 26, for the first two places and the number of different digits, 10, for the next three places. $26 \cdot 26 \cdot 10 \cdot 10 \cdot 10 = 26^2 \cdot 1000 = 676{,}000$ plates
There are 676,000 different license plates possible.

4. Your group is choosing $r = 4$ officers from a group of $n = 7$ people. The order in which the officers are chosen matters because the four officers to be chosen have different responsibilities. Thus, we are looking for the number of permutations of 7 things taken 4 at a time.
We use the formula ${}_nP_r = \dfrac{n!}{(n-r)!}$ with $n = 7$ and $r = 4$. ${}_7P_4 = \dfrac{7!}{(7-4)!} = \dfrac{7!}{3!} = 840$.
Thus, there are 840 different ways of filling the four offices.

5. Because you are using all six of your books in every possible arrangement, you are arranging $r = 6$ books from a group of $n = 6$ books. Thus, we are looking for the number of permutations of 6 things taken 6 at a time. We use the formula

$${}_nP_r = \frac{n!}{(n-r)!} \text{ with } n = 6 \text{ and } r = 6.$$

$${}_6P_6 = \frac{6!}{(6-6)!} = \frac{6!}{0!} = 6! = 720.$$

There are 720 different possible permutations. Thus, you can arrange the books in 720 ways.

6. a. The order does not matter; this is a combination.

b. Since what place each runner finishes matters, this is a permutation.

7. The order in which the four people are selected does not matter. This is a problem of selecting $r = 4$ people from a group of $n = 10$ people. We are looking for the number of combinations of 10 things taken 4 at a time. We use the formula

$${}_nC_r = \frac{n!}{(n-r)!\ r!} \text{ with } n = 10 \text{ and } r = 4.$$

$${}_{10}C_4 = \frac{10!}{(10-4)!4!} = \frac{10!}{6!4!} = \frac{10\cdot 9\cdot 8\cdot 7\cdot 6!}{6!\cdot 4\cdot 3\cdot 2\cdot 1}$$

$$= \frac{10\cdot 9\cdot 8\cdot 7}{4\cdot 3\cdot 2\cdot 1} = 210$$

Thus, 210 committees of 4 people each can be found from 10 people at the conference on acupuncture.

8. Because the order in which the 4 cards are dealt does not matter, this is a problem involving combinations. We are looking for the number of combinations of $n = 16$ cards drawn $r = 4$ at a time. We use the formula

$${}_nC_r = \frac{n!}{(n-r)!\ r!} \text{ with } n = 16 \text{ and } r = 4.$$

$${}_{16}C_4 = \frac{16!}{(16-4)!4!} = \frac{16!}{12!4!} = \frac{16\cdot 15\cdot 14\cdot 13\cdot 12!}{12!\cdot 4\cdot 3\cdot 2\cdot 1}$$

$$= 1820$$

Thus, there are 1820 different 4-card hands possible.

Exercise Set 8.6

1. ${}_9P_4 = \frac{9!}{5!} = 3024$

3. ${}_8P_5 = \frac{8!}{3!} = 8\cdot 7\cdot 6\cdot 5\cdot 4 = 6720$

5. ${}_6P_6 = \frac{6!}{0!} = 720$

7. ${}_8P_0 = \frac{8!}{8!} = 1$

9. ${}_9C_5 = \frac{9!}{4!5!} = \frac{9\cdot 8\cdot 7\cdot 6}{4\cdot 3\cdot 2\cdot 1} = \frac{3\cdot 7\cdot 6}{1} = 126$

11. ${}_{11}C_4 = \frac{11!}{7!4!} = \frac{11\cdot 10\cdot 9\cdot 8}{4\cdot 3\cdot 2\cdot 1} = \frac{11\cdot 10\cdot 3}{1} = 330$

13. ${}_7C_7 = \frac{7!}{0!7!} = 1$

15. ${}_5C_0 = \frac{5!}{5!0!} = 1$

17. combination; The order in which the volunteers are chosen does not matter.

19. permutation; The order of the letters matters because ABCD is not the same as BADC.

21. $9\cdot 3 = 27$ ways

23. $2\cdot 4\cdot 5 = 40$ ways

25. $3^5 = 243$ ways

27. $8\cdot 2\cdot 9 = 144$ area codes

29. $5\cdot 4\cdot 3\cdot 2\cdot 1\cdot 1 = 120$ ways

31. $1\cdot 3\cdot 2\cdot 1\cdot 1 = 6$ paragraphs

33. ${}_{10}P_3 = \frac{10!}{7!3!} = 10\cdot 9\cdot 8 = 720$ ways

35. $_{13}P_7 = \frac{13!}{6!} = 13\cdot 12\cdot 11\cdot 10\cdot 9\cdot 8\cdot 7$
$= 8,648,640$ ways

37. $_6P_3 = \frac{6!}{3!} = 6\cdot 5\cdot 4 = 120$ ways

39. $_9P_5 = \frac{9!}{4!} = 9\cdot 8\cdot 7\cdot 6\cdot 5 = 15,120$ lineups

41. $_6C_3 = \frac{6!}{3!3!} = \frac{6\cdot 5\cdot 4}{3\cdot 2\cdot 1} = 20$ ways

43. $_{12}C_4 = \frac{12!}{8!4!} = \frac{12\cdot 11\cdot 10\cdot 9}{4\cdot 3\cdot 2\cdot 1}$
$= 495$ collections

45. $_{17}C_8 = \frac{17!}{9!8!} = \frac{17\cdot 16\cdot 15\cdot 14\cdot 13\cdot 12\cdot 11\cdot 10}{8\cdot 7\cdot 6\cdot 5\cdot 4\cdot 3\cdot 2\cdot 1}$
$= 24,310$ groups

47. $_{49}C_6 = \frac{49!}{43!6!} = 13,983,816$ selections

49. $_6P_4 = \frac{6!}{2!} = 6\cdot 5\cdot 4\cdot 3 = 360$ ways

51. $_{13}C_6 = \frac{13!}{7!6!} = \frac{13\cdot 12\cdot 11\cdot 10\cdot 9\cdot 8}{6\cdot 5\cdot 4\cdot 3\cdot 2\cdot 1}$
$= 1716$ ways

53. $_{20}C_3 = \frac{20!}{17!3!} = \frac{20\cdot 19\cdot 18}{3\cdot 2\cdot 1} = 1140$ ways

55. $_7P_4 = \frac{7!}{3!} = 840$ passwords

57. $_{15}P_3 = \frac{15!}{12!} = 15\cdot 14\cdot 13 = 2730$ cones

59.–65. Answers may vary.

67. Answers may vary.

Exercises 1 and 3

```
9 nPr 4
                3024
8 nPr 5
                6720
```

Exercises 5 and 7

```
6 nPr 6
                 720
8 nPr 0
                   1
```

69. **a.** False; the number of ways is $_{10}C_4$.

b. False;

$_nP_r = \frac{n!}{(n-r)!} > \frac{n!}{(n-r)!r!} = {_nC_r}$ if $r>1$.

c. True; $_7P_3 = \frac{7!}{4!} = 3!\frac{7!}{4!3!} = 3!_7C_3$

d. False;
the number of ways is $20\cdot 19 = {_{20}P_2}$.

(c) is true.

71. $2\cdot 6\cdot 6\cdot 2 = 144$ numbers

Section 8.7

Check Point Exercises 8.7

1. P(seven hours sleep)

$= \frac{\text{number of Americans who sleep 7 hours}}{\text{total number of Americans}}$

$= \frac{82.5}{275} = 0.3$

The empirical probability of randomly selecting an American who gets seven hours of sleep on a typical night is 0.3.

2. The sample space of equally likely outcomes is $S = \{1, 2, 3, 4, 5, 6\}$. There are six outcomes in the sample space, so $n(S) = 6$. The event of getting a number greater than 4 can be represented by $E = \{5, 6\}$. There are two outcomes in this event, so $n(E) = 2$. The probability of rolling a number greater than 4 is $P(E) = \frac{n(E)}{n(S)} = \frac{2}{6} = \frac{1}{3}$.

3. We have $n(S) = 36$. The phrase "getting a sum of 5" describes the event $E = \{(1,4),(2,3),(3,2),(4,1)\}$. This event has 4 outcomes, so $n(E) = 4$. Thus, the probability of getting a sum of 5 is

$$P(E) = \frac{n(E)}{n(S)} = \frac{4}{36} = \frac{1}{9}.$$

4. Let E be the event of being dealt a king. Because there are 4 kings in the deck, the event of being dealt a king can occur in 4 ways, i.e., $n(E) = 4$. With 52 cards in the deck, $n(S) = 52$. The probability of being dealt a king is $P(E) = \frac{n(E)}{n(S)} = \frac{4}{52} = \frac{1}{13}$.

5. Because the order of the six numbers does not matter, this is a situation involving combinations. With one lottery ticket, there is only one way of winning so $n(E) = 1$. Using the combinations formula

${}_nC_r = \frac{n!}{(n-r)!r!}$ to find the number of outcomes in the sample space, we are selecting $r = 5$ numbers from a collection of $n = 30$ numbers.

$$\begin{aligned} {}_{30}C_5 &= \frac{30!}{(30-5)!5!} = \frac{30!}{25!5!} \\ &= \frac{30 \cdot 29 \cdot 28 \cdot 27 \cdot 26 \cdot 25!}{25!5 \cdot 4 \cdot 3 \cdot 2 \cdot 1} \\ &= 142{,}506. \end{aligned}$$

So $n(S) = 142{,}506$.

If a person buys one lottery ticket, the probability of winning is

$$\begin{aligned} P(E) &= \frac{n(E)}{n(S)} = \frac{1}{142{,}506} \\ &\approx 0.00000702. \end{aligned}$$

The probability of winning the state lottery is 0.00000702.

6.
$$\begin{aligned} P(\text{not winning}) &= 1 - P(\text{winning}) \\ &= 1 - \frac{1}{142{,}506} \\ &= \frac{142{,}505}{142{,}506} \approx 0.999993 \end{aligned}$$

The probability of not winning is about 0.999993.

7. We find the probability that either of these mutually exclusive events will occur by adding their individual probabilities.

$$\begin{aligned} P(4 \text{ or } 5) &= P(4) + P(5) \\ &= \frac{1}{6} + \frac{1}{6} = \frac{2}{6} = \frac{1}{3} \end{aligned}$$

The probability of selecting a 4 or a 5 is $\frac{1}{3}$.

8. It is possible for the pointer to land on a number that is odd and less than 5. Two of the numbers , 1 and 3, are odd and less than 5. These events are not mutually exclusive. The probability of landing on a number that is odd and less than 5 is

$$\begin{aligned} &P\text{ (odd or less than 5)} \\ &= P\text{ (odd)} + P\text{ (less than 5)} \\ &- P\text{ (odd and less than 5)} \\ &= \frac{4}{8} + \frac{4}{8} - \frac{2}{8} \\ &= \frac{6}{8} = \frac{3}{4} \end{aligned}$$

The probability that the pointer will stop on an odd number or a number less than 5 is $\frac{3}{4}$.

9. The group is comprised of 25 baboons. It is possible to select a baboon that enjoys picking fleas off of its neighbors that also screeches wildly. These events are not mutually exclusive.

$$\begin{aligned} &P\text{ (picking or screeching)} \\ &= P\text{ (picking)} + P\text{ (screeching)} \\ &\quad - P\text{ (picking and screeching)} \\ &= \frac{18}{25} + \frac{16}{25} - \frac{10}{25} = \frac{24}{25}. \end{aligned}$$

10. The wheel has 38 equally likely outcomes and 2 are green. Thus, the probability of a green occurring on a play is $\frac{2}{38}$, or $\frac{1}{19}$. The result that occurs on each play is independent of all previous results. Thus,
P (green and green)
$= P$ (green) $\cdot$ P (green)
$$= \frac{1}{19} \cdot \frac{1}{19} = \frac{1}{361} \approx 0.003.$$
The probability of green occurring on two consecutive plays is $\frac{1}{361}$.

11. If two or more events are independent, we can find the probability of them all occurring by multiplying the probabilities. The probability of a baby boy is $\frac{1}{2}$, so the probability of having four boys in a row is P (4 boys in a row)
$$= \frac{1}{2} \cdot \frac{1}{2} \cdot \frac{1}{2} \cdot \frac{1}{2}$$
$$= \frac{1}{16}.$$

Exercise Set 8.7

1. $P(\text{2 people}) = \dfrac{29,780,000}{70,241,000} \approx 0.42$

3. $P(\text{ African}) = \dfrac{761}{5926} \approx 0.13$

5. $P(R) = \dfrac{n(E)}{n(S)} = \dfrac{1}{6}$

7. $P(E) = \dfrac{n(E)}{n(S)} = \dfrac{3}{6} = \dfrac{1}{2}$

9. $P(E) = \dfrac{n(E)}{n(S)} = \dfrac{2}{6} = \dfrac{1}{3}$

11. $P(E) = \dfrac{n(E)}{n(S)} = \dfrac{4}{52} = \dfrac{1}{13}$

13. $P(E) = \dfrac{n(E)}{n(S)} = \dfrac{12}{52} = \dfrac{3}{13}$

15. $P(E) = \dfrac{n(E)}{n(S)} = \dfrac{1}{4}$

17. $P(E) = \dfrac{n(E)}{n(S)} = \dfrac{7}{8}$

19. $P(E) = \dfrac{n(E)}{n(S)} = \dfrac{3}{36} = \dfrac{1}{12}$

21. Buying 1 ticket:
$$P(E) = \frac{n(E)}{n(S)} = \frac{1}{{}_{51}C_6} = \frac{1}{18,009,460}$$
Buying 100 tickets:
$$P(E) = \frac{100}{18,009,460} = \frac{5}{900,473}$$

23. **a.** $${}_{52}C_5 = \frac{52!}{47!5!}$$
$$= \frac{52 \cdot 51 \cdot 50 \cdot 49 \cdot 48}{5 \cdot 4 \cdot 3 \cdot 2 \cdot 1} = 2,598,960$$

b. $${}_{13}C_5 = \frac{13!}{8!5!} = \frac{13 \cdot 12 \cdot 11 \cdot 10 \cdot 9}{5 \cdot 4 \cdot 3 \cdot 2 \cdot 1} = 1287$$

c. $$P(E) = \frac{n(E)}{n(S)} = \frac{1287}{2,598,960} \approx 0.0005$$

25. $P(\text{under 5}) = \dfrac{18,987}{274,634}$
$P(\text{not under 5}) = 1 - P(\text{under 5})$
$$= \frac{255,647}{274,634} \approx 0.93$$

27. $P(25 - 34) = \dfrac{37,233}{274,634}$
$P(\text{not } 25 - 34) = 1 - P(25 - 34)$
$$= \frac{237,401}{274,634} \approx 0.86$$

29. $P(E) = P(14 - 17) + P(18 - 24)$
$$= \frac{15,752}{274,634} + \frac{26,258}{274,634}$$
$$= \frac{42,010}{274,634} \approx 0.15$$

31. $P(E) = P(2) + P(3)$
$= \frac{4}{52} + \frac{4}{52} = \frac{8}{52} = \frac{2}{13}$

33. $P(E) = P(\text{even}) + P(\text{less than 5}) - P(\text{even and less than 5})$
$= \frac{3}{6} + \frac{4}{6} - \frac{2}{6} = \frac{5}{6}$

35. $P(E) = P(7) + P(\text{red}) - P(\text{red 7})$
$= \frac{4}{52} + \frac{26}{52} - \frac{2}{52} = \frac{28}{52} = \frac{7}{13}$

37. $P(E) = P(\text{odd}) + P(\text{less than 6}) - P(\text{odd and less than 6})$
$= \frac{4}{8} + \frac{5}{8} - \frac{3}{8} = \frac{6}{8} = \frac{3}{4}$

39. $P(E)$
$= P(\text{professor}) + P(\text{male}) - P(\text{male professor})$
$= \frac{19}{40} + \frac{22}{40} - \frac{8}{40} = \frac{33}{40}$

41. $P(E) = P(2) \cdot P(3) = \frac{1}{6} \cdot \frac{1}{6} = \frac{1}{36}$

43. $P(E) = P(\text{even}) \cdot P(\text{greater than 2})$
$= \frac{3}{6} \cdot \frac{4}{6} = \frac{1}{2} \cdot \frac{2}{3} = \frac{1}{3}$

45. $P(E) = \left(\frac{1}{2}\right)^6 = \frac{1}{64}$

47. **a.** $P(E) = \frac{1}{16} \cdot \frac{1}{16} = \frac{1}{256}$

b. $P(E) = \left(\frac{1}{16}\right)^3 = \frac{1}{4096}$

c. $P(E) = \left(\frac{15}{16}\right)^{10}$

d. $1 - \left(\frac{15}{16}\right)^{10}$

49.–59. Answers may vary.

Review Exercises

1. $a_n = 7n - 4$
$a_1 = 7 - 4 = 3$
$a_2 = 14 - 4 = 10$
$a_3 = 21 - 4 = 17$
$a_4 = 28 - 4 = 24$
The first four terms are 3, 10, 17, and 24.

2. $a_n = (-1)^n \frac{n+2}{n+1}$
$a_1 = (-1)^1 \frac{1+2}{1+1} = -\frac{3}{2}$
$a_2 = (-1)^2 \frac{2+2}{2+1} = \frac{4}{3}$
$a_3 = (-1)^3 \frac{3+2}{3+1} = -\frac{5}{4}$
$a_4 = (-1)^4 \frac{4+2}{4+1} = \frac{6}{5}$
The first four terms are $-\frac{3}{2}, \frac{4}{3}, -\frac{5}{4}$, and $\frac{6}{5}$.

3. $a_n = \frac{1}{(n-1)!}$
$a_1 = \frac{1}{0!} = 1$
$a_2 = \frac{1}{1!} = 1$
$a_3 = \frac{1}{2!} = \frac{1}{2}$
$a_4 = \frac{1}{3!} = \frac{1}{6}$
The first four terms are 1, 1, $\frac{1}{2}$, and $\frac{1}{6}$.

4. $a_n = \frac{(-1)^{n+1}}{2^n}$

$a_1 = \frac{(-1)^2}{2^1} = \frac{1}{2}$

$a_2 = \frac{(-1)^3}{2^2} = -\frac{1}{4}$

$a_3 = \frac{(-1)^4}{2^3} = \frac{1}{8}$

$a_4 = \frac{(-1)^5}{2^4} = -\frac{1}{16}$

The first four terms are $\frac{1}{2}$, $-\frac{1}{4}$, $\frac{1}{8}$, and $-\frac{1}{16}$.

5. $a_1 = 9$ and $a_n = \frac{2}{3a_{n-1}}$

$a_1 = 9$

$a_2 = \frac{2}{3 \cdot 9} = \frac{2}{27}$

$a_3 = \frac{2}{3} \cdot \frac{27}{2} = \frac{54}{6} = 9$

$a_4 = \frac{2}{3 \cdot 9} = \frac{2}{27}$

The first four terms are 9, $\frac{2}{27}$, 9, and $\frac{2}{27}$.

6. $a_1 = 4$ and $a_n = 2a_{n-1} + 3$

$a_1 = 4$

$a_2 = 2 \cdot 4 + 3 = 8 + 3 = 11$

$a_3 = 2 \cdot 11 + 3 = 22 + 3 = 25$

$a_4 = 2 \cdot 25 + 3 = 50 + 3 = 53$

The first four terms are 4, 11, 25, and 53.

7. $\frac{40!}{4! \cdot 38!} = \frac{40 \cdot 39 \cdot 38!}{4 \cdot 3 \cdot 2 \cdot 1 \cdot 38!} = 65$

8. $\sum_{i=1}^{5} \left(2i^2 - 3\right) = (2-3) + \left(2 \cdot 2^2 - 3\right) + \left(2 \cdot 3^2 - 3\right) + \left(2 \cdot 4^2 - 3\right) + \left(2 \cdot 5^2 - 3\right)$

$= -1 + 5 + 15 + 29 + 47$

$= 95$

9. $\sum_{i=0}^{4}(-3)^{i+1}i! = (-1)^1 0! + (-1)^2 1! + (-1)^3 2! + (-1)^4 3! + (-1)^5 4!$

$= -1 + 1 - 2 + 6 - 24$
$= -20$

10. $\frac{1}{3}+\frac{2}{4}+\frac{3}{5}+\cdots+\frac{15}{17}=\sum_{i=1}^{15}\frac{i}{i+2}$

11. $4^3+5^3+6^3+\cdots+13^3=\sum_{i=1}^{10}(i+3)^3$

12. $a_1 = 7,\ d = 4$
The first six terms are 7, 11, 15, 19, 23, and 27.

13. $a_1 = -4,\ d = -5$
The first six terms are $-4,\ -9,\ -14,\ -19,\ -24,$ and -29.

14. $a_1 = \frac{3}{2},\ d = -\frac{1}{2}$
The first six terms are $\frac{3}{2},\ 1,\ \frac{1}{2},\ 0,\ -\frac{1}{2},$ and -1.

15. $a_{n+1} = a_n + 5,\ a_1 = -2$
The first six terms are -2, 3, 8, 13, 18, and 23.

16. $a_1 = 5,\ d = 3$
$a_n = 5 + (n-1)3$
$a_6 = 5 + (5)3 = 20$

17. $a_1 = -8,\ d = -2$
$a_n = -8 + (n-1)(-2)$
$a_{12} = -8 + 11(-2) = -30$

18. $a_1 = 14,\ d = -4$
$a_n = 14 + (n-1)(-4)$
$a_{14} = 14 + (13)(-4) = -38$

19. $-7, -3, 1, 5, \ldots$
$d = -3 - (-7) = 4$
$a_n = -7 + (n-1)(4)$
$a_n = 4n - 11$
$a_{20} = 4(20) - 11$
$a_{20} = 69$

20. $a_1 = 200, d = -20$
$a_n = 200 + (n-1)(-20)$
$a_n = 220 - 20n$
$a_{20} = 220 - 20(20)$
$a_{20} = -180$

21. $a_n = a_{n-1} - 5, a_1 = 3$
$d = -5$
$a_n = 3 + (n-1)(-5) = 3 - 5n + 5$
$a_n = 8 - 5n$
$a_{20} = 8 - 5(20) = -92$

22. 5, 12, 19, 26, …
$d = 7$
$a_n = 5 + (n-1)(7)$
$a_{22} = 5 + 21(7) = 152$
$S_{22} = \frac{22}{2}(5 + 152) = 1727$

23. $-6, -3, 0, 3, \ldots$
$d = 3$
$a_n = -6 + (n-1)3$
$a_{15} = -6 + (14)3 = 36$
$S_{15} = \frac{15}{2}(-6 + 36) = 225$

24. $3 + 6 + 9 + \cdots + 300$
$S_{100} = \frac{100}{2}(3 + 300) = 15{,}150$

25. $\sum_{i=1}^{16}(3i + 2)$
$a_1 = 3 + 2 = 5$
$a_{16} = 3(16) + 2 = 50$
$S_{16} = \frac{16}{2}(5 + 50) = 440$

26. $\sum_{i=1}^{25}(-2i + 6)$
$a_1 = -2 + 6 = 4$
$a_{25} = -2(25) + 6 = -44$
$S_{25} = \frac{25}{2}(4 - 44) = -500$

27. $\sum_{i=1}^{30} -5i$
$a_1 = -5$
$a_{30} = -5(30) = -150$
$S_{30} = \frac{30}{2}(-5 - 150) = -2325$

28. **a.** $d = -0.4118$
$a_n = 1043.04 + (n-1)(-0.4118)$
$a_n = 1043.4518 - 0.4118n$

b. $n = 2010 - 1910 = 100$
$a_{100} = 1043.4518 - 0.4118(90)$
$a = 1002.2718$
1002.2718 seconds

29. $a_n = 31{,}500 + (n-1)2300$
$a_{10} = 31{,}500 + (9)2300 = 52{,}200$
$S_{10} = \frac{10}{2}(31{,}500 + 52{,}200) = 418{,}500$
The total salary is \$418, 500.

30. $a_n = 25 + (n-1)$
$a_{35} = 25 + 34 = 59$
$S_{35} = \frac{35}{2}(25 + 59) = 1470$
There are 1470 seats.

31. $a_1 = 3, r = 2$
The first five terms are 3, 6, 12, 24, and 48.

32. $a_1 = \frac{1}{2}, r = \frac{1}{2}$
The first five terms are
$\frac{1}{2}, \frac{1}{4}, \frac{1}{8}, \frac{1}{16}$, and $\frac{1}{32}$.

33. $a_1 = 16, r = -\frac{1}{2}$
The first five terms are
16, −8, 4, −2, and 1.

34. $a_n = -5a_{n-1}, a_1 = -1$
The first five terms are −1, 5, −25, 125, and −625.

35. $a_1 = 2, r = 3$
$a_n = 2 \cdot 3^{n-1}$
$a_7 = 2 \cdot 3^6 = 1458$

36. $a_1 = 16, r = \frac{1}{2}$
$a_n = 16\left(\frac{1}{2}\right)^{n-1}$
$a_6 = 16\left(\frac{1}{2}\right)^5 = \frac{16}{32} = \frac{1}{2}$

37. $a_1 = -3, r = 2$
$a_n = -3 \cdot 2^{n-1}$
$a_5 = -3 \cdot 2^4 = -48$

38. 1, 2, 4, 8, ...
$a_1 = 1, r = \frac{2}{1} = 2$
$a_n = 2^{n-1}$
$a_8 = 2^7 = 128$

39. $100, 10, 1, \frac{1}{10}, \ldots$
$a_1 = 100, r = \frac{10}{100} = \frac{1}{10}$
$a_n = 100\left(\frac{1}{10}\right)^{n-1}$
$a_8 = 100\left(\frac{1}{10}\right)^7 = \frac{1}{100,000}$

40. $12, -4, \frac{4}{3}, -\frac{4}{9}, \ldots$
$a_1 = 12, r = -\frac{4}{12} = -\frac{1}{3}$
$a_n = 12\left(-\frac{1}{3}\right)^{n-1}$
$a_8 = 12\left(-\frac{1}{3}\right)^7 = -\frac{4}{729}$

41. 5, −15, 45, −135, ...
$r = \frac{-15}{5} = -3$
$S_{15} = \frac{5\left[1-(-3)^{15}\right]}{1-(-3)} = 17,936,135$

42. $\frac{1}{3}, \frac{1}{9}, \frac{1}{27}, \frac{1}{81}, \ldots$
$r = \frac{1}{3}$
$S_7 = \frac{\frac{1}{3}\left[1-\left(\frac{1}{3}\right)^7\right]}{1-\frac{1}{3}} = \frac{\frac{1}{3}\left(\frac{2186}{2187}\right)}{\frac{2}{3}} = \frac{1093}{2187}$

43. $\sum_{i=1}^{6} 5^i$
$r = 5, a_1 = 5$
$S_6 = \frac{5(1-5^6)}{1-5} = \frac{5(-15624)}{-4} = 19,530$

44. $\sum_{i=1}^{7} 3(-2)^i$

$a_1 = -6,\ r = -2$

$S_7 = \frac{-6\left[1-(-2)^7\right]}{1-(-2)} = \frac{-6(129)}{3} = -258$

45. $\sum_{i=1}^{5} 2\left(\frac{1}{4}\right)^{i-1}$

$a_1 = 2,\ r = \frac{1}{4}$

$S_5 = \frac{2\left[1-\left(\frac{1}{4}\right)^5\right]}{1-\frac{1}{4}} = \frac{2\left(\frac{1023}{1024}\right)}{\frac{3}{4}} = \frac{341}{128}$

46. $9+3+1+\frac{1}{3}+\cdots$

$a_1 = 9,\ r = \frac{1}{3}$

$S_\infty = \frac{9}{1-\frac{1}{3}} = \frac{9}{\frac{2}{3}} = 9\cdot\frac{3}{2} = \frac{27}{2}$

47. $2-1+\frac{1}{2}-\frac{1}{4}+\cdots$

$a_1 = 2,\ r = -\frac{1}{2}$

$S_\infty = \frac{2}{1-\left(-\frac{1}{2}\right)} = \frac{2}{\frac{3}{2}} = \frac{4}{3}$

48. $-6+4-\frac{8}{3}+\frac{16}{9}-\cdots$

$a_1 = -6,\ r = -\frac{2}{3}$

$S_\infty = \frac{-6}{1-\left(-\frac{2}{3}\right)} = \frac{-6}{\frac{5}{3}} = -\frac{18}{5}$

49. $\sum_{i=1}^{\infty} 5(0.8)^i = 4+3.2+\cdots$

$r = 0.8$

$S_\infty = \frac{4}{1-0.8} = 20$

50. $0.\overline{6} = 0.6+0.06+0.006+\cdots$

$a_1 = \frac{6}{10},\ r = \frac{1}{10}$

$S_\infty = \frac{\frac{6}{10}}{1-\frac{1}{10}} = \frac{\frac{6}{10}}{\frac{9}{10}} = \frac{6}{9} = \frac{2}{3}$

51. $0.\overline{47} = 0.47+0.0047+0.000047+\cdots$

$a_1 = \frac{47}{100},\ r = \frac{1}{100}$

$S_\infty = \frac{\frac{47}{100}}{1-\frac{1}{100}} = \frac{\frac{47}{100}}{\frac{99}{100}} = \frac{47}{99}$

52. $a_1 = 32,000,\ r = 1.06$

$a_6 = 32,000(1.06)^5 \approx 42,823.22$

The sixth year salary is $42, 823.22.

$S_6 = \frac{32,000\left(1-1.06^6\right)}{1-1.06} = \frac{32,000\left(1-1.06^6\right)}{-0.06}$

$\approx 223,210.19$

The total salary paid is $223, 210.19.

53. $A = 200\frac{\left(1+\frac{0.1}{12}\right)^{18\cdot 12}-1}{\frac{0.1}{12}} \approx 120,112.64$

You will save $120,112.64.

54. $4(0.7)+4(0.7)^2+\cdots$

$r = 0.7$

$S_\infty = \frac{4(0.7)}{1-0.7} = 9.\overline{3}$

The total spending is $\$9\frac{1}{3}$ million.

55. $S_1: 5 = \frac{5(1)(1+1)}{2}$

$5 = \frac{5(2)}{2}$

$5 = 5$ is true.

$S_k: 5+10+15+\cdots+5k = \frac{5k(k+1)}{2}$

$S_{k+1}: 5+10+15+\cdots+5k+5(k+1) = \frac{5(k+1)(k+2)}{2}$

Add $5(k+1)$ to both sides of S_k:

$5+10+15+\cdots+5k+5(k+1) = \frac{5k(k+1)}{2}+5(k+1)$

Simplify the right-hand side:

$\frac{5k(k+1)}{2}+5(k+1) = \frac{5k(k+1)+10(k+1)}{2} = \frac{(5k+10)(k+1)}{2}$

$= \frac{5(k+1)(k+2)}{2}$

If S_k is true, then S_{k+1} is true.
The statement is true for all n.

56. $S_1: 1 = \frac{4^1-1}{3}$

$1 = \frac{3}{3}$

$1 = 1$ is true.

$S_k: 1+4+4^2+\cdots+4^{k-1} = \frac{4^k-1}{3}$

$S_{k+1}: 1+4+4^2+\cdots+4^{k-1}+4^k = \frac{4^{k+1}-1}{3}$

Add 4^k to both sides of S_k:

$1+4+4^2+\cdots+4^{k-1}+4^k = \frac{4^k-1}{3}+4^k$

Simplify the right-hand side:

$\frac{4^k-1}{3}+4^k = \frac{4^k-1+3\cdot 4^k}{3} = \frac{4\cdot 4^k-1}{3}$

$= \frac{4^{k+1}-1}{3}$

If S_k is true, then S_{k+1} is true. The statement is true for all n.

57. S_1: $2 = 2(1)^2$

$2 = 2$ is true.

S_k: $2 + 6 + 10 + \cdots + (4k - 2) = 2k^2$

S_{k+1}: $2 + 6 + 10 + \cdots + (4k - 2) + (4k + 2) = 2(k + 1)^2$

Add $(4k + 2)$ to both sides of S_k:

$2 + 6 + 10 + \cdots + (4k - 2) + (4k + 2) = 2k^2 + (4k + 2)$

Simplify the right-hand side:

$$2k^2 + 4k + 2 = 2(k^2 + 2k + 1) = 2(k + 1)^2$$

If S_k is true, then S_{k+1} is true. The statement is true for all n.

58. S_1: $1 \cdot 3 = \frac{1(1+1)[2(1)+7]}{6}$

$$3 = \frac{2 \cdot 9}{6}$$

$$3 = \frac{18}{6}$$

$3 = 3$ is true.

S_k: $1 \cdot 3 + 2 \cdot 4 + 3 \cdot 5 + \cdots + k(k+2) = \frac{k(k+1)(2k+7)}{6}$

S_{k+1}: $1 \cdot 3 + 2 \cdot 4 + 3 \cdot 5 + \cdots + k(k+2) + (k+1)(k+3) = \frac{(k+1)(k+2)(2k+9)}{6}$

Add $(k+1)(k+3)$ to both sides of S_k:

$1 \cdot 3 + 2 \cdot 4 + 3 \cdot 5 + \cdots + k(k+2) + (k+1)(k+3) = \frac{k(k+1)(2k+7)}{6} + (k+1)(k+3)$

Simplify the right-hand side:

$$= \frac{k(k+1)(2k+7)}{6} + (k+1)(k+3)$$

$$= \frac{k(k+1)(2k+7) + 6(k+1)(k+3)}{6}$$

$$= \frac{(k+1)[k(2k+7) + 6(k+3)]}{6}$$

$$= \frac{(k+1)(2k^2 + 13k + 18)}{6}$$

$$= \frac{(k+1)(k+2)(2k+9)}{6}$$

If S_k is true, then S_{k+1} is true. The statement is true for all n.

59. S_1: 2 is a factor of $1^2 + 5(1) = 6$ since $6 = 2 \cdot 3$.

S_k: 2 is a factor of $k^2 + 5k$.

S_{k+1}: 2 is a factor of $(k+1)^2 + 5(k+1)$.

$$\begin{aligned}(k+1)^2 + 5(k+1) &= k^2 + 2k + 1 + 5k + 5 \\ &= k^2 + 7k + 6 \\ &= k^2 + 5k + 2(k+3) \\ &= \left(k^2 + 5k\right) + 2(k+3)\end{aligned}$$

Because we assume S_k is true, we know 2 is a factor of $k^2 + 5k$. Since 2 is a factor of $2(k+3)$, we conclude 2 is a factor of the sum $\left(k^2 + 5k\right) + 2(k+3)$. If S_k is true, then S_{k+1} is true. The statement is true for all n.

60. $\binom{11}{8} = \dfrac{11!}{3!8!} = \dfrac{11 \cdot 10 \cdot 9}{3 \cdot 2 \cdot 1} = 165$

61. $\binom{90}{2} = \dfrac{90!}{88!2!} = \dfrac{90 \cdot 89}{2 \cdot 1} = 4005$

62. $$\begin{aligned}(2x+1)^3 &= \binom{3}{0}(2x)^3 + \binom{3}{1}(2x)^2 \cdot 1 + \binom{3}{2}(2x)1^2 + \binom{3}{3}1^3 = 8x^3 + 3\left(4x^2\right) + 3(2x) + 1 \\ &= 8x^3 + 12x^2 + 6x + 1\end{aligned}$$

63. $$\begin{aligned}\left(x^2 - 1\right)^4 &= \binom{4}{0}\left(x^2\right)^4 + \binom{4}{1}\left(x^2\right)^3(-1) + \binom{4}{2}\left(x^2\right)^2(-1)^2 + \binom{4}{3}x^2(-1)^3 + \binom{4}{4}(-1)^4 \\ &= x^8 - 4x^6 + 6x^4 - 4x^2 + 1\end{aligned}$$

64. $$\begin{aligned}(x+2y)^5 &= \binom{5}{0}x^5 + \binom{5}{1}x^4(2y) + \binom{5}{2}x^3(2y)^2 + \binom{5}{3}x^2(2y)^3 + \binom{5}{4}x(2y)^4 + \binom{5}{5}(2y)^5 \\ &= x^5 + 5(2)x^4y + 10(4)x^3y^2 + 10(8)x^2y^3 + 5(16)xy^4 + 32y^5 \\ &= x^5 + 10x^4y + 40x^3y^2 + 80x^2y^3 + 80xy^4 + 32y^5\end{aligned}$$

65. $$\begin{aligned}(x-2)^6 &= \binom{6}{0}x^6 + \binom{6}{1}x^5(-2) + \binom{6}{2}x^4(-2)^2 + \binom{6}{3}x^3(-2)^3 + \binom{6}{4}x^2(-2)^4 + \binom{6}{5}x(-2)^5\binom{6}{6}(-2)^6 \\ &= x^6 + 6x^5(-2) + 15x^4(4) + 20x^3(-8) + 15x^2(16) + 6x(-32) + 64 \\ &= x^6 - 12x^5 + 60x^4 - 160x^3 + 240x^2 - 192x + 64\end{aligned}$$

66. $$\begin{aligned}\left(x^2 + 3\right)^8 &= \binom{8}{0}\left(x^2\right)^8 + \binom{8}{1}\left(x^2\right)^7 \cdot 3 + \binom{8}{2}\left(x^2\right)^6 \cdot 3^2 + \cdots \\ &= x^{16} + 8x^{14} \cdot 3 + 28x^{12} \cdot 9 + \cdots \\ &= x^{16} + 24x^{14} + 252x^{12} + \cdots\end{aligned}$$

67. $(x-3)^9$
$= \binom{9}{0}x^9 + \binom{9}{1}x^8(-3) + \binom{9}{2}x^7(-3)^2 + \cdots$
$= x^9 + 9(-3)x^8 + 36(9)x^7 + \cdots$
$= x^9 - 27x^8 + 324x^7 - \cdots$

68. $(x+2)^5$
fourth term $= \binom{5}{3}x^2(2)^3 = 10(8)x^2 = 80x^2$

69. $(2x-3)^6$
fifth term $= \binom{6}{4}(2x)^2(-3)^4 = 15(4x^2)(81)$
$= 4860x^2$

70. ${}_8P_3 = \frac{8!}{5!} = 8 \cdot 7 \cdot 6 = 336$

71. ${}_9P_5 = \frac{9!}{4!} = 9 \cdot 8 \cdot 7 \cdot 6 \cdot 5 = 15{,}120$

72. ${}_8C_3 = \frac{8!}{5!3!} = \frac{8 \cdot 7 \cdot 6}{3 \cdot 2 \cdot 1} = 56$

73. ${}_{13}C_{11} = \frac{13!}{2!11!} = \frac{13 \cdot 12}{2 \cdot 1} = 78$

74. $4 \cdot 5 = 20$ choices

75. $3^5 = 243$ possibilities

76. ${}_{15}P_4 = \frac{15!}{11!} = 15 \cdot 14 \cdot 13 \cdot 12 = 32{,}760$ ways

77. ${}_{20}C_4 = \frac{20!}{16!4!} = \frac{20 \cdot 19 \cdot 18 \cdot 17}{4 \cdot 3 \cdot 2 \cdot 1} = 4845$ ways

78. ${}_{20}C_3 = \frac{20!}{17!3!} = \frac{20 \cdot 19 \cdot 18}{3 \cdot 2 \cdot 1} = 1140$ sets

79. ${}_{20}P_4 = \frac{20!}{16!} = 20 \cdot 19 \cdot 18 \cdot 17$
$= 116{,}280$ ways

80. $5! = 120$ ways

81. $P(E) = \frac{9{,}630{,}188}{31{,}878{,}234} \approx 0.302$

82. $P(E) = \frac{5{,}503{,}372}{19{,}128{,}261} \approx 0.288$

83. $P(E) = \frac{n(E)}{n(S)} = \frac{4}{6} = \frac{2}{3}$

84. $P(E) = \frac{2}{6} + \frac{2}{6} = \frac{4}{6} = \frac{2}{3}$

85. $P(E) = \frac{4}{52} + \frac{4}{52} = \frac{8}{52} = \frac{2}{13}$

86. $P(E) = \frac{4}{52} + \frac{26}{52} - \frac{2}{52} = \frac{28}{52} = \frac{7}{13}$

87. $P(\text{not yellow}) = 1 - P(\text{yellow}) = 1 - \frac{1}{6} = \frac{5}{6}$

88. $P(E) = \frac{3}{6} + \frac{3}{6} - \frac{1}{6} = \frac{5}{6}$

89. a. $P(E) = \frac{n(E)}{n(S)} = \frac{1}{{}_{20}C_5} = \frac{1}{15{,}504}$

b. $P(E) = \frac{100}{15{,}504} = \frac{25}{3876}$

90. $P(E) = \frac{70}{200} + \frac{140}{200} - \frac{50}{200} = \frac{160}{200} = \frac{4}{5}$

91. $P(E) = \frac{60}{200} + \frac{130}{200} - \frac{40}{200} = \frac{150}{200} = \frac{3}{4}$

92. $P(E) = \left(\frac{1}{2}\right)^5 = \frac{1}{32}$

93. a. $(0.2)^2 = 0.04$

b. $(0.2)^3 = 0.008$

c. $(1-0.2)^4 = (0.8)^4 = 0.4096$

Chapter 8 Test

1. $a_n = \frac{(-1)^{n+1}}{n^2}$

$a_1 = \frac{(-1)^2}{1^2} = 1$

$a_2 = \frac{(-1)^3}{2^2} = -\frac{1}{4}$

$a_3 = \frac{(-1)^4}{3^2} = \frac{1}{9}$

$a_4 = \frac{(-1)^5}{4^2} = -\frac{1}{16}$

$a_5 = \frac{(-1)^6}{5^2} = \frac{1}{25}$

The first five terms are

$1, -\frac{1}{4}, \frac{1}{9}, -\frac{1}{16}$, and $\frac{1}{25}$.

2. $\sum_{i=1}^{5}\left(i^2+10\right) = 11+14+19+26+35 = 105$

3. $\sum_{i=1}^{20}(3i-4)$

$a_1 = 3-4 = -1$

$d = 3$

$a_n = -1+(n-1)3$

$a_{20} = -1+(19)3 = 56$

$S_{20} = \frac{20}{2}(-1+56) = 550$

4. $\sum_{i=1}^{15}(-2)^i$

$a_1 = -2,\ r = -2$

$S_{15} = \frac{-2\left[1-(-2)^{15}\right]}{1-(-2)} = -21{,}846$

5. $\binom{9}{2} = \frac{9!}{7!2!} = \frac{9\cdot 8}{2\cdot 1} = 36$

6. ${}_{10}P_3 = \frac{10!}{7!} = 10\cdot 9\cdot 8 = 720$

7. ${}_{10}C_3 = \frac{10!}{7!3!} = \frac{10\cdot 9\cdot 8}{3\cdot 2\cdot 1} = 120$

8. $\frac{2}{3}+\frac{3}{4}+\frac{4}{5}+\cdots+\frac{21}{22} = \sum_{i=1}^{20}\frac{i+1}{i+2}$

9. 4, 9, 14, 19, . . .

$a_1 = 4,\ d = 5$

$a_n = 4+(n-1)\cdot 5 = 4+5n-1$

$a_n = 5n-1$

$a_{12} = 5(12)-1 = 59$

10. 16, 4, 1, $\frac{1}{4}$, . . .

$a_1 = 16,\ r = \frac{1}{4}$

$a_n = 16\left(\frac{1}{4}\right)^{n-1}$

$a_{12} = 16\left(\frac{1}{4}\right)^{11} = \frac{1}{262{,}144}$

11. 7, −14, 28, −56, . . .

$a_1 = 7,\ r = -2$

$S_{10} = \frac{7\left[1-(-2)^{10}\right]}{1-(-2)} = \frac{7(-1023)}{3} = -2387$

12. −7, −14, −21, −28, . . .

$a_1 = -7,\ d = -7$

$a_n = -7+(n-1)(-7)$

$a_{10} = -7+9(-7) = -70$

$S_{10} = \frac{10}{2}(-7-70) = -385$

13. $4+\frac{4}{2}+\frac{4}{2^2}+\frac{4}{2^3}+\cdots$

$r = \frac{1}{2}$

$S_\infty = \frac{4}{1-\frac{1}{2}} = 8$

14. $a_1 = 30,000, r = 1.04$

$$S_8 = \frac{30,000\left[1-(1.04)^8\right]}{1-1.04} \approx 276,426.79$$

The total salary is \$276,426.79.

15. $S_1: 1 = \frac{1[3(1)-1]}{2}$

$$1 = \frac{2}{2}$$

$1 = 1$ is true.

$$S_k: 1+4+7+\cdots+(3k-2) = \frac{k(3k-1)}{2}$$

$$S_{k+1}: 1+4+7+\cdots+(3k-2)+(3k+1) = \frac{(k+1)(3k+2)}{2}$$

Add $(3k+1)$ to both sides of S_k:

$$1+4+7+\cdots+(3k-2)+(3k+1) = \frac{k(3k-1)}{2}+(3k+1)$$

Simplify the right-hand side:

$$\frac{k(3k-1)}{2}+(3k+1) = \frac{k(3k-1)+2(3k+1)}{2} = \frac{3k^2+5k+2}{2} = \frac{(k+1)(3k+2)}{2}$$

If S_k is true, then S_{k+1} is true. The statement is true for all n.

16. $$\left(x^2-1\right)^5 = \binom{5}{0}\left(x^2\right)^5+\binom{5}{1}\left(x^2\right)^4(-1)+\binom{5}{2}\left(x^2\right)^3(-1)^2+\binom{5}{3}\left(x^2\right)^2(-1)^3+\binom{5}{4}x^2(-1)^4+\binom{5}{5}(-1)^5$$
$$= x^{10}-5x^8+10x^6-10x^4+5x^2-1$$

17. ${}_{11}P_3 = \frac{11!}{8!} = 11\cdot 10\cdot 9 = 990$ ways

18. ${}_{10}C_4 = \frac{10!}{6!4!} = \frac{10\cdot 9\cdot 8\cdot 7}{4\cdot 3\cdot 2\cdot 1} = 210$ sets

19. Four digits are open: $10^4 = 10,000$

20. ${}_{15}C_6 = \frac{15!}{9!6!} = \frac{15\cdot 14\cdot 13\cdot 12\cdot 11\cdot 10}{6\cdot 5\cdot 4\cdot 3\cdot 2} = 5005$

$$P(E) = \frac{50}{5005} = \frac{10}{1001}$$

21. $P(E) = \frac{26}{52} + \frac{12}{52} - \frac{6}{52} = \frac{32}{52} = \frac{8}{13}$

22. $P(E) = \frac{25}{50} + \frac{20}{50} - \frac{15}{50} = \frac{30}{50} = \frac{3}{5}$

23. $P(E) = \left(\frac{1}{4}\right)^4 = \frac{1}{256}$

24. $P(E) = \frac{2}{8} \cdot \frac{2}{8} = \frac{1}{16}$

Cumulative Review Exercises (Chapters 1–8)

1. $-(x-5)+10 = 3(x+2)$

$-2x + 10 + 10 = 3x + 6$

$14 = 5x$

$x = \frac{14}{5}$

The solution set is $\left\{\frac{14}{5}\right\}$.

2. $3x^2 - 6x + 2 = 0$

$x = \frac{6 \pm \sqrt{36-24}}{6}$

$= \frac{6 \pm \sqrt{12}}{6}$

$= \frac{6 \pm 2\sqrt{3}}{6}$

$= \frac{3 \pm \sqrt{3}}{3}$

The solution set is $\left\{\frac{3+\sqrt{3}}{3}, \frac{3-\sqrt{3}}{3}\right\}$.

3. $\log_2 x + \log_2 (2x-3) = 1$

$\log_2 x(2x-3) = 1$

$x(2x-3) = 2$

$2x^2 - 3x - 2 = 0$

$(2x+1)(x-2) = 0$

$2x+1 = 0$ or $x-2=0$

$x = -\frac{1}{2}$ $\quad x = 2$

$x = -\frac{1}{2}$ does not check since $\log_2\left(-\frac{1}{2}\right)$ does not exist.

The solution set is $\{2\}$.

4. $x^{1/2} - 6x^{1/4} + 8 = 0$

Let $t = x^{1/4}$.

$t^2 - 6t + 8 = 0$

$(t-2)(t-4) = 0$

$t-2=0$ or $t-4=0$

$t = 2$ $\quad t = 4$

$x^{1/4} = 2$ $\quad x^{1/4} = 4$

$x = 16$ $\quad x = 256$

The solution set is $\{16, 256\}$.

5. $\sqrt{2x+4} - \sqrt{x+3} - 1 = 0$

$\left(\sqrt{2x+4}\right)^2 = \left(\sqrt{x+3}+1\right)^2$

$2x+4 = (x+3) + 2\sqrt{x+3} + 1$

$x = 2\sqrt{x+3}$

$x^2 = 4(x+3)$

$x^2 - 4x - 12 = 0$

$(x-6)(x+2) = 0$

$x-6=0$ or $x+2=0$

$x = 6$ $\quad x = -2$

$x = -2$ does not check.

The solution set is $\{6\}$.

6. $|2x+1| \le 1$
$-1 \le 2x + 1 \le 1$
$-2 \le 2x \le 0$
$-1 \le x \le 0$ or $[-1, 0]$
The solution set is $\{x | -1 \le x \le 0\}$ or $[-1, 0]$.

7.
$$6x^2 - 6 < 5x$$
$$6x^2 - 5x - 6 < 0$$
$$6x^2 - 5x - 6 = 0$$
$$(3x+2)(2x-3) = 0$$
$$3x + 2 = 0 \text{ or } 2x - 3 = 0$$
$$x = -\frac{2}{3} \qquad x = \frac{3}{2}$$
The test intervals are $\left(-\infty, -\frac{2}{3}\right)$, $\left(-\frac{2}{3}, \frac{3}{2}\right)$, and $\left(\frac{3}{2}, \infty\right)$. Testing a point in each interval shows that the solution is $\left(-\frac{2}{3}, \frac{3}{2}\right)$.

8. $\dfrac{x-1}{x+3} \le 0$
The test intervals are $(-\infty, -3)$, $(-3, 1)$ and $(1, \infty)$.
Testing a point in each interval shows that the solution is $(-3, 1]$.

9.
$$30e^{0.7x} = 240$$
$$e^{0.7x} = 8$$
$$\ln e^{0.7x} = \ln 8$$
$$0.7x = \ln 8$$
$$x = \frac{\ln 8}{0.7}$$
The solution set is $\left\{\dfrac{\ln 8}{0.7}\right\}$, approximately 2.9706.

10. $2x^3 + 3x^2 - 8x + 3 = 0$
$p: \pm 1, \pm 3$
$q: \pm 1, \pm 2$
$\dfrac{p}{q}: \pm 1, \pm 3, \pm\dfrac{1}{2}, \pm\dfrac{3}{2}$

1	2	3	-8	3
		2	5	-3
	2	5	-3	0

$(x-1)(2x^2 + 5x - 3) = 0$
$(x-1)(2x-1)(x+3) = 0$
$x = 1$ or $x = \dfrac{1}{2}$ or $x = -3$
The solution set is $\left\{-3, \dfrac{1}{2}, 1\right\}$.

11. $4x^2 + 3y^2 = 48$
$3x^2 + 2y^2 = 35$
Multiply equation 1 by –2.
Multiply equation 2 by 3.
$$-8x^2 - 6y^2 = -96$$
$$9x^2 + 6y^2 = 105$$
Add: $x^2 = 9$
$$x = \pm 3$$
Let $x = -3$:
$$4(-3)^2 + 3y^2 = 48$$
$$36 + 3y^2 = 48$$
$$3y^2 = 12$$
$$y^2 = 4$$
$$y = \pm 2$$
Let $x = 3$:
$$4(3)^2 + 3y^2 = 48$$
$$36 + 3y^2 = 48$$
$$3y^2 = 12$$
$$y^2 = 4$$
$$y = \pm 2$$
The solution set is
$\{(3, 2), (3, -2), (-3, 2), (-3, -2)\}$.

12.
$$\begin{aligned} x - 2y + z &= 16 \\ 2x - y - z &= 14 \\ 3x + 5y - 4z &= -10 \end{aligned}$$

$$\left[\begin{array}{ccc|c} 1 & -2 & 1 & 16 \\ 0 & -1 & -1 & 14 \\ 3 & 5 & -4 & -10 \end{array}\right] \begin{array}{l} \\ -2R_1 + R_2 \\ -3R_1 + R_3 \end{array}$$

$$\left[\begin{array}{ccc|c} 1 & -2 & 1 & 16 \\ 0 & 3 & -3 & -18 \\ 0 & 11 & -7 & -58 \end{array}\right] \begin{array}{l} \\ \frac{1}{3}R_2 \\ \\ \end{array}$$

$$\left[\begin{array}{ccc|c} 1 & -2 & 1 & 16 \\ 0 & 1 & -1 & -6 \\ 0 & 11 & -7 & -58 \end{array}\right] \begin{array}{l} \\ 2R_2 + R_1 \\ -11R_2 + R_3 \end{array}$$

$$\left[\begin{array}{ccc|c} 1 & 0 & -1 & 4 \\ 0 & 1 & -1 & -6 \\ 0 & 0 & 4 & 8 \end{array}\right] \begin{array}{l} \\ \frac{1}{4}R_3 \\ \\ \end{array}$$

$$\left[\begin{array}{ccc|c} 1 & 0 & -1 & 4 \\ 0 & 1 & -1 & -6 \\ 0 & 0 & 1 & 2 \end{array}\right] \begin{array}{l} R_3 + R_1 \\ R_2 + R_1 \\ \\ \end{array}$$

$$\left[\begin{array}{ccc|c} 1 & 0 & 0 & 6 \\ 0 & 1 & 0 & -4 \\ 0 & 0 & 1 & 2 \end{array}\right] \begin{array}{l} R_3 + R_1 \\ R_2 + R_1 \\ \\ \end{array}$$

The solution set is $\{(6, -4, 2)\}$.

13.
$$\begin{aligned} x - y &= 1 \\ x^2 - x - y &= 1 \end{aligned}$$

Multiply $x - y = 1$ by -1, then add

$$\begin{aligned} -x + y &= -1 \\ x^2 - x - y &= 1 \\ \hline x^2 - 2x &= 0 \\ x(x - 2) &= 0 \end{aligned}$$

$x = 0$ or $x = 2$

If $x = 0$, $-y = 1$ so $y = -1$.

If $x = 2$, $2 - y = 1$ so $y = 1$.

The solution set is $\{(0, -1), (2, 1)\}$.

14. $100x^2 + y^2 = 25$

$$4x^2 + \frac{y^2}{25} = 1$$

$$\frac{x^2}{\left(\frac{1}{4}\right)} + \frac{y^2}{25} = 1$$

Ellipse

Foci on the y-axis

$a^2 = 25$ and $b^2 = \frac{1}{4}$, so $\frac{1}{4} = 25 - c^2$.

$$c^2 = \frac{99}{4}$$

$$c = \frac{3\sqrt{11}}{2}$$

Foci: $\left(0, -\frac{3\sqrt{11}}{2}\right), \left(0, \frac{3\sqrt{11}}{2}\right)$

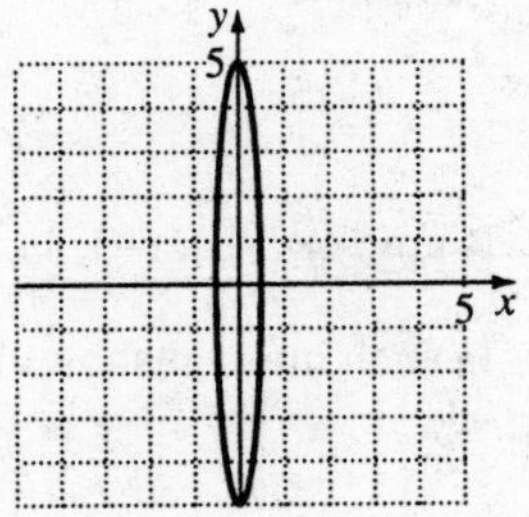

15. $4x^2 - 9y^2 - 16x + 54y - 29 = 0$

$4(x^2 - 4x) - 9(y^2 - 6y) = 29$

$4(x^2 - 4x + 4) - 9(y^2 - 6y + 9) = 16 - 81 + 29$

$4(x-2)^2 - 9(y-3)^2 = -36$

$\dfrac{(y-3)^2}{4} - \dfrac{(x-2)^2}{9} = 1$

Hyperbola with center at (2, 3)

Transverse axis vertical

$a^2 = 4$ and $b^2 = 9$, so $9 = c^2 - 4$.

$c^2 = 13$

$c = \sqrt{13}$

Foci: $\left(2, 3 - \sqrt{13}\right), \left(2, 3 + \sqrt{13}\right)$

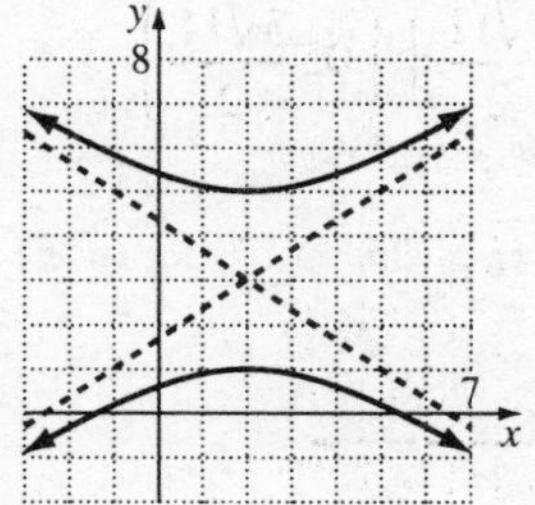

16. $f(x) = \dfrac{x^2 - 1}{x - 2}$

Symmetry:

$f(-x) = \dfrac{x^2 - 1}{-x - 2}$

No symmetry since $f(-x) \neq f(x)$ and $f(-x) \neq -f(-x)$.

x-intercepts:

$x^2 - 1 = 0$

$x = \pm 1$

y-intercept:

$f(0) = \dfrac{1}{2}$

$y = \dfrac{1}{2}$

Vertical asymptote:

$x - 2 = 0$

$x = 2$

Horizontal asymptote:

$n > m$, so no horizontal asymptote.

Slant asymptote:

$n = m + 1$

$f(x) = x + 2 + \dfrac{3}{x - 2}$

$y = x + 2$

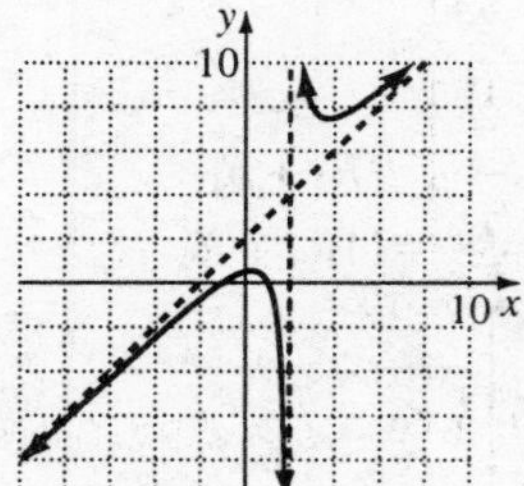

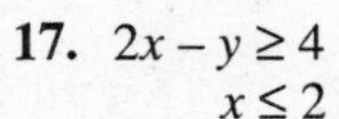
17. $2x - y \geq 4$

$x \leq 2$

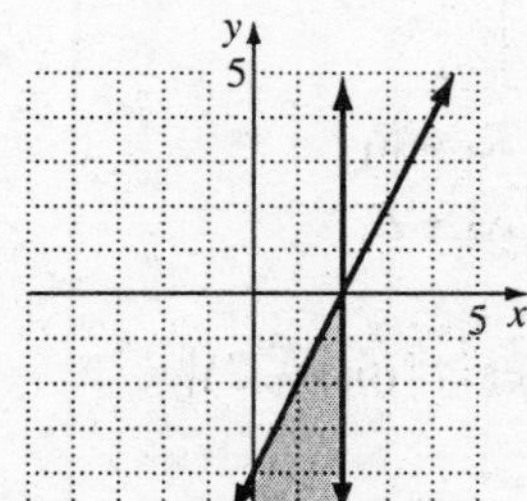

18. $f(x) = x^2 - 4x - 5$

$x = \frac{-b}{2a} = \frac{4}{2} = 2$

$f(2) = 2^2 - 8 - 5 = -9$

vertex: $(2, -9)$

x-intercepts:

$x^2 - 4x - 5 = 0$

$(x - 5)(x + 1) = 0$

$x = 5, -1$

y-intercept: $f(0) = -5$

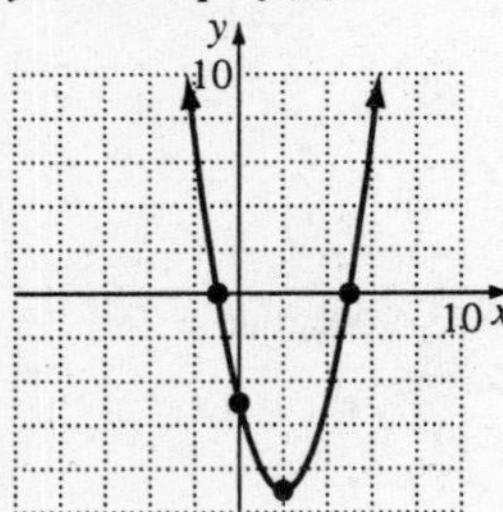

19. $y = \log_2 x$

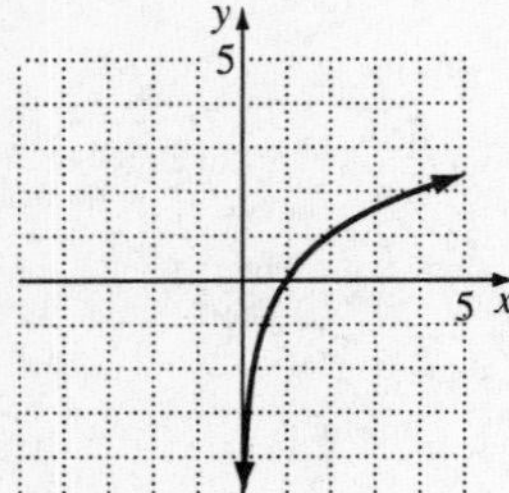

20.

$f(x) = \sqrt[3]{x+4}$

$y = \sqrt[3]{x+4}$

$x = \sqrt[3]{y+4}$

$x^3 = y + 4$

$y = x^3 - 4$

$f^{-1}(x) = x^3 - 4$

21.

$$AB - 4A = \begin{bmatrix} 4 & 2 \\ 1 & -1 \\ 0 & 5 \end{bmatrix} \begin{bmatrix} 2 & 4 \\ 3 & 1 \end{bmatrix} - 4 \begin{bmatrix} 4 & 2 \\ 1 & 1 \\ 0 & 5 \end{bmatrix}$$

$$= \begin{bmatrix} 14 & 18 \\ -1 & 3 \\ 15 & 5 \end{bmatrix} - \begin{bmatrix} 16 & 8 \\ 4 & -4 \\ 0 & 20 \end{bmatrix} = \begin{bmatrix} -2 & 10 \\ -5 & 7 \\ 15 & -15 \end{bmatrix}$$

22. $\frac{2x^2 - 10x + 2}{(x-2)(x^2 + 2x + 2)} = \frac{A}{x-2} + \frac{Bx + C}{x^2 + 2x + 2}$

$2x^2 - 10x + 2$

$= A(x^2 + 2x + 2) + (Bx + C)(x - 2)$

$= Ax^2 + 2Ax + 2A + Bx^2 - 2Bx + Cx - 2C$

$= (A + B)x^2 + (2A - 2B + C)x + 2A - 2C$

Thus we have the following system of equations.

$A + B = 2$

$2A - 2B + C = -10$

$2A - 2C = 2$

Add twice the first equation to the second equation.

$2A + 2B = 4$

$2A - 2B + C = -10$

$4A + C = -6$

Add twice the resulting equation to the third equation.

$8A + 2C = -12$

$2A - 2C = 2$

$10A = -10$

$A = -1$

Back-substitute to find B and C.

$2(-1) - 2C = 2$

$-2 - 2C = 2$

$-2C = 4$

$C = -2$

$-1 + B = 2$

$B = 3$

We have the following partial fraction decomposition.

$\frac{-1}{x-2} + \frac{3x - 2}{x^2 + 2x + 2}$

23. $(x^3+2y)^5 = \binom{5}{0}(x^3)^5 + \binom{5}{1}(x^3)^4(2y) + \binom{5}{2}(x^3)^3(2y)^2 + \binom{5}{3}(x^3)^2(2y)^3 + \binom{5}{4}(x^3)(2y)^4 + \binom{5}{5}(2y)^5$

$= x^{15} + 5x^{12}(2y) + 10x^9(4y^2) + 10x^6(8y^3) + 5x^3(16y^4) + 32y^5$

$= x^{15} + 10x^{12}y + 40x^9y^2 + 80x^6y^3 + 80x^3y^4 + 32y^5$

24. $\sum_{i=1}^{50}(4i-25)$

$a_1 = 4(1) - 25 = -21$

$a_{50} = 4(50) - 25 = 175$

$S_{50} = \frac{50}{2}(-21+175) = 3850$

25. a. $m = \frac{171.1-119.4}{10-0} = 5.17$

$y - 119.4 = 5.17x$

b. $y = 5.17x + 119.4$

c. $2000 - 1983 = 17$

$y = 5.17(17) + 119.4$

$= 207.29$

207.29 billion pieces of mail

26. x = height of Empire State Building

y = height of World Trade Center

$y = 2x - 790$

$\frac{x+y}{2} = 980$

Substitute the first equation into the second:

$\frac{x+2x-790}{2} = 980$

$3x - 790 = 1960$

$3x = 2750$

$x \approx 916.7$

$y \approx 1043.4$

The Empire State Building is about 916.7 feet tall and the World Trade Center is about 1043.4 feet tall.

27. $2L + 2W = 300$

$L = W + 50$

Rearrange the equations and add:

$L + W = 150$

$\underline{L - W = 50}$

$2L = 200$

$L = 100$

$W = 50$

length: 100 yards, width 50 yards

28. $10x + 12y = 42$

$5x + 10y = 29$

Multiply second equation by –2 and add:

$$\begin{aligned} 10x + 12y &= 42 \\ \underline{-10x - 20y} &\underline{= -58} \\ -8y &= -16 \\ y &= 2 \end{aligned}$$

Back substitute:

$$\begin{aligned} 5x + 10(2) &= 29 \\ 5x &= 9 \\ x &= 1.8 \end{aligned}$$

pen: \$1.80, pad: \$2

29. $s(t) = -16t^2 + 80t + 96$

a. $-16t^2 + 80t + 96 = 0$

$$\begin{aligned} t^2 - 5t - 6 &= 0 \\ (t + 1)(t - 6) &= 0 \\ t = -1 \text{ or } t &= 6 \end{aligned}$$

The ball will strike the ground after 6 seconds.

b. $t = \dfrac{-b}{2a} = \dfrac{-80}{-32} = \dfrac{5}{2}$ or 2.5

$S(2.5) = -16(2.5)^2 + 80(2.5) + 96 = 196$

The ball reaches a maximum height of 196 feet, 2.5 seconds after it is thrown.

30. $I = \dfrac{k}{R}$

$5 = \dfrac{k}{22}$

$k = 110$

$I = \dfrac{110}{10} = 11$

11 amperes